De Laval
Engineering Handbook

AMERICAN SOCIETY OF MECHANICAL ENGINEERS · ASME Handbooks:
Engineering Tables   Metals Engineering—Processes
Metals Engineering—Design   Metals Properties
BAUMEISTER AND MARKS · Standard Handbook for Mechanical Engineers
BEEMAN · Industrial Power Systems Handbook
BRADY · Materials Handbook
BURINGTON AND MAY · Handbook of Probability and Statistics with Tables
CALLENDER · Time-Saver Standards
CARRIER AIR CONDITIONING COMPANY · Handbook of Air Conditioning System Design
CARROLL · Industrial Instrument Servicing Handbook
CONSIDINE · Process Instruments and Controls Handbook
CONSIDINE AND ROSS · Handbook of Applied Instrumentation
CROCKER AND KING · Piping Handbook
DUDLEY · Gear Handbook
EMERICK · Handbook of Mechanical Specifications for Buildings and Plants
EMERICK · Heating Handbook
EMERICK · Troubleshooters' Handbook for Mechanical Systems
FACTORY MUTUAL ENGINEERING DIVISION · Handbook of Industrial Loss Prevention
FINK AND CARROLL · Standard Handbook for Electrical Engineers
FLÜGGE · Handbook of Engineering Mechanics
HARRIS · Handbook of Noise Control
HARRIS AND CREDE · Shock and Vibration Handbook
HEYEL · The Foreman's Handbook
KALLEN · Handbook of Instrumentation and Controls
KING AND BRATER · Handbook of Hydraulics
KLERER AND KORN · Digital Computer User's Handbook
KOELLE · Handbook of Astronautical Engineering
KORN AND KORN · Mathematical Handbook for Scientists and Engineers
LeGRAND · The New American Machinists' Handbook
MACHOL · System Engineering Handbook
MAGILL, HOLDEN, AND ACKLEY · Air Pollution Handbook
MANAS · National Plumbing Code Handbook
MANTELL · Engineering Materials Handbook
MAYNARD · Industrial Engineering Handbook
MERRITT · Building Construction Handbook
MORROW · Maintenance Engineering Handbook
PERRY · Chemical Engineers' Handbook
PERRY · Engineering Manual
ROSSNAGEL · Handbook of Rigging
ROTHBART · Mechanical Design and Systems Handbook
SHAND · Glass Engineering Handbook
SOCIETY OF MANUFACTURING ENGINEERS:
Die Design Handbook   Manufacturing Planning and
Handbook of Fixture Design   Estimating Handbook
                                 Tool Engineers Handbook
STANIAR · Plant Engineering Handbook
STREETER · Handbook of Fluid Dynamics
TOULOUKIAN · Retrieval Guide to Thermophysical Properties Research Literature
TRUXAL · Control Engineers' Handbook

De Laval Engineering Handbook

Compiled by
The Engineering Staff of De Laval Turbine Inc.

Edited by HANS GARTMANN

Third Edition

McGRAW-HILL BOOK COMPANY

New York   St. Louis   San Francisco   Düsseldorf   London
Mexico   Panama   Sydney   Toronto

Sponsoring Editor   Daniel N. Fischel
Director of Production   Stephen J. Boldish
Editing Supervisor   Stanley E. Redka
Editing and Production Staff   Gretlyn Blau, Teresa F. Leaden, George E. Oechsner

DE LAVAL ENGINEERING HANDBOOK

ISBN 07-022908-2

3 4 5 6 7 8 9   KPKP   7 9 8 7 6 5 4 3

Preface

This is the Third Edition of the "De Laval Engineering Handbook," an engineering data book for users of turbines, engines, pumps, compressors, gears, condensers, and filters. As before, the aim has been to offer quick answers to problems faced in everyday work by engineers designing or working in power plants, industrial plants, municipal water works, and similar installations.

The earlier editions of this work were prepared to provide reference data and other useful information for the convenience of De Laval's employees and customers. They were so well received that we saw the logic of making this edition available to an even larger audience through the facilities of the McGraw-Hill Book Company. For this edition, accordingly, all reference material has been updated, and new sections have been added, not only to reflect the widening interests of De Laval, but also to make the book more broadly useful.

The contents are still, of course, of a general nature; no attempt has been made to provide detailed data for all possible conditions of design and operation. For more detailed information on particular problems, inquiries may be addressed to the field offices of the company in all principal cities of the United States, or to the organization's headquarters: De Laval Turbine, Inc., Trenton, New Jersey 08602.

This Handbook represents the work of numerous contributors from the engineering staff of De Laval Turbine, Inc. The Editor is grateful to them for their effort and patience in submitting to modifications of their work.

Hans Gartmann

Contents

De Laval
Engineering Handbook

Mathematical Data and Conversion Tables

SQUARES AND CUBES OF NUMBERS

No.	Square	Cube	No.	Square	Cube
1	1	1	51	2,601	132,651
2	4	8	52	2,704	140,608
3	9	27	53	2,809	148,877
4	16	64	54	2,916	157,464
5	25	125	55	3,025	166,375
6	36	216	56	3,136	175,616
7	49	343	57	3,249	185,193
8	64	512	58	3,364	195,112
9	81	729	59	3,481	205,379
10	100	1,000	60	3,600	216,000
11	121	1,331	61	3,721	226,981
12	144	1,728	62	3,844	238,328
13	169	2,197	63	3,969	250,047
14	196	2,744	64	4,096	262,144
15	225	3,375	65	4,225	274,625
16	256	4,096	66	4,356	287,496
17	289	4,913	67	4,489	300,763
18	324	5,832	68	4,624	314,432
19	361	6,859	69	4,761	328,509
20	400	8,000	70	4,900	343,000
21	441	9,261	71	5,041	357,911
22	484	10,648	72	5,184	373,248
23	529	12,167	73	5,329	389,107
24	576	13,824	74	5,476	405,224
25	625	15,625	75	5,625	421,875
26	676	17,576	76	5,776	438,976
27	729	19,683	77	5,929	456,533
28	784	21,952	78	6,084	474,552
29	841	24,389	79	6,241	493,039
30	900	27,000	80	6,400	512,000
31	961	29,791	81	6,561	531,441
32	1,024	32,768	82	6,724	551,368
33	1,089	35,937	83	6,889	571,787
34	1,156	39,304	84	7,056	592,704
35	1,225	42,875	85	7,225	614,125
36	1,296	46,656	86	7,396	636,056
37	1,369	50,653	87	7,569	658,503
38	1,444	54,872	88	7,744	681,472
39	1,521	59,319	89	7,921	704,969
40	1,600	64,000	90	8,100	729,000
41	1,681	68,921	91	8,281	753,571
42	1,764	74,088	92	8,464	778,688
43	1,849	79,507	93	8,649	804,357
44	1,936	85,184	94	8,836	830,584
45	2,025	91,125	95	9,025	857,375
46	2,116	97,336	96	9,216	884,736
47	2,209	103,823	97	9,409	912,673
48	2,304	110,592	98	9,604	941,192
49	2,401	117,649	99	9,801	970,299
50	2,500	125,000	100	10,000	1,000,000

SQUARES AND CUBES OF NUMBERS (Continued)

No.	Square	Cube	No.	Square	Cube
101	10,201	1,030,301	151	22,801	3,442,951
102	10,404	1,061,208	152	23,104	3,511,008
103	10,609	1,092,727	153	23,409	3,581,577
104	10,816	1,124,864	154	23,716	3,652,264
105	11,025	1,157,625	155	24,025	3,723,875
106	11,236	1,191,016	156	24,336	3,796,416
107	11,449	1,225,043	157	24,649	3,869,893
108	11,664	1,259,712	158	24,964	3,944,312
109	11,881	1,295,029	159	25,281	4,019,679
110	12,100	1,331,000	160	25,600	4,096,000
111	12,321	1,367,631	161	25,921	4,173,281
112	12,544	1,404,928	162	26,244	4,251,528
113	12,769	1,442,897	163	26,569	4,330,747
114	12,996	1,481,544	164	26,896	4,410,944
115	13,225	1,520,875	165	27,225	4,492,125
116	13,456	1,560,896	166	27,556	4,574,296
117	13,689	1,601,613	167	27,889	4,657,463
118	13,924	1,643,032	168	28,224	4,741,632
119	14,161	1,685,159	169	28,651	4,826,809
120	14,400	1,728,000	170	28,900	4,913,000
121	14,641	1,771,561	171	29,241	5,000,211
122	14,884	1,815,848	172	29,584	5,088,448
123	15,129	1,860,867	173	29,929	5,177,717
124	15,376	1,906,624	174	30,276	5,268,024
125	15,625	1,953,125	175	30,625	5,359,375
126	15,876	2,000,376	176	30,976	5,451,776
127	16,129	2,048,383	177	31,329	5,545,233
128	16,384	2,097,152	178	31,684	5,639,752
129	16,641	2,146,689	179	32,041	5,735,339
130	16,900	2,197,000	180	32,400	5,832,000
131	17,161	2,248,091	181	32,761	5,929,741
132	17,424	2,299,968	182	33,124	6,028,568
133	17,689	2,352,637	183	33,489	6,128,487
134	17,956	2,406,104	184	33,856	6,229,504
135	18,225	2,460,375	185	34,225	6,331,625
136	18,496	2,515,456	186	34,596	6,434,856
137	18,769	2,571,353	187	34,969	6,539,203
138	19,044	2,628,072	188	35,344	6,644,672
139	19,321	2,685,619	189	35,721	6,751,269
140	19,600	2,744,000	190	36,100	6,859,000
141	19,881	2,803,221	191	36,481	6,967,871
142	20,164	2,863,288	192	36,864	7,077,888
143	20,449	2,924,207	193	37,249	7,189,057
144	20,736	2,985,984	194	37,636	7,301,384
145	21,025	3,048,625	195	38,025	7,414,875
146	21,316	3,112,136	196	38,416	7,529,536
147	21,609	3,176,523	197	38,809	7,645,373
148	21,904	3,241,792	198	39,204	7,762,392
149	22,201	3,307,949	199	39,601	7,880,599
150	22,500	3,375,000	200	40,000	8,000,000

SQUARES AND CUBES OF NUMBERS (Continued)

No.	Square	Cube	No.	Square	Cube
201	40,401	8,120,601	251	63,001	15,813,251
202	40,804	8,242,408	252	63,504	16,003,008
203	41,209	8,365,427	253	64,009	16,194,277
204	41,616	8,489,664	254	64,516	16,387,064
205	42,025	8,615,125	255	65,025	16,581,375
206	42,436	8,741,816	256	65,536	16,777,216
207	42,849	8,869,743	257	66,049	16,974,593
208	43,264	8,998,912	258	66,564	17,173,512
209	43,681	9,129,329	259	67,081	17,373,979
210	44,100	9,261,000	260	67,600	17,576,000
211	44,521	9,393,931	261	68,121	17,779,581
212	44,944	9,528,128	262	68,644	17,984,728
213	45,369	9,663,597	263	69,169	18,191,447
214	45,796	9,800,344	264	69,696	18,399,744
215	46,225	9,938,375	265	70,225	18,609,625
216	46,656	10,077,696	266	70,756	18,821,096
217	47,084	10,218,313	267	71,289	19,034,163
218	47,524	10,360,232	268	71,824	19,248,832
219	47,961	10,503,459	269	72,361	19,465,109
220	48,400	10,648,000	270	72,900	19,683,000
221	48,841	10,793,861	271	73,441	19,902,511
222	49,284	10,941,048	272	73,984	20,123,648
223	49,729	11,089,567	273	74,529	20,346,417
224	50,176	11,239,424	274	75,076	20,570,824
225	50,625	11,390,625	275	75,625	20,796,875
226	51,076	11,543,176	276	76,176	21,024,576
227	51,529	11,697,083	277	76,729	21,253,933
228	51,984	11,852,352	278	77,284	21,484,952
229	52,441	12,008,989	279	77,841	21,717,639
230	52,900	12,167,000	280	78,400	21,952,000
231	53,361	12,326,391	281	78,961	22,188,041
232	53,824	12,487,168	282	79,524	22,425,768
233	54,289	12,649,337	283	80,089	22,665,187
234	54,756	12,812,904	284	80,656	22,906,304
235	55,225	12,977,875	285	81,225	23,149,125
236	55,696	13,144,256	286	81,796	23,393,656
237	56,169	13,312,053	287	82,369	23,639,903
238	56,644	13,481,272	288	82,944	23,887,872
239	57,121	13,651,919	289	83,521	24,137,569
240	57,600	13,824,000	290	84,100	24,389,000
241	58,081	13,997,521	291	84,681	24,642,171
242	58,564	14,172,488	292	85,264	24,897,088
243	59,049	14,348,907	293	85,849	25,153,757
244	59,536	14,526,784	294	86,436	25,412,184
245	60,025	14,706,125	295	87,025	25,672,375
246	60,516	14,886,936	296	87,616	25,934,336
247	61,009	15,069,223	297	88,209	26,198,073
248	61,504	15,252,992	298	88,804	26,463,592
249	62,001	15,438,249	299	89,401	26,730,899
250	62,500	15,625,000	300	90,000	27,000,000

SQUARES AND CUBES OF NUMBERS (Continued)

No.	Square	Cube	No.	Square	Cube
301	90,601	27,270,901	351	123,201	43,243,551
302	91,204	27,543,608	352	123,904	43,614,208
303	91,809	27,818,127	353	124,609	43,986,977
304	92,416	28,094,464	354	125,316	44,361,864
305	93,025	28,372,625	355	126,025	44,738,875
306	93,636	28,652,616	356	126,736	45,118,016
307	94,249	28,934,443	357	127,449	45,499,293
308	94,864	29,218,112	358	128,164	45,882,712
309	95,481	29,503,629	359	128,881	46,268,279
310	96,100	29,791,000	360	129,600	46,656,000
311	96,721	30,080,231	361	130,321	47,045,881
312	97,344	30,371,328	362	131,044	47,437,928
313	97,969	30,664,297	363	131,769	47,832,147
314	98,596	30,959,144	364	132,496	48,228,544
315	99,225	31,255,875	365	133,225	48,627,125
316	99,856	31,554,496	366	133,956	49,027,986
317	100,489	31,855,013	367	134,689	49,430,863
318	101,124	32,157,432	368	135,424	49,836,032
319	101,761	32,461,759	369	136,161	50,243,409
320	102,400	32,768,000	370	136,900	50,653,000
321	103,041	33,076,161	371	137,641	51,064,811
322	103,684	33,386,248	372	138,384	51,478,848
323	104,329	33,698,267	373	139,129	51,895,117
324	104,976	34,012,224	374	139,876	52,313,624
325	105,625	34,328,125	375	140,625	52,734,375
326	106,276	34,645,976	376	141,376	53,157,376
327	106,929	34,965,783	377	142,129	53,582,633
328	107,584	35,287,552	378	142,884	54,010,152
329	108,241	35,611,289	379	143,641	54,439,939
330	108,900	35,937,000	380	144,400	54,872,000
331	109,561	36,264,691	381	145,161	55,306,341
332	110,224	36,594,368	382	145,924	55,742,968
333	110,889	36,926,037	383	146,689	56,181,887
334	111,556	37,259,704	384	147,456	56,623,104
335	112,225	37,595,375	385	148,225	57,066,625
336	112,896	37,933,056	386	148,996	57,512,456
337	113,569	38,272,753	387	149,769	57,960,603
338	114,244	38,614,472	388	150,544	58,411,072
339	114,921	38,958,219	389	151,321	58,863,869
340	115,600	39,304,000	390	152,100	59,319,000
341	116,281	39,651,821	391	152,881	59,776,471
342	116,964	40,001,688	392	153,664	60,236,288
343	117,649	40,353,607	393	154,449	60,698,457
344	118,336	40,707,584	394	155,236	61,162,984
345	119,025	41,063,625	395	156,025	61,629,875
346	119,716	41,421,736	396	156,816	62,099,136
347	120,409	41,781,923	397	157,609	62,570,773
348	121,104	42,144,192	398	158,404	63,044,792
349	121,801	42,508,549	399	159,201	63,521,199
350	122,500	42,875,000	400	160,000	64,000,000

SQUARES AND CUBES OF NUMBERS (Continued)

No.	Square	Cube	No.	Square	Cube
401	160,801	64,481,201	451	203,401	91,733,851
402	161,604	64,964,808	452	204,304	92,345,408
403	162,409	65,450,827	453	205,209	92,959,677
404	163,216	65,939,264	454	206,116	93,576,664
405	164,025	66,430,125	455	207,025	94,196,375
406	164,836	66,923,416	456	207,936	94,818,816
407	165,649	67,419,143	457	208,849	95,443,993
408	166,464	67,917,312	458	209,764	96,071,912
409	167,281	68,417,929	459	210,681	96,702,579
410	168,100	68,921,000	460	211,600	97,336,000
411	168,921	69,426,531	461	212,521	97,972,181
412	169,744	69,934,528	462	213,444	98,611,128
413	170,569	70,444,997	463	214,369	99,252,847
414	171,396	70,957,944	464	215,296	99,897,344
415	172,225	71,473,375	465	216,225	100,544,625
416	173,056	71,991,296	466	217,156	101,194,696
417	173,889	72,511,713	467	218,089	101,847,563
418	174,724	73,034,632	468	219,024	102,503,232
419	175,561	73,560,059	469	219,961	103,161,709
420	176,400	74,088,000	470	220,900	103,823,000
421	177,241	74,618,461	471	221,841	104,487,111
422	178,084	75,151,448	472	222,784	105,154,048
423	178,929	75,686,967	473	223,729	105,823,817
424	179,776	76,225,024	474	224,676	106,496,424
425	180,625	76,765,625	475	225,625	107,171,875
426	181,476	77,308,776	476	226,576	107,850,176
427	182,329	77,854,483	477	227,529	108,531,333
428	183,184	78,402,752	478	228,484	109,215,352
429	184,041	78,953,589	479	229,441	109,902,239
430	184,900	79,507,000	480	230,400	110,592,000
431	185,761	80,062,991	481	231,361	111,284,641
432	186,624	80,621,568	482	232,324	111,980,168
433	187,489	81,182,737	483	233,289	112,678,587
434	188,356	81,746,504	484	234,256	113,379,904
435	189,225	82,312,875	485	235,225	114,084,125
436	190,096	82,881,856	486	236,196	114,791,256
437	190,969	83,453,453	487	237,169	115,501,303
438	191,844	84,027,672	488	238,144	116,214,272
439	192,721	84,604,519	489	239,121	116,930,169
440	193,600	85,184,000	490	240,100	117,649,000
441	194,481	85,766,121	491	241,081	118,370,771
442	195,364	86,350,888	492	242,064	119,095,488
443	196,249	86,938,307	493	243,049	119,823,157
444	197,136	87,528,384	494	244,036	120,553,784
445	198,025	88,121,125	495	245,025	121,287,375
446	198,916	88,716,536	496	246,016	122,023,936
447	199,809	89,314,623	497	247,009	122,763,473
448	200,704	89,915,392	498	248,004	123,505,992
449	201,601	90,518,849	499	249,001	124,251,499
450	202,500	91,125,000	500	250,000	125,000,000

SQUARES AND CUBES OF NUMBERS (Continued)

No.	Square	Cube	No.	Square	Cube
501	251,001	125,751,501	551	303,601	167,284,151
502	252,004	126,506,008	552	304,704	168,196,608
503	253,009	127,263,527	553	305,809	169,112,377
504	254,016	128,024,064	554	306,916	170,031,464
505	255,025	128,787,625	555	308,025	170,953,875
506	256,036	129,554,216	556	309,136	171,879,616
507	257,049	130,323,843	557	310,249	172,808,693
508	258,064	131,096,512	558	311,364	173,741,112
509	259,081	131,872,229	559	312,481	174,676,879
510	260,100	132,651,000	560	313,600	175,616,000
511	261,121	133,432,831	561	314,721	176,558,481
512	262,144	134,217,728	562	315,844	177,504,328
513	263,169	135,005,697	563	316,969	178,453,547
514	264,196	135,796,744	564	318,096	179,406,144
515	265,225	136,590,875	565	319,225	180,362,125
516	266,256	137,388,096	566	320,356	181,321,496
517	267,289	138,188,413	567	321,489	182,284,263
518	268,324	138,991,832	568	322,624	183,250,432
519	269,361	139,798,359	569	323,761	184,220,009
520	270,400	140,608,000	570	324,900	185,193,000
521	271,441	141,420,761	571	326,041	186,169,411
522	272,484	142,236,648	572	327,184	187,149,248
523	273,529	143,055,667	573	328,329	188,132,517
524	274,576	143 877,824	574	329,476	189,119,224
525	275,625	144,703,125	575	330,625	190,109,375
526	276,676	145,531,576	576	331,776	191,102,976
527	277,729	146,363,183	577	332,929	192,100,033
528	278,784	147,197,952	578	334,084	193,100,552
529	279,841	148,035,889	579	335,241	194,104,539
530	280,900	148,877,000	580	336,400	195,112,000
531	281,961	149,721,291	581	337,561	196,122,941
532	283,024	150,568,768	582	338,724	197,137,368
533	284,089	151,419,437	583	339,889	198,155,287
534	285,156	152,273,304	584	341,056	199,176,704
535	286,225	153,130,375	585	342,225	200,201,625
536	287,296	153,990,656	586	343,396	201,230,056
537	288,369	154,854,153	587	344,569	202,262,003
538	289,444	155,720,872	588	345,744	203,297,472
539	290,521	156,590,819	589	346,921	204,336,469
540	291,600	157,464,000	590	348,100	205,379,000
541	292,681	158,340,421	591	349,281	206,425,071
542	293,764	159,220,088	592	350,464	207,474,688
543	294,849	160,103,007	593	351,649	208,527,857
544	295,936	160,989,184	594	352,836	209,584,584
545	297,025	161,878,625	595	354,025	210,644,875
546	298,116	162,771,336	596	355,216	211,708,736
547	299,209	163,667,323	597	356,409	212,776,173
548	300,304	164,566,592	598	357,604	213,847,192
549	301,401	165,469,149	599	358,801	214,921,799
550	302,500	166,375,000	600	360,000	216,000,000

SQUARES AND CUBES OF NUMBERS (Continued)

No.	Square	Cube	No.	Square	Cube
601	361,201	217,081,801	651	423,801	275,894,451
602	362,404	218,167,208	652	425,104	277,167,808
603	363,609	219,256,227	653	426,409	278,445,077
604	364,816	220,348,864	654	427,716	279,726,264
605	366,025	221,445,125	655	429,025	281,011,375
606	367,236	222,545,016	656	430,336	282,300,416
607	368,449	223,648,543	657	431,649	283,593,393
608	369,664	224,755,712	658	432,964	284,890,312
609	370,881	225,866,529	659	434,281	286,191,179
610	372,100	226,981,000	660	435,600	287,496,000
611	373,321	228,099,131	661	436,921	288,804,781
612	374,544	229,220,928	662	438,244	290,117,528
613	375,769	230,346,397	663	439,569	291,434,247
614	376,996	231,475,544	664	440,896	292,754,944
615	378,225	232,608,375	665	442,225	294,079,625
616	379,456	233,744,896	666	443,556	295,408,296
617	380,689	234,885,113	667	444,889	296,740,963
618	381,924	236,029,032	668	446,224	298,077,632
619	383,161	237,176,659	669	447,561	299,418,309
620	384,400	238,328,000	670	448,900	300,763,000
621	385,641	239,483,061	671	450,241	302,111,711
622	386,884	240,641,848	672	451,584	303,464,448
623	388,129	241,804,367	673	452,929	304,821,217
624	389,376	242,970,624	674	454,276	306,182,024
625	390,625	244,140,625	675	455,625	307,546,875
626	391,876	245,314,376	676	456,976	308,915,776
627	393,129	246,491,883	677	458,329	310,288,733
628	394,384	247,673,152	678	459,684	311,665,752
629	395,641	248,858,189	679	461,041	313,046,839
630	396,900	250,047,000	680	462,400	314,432,000
631	398,161	251,239,591	681	463,761	315,821,241
632	399,424	252,435,968	682	465,124	317,214,568
633	400,689	253,636,137	683	466,489	318,611,987
634	401,956	254,840,104	684	467,856	320,013,504
635	403,225	256,047,875	685	469,225	321,419,125
636	404,496	257,259,456	686	470,596	322,828,856
637	405,769	258,474,853	687	471,969	324,242,703
638	407,044	259,694,072	688	473,344	325,660,672
639	408,321	260,917,119	689	474,721	327,082,769
640	409,600	262,144,000	690	476,100	328,509,000
641	410,881	263,374,721	691	477,481	329,939,371
642	412,164	264,609,288	692	478,864	331,373,888
643	413,449	265,847,707	693	480,249	332,812,557
644	414,736	267,089,984	694	481,636	334,255,384
645	416,025	268,336,125	695	483,025	335,702,375
646	417,316	269,586,136	696	484,416	337,153,536
647	418,609	270,840,023	697	485,809	338,608,873
648	419,904	272,097,792	698	487,204	340,068,392
649	421,201	273,359,449	699	488,601	341,532,099
650	422,500	274,625,000	700	490,000	343,000,000

SQUARES AND CUBES OF NUMBERS (Continued)

No.	Square	Cube	No.	Square	Cube
701	491,401	344,472,101	751	564,001	423,564,751
702	492,804	345,948,408	752	565,504	425,259,008
703	494,209	347,428,927	753	567,009	426,957,777
704	495,616	348,913,664	754	568,516	428,661,064
705	497,025	350,402,625	755	570,025	430,368,875
706	498,436	351,895,816	756	571,536	432,081,216
707	499,849	353,393,243	757	573,049	433,798,093
708	501,264	354,894,912	758	574,564	435,519,512
709	502,681	356,400,829	759	576,081	437,245,479
710	504,100	357,911,000	760	577,600	438,976,000
711	505,521	359,425,431	761	579,121	440,711,081
712	506,944	360,944,128	762	580,644	442,450,728
713	508,369	362,467,097	763	582,169	444,194,947
714	509,796	363,994,344	764	583,696	445,943,744
715	511,225	365,525,875	765	585,225	447,697,125
716	512,656	367,061,696	766	586,756	449,455,096
717	514,089	368,601,813	767	588,289	451,217,663
718	515,524	370,146,232	768	589,824	452,984,832
719	516,961	371,694,959	769	591,361	454,756,609
720	518,400	373,248,000	770	592,900	456,533,000
721	519,841	374,805,361	771	594,441	458,314,011
722	521,284	376,367,048	772	595,984	460,099,648
723	522,729	377,933,067	773	597,529	461,889,917
724	524,176	379,503,424	774	599,076	463,684,824
725	525,625	381,078,125	775	600,625	465,484,375
726	527,076	382,657,176	776	602,176	467,288,576
727	528,529	384,240,583	777	603,729	469,097,433
728	529,984	385,828,352	778	605,284	470,910,952
729	531,441	387,420,489	779	606,841	472,729,139
730	532,900	389,017,000	780	608,400	474,552,000
731	534,361	390,617,891	781	609,961	476,379,541
732	535,824	392,223,168	782	611,524	478,211,768
733	537,289	393,832,837	783	613,089	480,048,687
734	538,756	395,446,904	784	614,656	481,890,304
735	540,225	397,065,375	785	616,225	483,736,625
736	541,696	398,688,256	786	617,796	485,587,656
737	543,169	400,315,553	787	619,369	487,443,403
738	544,644	401,947,272	788	620,944	489,303,872
739	546,121	403,583,419	789	622,521	491,169,069
740	547,600	405,224,000	790	624,100	493,039,000
741	549,081	406,869,021	791	625,681	494,913,671
742	550,564	408,518,488	792	627,264	496,793,088
743	552,049	410,172,407	793	628,849	498,677,257
744	553,536	411,830,784	794	630,436	500,566,184
745	555,025	413,493,625	795	632,025	502,459,875
746	556,516	415,160,936	796	633,616	504,358,336
747	558,009	416,832,723	797	635,209	506,261,573
748	559,504	418,508,992	798	636,804	508,169,592
749	561,001	420,189,749	799	638,401	510,082,399
750	562,500	421,875,000	800	640,000	512,000,000

SQUARES AND CUBES OF NUMBERS (Continued)

No.	Square	Cube	No.	Square	Cube
801	641.601	513,922,401	851	724.201	616.295,051
802	643.204	515 849,608	852	725.904	618,470,208
803	644,809	517.781 627	853	727,609	620,650,477
804	646,416	519,718,464	854	729,316	622,835,864
805	648,025	521,660,125	855	731,025	625,026,375
806	649,636	523,606,616	756	732,736	627,222,016
807	651,249	525,557,943	857	734,449	629,422,793
808	652,864	527.514.112	858	736,164	631,628,712
809	654,481	529,475,129	859	737,881	633,839,779
810	656,100	531,441,000	860	739,600	636,056,000
811	657,721	533,411,731	861	741,321	638,277,381
812	659,344	535,387,328	862	743,044	640.503,928
813	660,969	537,367,797	863	744,769	642,735,647
814	662,596	539,353,144	864	746,496	644,972,544
815	664,225	541,343,375	865	748,225	647,214,625
816	665,856	543.338.496	866	749,956	649,461,896
817	667,489	545,338,513	867	751.689	651,714 363
818	669,124	547,343,432	868	753,424	653,972,032
819	670,761	549,353,259	869	755,161	656,234,909
820	672,400	551,368,000	870	756,900	658,503,000
821	674,041	553,387,661	871	758,641	660,776.311
822	675,684	555,412,248	872	760,384	663,054,848
823	677,329	557,441,767	873	762.129	665,338 617
824	678,976	559,476,224	874	763,876	667,627,624
825	680,625	561,515,625	875	765,625	669,921,875
826	682,276	563.559 976	876	767,376	672,221,376
827	683,929	565,609,283	877	769.129	674,526,133
828	685,584	567,663,552	878	770,884	676,836,152
829	687,241	569,722,789	879	772,641	679,151,439
830	688,900	571,787,000	880	774,400	681,472,000
831	690,561	573,856,191	881	776,161	683,797,841
832	692.224	575,930,368	882	777,924	686.128.968
833	693,889	578,009,537	883	779,689	688,465,387
834	695,556	580,093,704	884	781,456	690,807,104
835	697,225	582,182,875	885	783,225	693,154,125
836	698,896	584,277.056	886	784,996	695,506,456
837	700,569	586,376,253	887	786,769	697,864,103
838	702,244	588,480,472	888	788,544	700,227,072
839	703,921	590,589,719	889	790,321	702,595,369
840	705,600	592,704,000	890	792,100	704,969,000
841	707,281	594,823,321	891	793,881	707,347,971
842	708.964	596,947,688	892	795,664	709,932,288
843	710,649	599,077,107	893	797,449	712,121,957
844	712,336	601,211,584	894	799,236	714,516,984
845	714,025	603,351,125	895	801,025	716,917,375
846	715,716	605,495,736	896	802,816	719,323,136
847	717,409	607,645,423	897	804,609	721,734,273
848	719,104	609,800 192	898	806,404	724,150,792
849	720,801	611,960,049	899	808,201	726,572,699
850	722,500	614,125,000	900	810,000	729,000,000

SQUARES AND CUBES OF NUMBERS (Continued)

No.	Square	Cube	No.	Square	Cube
901	811,801	731,432,701	951	904,401	860,085,351
902	813,604	733,870,808	952	906,304	862,801,408
903	815,409	736,314,327	953	908,209	865,523,177
904	817,216	738,763,264	954	910,116	868,250,664
905	819,025	741,217,625	955	912,025	870,983,875
906	820,836	743,677,416	956	913,936	873,722,816
907	822,649	746,142,643	957	915,849	876,467,493
908	824,464	748,613,312	958	917,764	879,217,912
909	826,281	751,089,429	959	919,681	881,974,079
910	828,100	753,571,000	960	921,600	884,736,000
911	829,921	756,058,031	961	923,521	887,503,681
912	831,744	758,550,528	962	925,444	890,277,128
913	833,569	761,048,497	963	927,369	893,056,347
914	835,396	763,551,944	964	929,296	895,841,344
915	837,225	766,060,875	965	931,225	898,632,125
916	839,056	768,575,296	966	933,156	901,428,696
917	840,889	771,095,213	967	935,089	904,231,063
918	842,724	773,620,632	968	937,024	907,039,232
919	844,561	776,151,559	969	938,961	909,853,209
920	846,400	778,688,000	970	940,900	912,673,000
921	848,241	781,229,961	971	942,841	915,498,611
922	850,084	783,777,448	972	944,784	918,330,048
923	851,929	786,330,467	973	946,729	921,167,317
924	853,776	788,889,024	974	948,676	924,010,424
925	855,625	791,453,125	975	950,625	926,859,375
926	857,476	794,022,776	976	952,576	929,714,176
927	859,329	796,597,983	977	954,529	932,574,833
928	861,184	799,178,752	978	956,484	935,441,352
929	863,041	801,765,089	979	958,441	938,313,739
930	864,900	804,357,000	980	960,400	941,192,000
931	866,761	806,954,491	981	962,361	944,076,141
932	868,624	809,557,568	982	964,324	946,966,168
933	870,489	812,166,237	983	966,289	949,862,087
934	872,356	814,780,504	984	968,256	952,763,904
935	874,225	817,400,375	985	970,225	955,671,625
936	876,096	820,025,856	986	972,196	958,585,256
937	877,969	822,656,953	987	974,169	961,504,803
938	879,844	825,293,672	988	976,144	964,430,272
939	881,721	827,936,019	989	978,121	967,361,669
940	883,600	830,584,000	990	980,100	970,299,000
941	885,481	833,237,621	991	982,081	973,242,271
942	887,364	835,896,888	992	984,064	976,191,488
943	889,249	838,561,807	993	986,049	979,146,657
944	891,136	841,232,384	994	988,036	982,107,784
945	893,025	843,908,625	995	990,025	985,074,875
946	894,916	846,590,536	996	992,016	988,047,936
947	896,809	849,278,123	997	994,009	991,026,973
948	898,704	851,971,392	998	996,004	994,011,992
949	900,601	854,670,349	999	998,001	997,002,999
950	902,500	857,375,000	1000	1,000,000	1,000,000,000

AREAS OF CIRCLES

Diameter	Area	Diameter	Area	Diameter	Area
1/32	0.00077	2	3.1416	5	19.635
1/16	0.00307				
3/32	0.00690	2-1/16	3.3410	5-1/16	20.129
1/8	0.01227	2-1/8	3.5466	5-1/8	20.629
5/32	0.01917	2-3/16	3.7583	5-3/16	21.135
3/16	0.02761	2-1/4	3.9761	5-1/4	21.648
7/32	0.03758	2-5/16	4.2000	5-5/16	22.166
1/4	0.04909	2-3/8	4.4301	5-3/8	22.691
9/32	0.06213	2-7/16	4.6664	5-7/16	23.221
5/16	0.07670	2-1/2	4.9087	5-1/2	23.758
11/32	0.09281	2-9/16	5.1572	5-9/16	24.301
3/8	0.11045	2-5/8	5.4119	5-5/8	24.850
13/32	0.12962	2-11/16	5.6727	5-11/16	25.406
7/16	0.15033	2-3/4	5.9396	5-3/4	25.967
15/32	0.17257	2-13/16	6.2126	5-13/16	26.535
		2-7/8	6.4918	5-7/8	27.109
		2-15/16	6.7771	5-15/16	27.688
½	0.19635				
17/32	0.22166	3	7.0686	6	28.274
9/16	0.24850	3-1/16	7.3662	6-1/16	28.866
19/32	0.27688	3-1/8	7.6699	6-1/8	29.465
5/8	0.30680	3-3/16	7.9798	6-3/16	30.069
21/32	0.33824	3-1/4	8.2958	6-1/4	30.680
11/16	0.37122	3-5/16	8.6179	6-5/16	31.296
23/32	0.40574	3-3/8	8.9462	6-3/8	31.919
3/4	0.44179	3-7/16	9.2806	6-7/16	32.548
25/32	0.47937	3-1/2	9.6211	6-1/2	33.183
13/16	0.51849	3-9/16	9.9678	6-9/16	33.824
27/32	0.55914	3-5/8	10.321	6-5/8	34.472
7/8	0.60132	3-11/16	10.680	6-11/16	35.125
29/32	0.64504	3-3/4	11.045	6-3/4	35.785
15/16	0.69029	3-13/16	11.416	6-13/16	36.450
31/32	0.73708	3-7/8	11.793	6-7/8	37.122
		3-15/16	12.177	6-15/16	37.800
1	0.7854	4	12.566	7	38.485
1-1/16	0.8866	4-1/16	12.962	7-1/16	39.175
1-1/8	0.9940	4-1/8	13.364	7-1/8	39.871
1-3/16	1.1075	4-3/16	13.772	7-3/16	40.574
1-1/4	1.2272	4-1/4	14.186	7-1/4	41.282
1-5/16	1.3530	4-5/16	14.607	7-5/16	41.997
1-3/8	1.4849	4-3/8	15.033	7-3/8	42.718
1-7/16	1.6230	4-7/16	15.466	7-7/16	43.445
1-1/2	1.7671	4-1/2	15.904	7-1/2	44.179
1-9/16	1.9175	4-9/16	16.349	7-9/16	44.918
1-5/8	2.0739	4-5/8	16.800	7-5/8	45.664
1-11/16	2.2365	4-11/16	17.257	7-11/16	46.415
1-3/4	2.4053	4-3/4	17.721	7-3/4	47.173
1-13/16	2.5802	4-13/16	18.190	7-13/16	47.937
1-7/8	2.7612	4-7/8	18.665	7-7/8	48.707
1-15/16	2.9483	4-15/16	19.147	7-15/16	49.483

AREAS OF CIRCLES (Continued)

Diameter	Area	Diameter	Area	Diameter	Area
8	50.265	13	132.73	18	254.47
8-1/8	51.849	13-1/8	135.30	18-1/8	258.02
8-1/4	53.456	13-1/4	137.89	18-1/4	261.59
8-3/8	55.088	13-3/8	140.50	18-3/8	265.18
8-1/2	56.745	13-1/2	143.14	18-1/2	268.80
8-5/8	58.426	13-5/8	145.80	18-5/8	272.45
8-3/4	60.132	13-3/4	148.49	18-3/4	276.12
8-7/8	61.862	13-7/8	151.20	18-7/8	279.81
9	63.617	14	153.94	19	283.53
9-1/8	65.397	14-1/8	156.70	19-1/8	287.27
9-1/4	67.201	14-1/4	159.48	19-1/4	291.04
9-3/8	69.029	14-3/8	162.30	19-3/8	294.83
9-1/2	70.882	14-1/2	165.13	19-1/2	298.65
9-5/8	72.760	14-5/8	167.99	19-5/8	302.49
9-3/4	74.662	14-3/4	170.87	19-3/4	306.35
9-7/8	76.589	14-7/8	173.78	19-7/8	310.24
10	78.540	15	176.71	20	314.16
10-1/8	80.516	15-1/8	179.67	20-1/8	318.10
10-1/4	82.516	15-1/4	182.65	20-1/4	322.06
10-3/8	84.541	15-3/8	185.66	20-3/8	326.05
10-1/2	86.590	15-1/2	188.69	20-1/2	330.06
10-5/8	88.664	15-5/8	191.75	20-5/8	334.10
10-3/4	90.763	15-3/4	194.83	20-3/4	338.16
10-7/8	92.886	15-7/8	197.93	20-7/8	342.25
11	95.033	16	201.06	21	346.36
11-1/8	97.205	16-1/8	204.22	21-1/8	350.50
11-1/4	99.402	16-1/4	207.39	21-1/4	354.66
11-3/8	101.62	16-3/8	210.60	21-3/8	358.84
11-1/2	103.87	16-1/2	213.82	21-1/2	363.05
11-5/8	106.14	16-5/8	217.08	21-5/8	367.28
11-3/4	108.43	16-3/4	220.35	21-3/4	371.54
11-7/8	110.75	16-7/8	223.65	21-7/8	375.83
12	113.10	17	226.98	22	380.13
12-1/8	115.47	17-1/8	230.33	22-1/8	384.86
12-1/4	117.86	17-1/4	233.71	22-1/4	388.82
12-3/8	120.28	17-3/8	237.10	22-3/8	393.20
12-1/2	122.72	17-1/2	240.53	22-1/2	397.61
12-5/8	125 19	17-5/8	243.98	22-5/8	402.04
12-3/4	127.68	17-3/4	247.45	22-3/4	406.49
12-7/8	130.19	17-7/8	250.95	22-7/8	410.97

AREAS OF CIRCLES (Continued)

Diameter	Area	Diameter	Area	Diameter	Area
23	415.48	28	615.75	33	855.30
23-1/8	420.00	28-1/8	621.26	33-1/8	861.79
23-1/4	424.56	28-1/4	626.80	33-1/4	868.31
23-3/8	429.13	28-3/8	632.36	33-3/8	874.85
23-1/2	433.74	28-1/2	637.94	33-1/2	881.41
23-5/8	438.36	28-5/8	643.55	33-5/8	888.00
23-3/4	443.01	28-3/4	649.18	33-3/4	894.62
23-7/8	447.69	28-7/8	654.84	33-7/8	901.26
24	452.39	29	660.52	34	907.92
24-1/8	457.11	29-1/8	666.23	34-1/8	914.61
24-1/4	461.86	29-1/4	671.96	34-1/4	921.32
24-3/8	466.64	29-3/8	677.71	34-3/8	928.06
24-1/2	471.44	29-1/2	683.49	34-1/2	934.82
24-5/8	476.26	29-5/8	689.30	34-5/8	941.61
24-3/4	481.11	29-3/4	695.13	34-3/4	948.42
24-7/8	485.98	29-7/8	700.98	34-7/8	955.25
25	490.87	30	706.86	35	962.11
25-1/8	495.79	30-1/8	712.76	35-1/8	969.00
25-1/4	500.74	30-1/4	718.69	35-1/4	975.91
25-3/8	505.71	30-3/8	724.64	35-3/8	982.84
25-1/2	510.71	30-1/2	730.62	35-1/2	989.80
25-5/8	515.72	30-5/8	736.62	35-5/8	996.78
25-3/4	520.77	30-3/4	742.64	35-3/4	1003.8
25-7/8	525.84	30-7/8	748.69	35-7/8	1010.8
26	530.93	31	754.77	36	1017.9
26-1/8	536.05	31-1/8	760.87	36-1/8	1025.0
26-1/4	541.19	31-1/4	766.99	36-1/4	1032.1
26-3/8	546.35	31-3/8	773.14	36-3/8	1039.2
26-1/2	551.55	31-1/2	779.31	36-1/2	1046.3
26-5/8	556.76	31-5/8	785.51	36-5/8	1053.5
26-3/4	562.00	31-3/4	791.73	36-3/4	1060.7
26-7/8	567.27	31-7/8	797.98	36-7/8	1068.0
27	572.56	32	804.25	37	1075.2
27-1/8	577.87	32-1/8	810.54	37-1/8	1082.5
27-1/4	583.21	32-1/4	816.86	37-1/4	1089.8
27-3/8	588.57	32-3/8	823.21	37-3/8	1097.1
27-1/2	593.96	32-1/2	829.58	37-1/2	1104.5
27-5/8	599.37	32-5/8	835.97	37-5/8	1111.8
27-3/4	604.81	32-3/4	842.39	37-3/4	1119.2
27-7/8	610.27	32-7/8	848.83	37-7/8	1126.7

AREAS OF CIRCLES (Continued)

Diameter	Area	Diameter	Area	Diameter	Area
38	1134.1	43	1452.2	48	1809.6
38-1/8	1141.6	43-1/8	1460.7	48-1/8	1819.0
38-1/4	1149.1	43-1/4	1469.1	48-1/4	1828.5
38-3/8	1156.6	43-3/8	1477.6	48-3/8	1837.9
38-1/2	1164.2	43-1/2	1486.2	48-1/2	1847.5
38-5/8	1171.7	43-5/8	1494.7	48-5/8	1857.0
38-3/4	1179.3	43-3/4	1503.3	48-3/4	1866.5
38-7/8	1186.9	43-7/8	1511.9	48-7/8	1876.1
39	1194.6	44	1520.5	49	1885.7
39-1/8	1202.3	44-1/8	1529.2	49-1/8	1895.4
39-1/4	1210.0	44-1/4	1537.9	49-1/4	1905.0
39-3/8	1217.7	44-3/8	1546.6	49-3/8	1914.7
39-1/2	1225.4	44-1/2	1555.3	49-1/2	1924.4
39-5/8	1233.2	44-5/8	1564.0	49-5/8	1934.2
39-3/4	1241.0	44-3/4	1572.8	49-3/4	1943.9
39-7/8	1248.8	44-7/8	1581.6	49-7/8	1953.7
40	1256.6	45	1590.4	50	1963.5
40-1/8	1264.5	45-1/8	1599.3	50-1/8	1973.3
40-1/4	1272.4	45-1/4	1608.2	50-1/4	1983.2
40-3/8	1280.3	45-3/8	1617.0	50-3/8	1993.1
40-1/2	1288.2	45-1/2	1626.0	50-1/2	2003.0
40-5/8	1296.2	45-5/8	1634.9	50-5/8	2012.9
40-3/4	1304.2	45-3/4	1643.9	50-3/4	2022.8
40-7/8	1312.2	45-7/8	1652.9	50-7/8	2032.8
41	1320.3	46	1661.9	51	2042.8
41-1/8	1328.3	46-1/8	1670.9	51-1/8	2052.8
41-1/4	1336.4	46-1/4	1680.0	51-1/4	2062.9
41-3/8	1344.5	46-3/8	1689.1	51-3/8	2073.0
41-1/2	1352.7	46-1/2	1698.2	51-1/2	2083.1
41-5/8	1360.8	46-5/8	1707.4	51-5/8	2093.2
41-3/4	1369.0	46-3/4	1716.5	51-3/4	2103.3
41-7/8	1377.2	46-7/8	1725.7	51-7/8	2113.5
42	1385.4	47	1734.9	52	2123.7
42-1/8	1393.7	47-1/8	1744.2	52-1/8	2133.9
42-1/4	1402.0	47-1/4	1753.5	52-1/4	2144.2
42-3/8	1410.3	47-3/8	1762.7	52-3/8	2154.5
42-1/2	1418.6	47-1/2	1772.1	52-1/2	2164.8
42-5/8	1427.0	47-5/8	1781.4	52-5/8	2175.1
42-3/4	1435.4	47-3/4	1790.8	52-3/4	2185.4
42-7/8	1443.8	47-7/8	1800.1	52-7/8	2195.8

AREAS OF CIRCLES (Continued)

Diameter	Area	Diameter	Area	Diameter	Area
53	2206.2	61	2922.5	71	3959.2
53-1/8	2216.6	61-1/4	2946.5	71-1/4	3987.1
53-1/4	2227.0	61-1/2	2970.6	71-1/2	4015.2
53-3/8	2237.5	61-3/4	2994.8	71-3/4	4043.3
53-1/2	2248.0	62	3019.1	72	4071.5
53-5/8	2258.5				
53-3/4	2269.1	62-1/4	3043.5	72-1/4	4099.8
53-7/8	2279.6	62-1/2	3068.0	72-1/2	4128.2
		62-3/4	3092.6	72-3/4	4156.8
54	2290.2	63	3117.2	73	4185.4
54-1/8	2300.8				
54-1/4	2311.5	63-1/4	3142.0	73-1/4	4214.1
54-3/8	2322.1	63-1/2	3166.9	73-1/2	4242.9
54-1/2	2332.8	63-3/4	3191.9	73-3/4	4271.8
54-5/8	2343.5	64	3217.0	74	4300.8
54-3/4	2354.3				
54-7/8	2365.0	64-1/4	3242.2	74-1/4	4329.9
		64-1/2	3267.5	74-1/2	4359.2
55	2375.8	64-3/4	3292.8	74-3/4	4388.5
55-1/4	2397.5	65	3318.3	75	4417.9
55-1/2	2419.2				
55-3/4	2441.1	65-1/4	3343.9	75-1/4	4447.4
		65-1/2	3369.6	75-1/2	4477.0
56	2463.0	65-3/4	3395.3	75-3/4	4506.7
56-1/4	2485.0	66	3421.2	76	4536.5
56-1/2	2507.2				
56-3/4	2529.4	66-1/4	3447.2	76-1/4	4566.4
		66-1/2	3473.2	76-1/2	4596.3
57	2551.8	66-3/4	3499.4	76-3/4	4626.4
57-1/4	2574.2	67	3525.7	77	4656.6
57-1/2	2596.7				
57-3/4	2619.4	67-1/4	3552.0	77-1/4	4686.9
		67-1/2	3578.5	77-1/2	4717.3
58	2642.1	67-3/4	3605.0	77-3/4	4747.8
58-1/8	2664.9	68	3631.7	78	4778.4
58-1/2	2687.8				
58-3/4	2710.9	68-1/4	3658.4	78-1/4	4809.0
		68-1/2	3685.3	78-1/2	4839.8
59	2734.0	68-3/4	3712.2	78-3/4	4870.7
59-1/4	2757.2	69	3739.3	79	4901.7
59-1/2	2780.5				
59-3/4	2803.9	69-1/4	3766.4	79-1/4	4932.7
		69-1/2	3793.7	79-1/2	4963.9
60	2827.4	69-3/4	3821.0	79-3/4	4995.2
60-1/4	2851.0	70	3848.5	80	5026.5
60-1/2	2874.0	70-1/4	3876.0	80-1/4	5058.0
60-3/4	2898.6	70-1/2	3903.6	80-1/2	5089.6
		70-3/4	3931.4	80-3/4	5121.2

AREAS OF CIRCLES (Continued)

Diameter	Area	Diameter	Area
81	5153.0	91	6503.9
81-1/4	5184.9	91-1/4	6539.7
81-1/2	5216.8	91-1/2	6575.5
81-3/4	5248.9	91-3/4	6611.5
82	5281.0	92	6647.6
82-1/4	5313.3		
82-1/2	5345.6	92-1/4	6683.8
82-3/4	5378.1	92-1/2	6720.1
		92-3/4	6756.4
83	5410.6		
83-1/4	5443.3	93	6792.9
83-1/2	5476.0	93-1/4	6829.5
83-3/4	5508.8	93-1/2	6866.1
		93-3/4	6902.9
84	5541.8		
84-1/4	5574.8	94	6939.8
84-1/2	5607.9	94-1/4	6976.7
84-3/4	5641.2	94-1/2	7013.8
		94-3/4	7051.0
85	5674.5		
85-1/4	5707.9	95	7088.2
85-1/2	5741.5	95-1/4	7125.6
85-3/4	5775.1	95-1/2	7163.0
		95-3/4	7200.6
86	5808.8		
86-1/4	5842.6	96	7238.2
86-1/2	5876.5	96-1/4	7276.0
86-3/4	5910.6	96-1/2	7313.8
		96-3/4	7351.8
87	5944.7		
87-1/4	5978.9	97	7389.8
87-1/2	6013.2	97-1/4	7428.0
87-3/4	6047.6	97-1/2	7466.2
		97-3/4	7504.5
88	6082.1		
88-1/4	6256.7	98	7543.0
88-1/2	6151.4	98-1/4	7581.5
88-3/4	6186.2	98-1/2	7620.1
		98-3/4	7658.9
89	6221.1		
89-1/4	6256.1	99	7697.7
89-1/2	6291.2	99-1/4	7736.6
89-3/4	6326.4	99-1/2	7775.6
		99-3/4	7814.8
90	6361.7		
90-1/4	6397.1	100	7854.0
90-1/2	6432.6		
90-3/4	6468.2		

LOGARITHMS

If $x = \log_e n$, then $e^x = n$ $\log n^c = c \log n$ $\log 1 = 0$

$\log ab = \log a + \log b$ $\log \sqrt[c]{n} = (1/c) \log n$ $\pi = 3.141593$

$\log a/b = \log a - \log b$ $\log_e x = 2.3026 \log_{10} x$ $\log_{10} \pi = .497150$

$\quad\quad\quad = -\log b/a$ $\log_{10} x = 0.4343 \log_e x$

$\log 1/n = -\log n$ $e = 2.718282$

LOGARITHMS TO BASE 10

Number	0	1	2	3	4	5	6	7	8	9	1 2 3	4 5 6	7 8 9
1.0	0000	0043	0086	0128	0170	0212	0253	0294	0334	0374	4 8 12	17 21 25	29 33 37
1.1	0414	0453	0492	0531	0569	0607	0645	0682	0719	0755	4 8 11	15 19 23	26 30 34
1.2	0792	0828	0864	0899	0934	0969	1004	1038	1072	1106	3 7 10	14 17 21	24 28 31
1.3	1139	1173	1206	1239	1271	1303	1335	1367	1399	1430	3 6 10	13 16 19	23 26 29
1.4	1461	1492	1523	1553	1584	1614	1644	1673	1703	1732	3 6 9	12 15 18	21 24 27
1.5	1761	1790	.1818	1847	1875	1903	1931	1959	1987	2014	3 6 8	11 14 17	20 22 25
1.6	2041	2068	2095	2122	2148	2175	2201	2227	2253	2279	3 5 8	11 13 16	18 21 24
1.7	2304	2330	2355	2380	2405	2430	2455	2480	2504	2529	2 5 7	10 12 15	17 20 22
1.8	2553	2577	2601	2625	2648	2672	2695	2718	2742	2765	2 5 7	9 12 14	16 19 21
1.9	2788	2810	2833	2856	2878	2900	2923	2945	2967	2989	2 4 7	9 11 13	16 18 20
2.0	3010	3032	3054	3075	3096	3118	3139	3160	3181	3201	2 4 6	8 11 13	15 17 19
2.1	3222	3243	3263	3284	3304	3324	3345	3365	3385	3404	2 4 6	8 10 12	14 16 18
2.2	3424	3444	3464	3483	3502	3522	3541	3560	3579	3598	2 4 6	8 10 12	14 15 17
2.3	3617	3636	3655	3674	3692	3711	3729	3747	3766	3784	2 4 6	7 9 11	13 15 17
2.4	3802	3820	3838	3856	3874	3892	3909	3927	3945	3962	2 4 5	7 9 11	12 14 16
2.5	3979	3997	4014	4031	4048	4065	4082	4099	4116	4133	2 3 5	7 9 10	12 14 15
2.6	4150	4166	4183	4200	4216	4232	4249	4265	4281	4298	2 3 5	7 8 10	11 13 15
2.7	4314	4330	4346	4362	4378	4393	4409	4425	4440	4456	2 3 5	6 8 9	11 13 14
2.8	4472	4487	4502	4518	4533	4548	4564	4579	4594	4609	2 3 5	6 8 9	11 12 14
2.9	4624	4639	4654	4669	4683	4698	4713	4728	4742	4757	1 3 4	6 7 9	10 12 13
3.0	4771	4786	4800	4814	4829	4843	4857	4871	4886	4900	1 3 4	6 7 9	10 11 13
3.1	4914	4928	4942	4955	4969	4983	4997	5011	5024	5038	1 3 4	6 8 9	10 11 12
3.2	5051	5065	5079	5092	5105	5119	5132	5145	5159	5172	1 3 4	5 7 8	9 11 12
3.3	5185	5198	5211	5224	5237	5250	5263	5276	5289	5302	1 3 4	5 6 8	9 10 12
3.4	5315	5328	5340	5353	5366	5378	5391	5403	5416	5428	1 3 4	5 6 8	9 10 11
3.5	5441	5453	5465	5478	5490	5502	5514	5527	5539	5551	1 2 4	5 6 7	9 10 11
3.6	5563	5575	5587	5599	5611	5623	5635	5647	5658	5670	1 2 4	5 6 7	8 10 11
3.7	5682	5694	5705	5717	5729	5740	5752	5763	5775	5786	1 2 3	5 6 7	8 9 10
3.8	5798	5809	5821	5832	5843	5855	5866	5877	5888	5899	1 2 3	5 6 7	8 9 10
3.9	5911	5922	5933	5944	5955	5966	5977	5988	5999	6010	1 2 3	4 5 7	8 9 10
4.0	6021	6031	6042	6053	6064	6075	6085	6096	6107	6117	1 2 3	4 5 6	8 9 10
4.1	6128	6138	6149	6160	6170	6180	6191	6201	6212	6222	1 2 3	4 5 6	7 8 9
4.2	6232	6243	6253	6263	6274	6284	6294	6304	6314	6325	1 2 3	4 5 6	7 8 9
4.3	6335	6345	6355	6365	6375	6385	6395	6405	6415	6425	1 2 3	4 5 6	7 8 9
4.4	6435	6444	6454	6464	6474	6484	6493	6503	6513	6522	1 2 3	4 5 6	7 8 9
4.5	6532	6542	6551	6561	6571	6580	6590	6599	6609	6618	1 2 3	4 5 6	7 8 9
4.6	6628	6637	6646	6656	6665	6675	6684	6693	6702	6712	1 2 3	4 5 6	7 7 8
4.7	6721	6730	6739	6749	6758	6767	6776	6785	6794	6803	1 2 3	4 5 6	6 7 8
4.8	6812	6821	6830	6839	6848	6857	6866	6875	6884	6893	1 2 3	4 4 5	6 7 8
4.9	6902	6911	6920	6928	6937	6946	6955	6964	6972	6981	1 2 3	4 4 5	6 7 8
5.0	6990	6998	7007	7016	7024	7033	7042	7050	7059	7067	1 2 3	3 4 5	6 7 8
5.1	7076	7084	7093	7101	7110	7118	7126	7135	7143	7152	1 2 3	3 4 5	6 7 8
5.2	7160	7168	7177	7185	7193	7202	7210	7218	7226	7235	1 2 2	3 4 5	6 7 7
5.3	7243	7251	7259	7267	7275	7284	7292	7300	7308	7316	1 2 2	3 4 5	6 6 7
5.4	7324	7332	7340	7348	7356	7364	7372	7380	7388	7396	1 2 2	3 4 5	6 6 7

LOGARITHMS TO BASE 10 (Continued)

Num-ber	0	1	2	3	4	5	6	7	8	9	Proportional Parts								
											1	2	3	4	5	6	7	8	9
5.5	7404	7412	7419	7427	7435	7443	7451	7459	7466	7474	1	2	2	3	4	5	5	6	7
5.6	7482	7490	7497	7505	7513	7520	7528	7536	7543	7551	1	2	2	3	4	5	5	6	7
5.7	7559	7566	7574	7582	7589	7597	7604	7612	7619	7627	1	2	2	3	4	5	5	6	7
5.8	7634	7642	7649	7657	7664	7672	7679	7686	7694	7701	1	1	2	3	4	4	5	6	7
5.9	7709	7716	7723	7731	7738	7745	7752	7760	7767	7774	1	1	2	3	4	4	5	6	7
6.0	7782	7789	7796	7803	7810	7818	7825	7832	7839	7846	1	1	2	3	4	4	5	6	6
6.1	7853	7860	7868	7875	7882	7889	7896	7903	7910	7917	1	1	2	3	4	4	5	6	6
6.2	7924	7931	7938	7945	7952	7959	7966	7973	7980	7987	1	1	2	3	3	4	5	6	6
6.3	7993	8000	8007	8014	8021	8028	8035	8041	8048	8055	1	1	2	3	3	4	5	5	6
6.4	8062	8069	8075	8082	8089	8096	8102	8109	8116	8122	1	1	2	3	3	4	5	5	6
6.5	8129	8136	8142	8149	8156	8162	8169	8176	8182	8189	1	1	2	3	3	4	5	5	6
6.6	8195	8202	8209	8215	8222	8228	8235	8241	8248	8254	1	1	2	3	3	4	5	5	6
6.7	8261	8267	8274	8280	8287	8293	8299	8306	8312	8319	1	1	2	3	3	4	5	5	6
6.8	8325	8331	8338	8344	8351	8357	8363	8370	8376	8382	1	1	2	3	3	4	4	5	6
6.9	8388	8395	8401	8407	8414	8420	8426	8432	8439	8445	1	1	2	2	3	4	4	5	6
7.0	8451	8457	8463	8470	8476	8482	8488	8494	8500	8506	1	1	2	2	3	4	4	5	6
7.1	8513	8519	8525	8531	8537	8543	8549	8555	8561	8567	1	1	2	2	3	4	4	5	5
7.2	8573	8579	8585	8591	8597	8603	8609	8615	8621	8627	1	1	2	2	3	4	4	5	5
7.3	8633	8639	8645	8651	8657	8663	8669	8675	8681	8686	1	1	2	2	3	4	4	5	5
7.4	8692	8698	8704	8710	8716	8722	8727	8733	8739	8745	1	1	2	2	3	4	4	5	5
7.5	8751	8756	8762	8768	8774	8779	8785	8791	8797	8802	1	1	2	2	3	3	4	5	5
7.6	8808	8814	8820	8825	8831	8837	8842	8848	8854	8859	1	1	2	2	3	3	4	5	5
7.7	8865	8871	8876	8882	8887	8893	8899	8904	8910	8915	1	1	2	2	3	3	4	4	5
7.8	8921	8927	8932	8938	8943	8949	8954	8960	8965	8971	1	1	2	2	3	3	4	4	5
7.9	8976	8982	8987	8993	8998	9004	9009	9015	9020	9025	1	1	2	2	3	3	4	4	5
8.0	9031	9036	9042	9047	9053	9058	9063	9069	9074	9079	1	1	2	2	3	3	4	4	5
8.1	9085	9090	9096	9101	9106	9112	9117	9122	9128	9133	1	1	2	2	3	3	4	4	5
8.2	9138	9143	9149	9154	9159	9165	9170	9175	9180	9186	1	1	2	2	3	3	4	4	5
8.3	9191	9196	9201	9206	9212	9217	9222	9227	9232	9238	1	1	2	2	3	3	4	4	5
8.4	9243	9248	9253	9258	9263	9269	9274	9279	9284	9289	1	1	2	2	3	3	4	4	5
8.5	9294	9299	9304	9309	9315	9320	9325	9330	9335	9340	1	1	2	2	3	3	4	4	5
8.6	9345	9350	9355	9360	9365	9370	9375	9380	9385	9390	1	1	2	2	3	3	4	4	5
8.7	9395	9400	9405	9410	9415	9420	9425	9430	9435	9440	0	1	1	2	2	3	3	4	4
8.8	9445	9450	9455	9460	9465	9469	9474	9479	9484	9489	0	1	1	2	2	3	3	4	4
8.9	9494	9499	9504	9509	9513	9518	9523	9528	9533	9538	0	1	1	2	2	3	3	4	4
9.0	9542	9547	9552	9557	9562	9566	9571	9576	9581	9586	0	1	1	2	2	3	3	4	4
9.1	9590	9595	9600	9605	9609	9614	9619	9624	9628	9633	0	1	1	2	2	3	3	4	4
9.2	9638	9643	9647	9652	9657	9661	9666	9671	9675	9680	0	1	1	2	2	3	3	4	4
9.3	9685	9689	9694	9699	9703	9708	9713	9717	9722	9727	0	1	1	2	2	3	3	4	4
9.4	9731	9736	9741	9745	9750	9754	9759	9763	9768	9773	0	1	1	2	2	3	3	4	4
9.5	9777	9782	9786	9791	9795	9800	9805	9809	9814	9818	0	1	1	2	2	3	3	4	4
9.6	9823	9827	9832	9836	9841	9845	9850	9854	9859	9863	0	1	1	2	2	3	3	4	4
9.7	9868	9872	9877	9881	9886	9890	9894	9899	9903	9908	0	1	1	2	2	3	3	4	4
9.8	9912	9917	9921	9926	9930	9934	9939	9943	9948	9952	0	1	1	2	2	3	3	4	4
9.9	9956	9961	9965	9969	9974	9978	9983	9987	9991	9996	0	1	1	2	2	3	3	3	4

GREEK ALPHABET

A, α	Alpha	H, η	Eta	N, ν	Nu	T, τ	Tau
B, β	Beta	Θ, ϑ	Theta	Ξ, ξ	Xi	Y, υ	Upsilon
Γ, γ	Gamma	I, ι	Iota	O, o	Omicron	Φ, φ	Phi
Δ, δ	Delta	K, κ	Kappa	Π, π	Pi	X, χ	Chi
E, ϵ	Epsilon	Λ, λ	Lambda	P, ρ	Rho	Ψ, ψ	Psi
Z, ζ	Zeta	M, μ	Mu	Σ, σ	Sigma	Ω, ω	Omega

TRIGONOMETRIC SOLUTION OF TRIANGLES

Right-angle Triangle

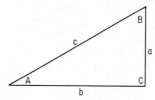

$$a^2 + b^2 = c^2 \qquad A + B = 90° \qquad Area = \tfrac{1}{2}ab$$
$$\sin A = a/c \qquad \cos A = b/c \qquad \tan A = a/b$$
$$\csc A = c/a \qquad \sec A = c/b \qquad \cot A = b/a$$
$$a = \sqrt{c^2 - b^2} = c \sin A = b \tan A = b/\cot A = c/\csc A$$
$$b = \sqrt{c^2 - a^2} = c \cos A = a/\tan A = a \cot A = c/\sec A$$
$$c = \sqrt{a^2 + b^2} = a/\sin A = b/\cos A = a \csc A = b \sec A$$
$$A = 90° - B \qquad B = 90° - A \qquad C = 90°$$

Oblique-angle Triangle

$$a = \sqrt{b^2 + c^2 - 2bc \cos A} = \frac{b \sin A}{\sin B} = \frac{\sin C}{c \sin A}$$

$$b = \sqrt{a^2 + c^2 - 2ac \cos B} = \frac{a \sin B}{\sin A} = \frac{c \sin B}{\sin C}$$

$$c = \sqrt{a^2 + b^2 - 2ab \cos C} = \frac{a \sin C}{\sin A} = \frac{b \sin C}{\sin B}$$

$$A = 180° - B - C; \sin A = \frac{a \sin B}{b} = \frac{a \sin C}{c}$$

$$B = 180° - A - C; \sin B = \frac{b \sin A}{a} = \frac{b \sin C}{c}$$

$$C = 180° - A - B; \sin C = \frac{c \sin A}{a} = \frac{c \sin B}{b}$$

$$Area = \tfrac{1}{2}ab \sin C = \frac{a^2 \sin B \sin C}{2 \sin A} = \frac{bc \sin A}{2} = \frac{ac \sin B}{2}$$

TRIGONOMETRIC FORMULAS*

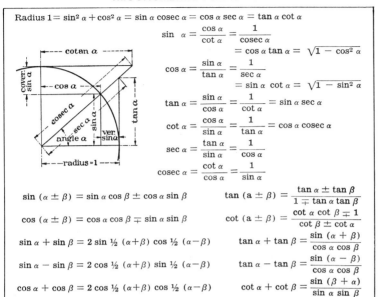

Radius $1 = \sin^2\alpha + \cos^2\alpha = \sin\alpha\,\mathrm{cosec}\,\alpha = \cos\alpha\sec\alpha = \tan\alpha\cot\alpha$

$$\sin\alpha = \frac{\cos\alpha}{\cot\alpha} = \frac{1}{\mathrm{cosec}\,\alpha}$$
$$= \cos\alpha\tan\alpha = \sqrt{1-\cos^2\alpha}$$

$$\cos\alpha = \frac{\sin\alpha}{\tan\alpha} = \frac{1}{\sec\alpha}$$
$$= \sin\alpha\cot\alpha = \sqrt{1-\sin^2\alpha}$$

$$\tan\alpha = \frac{\sin\alpha}{\cos\alpha} = \frac{1}{\cot\alpha} = \sin\alpha\sec\alpha$$

$$\cot\alpha = \frac{\cos\alpha}{\sin\alpha} = \frac{1}{\tan\alpha} = \cos\alpha\,\mathrm{cosec}\,\alpha$$

$$\sec\alpha = \frac{\tan\alpha}{\sin\alpha} = \frac{1}{\cos\alpha}$$

$$\mathrm{cosec}\,\alpha = \frac{\cot\alpha}{\cos\alpha} = \frac{1}{\sin\alpha}$$

$$\sin(\alpha\pm\beta) = \sin\alpha\cos\beta \pm \cos\alpha\sin\beta$$

$$\tan(a\pm\beta) = \frac{\tan\alpha\pm\tan\beta}{1\mp\tan\alpha\tan\beta}$$

$$\cos(\alpha\pm\beta) = \cos\alpha\cos\beta \mp \sin\alpha\sin\beta$$

$$\cot(a\pm\beta) = \frac{\cot\alpha\cot\beta\mp1}{\cot\beta\pm\cot\alpha}$$

$$\sin\alpha + \sin\beta = 2\sin\tfrac{1}{2}(\alpha+\beta)\cos\tfrac{1}{2}(\alpha-\beta)$$

$$\tan\alpha + \tan\beta = \frac{\sin(\alpha+\beta)}{\cos\alpha\cos\beta}$$

$$\sin\alpha - \sin\beta = 2\cos\tfrac{1}{2}(\alpha+\beta)\sin\tfrac{1}{2}(\alpha-\beta)$$

$$\tan\alpha - \tan\beta = \frac{\sin(\alpha-\beta)}{\cos\alpha\cos\beta}$$

$$\cos\alpha + \cos\beta = 2\cos\tfrac{1}{2}(\alpha+\beta)\cos\tfrac{1}{2}(\alpha-\beta)$$

$$\cot\alpha + \cot\beta = \frac{\sin(\beta+\alpha)}{\sin\alpha\sin\beta}$$

$$\cos\beta - \cos\alpha = 2\sin\tfrac{1}{2}(\alpha+\beta)\sin\tfrac{1}{2}(\alpha-\beta)$$

$$\cot\alpha - \cot\beta = \frac{\sin(\beta-\alpha)}{\sin\alpha\sin\beta}$$

$$\sin2\alpha = 2\sin\alpha\cos\alpha \qquad \cos2\alpha = \cos^2\alpha - \sin^2\alpha \qquad \tan2\sigma = \frac{2\tan\alpha}{1-\tan^2\alpha}$$

$$\cot2\alpha = \frac{\cot^2\alpha-1}{2\cot\alpha} \qquad \sin\tfrac{1}{2}\alpha = \sqrt{\frac{1-\cos\alpha}{2}} \qquad \cos\tfrac{1}{2}\alpha = \sqrt{\frac{1+\cos\alpha}{2}}$$

$$\tan\tfrac{1}{2}\alpha = \frac{\sin\alpha}{1+\cos\alpha} \qquad \cot\tfrac{1}{2}\alpha = \frac{\sin\alpha}{1-\cos\alpha} \qquad \sin^2\alpha = \frac{1-\cos2\alpha}{2}$$

$$\cos^2\alpha = \frac{1+\cos2\alpha}{2} \qquad \tan^2\alpha = \frac{1-\cos2\alpha}{1+\cos2\alpha} \qquad \cot^2\alpha = \frac{1+\cos2\alpha}{1-\cos2\alpha}$$

$$\sin^2\alpha - \sin^2\beta = \sin(\alpha+\beta)\sin(\alpha-\beta) \qquad \cos^2\alpha - \sin^2\beta = \cos(\alpha+\beta)\cos(\alpha-\beta)$$

$$\frac{\sin\alpha\pm\sin\beta}{\cos\alpha+\cos\beta} = \tan\tfrac{1}{2}(\alpha\pm\beta), \qquad \frac{\sin\alpha\pm\sin\beta}{\cos\beta-\cos\alpha} = \cot\tfrac{1}{2}(\alpha\mp\beta)$$

The numerical values of angular functions increase or decrease from:

Function	In Quadrant I 0°—90°	In Quadrant II 90°—180°	In Quadrant III 180°—270°	In Quadrant IV 270°—360°
sin	0 to +1	+1 to 0	0 to −1	−1 to 0
cos	+1 to 0	0 to −1	−1 to 0	0 to +1
tan	0 to +∞	−∞ to 0	0 to +∞	−∞ to 0
cot	+∞ to 0	0 to −∞	+∞ to 0	0 to −∞
sec	+1 to +∞	−∞ to −1	−1 to −∞	+∞ to +1
cosec	+∞ to +1	+1 to +∞	−∞ to −1	−1 to −∞

* *Courtesy of* New Departure-Hyatt Bearings Division of General Motors Corp.

TRIGONOMETRIC FUNCTIONS

SINES

De-grees	Ra-dians	0'	10'	20'	30'	40'	50'	60'	
0	.0000	.0000	.0029	.0058	.0087	.0116	.0145	.0175	89
1	.0175	.0175	.0204	.0233	.0262	.0291	.0320	.0349	88
2	.0349	.0349	.0378	.0407	.0436	.0465	.0494	.0523	87
3	.0524	.0523	.0552	.0581	.0610	.0640	.0669	.0698	86
4	.0698	.0698	.0727	.0756	.0785	.0814	.0843	.0872	85
5	.0873	.0872	.0901	.0929	.0958	.0987	.1016	.1045	84
6	.1047	.1045	.1074	.1103	.1132	.1161	.1190	.1219	83
7	.1222	.1219	.1248	.1276	.1305	.1334	.1363	.1392	82
8	.1396	.1392	.1421	.1449	.1478	.1507	.1536	.1564	81
9	.1571	.1564	.1593	.1622	.1650	.1679	.1708	.1736	80
10	.1745	.1736	.1765	.1794	.1822	.1851	.1880	.1908	79
11	.1920	.1908	.1937	.1965	.1994	.2022	.2051	.2079	78
12	.2094	.2079	.2108	.2136	.2164	.2193	.2221	.2250	77
13	.2269	.2250	.2278	.2306	.2334	.2363	.2391	.2419	76
14	.2443	.2419	.2447	.2476	.2504	.2532	.2560	.2588	75
15	.2618	.2588	.2616	.2644	.2672	.2700	.2728	.2756	74
16	.2793	.2756	.2784	.2812	.2840	.2868	.2896	.2924	73
17	.2967	.2924	.2952	.2979	.3007	.3035	.3062	.3090	72
18	.3142	.3090	.3118	.3145	.3173	.3201	.3228	.3256	71
19	.3316	.3256	.3283	.3311	.3338	.3365	.3393	.3420	70
20	.3491	.3420	.3448	.3475	.3502	.3529	.3557	.3584	69
21	.3665	.3584	.361▶	.3638	.3665	.3692	.3719	.3746	68
22	.3840	.3746	.3773	.3800	.3827	.3854	.3881	.3907	67
23	.4014	.3907	.3934	.3961	.3987	.4014	.4041	.4067	66
24	.4189	.4067	.4094	.4120	.4147	.4173	.4200	.4226	65
25	.4363	.4226	.4253	.4279	.4305	.4331	.4358	.4384	64
26	.4538	.4384	.4410	.4436	.4462	.4488	.4514	.4540	63
27	.4712	.4540	.4566	.4592	.4617	.4643	.4669	.4695	62
28	.4887	.4695	.4720	.4746	.4772	.4797	.4823	.4848	61
29	.5061	.4848	.4874	.4899	.4924	.4950	.4975	.5000	60
30	.5236	.5000	.5025	.5050	.5075	.5100	.5125	.5150	59
31	.5411	.5150	.5175	.5200	.5225	.5250	.5275	.5299	58
32	.5585	.5299	.5324	.5348	.5373	.5398	.5422	.5446	57
33	.5760	.5446	.5471	.5495	.5519	.5544	.5568	.5592	56
34	.5934	.5592	.5616	.5640	.5664	.5688	.5712	.5736	55
35	.6109	.5736	.5760	.5783	.5807	.5831	.5854	.5878	54
36	.6283	.5878	.5901	.5925	.5948	.5972	.5995	.6018	53
37	.6458	.6018	.6041	.6065	.6088	.6111	.6134	.6157	52
38	.6632	.6157	.6180	.6202	.6225	.6248	.6271	.6293	51
39	.6807	.6293	.6316	.6338	.6361	.6383	.6406	.6428	50
40	.6981	.6428	.6450	.6472	.6494	.6517	.6539	.6561	49
41	.7156	.6561	.6583	.6604	.6626	.6648	.6670	.6691	48
42	.7330	.6691	.6713	.6734	.6756	.6777	.6799	.6820	47
43	.7505	.6820	.6841	.6862	.6884	.6905	.6926	.6947	46
44	.7679	.6947	.6967	.6988	.7009	.7030	.7050	.7071	45
45	.7854	.7071							
		60'	50'	40'	30'	20'	10'	0'	De-grees

COSINES

TRIGONOMETRIC FUNCTIONS (Continued)

SINES

De-grees	Ra-dians	0'	10'	20'	30'	40'	50'	60'	
45	0.7854	.7071	.7092	.7112	.7133	.7153	.7173	.7193	44
46	0.8029	.7193	.7214	.7234	.7254	.7274	.7294	.7314	43
47	0.8203	.7314	.7333	.7353	.7373	.7392	.7412	.7431	42
48	0.8378	.7431	.7451	.7470	.7490	.7509	.7528	.7547	41
49	0.8552	.7547	.7566	.7585	.7604	.7623	.7642	.7660	40
50	0.8727	.7660	.7679	.7698	.7716	.7735	.7753	.7771	39
51	0.8901	.7771	.7790	.7808	.7826	.7844	.7862	.7880	38
52	0.9076	.7880	.7898	.7916	.7934	.7951	.7969	.7986	37
53	0.9250	.7986	.8004	.8021	.8039	.8056	.8073	.8090	36
54	0.9425	.8090	.8107	.8124	.8141	.8158	.8175	.8192	35
55	0.9599	.8192	.8208	.8225	.8241	.8258	.8274	.8290	34
56	0.9774	.8290	.8307	.8323	.8339	.8355	.8371	.8387	33
57	0.9948	.8387	.8403	.8418	.8434	.8450	.8465	.8480	32
58	1.0123	.8480	.8496	.8511	.8526	.8542	.8557	.8572	31
59	1.0297	.8572	.8587	.8601	.8616	.8631	.8646	.8660	30
60	1.0472	.8660	.8675	.8689	.8704	.8718	.8732	.8746	29
61	1.0647	.8746	.8760	.8774	.8788	.8802	.8816	.8829	28
62	1.0821	.8829	.8843	.8857	.8870	.8884	.8897	.8910	27
63	1.0996	.8910	.8923	.8936	.8949	.8962	.8975	.8988	26
64	1.1170	.8988	.9001	.9013	.9026	.9038	.9051	.9063	25
65	1.1345	.9063	.9075	.9088	.9100	.9112	.9124	.9135	24
66	1.1519	.9135	.9147	.9159	.9171	.9182	.9194	.9205	23
67	1.1694	.9205	.9216	.9228	.9239	.9250	.9261	.9272	22
68	1.1868	.9272	.9283	.9293	.9304	.9315	.9325	.9336	21
69	1.2043	.9336	.9346	.9356	.9367	.9377	.9387	.9397	20
70	1.2217	.9397	.9407	.9417	.9426	.9436	.9446	.9455	19
71	1.2392	.9455	.9465	.9474	.9483	.9492	.9502	.9511	18
72	1.2566	.9511	.9520	.9528	.9537	.9546	.9555	.9563	17
73	1.2741	.9563	.9572	.9580	.9588	.9596	.9605	.9613	16
74	1.2915	.9613	.9621	.9628	.9636	.9644	.9652	.9659	15
75	1.3090	.9659	.9667	.9674	.9681	.9689	.9696	.9703	14
76	1.3265	.9703	.9710	.9717	.9724	.9730	.9737	.9744	13
77	1.3439	.9744	.9750	.9757	.9763	.9769	.9775	.9781	12
78	1.3614	.9781	.9787	.9793	.9799	.9805	.9811	.9816	11
79	1.3788	.9816	.9822	.9827	.9833	.9838	.9843	.9848	10
80	1.3963	.9848	.9853	.9858	.9863	.9868	.9872	.9877	9
81	1.4137	.9877	.9881	.9886	.9890	.9894	.9899	.9903	8
82	1.4312	.9903	.9907	.9911	.9914	.9918	.9922	.9925	7
83	1.4486	.9925	.9929	.9932	.9936	.9939	.9942	.9945	6
84	1.4661	.9945	.9948	.9951	.9954	.9957	.9959	.9962	5
85	1.4835	.9962	.9964	.9967	.9969	.9971	.9974	.9976	4
86	1.5010	.9976	.9978	.9980	.9981	.9983	.9985	.9986	3
87	1.5184	.9986	.9988	.9989	.9990	.9992	.9993	.9994	2
88	1.5359	.9994	.9995	.9996	.9997	.9997	.9998	.9998	1
89	1.5533	.9998	.9999	.9999	.9999	1.0000	1.0000	1.0000	0
90	1.5708	1.0000							
		60'	50'	40'	30'	20'	10'	0'	De-grees

COSINES

TRIGONOMETRIC FUNCTIONS (Continued)

TANGENTS

De-grees	Ra-dians	0'	10'	20'	30'	40'	50'	60'	
0	.0000	.0000	.0029	.0058	.0087	.0116	.0145	.0175	89
1	.0175	.0175	.0204	.0233	.0262	.0291	.0320	.0349	88
2	.0349	.0349	.0378	.0407	.0437	.0466	.0495	.0524	87
3	.0524	.0524	.0553	.0582	.0612	.0641	.0670	.0699	86
4	.0698	.0699	.0729	.0758	.0787	.0816	.0846	.0875	85
5	.0873	.0875	.0904	.0934	.0963	.0992	.1022	.1051	84
6	.1047	.1051	.1080	.1110	.1139	.1169	.1198	.1228	83
7	.1222	.1228	.1257	.1287	.1317	.1346	.1376	.1405	82
8	.1396	.1405	.1435	.1465	.1495	.1524	.1554	.1584	81
9	.1571	.1584	.1614	.1644	.1673	.1703	.1733	.1763	80
10	.1745	.1763	.1793	.1823	.1853	.1883	.1914	.1944	79
11	.1920	.1944	.1974	.2004	.2035	.2065	.2095	.2126	78
12	.2094	.2126	.2156	.2186	.2217	.2247	.2278	.2309	77
13	.2269	.2309	.2339	.2370	.2401	.2432	.2462	.2493	76
14	.2443	.2493	.2524	.2555	.2586	.2617	.2648	.2679	75
15	.2618	.2679	.2711	.2742	.2773	.2805	.2836	.2867	74
16	.2793	.2867	.2899	.2931	.2962	.2994	.3026	.3057	73
17	.2967	.3057	.3089	.3121	.3153	.3185	.3217	.3249	72
18	.3142	.3249	.3281	.3314	.3346	.3378	.3411	.3443	71
19	.3316	.3443	.3476	.3508	.3541	.3574	.3607	.3640	70
20	.3491	.3640	.3673	.3706	.3739	.3772	.3805	.3839	69
21	.3665	.3839	.3872	.3906	.3939	.3973	.4006	.4040	68
22	.3840	.4040	.4074	.4108	.4142	.4176	.4210	.4245	67
23	.4014	.4245	.4279	.4314	.4348	.4383	.4417	.4452	66
24	.4189	.4452	.4487	.4522	.4557	.4592	.4628	.4663	65
25	.4363	.4663	.4699	.4734	.4770	.4806	.4841	.4877	64
26	.4538	.4877	.4913	.4950	.4986	.5022	.5059	.5095	63
27	.4712	.5095	.5132	.5169	.5206	.5243	.5280	.5317	62
28	.4887	.5317	.5354	.5392	.5430	.5467	.5505	.5543	61
29	.5061	.5543	.5581	.5619	.5658	.5696	.5735	.5774	60
30	.5236	.5774	.5812	.5851	.5890	.5930	.5969	.6009	59
31	.5411	.6009	.6048	.6088	.6128	.6168	.6208	.6249	58
32	.5585	.6249	.6289	.6330	.6371	.6412	.6453	.6494	57
33	.5760	.6494	.6536	.6577	.6619	.6661	.6703	.6745	56
34	.5934	.6745	.6787	.6830	.6873	.6916	.6959	.7002	55
35	.6109	.7002	.7046	.7089	.7133	.7177	.7221	.7265	54
36	.6283	.7265	.7310	.7355	.7400	.7445	.7490	.7536	53
37	.6458	.7536	.7581	.7627	.7673	.7720	.7766	.7813	52
38	.6632	.7813	.7860	.7907	.7954	.8002	.8050	.8098	51
39	.6807	.8098	.8146	.8195	.8243	.8292	.8342	.8391	50
40	.6981	.8391	.8441	.8491	.8541	.8591	.8642	.8693	49
41	.7156	.8693	.8744	.8796	.8847	.8899	.8952	.9004	48
42	.7330	.9004	.9057	.9110	.9163	.9217	.9271	.9325	47
43	.7505	.9325	.9380	.9435	.9490	.9545	.9601	.9657	46
44	.7679	.9657	.9713	.9770	.9827	.9884	.9942	1.0000	45
45	.7854	1.0000							
		60'	50'	40'	30'	20'	10'	0'	De-grees

COTANGENTS

TRIGONOMETRIC FUNCTIONS (Continued)

TANGENTS

De-grees	Ra-dians	0'	10'	20'	30'	40'	50'	60'	
45	0.7854	1.000	1.006	1.012	1.018	1.024	1.030	1.036	44
46	0.8029	1.036	1.042	1.048	1.054	1.060	1.066	1.072	43
47	0.8203	1.072	1.079	1.085	1.091	1.098	1.104	1.111	42
48	0.8378	1.111	1.117	1.124	1.130	1.137	1.144	1.150	41
49	0.8552	1.150	1.157	1.164	1.171	1.178	1.185	1.192	40
50	0.8727	1.192	1.199	1.206	1.213	1.220	1.228	1.235	39
51	0.8901	1.235	1.242	1.250	1.257	1.265	1.272	1.280	38
52	0.9076	1.280	1.288	1.295	1.303	1.311	1.319	1.327	37
53	0.9250	1.327	1.335	1.343	1.351	1.360	1.368	1.376	36
54	0.9425	1.376	1.385	1.393	1.402	1.411	1.419	1.428	35
55	0.9599	1.428	1.437	1.446	1.455	1.464	1.473	1.483	34
56	0.9774	1.483	1.492	1.501	1.511	1.520	1.530	1.540	33
57	0.9948	1.540	1.550	1.560	1.570	1.580	1.590	1.600	32
58	1.0123	1.600	1.611	1.621	1.632	1.643	1.653	1.664	31
59	1.0297	1.664	1.675	1.686	1.698	1.709	1.720	7.732	30
60	1.0472	1.732	1.744	1.756	1.767	1.780	1.792	1.804	29
61	1.0647	1.804	1.816	1.829	1.842	1.855	1.868	1.881	28
62	1.0821	1.881	1.894	1.907	1.921	1.935	1.949	1.963	27
63	1.0996	1.963	1.977	1.991	2.006	2.020	2.035	2.050	26
64	1.1170	2.050	2.066	2.081	2.097	2.112	2.128	2.145	25
65	1.1345	2.145	2.161	2.177	2.194	2.211	2.229	2.246	24
66	1.1519	2.246	2.264	2.282	2.300	2.318	2.337	2.356	23
67	1.1694	2.356	2.375	2.394	2.414	2.434	2.455	2.475	22
68	1.1868	2.475	2.496	2.517	2.539	2.560	2.583	2.605	21
69	1.2043	2.605	2.628	2.651	2.675	2.699	2.723	2.747	20
70	1.2217	2.747	2.773	2.798	2.824	2.850	2.877	2.904	19
71	1.2392	2.904	2.932	2.960	2.989	3.018	3.047	3.078	18
72	1.2566	3.078	3.108	3.140	3.172	3.204	3.237	3.271	17
73	1.2741	3.271	3.305	3.340	3.376	3.412	3.450	3.487	16
74	1.2915	3.487	3.526	3.566	3.606	3.647	3.689	3.732	15
75	1.3090	3.732	3.776	3.821	3.867	3.914	3.962	4.011	14
76	1.3265	4.011	4.061	4.113	4.165	4.219	4.275	4.331	13
77	1.3439	4.331	4.390	4.449	4.511	4.574	4.638	4.705	12
78	1.3614	4.705	4.773	4.843	4.915	4.989	5.066	5.145	11
79	1.3788	5.145	5.226	5.309	5.396	5.485	5.576	5.671	10
80	1.3963	5.671	5.769	5.871	5.976	6.084	6.197	6.314	9
81	1.4137	6.314	6.435	6.561	6.691	6.827	6.968	7.115	8
82	1.4312	7.115	7.269	7.429	7.596	7.770	7.953	8.144	7
83	1.4486	8.144	8.345	8.556	8.777	9.010	9.255	9.514	6
84	1.4661	9.514	9.788	10.078	10.385	10.712	11.059	11.430	5
85	1.4835	11.430	11.826	12.251	12.706	13.197	13.727	14.301	4
86	1.5010	14.301	14.924	15.605	16.350	17.169	18.075	19.081	3
87	1.5184	19.081	20.206	21.470	22.904	24.542	26.432	28.636	2
88	1.5359	28.636	31.242	34.368	38.188	42.964	49.104	57.290	1
89	1.5533	57.290	68.750	85.940	114.59	171.89	343.77	infinity	0
90	1.5708	infinity							
		60'	50'	40'	30'	20'	10'	0'	De-grees

COTANGENTS

CALCULUS

FORMULAS FOR DIFFERENTIATION $\left(D_x = \dfrac{d}{d_x}\right)$

$D_x(c) = 0$

$D_x(x) = 1$

$D_x(u + v - w) = D_x(u) + D_x(v) - D_x(w)$

$D_x(cv) = c \cdot D_x(v)$

$D_x(uv) = u \cdot D_x(v) + v \, D_x(u)$

$D_x(v^n) = n \cdot v^{n-1} \, D_x(v)$

$D_x(\sqrt{v}) = D_x(v)/2\sqrt{v}$

$D_x\left(\dfrac{c}{v^n}\right) = -\,c \cdot n \cdot D_x(v)/v^{n+1}$

$D_x\left(\dfrac{u}{v}\right) = \dfrac{v \cdot D_x(u) - u \cdot D_x(v)}{v^2}$

$D_x\left(\dfrac{u}{c}\right) = \dfrac{1}{c} \cdot D_x(u)$

$D_x\left(\dfrac{c}{v}\right) = -\,c \cdot D_x(v)/v^2$

$D_x(\log_a v) = \log_a e \cdot \dfrac{D_x(v)}{v}$

$D_x(\log v) = \dfrac{D_x(v)}{v}$

$D_x(a^v) = a^v \log a \, D_x(v)$

$D_x(e^v) = e^v \, D_x(v)$

$D_x(u^v) = v \cdot u^{v-1} \, D_x(u) + u^v \log u \cdot D_x(v)$

$D_x(\sin v) = \cos v \cdot D_x(v)$

$D_x(\cos v) = -\sin v \cdot D_x(v)$

$D_x(\tan v) = \sec^2 v \cdot D_x(v)$

$D_x(\cot v) = -\csc^2 v \cdot D_x(v)$

$D_x(\sec v) = \sec v \cdot \tan v \cdot D_x(v)$

$D_x(\csc v) = -\csc v \cdot \cot v \cdot D_x(v)$

FORMULAS FOR INTEGRATION

$\displaystyle \int dv = v + C$

$\displaystyle \int a \, dv = a \int dv$

$\displaystyle \int (du + dv - dw) = \int du + \int dv - \int dw$

$\displaystyle \int v^n \, dv = \dfrac{v^{n+1}}{n+1} + C$

$\displaystyle \int \dfrac{dv}{v^n} = \dfrac{1}{(1-n)v^{n-1}} + C$

$\displaystyle \int \dfrac{dv}{\sqrt{v}} = 2\sqrt{v} + C$

$\displaystyle \int \dfrac{dv}{v} = \log v + C = \log cv$

$\displaystyle \int a^v dv = \dfrac{a^v}{\log a} + C$

$\displaystyle \int e^v \, dv = e^v + C$

$\displaystyle \int \sin v \cdot dv = -\cos v + C$

$\displaystyle \int \cos v \cdot dv = \sin v + C$

$\displaystyle \int \sec^2 v \cdot dv = \tan v + C$

$\displaystyle \int \csc^2 v \cdot dv = -\cot v + C$

$\displaystyle \int \sec v \cdot \tan v \cdot dv = \sec v + C$

$\displaystyle \int \csc v \cdot \cot v \cdot dv = -\csc v + C$

$\displaystyle \int \tan v \cdot dv = \begin{cases} \log \sec v + C, \text{ or} \\ -\log \cos v + C \end{cases}$

$\displaystyle \int \cot v \cdot dv = \begin{cases} \log \sin v + C, \text{ or} \\ -\log \csc v + C \end{cases}$

$\displaystyle \int \sec v \cdot dv = \begin{cases} \log (\sec v + \tan v) + C, \text{ or} \\ \log \tan (v/2 + \pi/4) + C \end{cases}$

$\displaystyle \int \csc v \cdot dv = \begin{cases} \log (\csc v - \cot v) + C, \text{ or} \\ \log \tan v/2 + C \end{cases}$

$\displaystyle \int \dfrac{dv}{\sqrt{a^2 - v^2}} = \sin^{-1} \dfrac{v}{a} + C$

$\displaystyle \int \dfrac{dv}{v^2 + a^2} = \dfrac{1}{a} \tan^{-1} \dfrac{v}{a} + C$

$\displaystyle \int \dfrac{dv}{v\sqrt{v^2 - a^2}} = \dfrac{1}{a} \sec^{-1} \dfrac{v}{a} + C$

$\displaystyle \int \dfrac{dv}{v^2 - a^2} = \dfrac{1}{2a} \log \dfrac{v-a}{v+a} + C, \left[\text{or } \dfrac{a-v}{a+v}\right]$

$\displaystyle \int \dfrac{dv}{a^2 - v^2} = \dfrac{1}{2a} \log \dfrac{a+v}{a-v} + C, \left[\text{or } \dfrac{v+a}{v-a}\right]$

$\displaystyle \int \dfrac{dv}{\sqrt{v^2 \pm a^2}} = \log (v + \sqrt{v^2 \pm a^2}) + C$

$\displaystyle \int \sqrt{a^2 - v^2} \cdot dv = \dfrac{v}{2} \sqrt{a^2 - v^2} + \dfrac{a^2}{2} \sin^{-1} \dfrac{v}{a} + C$

$\displaystyle \int \sqrt{v^2 \pm a^2} \cdot dv = \dfrac{v}{2} \sqrt{v^2 \pm a^2} \pm \dfrac{a^2}{2} \log (v + \sqrt{v^2 \pm a^2}) + C$

DECIMAL EQUIVALENTS

1/64——	.015625	
1/32————	.03125	
3/64——	.046875	
1/16————————	.0625	
5/64——	.078125	
3/32————	.09375	
7/64——	.109375	
1/8————————	.125	
9/64——	.140625	
5/32————	.15625	
11/64——	.171875	
3/16———————	.1875	
13/64——	.203125	
7/32————	.21875	
15/64——	.234375	
1/4————————	.250	
17/64——	.265625	
9/32————	.28125	
19/64——	.296875	
5/16———————	.3125	
21/64——	.328125	
11/32————	.34375	
23/64——	.359375	
3/8————————	.375	
25/64——	.390625	
13/32————	.40625	
27/64——	421875	
7/16———————	.4375	
29/64——	.453125	
15/32————	.46875	
31/64——	.484375	
1/2————————	.500	

33/64——	.515625	
17/32————	.53125	
35/64——	.546875	
9/16———————	.5625	
37/64——	.578125	
19/32————	.59375	
39/64——	.609375	
5/8————————	.625	
41/64——	.640625	
21/32————	.65625	
43/64——	.671875	
11/16———————	.6875	
45/64——	.703125	
23/32————	.71875	
47/64——	.734375	
3/4————————	.750	
49/64——	.765625	
25/32————	.78125	
51/64——	.796875	
13/16———————	.8125	
53/64——	.828125	
27/32————	.84375	
55/64——	.859375	
7/8————————	.875	
57/64——	.890625	
29/32————	.90625	
59/64——	.921875	
15/16———————	.9375	
61/64——	.953125	
31/32————	.96875	
63/64——	.984375	
1 ————————	1.000	

CONVERSION TABLES: ENGLISH SYSTEM

To convert	Multiply by	To obtain	To convert	Multiply by	To obtain
		Units of Length			
in.	0.0833	ft	yd	36	in.
in.	0.0278	yd	yd	3	ft
in.	0.0000158	miles	yd	0.000568	miles
ft	12	in.	miles	63,360	in.
ft	0.3333	yd	miles	5,280	ft
ft	0.000189	miles	miles	1,760	yd
ft	0.000165	miles (naut.)	miles (naut.)	6,076	ft
		Units of Area			
sq in.	0.00694	sq ft	sq yd	9	sq ft
sq in.	0.000772	sq yd	sq yd	0.0002066	acres
sq ft	144	sq in.	acres	43,560	sq ft
sq ft	0.1111	sq yd	acres	4,840	sq yd
sq ft	0.00002296	acres	sq yd	1,296	sq in.
		Units of Volume			
cu in.	0.00433	gal	cu ft	0.0370	cu yd
cu in.	0.000579	cu ft	cu ft	0.0000230	acre-ft
cu in.	0.0000214	cu yd	cu yd	46,656	cu in.
gal	231	cu in.	cu yd	202	gal
gal	0.1337	cu ft	cu yd	27	cu ft
gal	0.00495	cu yd			
gal	0.00000307	acre-ft	acre-ft	325,800	gal
gal	0.0238	bbl (oil)	bbl (oil)	42	gal
gal	0.8327	Imperial gal	Imperial gal	1.2	gal
cu ft	1,728	cu in.	acre-ft	43,560	cu ft
cu ft	7.48	gal			
		Units of Weight			
grains	0.00229	oz	lb	7,000	grains
grains	0.0001429	lb	lb	16	oz
grains	0.0000000714	tons	lb	0.0005	tons
oz	438	grains	tons	14,000,000	grains
oz	0.0625	lb	tons	32,000	oz
oz	0.00003125	tons	tons	2,000	lb
gal	8.3322	lb°	lb/hr°	0.0020003	gpm
lb	0.12002	gal°	gpm	499.925	lb/hr°
		Units of Velocity			
fps	60	fpm	ft/hr	0.0002778	fps
fps	3,600	ft/hr	ft/hr	0.01667	fpm
fps	0.682	mph	ft/hr	0.0001894	mph
fps	0.592	knots	knots	1.689	fps
fpm	0.01667	fps	mph	1.467	fps
fpm	60	ft/hr	mph	88	fpm
fpm	0.01136	mph	mph	5,280	ft/hr

° Water at 68°F.

CONVERSION TABLES: ENGLISH SYSTEM (Continued)

To convert	Multiply by	To obtain	To convert	Multiply by	To obtain

Units of Time

To convert	Multiply by	To obtain	To convert	Multiply by	To obtain
Seconds	0.01667	Minutes	Days	24	Hours
Seconds	0.0002778	Hours	Days	0.0329	Months
Seconds	0.00001157	Days	Days	0.00274	Years
Minutes	60	Seconds	Months	2,628,000	Seconds
Minutes	0.01667	Hours	Months	43,800	Minutes
Minutes	0.000694	Days	Months	730	Hours
Hours	3,600	Seconds	Months	30.42	Days
Hours	60	Minutes	Months	0.0833	Years
Hours	0.0417	Days	Years	31,536,000	Seconds
Hours	0.001370	Months	Years	525,600	Minutes
Hours	0.0001142	Years	Years	8,760	Hours
Days	86,400	Seconds	Years	365	Days
Days	1,440	Minutes	Years	12	Months

Units of Work, Energy, and Heat

To convert	Multiply by	To obtain	To convert	Multiply by	To obtain
Btu	9,340	in.-lb	ft-lb	0.0000003766	kwhr
Btu	778.3	ft-lb	ft-lb	0.000000505	hp-hr
Btu	0.000293	kwhr	kwhr	3,413	Btu
Btu	0.000393	hp-hr	kwhr	31,872,000	in.-lb
in.-lb	0.000107	Btu	kwhr	2,656,000	ft-lb
in.-lb	0.0833	ft-lb	kwhr	1.341	hp-hr
in.-lb	0.00000003138	kwhr	hp-hr	2,545	Btu
in.-lb	0.0000000421	hp-hr	hp-hr	23,760,000	in.-lb
ft-lb	0.001285	Btu	hp-hr	1,980,000	ft-lb
ft-lb	12	in.-lb	hp-hr	0.7455	kwhr

Units of Power

To convert	Multiply by	To obtain	To convert	Multiply by	To obtain
kw	1.341	hp	ft-lb/sec	0.0771	Btu/min
kw	738	ft-lb/sec	ft-lb/min	0.00002260	kw
kw	44,260	ft-lb/min	ft-lb/min	0.0000303	hp
kw	0.948	Btu/sec	ft-lb/min	0.01667	ft-lb/sec
kw	56.9	Btu/min	ft-lb/min	0.00002141	Btu/sec
kw	3,413	Btu/hr	ft-lb/min	0.001285	Btu/min
hp	0.7455	kw	Btu/sec	1.055	kw
hp	550	ft-lb/sec	Btu/sec	1.415	hp
hp	33,000	ft-lb/min	Btu/sec	778.3	ft-lb/sec
hp	0.707	Btu/sec	Btu/sec	46,700	ft-lb/min
hp	42.41	Btu/min	Btu/sec	60	Btu/min
hp	2,545	Btu/hr	Btu/min	0.01758	kw
ft-lb/sec	0.001356	kw	Btu/min	0.02357	hp
ft-lb/sec	0.001818	hp	Btu/min	12.97	ft-lb/sec
ft-lb/sec	60	ft-lb/min	Btu/min	778.3	ft-lb/min
ft-lb/sec	0.001285	Btu/sec	Btu/min	0.01667	Btu/sec

CONVERSION TABLES: ENGLISH SYSTEM (Continued)

To convert	Multiply by	To obtain	To convert	Multiply by	To obtain
		Units of Pressure (Water, Mercury at 68°F)			
in. water	0.0833	ft water	oz/sq ft	0.01205	in. water
in. water	0.0736	in. mercury	oz/sq ft	0.001004	ft water
in. water	82.98	oz/sq ft	oz/sq ft	0.000887	in. mercury
in. water	0.03602	psi	oz/sq ft	0.000434	psi
in. water	5.1869	psf	oz/sq ft	0.0625	psf
ft water	12	in. water	psi	27.762	in. water
ft water	0.8832	in. mercury	psi	2.314	ft water
ft water	995.8	oz/sq ft	psi	2.314/sp gr	ft (any liq.)
ft water	0.4322	psi	psi	2.043	in. mercury
ft water	62.24	psf	psi	230.4	oz/sq ft
ft (any liq.)	0.4322 × sp gr	psi	psi	144	psf
in. mercury	13.57	in. water	psi	0.06802	atm
in. mercury	1.131	ft water	psf	0.1928	in. water
in. mercury	1128	oz/sq ft	psf	0.01607	ft water
in. mercury	0.4894	psi	psf	0.01419	in. mercury
in. mercury	70.47	psf	psf	16	oz/sq ft
in. mercury	0.03342	atm	psf	0.00694	psi
atm	29.92	in. mercury	atm	14.7	psi
		Weight—Time Rates			
lb/sec	60	lb/min	lb/hr°	0 0020003	gpm
lb/sec	3,600	lb/hr	lb/hr	0.0002778	lb/sec
lb/sec	86,400	lb/day	lb/hr	0.01667	lb/min
lb/min	0.01667	lb/sec	lb/hr	24	lb/day
lb/min	60	lb/hr	lb/day	0.00001157	lb/sec
lb/min	1,440	lb/day	lb/day	0.000694	lb/min
			lb/day	0.0417	lb/hr
		Volume—Flow Rates			
cfs	60	cfm	gps	8.022	cfm
cfs	3,600	cu ft/hr	gps	481.3	cu ft/hr
cfs	7.48	gps	gps	60	gpm
cfs	448.8	gpm	gps	3,600	gal/hr
cfs	26,930	gal/hr	gpm	0.00223	cfs
cfs	646,317	gal/day	gpm	0.1337	cfm
cfs	1.983	acre-ft/day	gpm	8.022	cu ft/hr
cfm	0.01667	cfs	gpm	0.01667	gps
cfm	60	cu ft/hr	gpm	60	gal/hr
cfm	0.1247	gps	gpm	499.925	lb/hr°
cfm	7.48	gpm	gal/hr	0.0000371	cfs
cfm	448.8	gal/hr	gal/hr	0.00223	cfm
cu ft/hr	0.0002778	cfs	gal/hr	0.1337	cu ft/hr
cu ft/hr	0.01667	cfm	gal/hr	0.0002778	gps
cu ft/hr	0.002078	gps	gal/hr	0.01667	gpm
cu ft/hr	0.1247	gpm	bbl/min (oil)	42	gpm
cu ft/hr	7.48	gal/hr	bbl/day (oil)	0.0292	gpm
gps	0.1337	cfs	acre-ft/day	0.5042	cfs

° Water at 68°F.

CONVERSION TABLES: METRIC SYSTEM

To convert	Multiply by	To obtain	To convert	Multiply by	To obtain
			Units of Length		
mm	0.03937	in.	in.	25.40	mm
cm	0.3937	in.	in.	2.540	cm
meters	39.37	in.	in.	0.0254	meters
meters	3.281	ft	ft	0.3048	meters
meters	1.0936	yd	ft	0.0003048	km
km	3,281	ft	yd	0.9144	meters
km	1,093.6	yd	yd	0.0009144	km
km	0.6214	miles	miles	1.609	km
microns	0.00003937	in.	in.	25,400	microns
			Units of Area		
sq mm	0.00155	sq in.	sq in.	645.2	sq mm
sq cm	0.155	sq in.	sq in.	6.452	sq cm
sq meters	10.764	sq ft	sq ft	0.09290	sq meters
sq meters	1.196	sq yd	sq yd	0.8361	sq meters
sq km	0.3861	sq miles	sq miles	2.590	sq km
hectares	2.471	acres	acres	0.4047	hectares
			Units of Volume		
cu cm	0.06102	cu in.	cu in.	16.39	cu cm
cu cm	0.03381	fl oz	cu in.	0.01639	liters
cu meters	35.31	cu ft	cu ft	0.02832	cu meters
cu meters	1.308	cu yd	cu ft	28.317	liters
cu meters	264.2	US gal	cu yd	0.7646	cu meters
liters	61.02	cu in.	fl oz	29.58	cu cm
liters	0.03531	cu ft	US gal	0.003786	cu meters
liters	0.2642	US gal	US gal	3.786	liters
			Units of Weight		
grams	15.43	grains	grains	0.0648	grams
grams	0.0353	oz	oz	28.350	grams
kg	35.27	oz	oz	0.02835	kg
kg	2.2046	lb	lb	0.4536	kg
kg	0.001102	US tons	lb	0.000454	tonnes
tonnes	2,204.6	lb	US tons	907.2	kg
tonnes	1.1023	US tons	US tons	0.9072	tonnes
			Unit Weight and Pressure		
gr/sq cm	0.01422	psi	lb/ft	1.4881	kg/m
gr/cu cm	0.0361	lb/cu in.	psi	70.31	gr/sq cm
kg/sq cm	14.22	psi	psi	0.07031	kg/sq cm
kg/cu m	0.0624	lb/cu ft	psi	0.7042	meters water
kg/m	0.6720	lb/ft	psi	0.7042/sp gr	meters (any liq.)
meters water	1.42	psi	lb/cu in.	27.68	gr/cu cm
meters (any liq.)	1.42 × sp gr	psi	lb/cu ft	16.018	kg/cu m
mm mercury	0.001316	atm	atm	760	mm mercury

CONVERSION TABLES: METRIC SYSTEM (Continued)

To convert	Multiply by	To obtain	To convert	Multiply by	To obtain

Volume—Flow Rates

To convert	Multiply by	To obtain	To convert	Multiply by	To obtain
liters/sec	15.85	US gpm	US gpm	0.0631	liters/sec
liters/min	0.2642	US gpm	US gpm	227.1	liters/hr
liters/min	0.03531	cfm	US gpm	3.785	liters/min
liters/hr	0.0044	US gpm	US gpm	0.003786	cu m/min
cu m/min	35.314	cfm	US gpm	0.2271	cu m/hr
cu m/min	264.17	US gpm	cfm	28.317	liters/min
cu m/hr	0.5883	cfm	cfm	0.02832	cu m/min
cu m/hr	4.4028	US gpm	cfm	1.6992	cu m/hr

Units of Power

To convert	Multiply by	To obtain	To convert	Multiply by	To obtain
watts	0.7376	ft-lb/sec	ft-lb/sec	1.356	watts
watts	0.001341	hp	hp	745.7	watts
kw	1.3410	hp	hp	0.7457	kw
cheval-vap	0.9863	hp	hp	1.0139	cheval-vap

Units of Heat and Energy

To convert	Multiply by	To obtain	To convert	Multiply by	To obtain
gr-cal	0.003969	Btu	Btu	252	gr-cal
kg-cal	3.9693	Btu	Btu	0.252	kg-cal
kg-cal/kg	1.800	Btu/lb	Btu/lb	0.5556	kg-cal/kg
gr-cal/sq cm	3.687	Btu/sq ft	Btu/sq ft	0.2713	gr-cal/sq cm
kg-cal/cu m	0.1124	Btu/cu ft	Btu/cu ft	8.896	kg-cal/cu m
joule	0.7376	ft-lb	ft-lb	1.356	joule
meter-kg	7.2330	ft-lb	ft-lb	0.1383	meter kg
gr-cal	3.087	ft-lb	ft-lb	0.3239	gr-cal
kg-cal	3,087	ft-lb	ft-lb	0.000324	kg-cal
hp-hr	1,980,000	ft-lb	ft-lb	0.000000505	hp-hr
kwhr	2,655,000	ft-lb	ft-lb	0.000000377	kwhr
Btu	778.3	ft-lb	ft-lb	0.001285	Btu

TEMPERATURE CONVERSION TABLE

Degrees Fahrenheit to Degrees Centigrade: $°F = \frac{9}{5} °C + 32°$ $°C = \frac{5}{9} (°F - 32°)$

F	C	F	C	F	C	F	C	F	C	F	C
−40	−40.00	+30	−1.11	+80	+26.67	+250	+121.11	+500	+260.00	+900	+482.22
−38	−38.89	31	−0.56	81	27.22	255	123.89	505	262.78	910	487.78
−36	−37.78	32	0.00	82	27.78	260	126.67	510	265.56	920	493.33
−34	−36.67	33	+0.56	83	28.33	265	129.44	515	268.33	930	498.89
−32	−35.56	34	1.11	84	28.89	270	132.22	520	271.11	940	504.44
−30	−34.44	35	1.67	85	29.44	275	135.00	525	273.89	950	510.00
−28	−33.33	36	2.22	86	30.00	280	137.78	530	276.67	960	515.56
−26	−32.22	37	2.78	87	30.56	285	140.55	535	279.44	970	521.11
−24	−31.11	38	3.33	88	31.11	290	143.33	540	282.22	980	526.67
−22	−30.00	39	3.89	89	31.67	295	146.11	545	285.00	990	532.22
−20	−28.89	40	4.44	90	32.22	300	148.89	550	287.78	1000	537.78
−18	−27.78	41	5.00	91	32.78	305	151.67	555	290.55	1050	565.56
−16	−26.67	42	5.56	92	33.33	310	154.44	560	293.33	1100	593.33
−14	−25.56	43	6.11	93	33.89	315	157.22	565	296.11	1150	612.11
−12	−24.44	44	6.67	94	34.44	320	160.00	570	298.89	1200	648.89
−10	−23.33	45	7.22	95	35.00	325	162.78	575	301.67	1250	676.67
− 8	−22.22	46	7.78	96	35.56	330	165.56	580	304.44	1300	704.44
− 6	−21.11	47	8.33	97	36.11	335	168.33	585	307.22	1350	732.22
− 4	−20.00	48	8.89	98	36.67	340	171.11	590	310.00	1400	760.00
− 2	−18.89	49	9.44	99	37.22	345	173.89	595	312.78	1450	787.78
0	−17.78	50	10.00	100	37.78	350	176.67	600	315.56	1500	815.56
+ 1	−17.22	51	10.56	105	40.55	355	179.44	610	321.11	1550	843.33
2	−16.67	52	11.11	110	43.33	360	182.22	620	326.67	1600	871.11
3	−16.11	53	11.67	115	46.11	365	185.00	630	332.22	1650	898.89
4	−15.56	54	12.22	120	48.89	370	187.78	640	337.78	1700	926.67
5	−15.00	55	12.78	125	51.67	375	190.55	650	343.33	1750	954.44
6	−14.44	56	13.33	130	54.44	380	193.33	660	348.89	1800	982.22
7	−13.89	57	13.89	135	57.22	385	196.11	670	354.44	1850	1010.00
8	−13.33	58	14.44	140	60.00	390	198.89	680	360.00	1900	1037.78
9	−12.78	59	15.00	145	62.78	395	201.67	690	365.56	1950	1065.56
10	−12.22	60	15.56	150	65.56	400	204.44	700	371.11	2000	1093.33
11	−11.67	61	16.11	155	68.33	405	207.22	710	376.67	2050	1121.11
12	−11.11	62	16.67	160	71.11	410	210.00	720	382.22	2100	1148.89
13	−10.56	63	17.22	165	73.89	415	212.78	730	387.78	2150	1176.67
14	−10.00	64	17.78	170	76.67	420	215.56	740	393.33	2200	1204.44
15	− 9.44	65	18.33	175	79.44	425	218.33	750	398.89	2250	1232.22
16	− 8.89	66	18.89	180	82.22	430	221.11	760	404.44	2300	1260.00
17	− 8.33	67	19.44	185	85.00	435	223.89	770	410.00	2350	1287.78
18	− 7.78	68	20.00	190	87.78	440	226.67	780	415.56	2400	1315.56
19	− 7.22	69	20.56	195	90.55	445	229.44	790	421.11	2450	1343.33
20	− 6.67	70	21.11	200	93.33	450	232.22	800	426.67	2500	1371.11
21	− 6.11	71	21.67	205	96.11	455	235.00	810	432.22	2550	1398.89
22	− 5.56	72	22.22	210	98.89	460	237.78	820	437.78	2600	1426.67
23	− 5.00	73	22.78	215	101.67	465	240.55	830	443.33	2650	1454.44
24	− 4.44	74	23.33	220	104.44	470	243.33	840	448.89	2700	1482.22
25	− 3.89	75	23.89	225	107.22	475	246.11	850	454.44	2750	1510.00
26	− 3.33	76	24.44	230	110.00	480	248.89	860	460.00	2800	1537.78
27	− 2.78	77	25.00	235	112.78	485	251.67	870	465.56	2850	1565.59
28	− 2.22	78	25.56	240	115.56	490	254.44	880	471.11	2900	1593.33
29	− 1.67	79	26.11	245	118.33	495	257.22	890	476.67	2950	1621.11

Mechanical and Physical Data

MECHANICAL PROPERTIES OF MATERIALS

All materials have properties which must be known in order to promote their proper use. These properties are essential to selection of the best material for a given member.

In the design of machine members the properties of materials which are of primary concern are those that indicate material behavior under certain types of load. Some property of a material is called for in each of the basic design formulas.

Mechanical properties commonly used by engineers are:

1. Ultimate tensile strength
2. Tensile yield strength
3. Elongation
4. Modulus of elasticity
5. Compressive strength
6. Shear strength
7. Endurance limit

1. *Ultimate tensile strength* is defined as the maximum load per unit of original cross-sectional area sustained by a material during a tension test.

2. *Tensile yield strength* is defined as the stress corresponding to some permanent deformation from the modulus slope, e.g., 0.2 percent offset in the case of heat-treated alloy steels.

3. *Elongation* is defined as the amount of permanent extension in a ruptured tensile test specimen; it is usually expressed as a percentage of the original gage length. Elongation is usually taken as a measure of ductility.

4. *Modulus of elasticity* is the property of material which indicates its rigidity. This property is the ratio of stress to the strain within the elastic range.

$$\frac{\text{Stress } \sigma}{\text{Strain } \epsilon} = \text{modulus of elasticity } E$$

On a stress-strain diagram, the modulus of elasticity is represented usually by the straight portion of the curve when the stress is directly proportional to the strain. The steeper the curve the higher the modulus of elasticity and the stiffer the material. Any steel has a modulus of elasticity in tension of approximately 30,000,000 psi. Other materials may vary according to the specific alloy. Cast iron, for example, has a modulus of elasticity in tension between 10,000,000 and 25,000,000 psi, depending on the grade.

5. *Compressive strength* is defined as the maximum compressive stress that a material is capable of developing based on the original cross-sectional area. The general design practice is to assume the compressive strength of a steel is equal to its tensile strength, although it is actually somewhat greater.

6. *Shear strength* is defined as the stress required to produce fracture in the plane of cross section, the conditions of loading being such that the directions of force and of resistance are parallel and opposite although their paths are offset a specified minimum amount. The ultimate shear strength is generally assumed to be three-fourths the material's ultimate tensile strength.

7. *Endurance limit* is defined as the maximum stress to which the material can be subjected for an indefinite service life. Although the standards vary for various types of members and different industries, it is common practice to accept the assumption that carrying a certain load for several million cycles of stress reversals indicates that load can be carried for an indefinite time. When a load on a member is constantly varying in value, is repeated by relatively high frequency, or constitutes a complete reversal of stresses with each operating cycle, the material's endurance limit must be substituted for the ultimate strength where called for by the design formulas. The geometry of the member, the presence of local areas of high stress concentration, and the condition of the material (pits, surface irregularities, and corrosion) have considerable influence on the real endurance limit.

DEFINITIONS OF TYPES OF STEELS

1. *Carbon Steel.* Steel is classed as carbon steel when no minimum content is specified or required for aluminum, boron, chromium, cobalt, columbium, molybdenum, nickel, titanium, tungsten, vanadium, or zirconium or any other element added to obtain a desired alloying effect; when the specified minimum copper does not exceed 0.40 percent; or when the maximum content specified for any of the following elements does not exceed the percentage noted: manganese 1.65, silicon 0.60, copper 0.60.

2. *Alloy Steel.* Steel is classed as alloy steel when the maximum range specified

for the content of alloying elements exceeds one or more of the following limits: manganese 1.65 percent; silicon 0.60 percent; copper 0.60 percent; or in which a definite minimum quantity for any of the following elements is specified or required within the limits of the recognized commercial field of alloy steels: aluminum, boron, chromium up to 3.99 percent, cobalt, columbium, molybdenum, nickel, titanium, tungsten, vanadium, zirconium, or any other alloyed elements added to obtain a desired alloying effect. Small percentages of chromium, molybdenum, and vanadium increase the high-temperature strength of an alloy steel.

3. *Stainless Steel.* Stainless steel is not a single alloy composition but rather the name applied to a group of low-carbon alloy steels containing at least 10 percent chromium and to which other alloying elements, principally nickel, may be added for increased corrosion resistance and/or improved fabricating characteristics.

The three basic types of stainless steels are:

Group A—Martensitic Hardenable Steels. These steels contain chromium and carbon as the principal alloying elements. They are the cutlery-type steels. They respond to heat treatment and can be hardened in a manner similar to that employed with the familiar alloy and tool steels to provide a wide range of mechanical properties. They are magnetic.

Group B—Ferritic Nonhardenable Steels. This group comprises the chromium-iron alloys much used for decorator trim. Like group A they are magnetic; however, they do not respond to heat treatment and are normally used in the annealed state where they exhibit their maximum softness, ductility, and corrosion resistance. The mechanical properties of these steels can be increased to a small extent by cold working.

Group C—Austenitic Nonhardenable Steels. The chromium-nickel alloys which form the basis of this group offer a greater degree of corrosion resistance than the steels of groups A and B. They are strong, tough, and ductile, and although they cannot be hardened by heat treatment, they can be appreciably strengthened by cold working. These austenitic steels are nonmagnetic.

The following is a partial glossary of terms related to testing, metallurgy, heat treatment, corrosion, etc., extracted from the "National Metals Handbook."

Hardening. Any process for increasing the hardness of metal by suitable treatment, usually involving heating and cooling.

Heat Treatment. A combination of heating and cooling operations, timed and applied to a metal or alloy in the solid state in a way that will produce desired properties. Heating for the sole purpose of hot working is excluded from the meaning of this definition.

Age Hardening. A process of aging that increases hardness and strength and ordinarily decreases ductility. Age hardening usually follows rapid cooling or cold working.

Case Hardening. A process of hardening a ferrous alloy so that the surface layer or case is made substantially harden than the interior or core. Typical case-hardening processes are carburizing, cyaniding, carbonitriding, nitriding, induction hardening and flame hardening.

Carburizing. A process that introduces carbon into a solid ferrous alloy by heating the metal in contact with a carbonaceous material—solid, liquid or gas—to a temperature above the transformation range and holding at that temperature. Carburizing is generally followed by quenching to produce a hardened case.

Carbonitriding. A process in which a ferrous alloy is case hardened by first being heated in a gaseous atmosphere of such composition that the alloy absorbs carbon and nitrogen simultaneously, and then being cooled at a rate that will produce desired properties.

Austenitizing. The process of forming austenite by heating a ferrous alloy into the transformation range (partial austenitizing) or above the transformation range (complete austenitizing).

Cold Work. Plastic deformation at such temperatures and rates that substantial increases occur in the strength and hardness of the metal. Visible structural changes include changes in grain shape and, in some instances, mechanical twinning or banding.

Normalizing. A process in which a ferrous alloy is heated to a suitable temperature above the transformation range and is subsequently cooled in still air to room temperature.

Nitriding. A process of case hardening in which a ferrous alloy, usually of special composition, is heated in an atmosphere of ammonia or in contact with nitrogenous material to produce surface hardening by the absorption of nitrogen, without quenching.

Precipitation Hardening. A process of hardening an alloy in which a constituent precipitates from a supersaturated solid solution.

This hardening usually consists of two steps: (1) Solution heat treatment (as described elsewhere) at a high temperature that softens and prepares the part. (2) Age hardening at a lower temperature that hardens and strengthens the part.

Quenching.   A process of rapid cooling from an elevated temperature by contact with liquids, gases or solids.

Solution Heat Treatment.   A process in which an alloy is heated to a suitable temperature, is held at this temperature long enough to allow a certain constituent to enter into solid solution and is then cooled rapidly to hold the constituent in solution.   The metal is left in a supersaturated, unstable state and may subsequently exhibit age hardening.

Temper.   A condition produced in a metal or alloy by mechanical or thermal treatment and having characteristic structure and mechanical properties.   A given alloy may be in the fully softened or annealed temper, or it may be cold worked to the hard temper, or further to spring temper.   Intermediate tempers produced by cold working (rolling or drawing) are called "quarter hard," "half hard" and "three-quarters hard," and are determined by the amount of cold reduction and the resulting tensile properties.   In addition to the annealed temper, conditions produced by thermal treatment are the solution heat treated temper and the heat treated and artificially aged temper. Other tempers involve a combination of mechanical and thermal treatments and include that temper produced by cold working after heat treating, and that produced by artificial aging of alloys that are as-cast, as-extruded, as-forged and heat treated, and worked.

Stress Relieving.   A process of reducing residual stresses in a metal object by heating the object to a suitable temperature and holding for a sufficient time.   This treatment may be applied to relieve stresses induced by casting, quenching, normalizing, machining, cold working, or welding.

Stabilizing Anneal.   A treatment applied to austenitic stainless steels that contain titanium or columbium.   This treatment consists of heating to a temperature below that of a full anneal in order to precipitate the maximum amount of carbon as titanium carbide or columbium carbide.   This eliminates precipitation at lower temperatures, which might reduce the resistance of the steel to corrosion.

Residual Stress.   Macroscopic stresses that are set up within a metal as the result of nonuniform plastic deformation.   This deformation may be caused by cold working or by drastic gradients of temperature from quenching or welding.

Cyaniding.   A process of case hardening a ferrous alloy by heating in a molten cyanide, thus causing the alloy to absorb carbon and nitrogen simultaneously.   Cyaniding is usually followed by quenching to produce a hard case.

Annealing.   A process involving heating and cooling, usually applied to induce softening.   The term also refers to treatments intended to alter mechanical or physical properties, produce a definite microstructure, or remove gases.   When applicable, the following more specific terms should be used:

black annealing	isothermal annealing
blue annealing	malleablizing
box annealing	process annealing
bright annealing	spheroidizing
full annealing	stabilizing annealing
graphitizing	

Definitions of the above terms will not be given in this brief glossary.   When applied to ferrous alloys, the term "annealing," without qualification, implies full annealing.   Any process of annealing will usually reduce stresses, but if the treatment is applied for the sole purpose of such relief, it should be designated as "stress relieving."

Tempering.   A process of reheating quench-hardened or normalized steel to a temperature below the transformation range, and then cooling at any rate desired.

Alloy.   A substance that has metallic properties and is composed of two or more chemical elements of which at least one is a metal.

Physical Metallurgy.   The science concerned with the physical and mechanical characteristics of metals and alloys.

Physical Properties.   Those properties familiarly discussed in physics, exclusive of those described under mechanical properties; for example, density, electrical conductivity, coefficient of thermal expansion.   This term has often been used to describe mechanical properties, but this usage is not recommended.

Mechanical Properties.   Those properties of a material that reveal the elastic and inelastic reaction when force is applied, or that involve the relationship between stress and strain; for example, the modulus of elasticity, tensile strength and fatigue limit.   These properties have often been designated as "physical properties," but the term "mechanical properties" is much to be preferred.

Modulus of Elasticity.   The slope of the elastic portion of the stress-strain curve in mechanical testing.   The stress is divided by the unit elongation.   The tensile or compressive elastic modulus is called "Young's modulus"; the torsional elastic modulus is known as the "shear modulus" or "modulus of rigidity."

Proof Stress.   In a test, stress that will cause a specified permanent deformation in a material, usually 0.01 percent or less.

Proportional Limit. The greatest stress that the material is capable of sustaining without a deviation from the law of proportionality of stress to strain.

Reduction in Area. The difference between the original cross-sectional area and that of the smallest area at the point of rupture; usually stated as a percentage of the original area; also called "contraction of area."

Tensile Strength. The value obtained by dividing the maximum load observed during tensile straining by the specimen cross-sectional area before straining. Also called "ultimate strength."

Yield Point. In mild or medium-carbon steel, the stress at which a marked increase in deformation occurs without increase in load. In other steels and in nonferrous metals this phenomenon is not observed.

Yield Strength. The stress at which a material exhibits a specified limiting deviation from proportionality of stress to strain. An offset of 0.2 percent is used for many metals. Copper-base alloys often use 0.5 percent total elongation under load.

Charpy Test. A pendulum type of impact test in which a specimen supported at both ends as a simple beam, is broken by the impact of the falling pendulum. The energy absorbed in breaking the specimen, as determined by the decreased rise of the pendulum, is a measure of the impact strength of the metal.

Endurance Limit. The maximum stress that a metal will withstand without failure during a specified large number of cycles of stress. If the term is employed without qualification, the cycles of stress are usually such as to produce complete reversal of flexural stress.

Corrosion Fatigue. The repeated cyclic stressing of a metal in a corrosive medium, resulting in more rapid deterioration of properties than would be encountered as a result of either cyclic stressing or of corrosion alone.

Corrosion Embrittlement. The embrittlement caused in certain alloys by exposure to a corrosive environment. Such material is usually susceptible to the intergranular type of corrosion attack.

Dezincification. Corrosion of an alloy containing zinc (usually brass), involving loss of zinc and a surface residue or deposit of one or more less active components (usually copper).

CHEMICAL COMPOSITION, MECHANICAL PROPERTIES, AND PHYSICAL CONSTANTS OF SOME METALS AND ALLOYS[a]

Material	Approx chemical composition, %	Form and condition	Average mechanical properties				Average physical constants				
			Yield strength (0.2% offset), 1,000 psi	Tensile strength, 1,000 psi	Elongation, % in 2 in.	Brinell hardness	Density, lb/cu in.	Specific gravity	Thermal expansion coefficient (32–212°F), 10^6 in./(in.)(°F)	Tensile modulus of elasticity, 10^{-6} psi	Torsional modulus of elasticity, 10^{-6} psi
Monel alloy 410 (cast)	Ni 66, Cu 30.5, Fe 1.0, Mn 0.8, Si 1.6	As cast	35	75	40	150	0.312	8.63	9.2	23	
Monel alloy K-500 bars and forgings AMS-4676	Ni bal, Cu 29.5, Al 2.8, Fe 1.0, Ti 0.5, Mn 0.6, C 0.15, Si 0.15	Rod as hot-rolled	49	97	44	155	0.306	8.46	7.6[e]	26	9.5
		Hot-rolled aged	111	160	23.5	300					
Monel alloy 505 (cast)	Ni 64, Cu 29, Si 4, Fe 2, Mn 0.8	Casting annealed	75	115	10	225	0.302	8.36	8.9[d]	24	
		As cast or annealed and aged	110	135	2	340					
Nickel (cast)	Ni 95.6, Cu 0.5, Fe 0.5, Mn 0.8, Si 1.5, C 0.8	As cast	25	57	22	110	0.301	8.34	8.85	21.5	
Hastelloy B	Ni 61, Mo 28, Fe 5.0, Co 2.5, Cr 1.0, C 0.05, others 3	Cast or wrought	50	90	10	180	0.334	8.81	5.3[c]	27	
Aluminum alloy 2017 bar, rod, and wire ASTM B 211	Al bal, Cu 4.0, Mn 0.5, Mg 0.5	Bar annealed	10	26	22	45	0.101	2.79	12.7[b]	10.5	4.0
		Heat-treated	40	62	22	105	. . .	. . .	. . .	10.5	4.0
Ni-Resist type 1 ASTM A 436	C 3 max, Si 2, Mn 1.25, Ni 15.5, Cr 2.0, Cu 6.5, Fe bal	As cast	. . .	27	. . .	150	0.264	7.30	10.4[c]	15.6	4.5
Cast gray iron ASTM A 48 C 1.30	C 3.4, Si 1.8, Mn 0.8, Fe bal	As cast	. . .	32	. . .	190	0.260	7.20	6.7	14	
Cast carbon steel	Fe bal, Mn 0.7, Si 0.4, C 0.3	Cast	40	72	26	140	0.283	7.84	6.7	30	
Carbon steel SAE 1020 ASTM A 285	Fe bal, Mn 0.45, Si 0.25, C 0.20	Annealed	38	65	30	130	0.284	7.86	6.7	30	
		Quenched and tempered at 1000F	62	90	25	179					

Material	Composition	Condition									
AISI 4340 low-alloy steel	Fe bal, Ni 1.75, Cr 0.80, Mo 0.25	Heat-treated	125	140	17	285	0.280	7.80	6.5	29	10.5
Stainless steel type 304	Fe bal, Cr 19, Ni 9, C 0.98, max	Annealed / Cold-rolled[h]	30 / 160	85 / 185	50 / 8	160 / 400	0.286	7.92	9.3	29	10.5
Stainless steel type 310	Fe bal, Cr 25, Ni 20, C 0.25 max	Annealed	40	100	50	165	0.285	7.90	8.5	29.5	11.1
Cast stainless steel type 316	Fe bal, Cr 19, Ni 9, Mo 3, C 0.1	Cast	44	80	50	150	0.286	7.92	8.9	29	
Stainless steel type 410	Fe bal, Cr 12.5, C 0.15 max	Annealed / Heat-treated	40 / 115	75 / 150	30 / 15	150 / 300	0.277	7.67	6.1	28	10
Stainless steel type 420	Fe bal, Cr 13, C 0.35	Annealed / Heat-treated	60 / 200	98 / 250	28 / 8	180 / 480	0.278	7.70	5.7	28	10
Stainless steel type 430	Fe bal, Cr 16, C 0.12 max	Annealed / Cold-rolled	40 / 95	70 / 110	35 / 10	165 / 225	0.275	7.61	6.0	29	10.5
Stainless steel 17-4 PH	Fe bal, Cr 17, Ni 4, Cu 4	Heat-treated	155	165	12	330	0.280	7.80	6.0	29	10.5
Stainless steel type 422	Cr 13, Ni 0.75, Va 0.30, W 1.00, Mo 1.00	Heat-treated	90	125	18	250	0.280	7.78	5.9	28	10.0
Copper CA110: sheet—ASTM B 152, rod—B 124, B 133, wire—B 1, B 2, B 3	Cu 99.9 min	Strip annealed / Spring temper	10[b] / 50[b]	32 / 55	45 / 4	42 / 107	0.322 /	8.91 /	9.4[g] / 9.8[h]	17	6.4
Phosphor bronze CA-524: sheet—ASTM B 103, rod—ASTM B 139, wire—ASTM B 159	Cu bal, Sn 10, P 0.2	Annealed / Spring temper	28[b] /	66 / 122	68 / 4	100 / 119	0.317	8.78	10.2[h]	16	6.0
G bronze (88-10-2) castings, ASTM B 143 A1.1A	Cu bal, Sn 10, Zn 2	As cast	21[b]	45	31	80	0.315	8.72	. . . .	15	
Leaded red brass (85-5-5-5) castings, ASTM B 145	Cu 85, Zn 5, Pb 5, Sn 5	As cast	17[b]	35	25	60	0.317	8.75	10.2	13	

[a] Abridged with permission from "Properties of Some Metals and Alloys," The International Nickel Co., Inc.
[b] 0.5 percent extension.
[c] 68 to 392°F.
[d] 70 to 1100°F.
[e] 70 to 200°F.
[f] Maximum for wrought alloy. Cast alloys have slightly different composition, notably higher carbon.
[g] 68 to 212°F.
[h] 68 to 572°F.

HARDNESS—TENSILE-STRENGTH CONVERSION TABLE

| Brinell, 10-mm carbide ball, 3,000-kg load | | Diamond pyramid hardness No. | Rockwell | | Shore | Tensile strength, 1,000 psi |
| | | | C scale 150-kg Brale | B scale 100-kg 1/16-in. ball | | |
Indentation dia, mm	Hardness No.					
. . . .	. . . .	940	68	. . . .	97	
. . . .	767	880	66.5	. . . .	93	
2.25	745	840	65.5	. . . .	91	
2.30	712					
2.35	682	737	61.5	. . . .	84	
2.40	653	697	60	. . . .	81	
2.45	627	667	58.5	. . . .	79	
2.50	601	640	57.5	. . . .	77	
2.55	578	615	56	. . . .	75	
2.60	555	591	54.5	. . . .	73	298
2.65	534	569	53.5	. . . .	71	279
2.70	514	547	52	. . . .	70	266
2.75	495	528	51	. . . .	68	259
2.80	477	508	50	. . . .	66	247
2.85	461	491	48.5	. . . .	65	237
2.90	444	472	47	. . . .	63	226
2.95	429	455	45.5	. . . .	61	219
3.00	415	440	44.5	. . . .	59	212
3.05	401	425	43	. . . .	58	202
3.10	388	410	42	. . . .	56	193
3.15	375	396	40.5	. . . .	54	184
3.20	363	383	39	. . . .	52	182
3.25	352	372	38	(110)	51	177
3.30	341	360	36.5	(109)	50	170
3.35	331	350	35.5	(108.5)	48	166
3.40	321	339	34.5	(108)	47	160
3.45	311	328	33	(107.5)	46	155
3.50	302	319	32	(107)	45	150
3.55	293	309	31	(106)	43	145
3.60	285	301	30	(105.5)	42	138
3.65	277	292	29	(104.5)	41	134
3.70	269	284	27.5	(104)	40	130
3.75	262	276	26.5	(103)	39	127
3.80	255	269	25.5	(102)	38	123
3.85	248	261	24	(101)	37	120
3.90	241	253	23	100	36	116
3.95	235	247	21.5	99	35	114
4.00	229	241	20.5	98	34	111
4.05	223	234	(19)	97.5	33	110
4.10	217	228	(17.5)	96.5	33	105
4.20	207	218	(15)	94.5	32	100
4.30	197	207	(12.5)	93	30	95
4.40	187	196	(10)	90.5	28	90
4.50	179	188	(8)	89	27	87
4.60	170	178	(5)	87	26	83
4.70	163	171	(3)	85	25	79
4.80	156	163	(1)	83	. . . .	76
5.00	143	150	. . . .	78.5	22	71
5.20	131	137	. . . .	74		65
5.40	121	127	. . . .	70	19	60
5.60	111	117	. . . .	65.5	15	56

Approximate data from 1966 SAE Handbook.
Values in parentheses are beyond normal range and are for information only.

PROPERTIES OF SECTIONS

SECTION	A	I	c	k
rectangle	$A = bh$	$I_G = \dfrac{bh^3}{12}$, $\quad I_F = \dfrac{bh^3}{3}$	$c = \dfrac{h}{2}$	$k_G = \dfrac{h'}{\sqrt{12}}$, $\quad k_F = \dfrac{h}{\sqrt{3}}$
triangle	$A = \tfrac{1}{2}bh$	$I_G = \dfrac{bh^3}{36}$, $\quad I_F = \dfrac{bh^3}{12}$	$c_1 = \dfrac{h}{3}$, $\quad c_2 = \dfrac{2h}{3}$	$k_G = \dfrac{h}{\sqrt{18}}$, $\quad k_F = \dfrac{h}{\sqrt{6}}$
circle	$A = \dfrac{\pi}{4}d^2$	$I_G = \dfrac{\pi d^4}{64}$	$c = \dfrac{d}{2}$	$k_G = \dfrac{d}{4}$
hollow circle	$A = \dfrac{\pi}{4}(D^2 - d^2)$	$I_G = \dfrac{\pi}{64}(D^4 - d^4)$	$c = \dfrac{D}{2}$	$k_G = \dfrac{\sqrt{D^2 + d^2}}{4}$
trapezoid	$A = \dfrac{h(b + b')}{2}$	$I_G = \dfrac{h^3(b^2 + 4bb' + b'^2)}{36(b + b')}$	$c_1 = \dfrac{h(b + 2b')}{3(b + b')}$, $\quad c_2 = \dfrac{h(b' + 2b)}{3(b + b')}$	$k_G = \dfrac{h\sqrt{2(b^2 + 4bb' + b'^2)}}{6(b + b')}$
ellipse	$A = \dfrac{\pi bh}{4}$	$I_G = \dfrac{\pi bh^3}{64}$	$c = \dfrac{h}{2}$	$k_G = \dfrac{h}{4}$
I / channel	$A = 2ht + (b - 2t)e$	$I_G = \dfrac{2th^3 + (b - 2t)e^3}{3} - Ac_1^2$	$c_1 = \dfrac{h^2t + \tfrac{1}{2}e^2(b - 2t)}{A}$, $\quad c_2 = h - c_1$	$k_G = \sqrt{\dfrac{I_G}{A}}$
hollow rectangle	$A = bh - a(h - 2e)$	$I_G = \dfrac{bh^3 - a(h - 2e)^3}{12}$	$c = \dfrac{h}{2}$	$k_G = \sqrt{\dfrac{bh^3 - a(h - 2e)^3}{12A}}$

The above table gives the properties of various sections where A = area, I = moment of inertia, c = distance from the center of gravity to the extreme point or edge, and k = radius of gyration. In the sections shown, the axis GG passes through the center of gravity, while the axis FF passes through one edge. If e is the distance between the GG and any parallel axis BB, the moment of inertia of the section about the BB axis is $I_B = I_G + Ae^2$. In general, the radius of gyration about axis BB of a section is $k_B = \sqrt{I_B/A}$.

BEAM FORMULAS (UNIFORM SECTION)

Loading	Reaction R	Bending moment M	Deflection y
	$R_B = F$	$M_B = FL$	$y_A = \dfrac{1}{3}\dfrac{FL^3}{EI}$
	$R_B = F$	$M_B = \dfrac{FL}{2}$	$y_A = \dfrac{1}{8}\dfrac{FL^2}{EI}$
	$R_B = F$	$M_B = Fb;\; M_C = 0$	$y_A = \dfrac{F(2L^3 - 3L^2 a + a^3)}{6\,EI}$
	$R_A = \dfrac{5}{16} F;\; R_B = \dfrac{11}{16} F$	$M_B = \dfrac{3}{16} FL;\; M_C = \dfrac{5}{32} FL$	$y_C = 0.0093\,\dfrac{FL^3}{EI}$
	$R_A = \dfrac{3}{8} F;\; R_B = \dfrac{5}{8} F$	$M_B = \dfrac{1}{8} FL;\; M_C = 0.07FL$	$y_C = 0.0054\,\dfrac{FL^2}{EI}$
	$R_B = \dfrac{F}{2}$	$M_B = \dfrac{FL}{12};\; M_C = \dfrac{FL}{24}$	$y_C = \dfrac{1}{384}\dfrac{FL^3}{EI}$
	$R_B = \dfrac{F}{2}$	$M_B = M_C = \dfrac{FL}{8}$	$y_C = \dfrac{1}{192}\dfrac{FL^3}{EI}$
	$R_B = \dfrac{F}{2}$	$M_C = \dfrac{FL}{4}$	$y_C = \dfrac{1}{48}\dfrac{FL^3}{EI}$
	$R_A = \dfrac{Fb}{L};\; R_B = \dfrac{Fa}{L}$	$M_C = \dfrac{Fab}{L}$	$y_{max} = \dfrac{Fab(a + 2b)\sqrt{3a(a + 2b)}}{27EIL}$
	$R_B = \dfrac{F}{2}$	$M_C = \dfrac{1}{8} FL$	$y_C = \dfrac{5}{384}\dfrac{FL^3}{EI}$
	$R_B = \dfrac{F}{2}$	$M_C = \dfrac{F}{8} (2b + 1)$	$y_C = \dfrac{(5 - 24b^2 + 16b^4)}{384\,(1 - 2b)}\dfrac{FL^3}{EI}$
	$R_B = \dfrac{F}{2}$	$M_A = M_C = \dfrac{Fb}{2}$	$y_C = \dfrac{Fb}{12EI} (\tfrac{3}{4} L^2 - b^2)$
	$R_B = \dfrac{F}{2}$	$M_B = M_C = \dfrac{Fa}{2}$	$y_A = \dfrac{Fa^2(3L - 4a)}{12\,EI}$ $y_C = \dfrac{Fa(L - 2a)^2}{16\,EI}$

The units to be used in the above equations should be inches and pounds. The bending stress in the beam is given by the equation $s = Mc/I$, where s = stress, psi; M = bending moment, in.-lb; c = distance from neutral axis or center of gravity to outer fiber, in.; and I = moment of inertia, in.[4] (see page 2-9 for calculation of I and c).

SHAFT DESIGN

Shafts are designed on the basis of the torsional moment or torque which they must transmit. This torque may be found from the equation $T = 63{,}025\ hp/n$, where $T =$ torque, in.-lb, hp $=$ transmitted horsepower, and $n =$ shaft rpm. The shear stress developed for a given transmitted torque is given by the formula

$$s_s = \frac{16T}{\pi d^3}$$

where $d =$ shaft diameter, in.

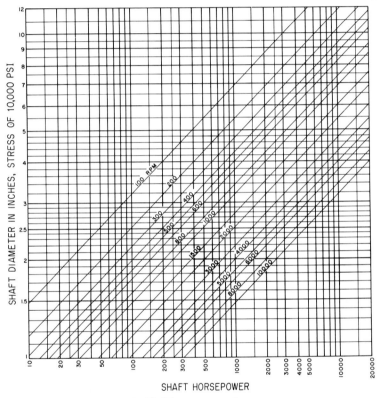

Fig. 2-1   Shaft-horsepower rating curve.

The curve in Fig. 2-1 may be used to determine the shaft diameter required for a shear stress of 10,000 psi for a given horsepower and speed. If it is desired to use some other design stress, the shaft diameter found in Fig. 2-1 may be corrected from the graph in Fig. 2-2.

Example: If 1,000 hp is to be transmitted at a shaft speed of 1,500 rpm, the shaft diameter as read from the chart in Fig. 2-1 for a shear stress of 10,000 psi is 2.78 in. If a stress of 5,000 psi is desired, the correction graph in Fig. 2-2 shows that a shaft diameter of 3.5 in. is required.

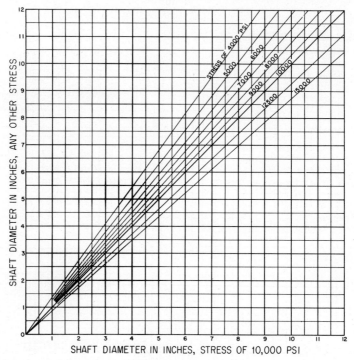

Fig. 2-2 Correction curve for shaft diameters at various stresses.

HOLLOW SHAFTS

Figure 2-3 can be used for hollow shafts by applying the factors and following the simple procedure indicated.   This curve has been calculated by the formula

$$1 - \left(\frac{\text{inside diameter}}{\text{outside diameter}}\right)^4$$

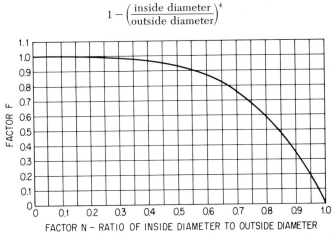

FACTOR N – RATIO OF INSIDE DIAMETER TO OUTSIDE DIAMETER

Fig. 2-3 Torsional conversion factor for hollow shafts. (1) Compute factor N. (2) Select F from curve. (3) Rating equals product of F and rating of solid shaft.

EFFECT OF KEYWAYS

For standard keyways where the width equals one-fourth the shaft diameter and the depth is one-half the width, the approximate effect on the torsional strength of a solid shaft is as follows:

No. keyways	Comparison with strength of shaft without keyways, %
1	85
2	78
3	73
4	70

BENDING MOMENTS OF SHAFTS

The maximum bending moment M at a for a shaft having an overhang load P at b, as shown in Fig. 2-4, is

$$M = PL$$

where M = bending moment, in.-lb
  P = load, lb
  L = distance from P to bearing support, in.

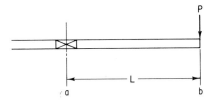

Fig. 2-4 Bending moment.

COMBINED TORSIONAL AND BENDING LOADS OF SHAFTS

For shafts which are subjected to bending as well as torsion, the following formula is recommended:

$$\text{Equivalent torsion} = \sqrt{T^2 + M^2}$$

where T = actual torsional moment
M = actual bending moment

Figure 2-5 simplifies this operation. These curves can be used for any range of loads by considering the bending and torsional moment graduations as units rather than as absolute figures and then pointing off the desired decimal places, just as is done in making calculations by means of a slide rule.

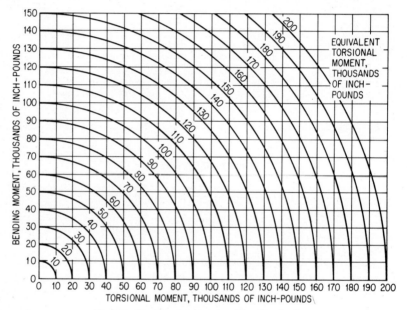

Fig. 2-5 Combined torsional and bending loads.

STEPPED SHAFTS

Too little attention has been paid in the past to the effect of shoulders in producing stress concentrations, often resulting in failures which could easily have been prevented simply by the use of a properly proportioned fillet.

Figure 2-6a, b, c, and d shows the proper fillet proportions based upon data presented by L. S. Jacobsen in *ASME Transactions* (vol. 47, p. 619, 1925).

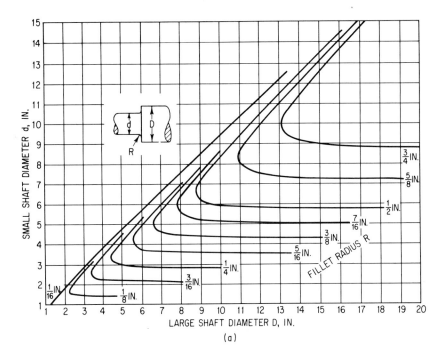

(a)

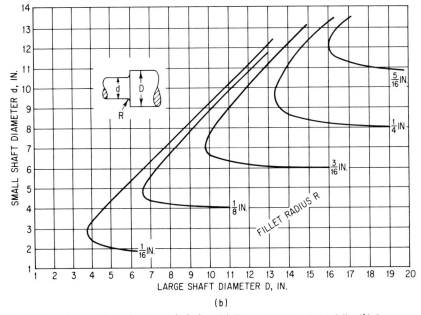

(b)

Fig. 2-6 Fillet proportions for stepped shafts. (*a*) Stress concentration = 1.5. (*b*) Stress concentration = 2.0.

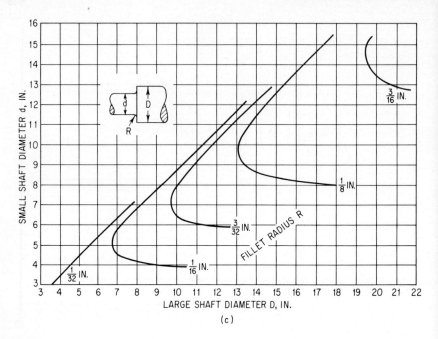

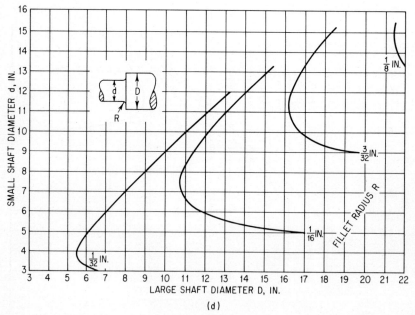

Fig. 2-6 (*Continued*) Fillet proportions for stressed shafts. (*c*) Stress concentration $= 2.5$. (*d*) Stress concentration $= 3.0$.

SAFE SPEEDS OF SHAFTS

Figure 2-7 has been included to show the maximum safe speeds with regard to whipping for plain shafts of uniform diameter without other members and of various lengths between supports.

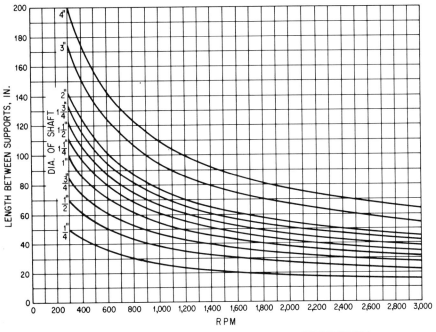

Fig. 2-7 Maximum safe speed of uniform-diameter shaft. $L = \sqrt{3,000,000 \times D/n}$, where $D =$ diameter in inches and $n =$ rpm. This formula permits operation up to approximately 63 percent of the critical speed.

ALLOWABLE STRESSES IN TYPICAL STEELS

As steady torsional loads cause failure in shear, shafts should be designed on the basis of the yield strength in shear, which is usually taken at 60 percent of the yield strength in tension. The following table gives the average mechanical properties of some popular steels.

Material	Size rounds, in.	Tensile strength	Yield point	Elongation, %	Reduction area	Brinell hardness
SAE 1020 hot-rolled	1	65,000	40,000	30	55	130
SAE 1020 hot-rolled	6	60,000	35,000	30	40	120
SAE 1020 forged	12	55,000	30,000	20	30	110
SAE 1040 hot-rolled	1	94,000	58,000	27	52	187
SAE 1040 hot-rolled	6	84,000	46,000	19	30	160
SAE 1040 forged	12	82,000	44,000	16	28	160
SAE 1040 hot-rolled, water-quenched, tempered at 1200°F	1	100,000	70,000	27	60	200
SAE 1040 hot-rolled, water-quenched, tempered at 1200°F	6	82,000	52,000	25	48	160

ALLOWABLE STRESSES IN TYPICAL STEELS (Continued)

Material	Size rounds, in.	Tensile strength	Yield point	Elonga-tion, %	Reduc-tion area	Brinell hardness
SAE 1040 forged, water-quenched, tempered at 1200°F	12	78,000	44,000	23	44	155
SAE 2340 hot-rolled, oil-quenched, tempered at 1200°F	1	112,000	85,000	25	63	230
SAE 2340 hot-rolled, oil-quenched, tempered at 1200°F	6	104,000	75,000	27	58	210
SAE 2340 forged, oil-quenched, tempered at 1200°F°.	12	100,000	70,000	21	48	200
SAE 2340 forged, normalized, tempered at 1200°F	12	100,000	65,000	20	45	200
SAE 4140 hot-rolled, oil-quenched, tempered at 1200°F	1	145,000	125,000	17	56	293
SAE 4140 hot-rolled, oil-quenched, tempered at 1200°F	6	108,000	80,000	21	54	220
SAE 4140 forged, oil-quenched, tempered at 1200°F°.	12	103,000	65,000	20	45	210
SAE 4140 forged, normalized, tempered at 1200°F	12	95,000	57,000	21	48	190
SAE 4340 hot-rolled, oil-quenched, tempered at 1200°F	1	150,000	130,000	20	58	302
SAE 4340 hot-rolled, oil-quenched, tempered at 1200°F	6	125,000	100,000	18	54	250
SAE 4340 forged, oil-quenched, tempered at 1200°F°.	12	110,000	90,000	17	50	230
SAE 4340 forged, normalized, tempered at 1200°F	12	95,000	70,000	20	45	220

° It is not generally considered good practice to liquid-quench solid diameters larger than 10 in.

When reversing or shock loads are encountered, the shafts should be designed on the basis of the endurance limit in shear. This is taken as one-fourth of the ultimate tensile strength.

These are the stresses where failure will begin, and in order to guard against breakdowns it is necessary to apply a factor of safety.

The usual factor for ordinary service is 3, but where exceptionally heavy shocks are encountered or with smooth loads where an occasional shock occurs, larger factors should be used. It is difficult to recommend the precise factor to be used, as this depends upon the intensity and frequency of the shock, and this is where experience and good judgment play an important part.

It must also be borne in mind that when mechanical properties of steels are given, the specimens are usually heat-treated in 1 in. diameter and then turned to a standard test diameter of 0.505 for testing.

WR^2 CALCULATION

Figure 2-8 may be found useful in calculating the WR^2 for cylindrical bodies often required in determining the flywheel effect.

$$WR^2 = W \times R^2$$

where WR^2 is in lb-ft^2

W = weight, lb

R^2 = radius of gyration squared from Fig. 2-8

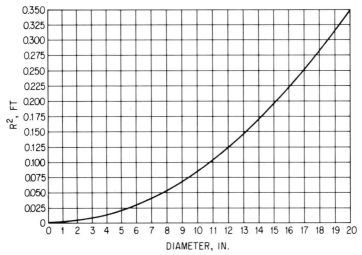

Fig. 2-8 Determination of WR^2 of cylindrical bodies. To determine the WR^2 for flywheel effect, multiply the weight in pounds by the value taken from curve. For members composed of various diameters, calculate the WR^2 of each diameter separately and take their sum, deducting for hollow sections. This curve follows the formula $R^2 = $(diameter in inches/24)^2/2 and gives R^2 in feet.

SQUARE AND FLAT KEYS

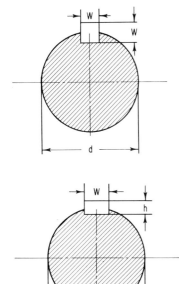

Dimensions of Standard Sizes in Inches

Shaft dia d (inclusive)	W	h
$7/16$–$9/16$	$1/8$	$3/32$
$9/16$–$7/8$	$3/16$	$1/8$
$7/8$–$1\frac{1}{4}$	$1/4$	$3/16$
$1\frac{1}{4}$–$1\frac{3}{8}$	$5/16$	$1/4$
$1\frac{3}{8}$–$1\frac{3}{4}$	$3/8$	$1/4$
$1\frac{3}{4}$–$2\frac{1}{4}$	$1/2$	$3/8$
$2\frac{1}{4}$–$2\frac{3}{4}$	$5/8$	$7/16$
$2\frac{3}{4}$–$3\frac{1}{4}$	$3/4$	$1/2$
$3\frac{1}{4}$–$3\frac{3}{4}$	$7/8$	$5/8$
$3\frac{3}{4}$–$4\frac{1}{2}$	1	$3/4$
$4\frac{1}{2}$–$5\frac{1}{2}$	$1\frac{1}{4}$	$7/8$
$5\frac{1}{2}$–$6\frac{1}{2}$	$1\frac{1}{2}$	1
$6\frac{1}{2}$–$7\frac{1}{2}$	$1\frac{3}{4}$	$1\frac{1}{2}$°
$7\frac{1}{2}$–9	2	$1\frac{1}{2}$

From ANSI Standard B17.1–1967.
° Some key standards show $1\frac{1}{4}$ in. Preferred size in $1\frac{1}{2}$ in.

UNIFIED SCREW THREADS

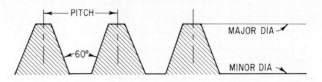

Size	Basic major dia	Course-thread series			Fine-thread series		
		Threads per inch	Minor dia	Area minor dia	Threads per inch	Minor dia	Area minor dia
0	0.0600				80	0.0447	0.00151
1	0.0730	64	0.0538	0.00218	72	0.0560	0.00237
2	0.0860	56	0.0641	0.00310	64	0.0668	0.00339
3	0.0990	48	0.0734	0.00406	56	0.0771	0.00451
4	0.1120	40	0.0813	0.00496	48	0.0864	0.00566
5	0.1250	40	0.0943	0.00672	44	0.0971	0.00716
6	0.1380	32	0.0997	0.00745	40	0.1073	0.00874
8	0.1640	32	0.1257	0.01196	36	0.1299	0.01285
10	0.1900	24	0.1389	0.01450	32	0.1517	0.0175
12	0.2160	24	0.1649	0.0206	28	0.1722	0.0226
$1/4$	0.2500	20	0.1887	0.0269	28	0.2062	0.0326
$5/16$	0.3125	18	0.2443	0.0454	24	0.2614	0.0524
$3/8$	0.3750	16	0.2983	0.0678	24	0.3239	0.0809
$7/16$	0.4375	14	0.3499	0.0933	20	0.3762	0.1090
$1/2$	0.5000	13	0.4056	0.1257	20	0.4387	0.1486
$9/16$	0.5625	12	0.4603	0.162	18	0.4943	0.189
$5/8$	0.6250	11	0.5135	0.202	18	0.5568	0.240
$3/4$	0.7500	10	0.6273	0.302	16	0.6733	0.351
$7/8$	0.8750	9	0.7387	0.419	14	0.7874	0.480
1	1.0000	8	0.8466	0.551	12	0.8978	0.625
$1\,1/8$	1.1250	7	0.9497	0.693	12	1.0228	0.812
$1\,1/4$	1.2500	7	1.0747	0.890	12	1.1478	1.024
$1\,3/8$	1.3750	6	1.1705	1.054	12	1.2728	1.260
$1\,1/2$	1.5000	6	1.2955	1.294	12	1.3978	1.521
$1\,3/4$	1.7500	5	1.5046	1.74			
2	2.0000	$4\,1/2$	1.7274	2.30			
$2\,1/4$	2.2500	$4\,1/2$	1.9774	3.02			
$2\,1/2$	2.5000	4	2.1933	3.72			
$2\,3/4$	2.7500	4	2.4433	4.62			
3	3.0000	4	2.6933	5.62			
$3\,1/4$	3.2500	4	2.9433	6.72			
$3\,1/2$	3.5000	4	3.1933	7.92			
$3\,3/4$	3.7500	4	3.4433	9.21			
4	4.0000	4	3.6933	10.61			

Abridged from ANSI Standard B1.1–1960.

DIMENSIONS OF HEXAGON-HEAD CAP SCREWS AND NUTS
ANSI Standard

Size	Hexagon-head cap screws°			Hexagon nuts†		
	Width across flats	Width across corners (max)	Nominal height	Width across flats	Width across corners (max)	Nominal height
1/4	7/16	0.505	5/32	7/16	0.505	7/32
5/16	1/2	0.577	13/64	1/2	0.577	17/64
3/8	9/16	0.650	15/64	9/16	0.650	21/64
7/16	5/8	0.722	9/32	11/16	0.794	3/8
1/2	3/4	0.866	5/16	3/4	0.866	7/16
9/16	13/16	0.938	23/64	7/8	1.010	31/64
5/8	15/16	1.083	25/64	15/16	1.083	35/64
3/4	1 1/8	1.299	15/32	1 1/8	1.299	41/64
7/8	1 5/16	1.516	35/64	1 5/16	1.516	3/4
1	1 1/2	1.732	39/64	1 1/2	1.732	55/64
1 1/8	1 11/16	1.949	11/16	1 11/16	1.949	31/32
1 1/4	1 7/8	2.165	25/32	1 7/8	2.165	1 1/16
1 3/8	2 1/16	2.382	27/32	2 1/16	2.382	1 11/64
1 1/2	2 1/4	2.598	15/16	2 1/4	2.598	1 9/32
1 3/4	2 5/8	3.031	1 3/32			
2	3	3.464	1 7/32			
2 1/4	3 3/8	3.897	1 3/8			
2 1/2	3 3/4	4.330	1 17/32			
2 3/4	4 1/8	4.763	1 11/16			
3	4 1/2	5.196	1 7/8			

° From ANSI Standard B18.2.1–1965.
† From ANSI Standard B18.2.2–1965.

DIMENSIONS OF HEXAGON-HEAD CAP SCREWS AND NUTS
ANSI Standard Heavy

Size	Hexagon-head cap screws°			Hexagon nuts†		
	Width across flats	Width across corners (max)	Nominal height	Width across flats	Width across corners (max)	Nominal height
1/4	....	....	.....	1/2	0.577	15/64
5/16	....	....	.....	9/16	0.650	19/64
3/8	....	....	.....	11/16	0.794	23/64
7/16	....	....	.....	3/4	0.866	27/64
1/2	7/8	1.010	5/16	7/8	1.010	31/64
9/16	....	....	.....	15/16	1.083	35/64
5/8	1 1/16	1.227	25/64	1 1/16	1.227	39/64
3/4	1 1/4	1.443	15/32	1 1/4	1.443	47/64
7/8	1 7/16	1.660	35/64	1 7/16	1.660	55/64
1	1 5/8	1.876	39/64	1 5/8	1.876	63/64
1 1/8	1 13/16	2.093	11/16	1 13/16	2.093	1 7/64
1 1/4	2	2.309	25/32	2	2.309	1 7/32
1 3/8	2 3/16	2.526	27/32	2 3/16	2.526	1 11/32

° From ANSI Standard B18.2.1–1965.
† From ANSI Standard B18.2.2–1965.

DIMENSIONS OF HEXAGON-HEAD CAP SCREWS AND NUTS (Continued)
ANSI Standard Heavy

Size	Hexagon-head cap screws°			Hexagon nuts†		
	Width across flats	Width across corners (max)	Nominal height	Width across flats	Width across corners (max)	Nominal height
$1\frac{1}{2}$	$2\frac{3}{8}$	2.742	$^{15}/_{16}$	$2\frac{3}{8}$	2.742	$1^{15}/_{32}$
$1\frac{5}{8}$	....	....	....	$2\frac{9}{16}$	2.959	$1^{19}/_{32}$
$1\frac{3}{4}$	$2\frac{3}{4}$	3.175	$1^{3}/_{32}$	$2\frac{3}{4}$	3.175	$1^{23}/_{32}$
$1\frac{7}{8}$	....	....	....	$2^{15}/_{16}$	3.392	$1^{27}/_{32}$
2	$3\frac{1}{8}$	3.608	$1^{7}/_{32}$	$3\frac{1}{8}$	3.608	$1^{31}/_{32}$
$2\frac{1}{4}$	$3\frac{1}{2}$	4.041	$1\frac{3}{8}$	$3\frac{1}{2}$	4.041	$2^{13}/_{64}$
$2\frac{1}{2}$	$3\frac{7}{8}$	4.474	$1^{17}/_{32}$	$3\frac{7}{8}$	4.474	$2^{29}/_{64}$
$2\frac{3}{4}$	$4\frac{1}{4}$	4.907	$1^{11}/_{16}$	$4\frac{1}{4}$	4.907	$2^{45}/_{64}$
3	$4\frac{5}{8}$	5.340	$1\frac{7}{8}$	$4\frac{5}{8}$	5.340	$2^{16}/_{64}$
$3\frac{1}{4}$	....	....	....	5	5.774	$3\frac{3}{16}$
$3\frac{1}{2}$	....	....	....	$5\frac{3}{8}$	6.207	$3\frac{7}{16}$
$3\frac{3}{4}$	....	....	....	$5\frac{3}{4}$	6.640	$3^{11}/_{16}$
4	....	....	....	$6\frac{1}{8}$	7.073	$3^{15}/_{16}$

° From ANSI Standard B18.2.1–1965.   † From ANSI Standard B18.2.2–1965.

ANSI STANDARD PIPE THREADS

Nominal pipe size	Pipe OD	Threads per inch	Length of effective threads	Length of hand-tight engagement	Total thread length	Tap drill in cast iron°
$^{1}/_{16}$	0.3125	27	0.26	0.16	0.39	D
$^{1}/_{8}$	0.405	27	0.26	0.16	0.39	Q
$^{1}/_{4}$	0.540	18	0.40	0.23	0.60	$^{7}/_{16}$
$^{3}/_{8}$	0.675	18	0.41	0.24	0.60	$^{9}/_{16}$
$^{1}/_{2}$	0.840	14	0.53	0.32	0.78	$^{45}/_{64}$
$^{3}/_{4}$	1.050	14	0.55	0.34	0.79	$^{29}/_{32}$
1	1.315	$11\frac{1}{2}$	0.68	0.40	0.99	$1^{9}/_{64}$
$1\frac{1}{4}$	1.660	$11\frac{1}{2}$	0.71	0.42	1.01	$1^{31}/_{64}$
$1\frac{1}{2}$	1.900	$11\frac{1}{2}$	0.72	0.42	1.03	$1^{47}/_{64}$
2	2.375	$11\frac{1}{2}$	0.76	0.44	1.06	$2^{13}/_{64}$
$2\frac{1}{2}$	2.875	8	1.14	0.68	1.57	$2\frac{5}{8}$
3	3.500	8	1.20	0.77	1.63	
$3\frac{1}{2}$	4.000	8	1.25	0.82	1.68	
4	4.500	8	1.30	0.84	1.73	
5	5.563	8	1.41	0.94	1.84	
6	6.625	8	1.51	0.96	1.95	
8	8.625	8	1.71	1.06	2.15	
10	10.750	8	1.93	1.21	2.36	
12	12.750	8	2.13	1.36	2.56	
14 OD	14.000	8	2.25	1.56	2.68	
16 OD	16.000	8	2.45	1.81	2.88	
18 OD	18.000	8	2.65	2.00	3.08	
20 OD	20.000	8	2.85	2.13	3.28	
24 OD	24.000	8	3.25	2.38	3.68	

Table abridged from ANSI Standard B2.1–1968.
° ANSI Standard twist drill sizes, without use of reamer.

PROPERTIES OF WELDED AND SEAMLESS STEEL PIPE

Size, nominal and outside dia, in.	Identification		Wall thickness, in.	ID, in.	Inside area, sq in.	Wt/ft, lb	Wt of water, lb/ft	External surface, sq ft/ft
	Schedule No.	Standard, X-strong, XX-strong						
⅛ (0.405)	40	STD	0.068	0.269	0.0568	0.244	0.025	0.106
	80	XS	0.095	0.215	0.0364	0.314	0.016	
¼ (0.540)	40	STD	0.088	0.364	0.1041	0.424	0.045	0.141
	80	XS	0.119	0.302	0.0716	0.535	0.031	
⅜ (0.675)	40	STD	0.091	0.493	0.1910	0.567	0.083	0.177
	80	XS	0.126	0.423	0.1405	0.738	0.061	
½ (0.840)	40	STD	0.109	0.622	0.3040	0.850	0.132	0.220
	80	XS	0.147	0.546	0.2340	1.087	0.101	
	160	. . . . . .	0.188	0.464	0.1691	1.311	0.073	
		XXS	0.294	0.252	0.0499	1.714	0.022	
¾ (1.050)	40	STD	0.113	0.824	0.5330	1.130	0.230	0.275
	80	XS	0.154	0.742	0.4330	1.473	0.187	
	160	. . . . . .	0.219	0.612	0.2942	1.944	0.127	
		XXS	0.308	0.434	0.1479	2.440	0.063	
1 (1.315)	40	STD	0.133	1.049	0.8640	1.678	0.374	0.344
	80	XS	0.179	0.957	0.7190	2.171	0.311	
	160	. . . . . .	0.250	0.815	0.5217	2.840	0.226	
		XXS	0.358	0.599	0.2818	3.659	0.122	
1¼ (1.660)	40	STD	0.140	1.380	1.495	2.272	0.647	0.434
	80	XS	0.191	1.278	1.283	2.996	0.555	
	160	. . . . . .	0.250	1.160	1.057	3.764	0.457	
		XXS	0.382	0.896	0.630	5.214	0.273	
1½ (1.900)	40	STD	0.145	1.610	2.036	2.717	0.882	0.497
	80	XS	0.200	1.500	1.767	3.631	0.765	
	160	. . . . . .	0.281	1.338	1.406	4.858	0.610	
		XXS	0.400	1.100	0.950	6.408	0.412	
2 (2.375)	40	STD	0.154	2.067	3.355	3.65	1.45	0.622
	80	XS	0.218	1.939	2.953	5.02	1.28	
	160	. . . . . .	0.344	1.687	2.235	7.46	0.97	
		XXS	0.436	1.503	1.774	9.03	0.77	
2½ (2.875)	40	STD	0.203	2.469	4.788	5.79	2.07	0.753
	80	XS	0.276	2.323	4.238	7.66	1.83	
	160	. . . . . .	0.375	2.125	3.547	10.01	1.54	
		XXS	0.552	1.771	2.464	13.70	1.07	
3 (3.500)	40	STD	0.216	3.068	7.393	7.58	3.20	0.916
	80	XS	0.300	2.900	6.605	10.25	2.86	
	160	. . . . . .	0.438	2.624	5.407	14.31	2.34	
		XXS	0.600	2.300	4.155	18.58	1.80	
3½ (4.000)	40	STD	0.226	3.548	9.886	9.11	4.28	1.047
	80	XS	0.318	3.364	8.888	12.51	3.85	
4 (4.500)	40	STD	0.237	4.026	12.730	10.79	5.51	1.178
	80	XS	0.337	3.826	11.497	14.98	4.98	
	120	. . . . . .	0.438	3.624	10.315	18.98	4.47	
	160	. . . . . .	0.531	3.438	9.283	22.52	4.02	
		XXS	0.674	3.152	7.803	27.54	3.38	
5 (5.563)	40	STD	0.258	5.047	20.006	14.62	8.66	1.456
	80	XS	0.375	4.813	18.194	20.78	7.87	
	120	. . . . . .	0.500	4.563	16.353	27.04	7.08	
	160	. . . . . .	0.625	4.313	14.610	32.96	6.32	
		XXS	0.750	4.063	12.966	38.55	5.62	

PROPERTIES OF WELDED AND SEAMLESS STEEL PIPE (Continued)

Size, nominal and outside dia, in.	Identification		Wall thickness, in.	ID, in.	Inside area, sq in.	Wt/ft, lb	Wt of water, lb/ft	External surface, sq ft/ft
	Schedule No.	Standard, X-strong, XX-strong						
6	40	STD	0.280	6.065	29.90	18.97	12.5	1.734
(6.625)	80	XS	0.432	5.761	26.07	28.57	11.3	
	120	. . . . . .	0.562	5.501	23.77	36.42	10.3	
	160	. . . . . .	0.719	5.187	21.13	45.34	9.2	
		XXS	0.864	4.897	18.83	53.16	8.1	
8	20	. . . . . .	0.250	8.125	51.8	22.36	22.5	2.258
(8.625)	30	. . . . . .	0.277	8.071	51.2	24.70	22.2	
	40	STD	0.322	7.981	50.0	28.55	21.6	
	60	. . . . . .	0.406	7.813	47.9	35.66	20.8	
	80	XS	0.500	7.625	45.7	43.39	19.8	
	100	. . . . . .	0.594	7.437	43.4	50.93	18.8	
	120	. . . . . .	0.719	7.187	40.6	60.69	17.6	
	140	. . . . . .	0.812	7.001	38.5	67.79	16.7	
		XXS	0.875	6.875	37.1	72.42	16.1	
	160	. . . . . .	0.906	6.813	36.5	74.71	15.8	
10	20	. . . . . .	0.250	10.250	82.5	28.04	35.9	2.814
(10.750)	30	. . . . . .	0.307	10.136	80.7	34.24	35.0	
	40	STD	0.365	10.020	78.9	40.48	34.1	
	60	XS	0.500	9.750	74.7	54.74	32.3	
	80	. . . . . .	0.594	9.562	71.8	64.40	31.1	
	100	. . . . . .	0.719	9.312	68.1	77.00	29.5	
	120	. . . . . .	0.844	9.062	64.5	89.27	27.9	
	140	XXS	1.000	8.750	60.1	104.13	26.1	
	160	. . . . . .	1.125	8.500	56.7	115.65	24.6	
12	20	. . . . . .	0.250	12.250	118.0	33.38	51.3	3.338
(12.750)	30	. . . . . .	0.330	12.090	114.8	43.77	49.7	
		STD	0.375	12.000	113.1	49.56	48.9	
	40	. . . . . .	0.406	11.938	111.9	53.56	48.5	
		XS	0.500	11.750	108.4	65.42	46.9	
	60	. . . . . .	0.562	11.626	106.2	73.22	46.0	
	80	. . . . . .	0.688	11.374	101.6	88.57	44.0	
	100	. . . . . .	0.844	11.062	96.1	107.29	41.6	
	120	XXS	1.000	10.750	90.8	125.49	39.3	
	140	. . . . . .	1.125	10.500	86.6	139.68	37.5	
	160	. . . . . .	1.312	10.126	80.5	160.33	34.9	
14	10	. . . . . .	0.250	13.500	143.0	36.71	62.1	3.665
(14.000)	20	. . . . . .	0.312	13.376	140.5	45.68	60.9	
	30	STD	0.375	13.250	137.9	54.57	59.7	
	40	. . . . . .	0.438	13.124	135.3	63.37	58.5	
		XS	0.500	13.000	132.7	72.09	57.4	
	60	. . . . . .	0.594	12.812	128.9	85.01	55.8	
	80	. . . . . .	0.750	12.500	122.7	106.13	53.2	
	100	. . . . . .	0.938	12.124	115.4	130.79	50.0	
	120	. . . . . .	1.094	11.812	109.6	150.76	47.5	
	140	. . . . . .	1.250	11.500	103.9	170.22	45.0	
	160	. . . . . .	1.406	11.188	98.3	189.15	42.6	
16	10	. . . . . .	0.250	15.500	188.7	42.05	81.7	4.189
(16.000)	20	. . . . . .	0.312	15.376	185.7	52.36	80.4	
	30	STD	0.375	15.250	182.6	62.58	79.1	
	40	XS	0.500	15.000	176.7	82.77	76.5	
	60	. . . . . .	0.656	14.688	169.4	107.54	73.4	
	80	. . . . . .	0.844	14.312	160.9	136.58	69.7	
	100	. . . . . .	1.031	13.938	152.6	164.86	66.0	
	120	. . . . . .	1.219	13.562	144.5	192.40	62.6	
	140	. . . . . .	1.438	13.124	135.3	223.57	58.6	
	160	. . . . . .	1.594	12.812	129.0	245.22	55.8	

PROPERTIES OF WELDED AND SEAMLESS STEEL PIPE (Continued)

Size, nominal and outside dia, in.	Identification		Wall thickness, in.	ID, in.	Inside area, sq in.	Wt/ft, lb	Wt of water, lb/ft	External surface, sq ft/ft
	Schedule No.	Standard, X-strong, XX-strong						
18 (18.000)	10	......	0.250	17.500	241.0	47.39	104.6	4.712
	20	......	0.312	17.376	237.1	59.03	102.7	
		STD	0.375	17.250	233.7	70.59	101.2	
	30	......	0.438	17.124	229.5	82.06	99.5	
		XS	0.500	17.000	227.0	93.45	98.2	
	40	......	0.562	16.876	224.0	104.76	97.2	
	60	......	0.750	16.500	213.8	138.17	92.5	
	80	......	0.938	16.124	204.2	170.84	88.4	
	100	......	1.156	15.688	193.3	208.00	83.7	
	120	......	1.375	15.250	182.7	244.14	79.2	
	140	......	1.562	14.876	173.8	274.30	75.3	
	160	......	1.781	14.438	163.7	308.55	71.0	
20 (20.000)	10	......	0.250	19.500	299.0	52.73	130.0	5.236
	20	STD	0.375	19.250	291.1	78.60	126.0	
	30	XS	0.500	19.000	283.5	104.13	122.8	
	40	......	0.594	18.812	277.9	123.06	120.4	
	60	......	0.812	18.376	265.2	166.50	114.9	
	80	......	1.031	17.938	252.7	208.92	109.4	
	100	......	1.281	17.438	238.8	256.15	103.4	
	120	......	1.500	17.000	227.0	296.37	98.3	
	140	......	1.750	16.500	213.8	341.10	92.6	
	160	......	1.969	16.062	202.6	379.14	87.8	
22 (22.000)	10	......	0.250	21.500	363.1	58.07	157.4	5.760
	20	STD	0.375	21.250	354.7	86.61	153.7	
	30	XS	0.500	21.000	346.4	114.81	150.2	
	60	......	0.875	20.250	322.1	197.42	139.6	
	80	......	1.125	19.750	306.4	250.82	132.8	
	100	......	1.375	19.250	291.0	302.88	126.2	
	120	......	1.625	18.750	276.1	353.61	119.6	
	140	......	1.875	18.250	261.6	403.01	113.3	
	160	......	2.125	17.750	247.4	451.07	107.2	
24 (24.000)	10	......	0.250	23.500	435.0	63.41	187.9	6.283
	20	STD	0.375	23.250	424.6	94.62	183.9	
		XS	0.500	23.000	416.0	125.49	180.0	
	30	......	0.562	22.876	411.0	140.80	178.0	
	40	......	0.688	22.624	402.0	171.17	174.1	
	60	......	0.969	22.062	382.3	238.29	165.6	
	80	......	1.219	21.562	365.2	296.53	158.2	
	100	......	1.531	20.938	344.3	367.45	149.3	
	120	......	1.812	20.376	326.1	429.50	141.4	
	140	......	2.062	19.876	310.3	483.24	134.4	
	160	......	2.344	19.312	292.9	542.09	126.9	
26 (26.000)	10	......	0.312	25.376	505.8	85.73	219.2	6.807
		STD	0.375	25.250	500.7	102.63	217.1	
	20	XS	0.500	25.000	490.9	136.17	212.8	
28 (28.000)	10	......	0.312	27.376	588.6	92.41	255.0	7.330
		STD	0.375	27.250	583.2	110.64	252.6	
	20	XS	0.500	27.000	572.6	146.85	248.0	
	30	......	0.625	26.750	562.0	182.73	243.4	
30 (30.000)	10	......	0.312	29.376	677.8	99.08	293.7	7.854
		STD	0.375	29.250	672.0	118.65	291.2	
	20	XS	0.500	29.000	660.5	157.53	286.2	
	30	......	0.625	28.750	649.2	196.08	281.3	
32 (32.000)	10	......	0.312	31.376	773.2	105.76	335.2	8.378
		STD	0.375	31.250	766.9	126.66	332.5	

PROPERTIES OF WELDED AND SEAMLESS STEEL PIPE (Continued)

Size, nominal and outside dia, in.	Identification Schedule No.	Standard, X-strong, XX-strong	Wall thickness, in.	ID, in.	Inside area, sq in.	Wt/ft, lb	Wt of water, lb/ft	External surface, sq ft/ft
	20	XS	0.500	31.000	754.7	168.21	327.2	
	30	. . . . . .	0.625	30.750	742.5	209.43	321.9	
	40	. . . . . .	0.688	30.624	736.6	229.92	319.0	
34	10	. . . . . .	0.312	33.376	874.9	112.43	379.3	8.901
(34.000)		STD	0.375	33.250	868.3	134.67	376.2	
	20	XS	0.500	33.000	855.3	178.89	370.8	
	30	. . . . . .	0.625	32.750	842.4	222.78	365.0	
	40	. . . . . .	0.688	32.624	835.9	244.60	362.1	
36	10	. . . . . .	0.312	35.376	982.9	119.11	426.1	9.425
(36.000)		STD	0.375	35.250	975.8	142.68	423.1	
	20	XS	0.500	35.000	962.1	189.57	417.1	
	30	. . . . . .	0.625	34.750	948.3	236.13	411.1	
	40	. . . . . .	0.750	34.500	934.7	282.36	405.3	

From ANSI Standard, Wrought Steel and Wrought Iron Pipe, B36.10–1959, and data of Crane Co. NOTE: Two systems of rating pipe wall thickness are utilized. The newer schedule numbers corresponde to definite pressures-stress ratios and are expressed simply as follows:

$$\text{Schedule No.} = 1{,}000 \times \frac{p}{s}$$

where p = internal pressure, psig
  s = allowable fiber stress, psi

Properties of the traditional designation for pipe entitled "standard," "extra strong," and "double extra strong" are also shown in the tables.

ANSI STANDARD STEEL PIPE FLANGES

Nominal pipe size	Flange OD	Flange thickness	Bolt circle dia	Bore weld neck socket weld‡	No. of bolts	Bolt dia
			150-lb Standard°			
$1/2$	$3^{1/2}$	$7/16$	$2^{3/8}$	0.62	4	$1/2$
$3/4$	$3^{7/8}$	$1/2$	$2^{3/4}$	0.82	4	$1/2$
1	$4^{1/4}$	$9/16$	$3^{1/8}$	1.05	4	$1/2$
$1^{1/4}$	$4^{5/8}$	$5/8$	$3^{1/2}$	1.38	4	$1/2$
$1^{1/2}$	5	$11/16$	$3^{7/8}$	1.61	4	$1/2$
2	6	$3/4$	$4^{3/4}$	2.07	4	$5/8$
$2^{1/2}$	7	$7/8$	$5^{1/2}$	2.47	4	$5/8$
3	$7^{1/2}$	$15/16$	6	3.07	4	$5/8$
$3^{1/2}$	$8^{1/2}$	$15/16$	7	3.55	8	$5/8$
4	9	$15/16$	$7^{1/2}$	4.03	8	$5/8$
5	10	$15/16$	$8^{1/2}$	5.05	8	$3/4$
6	11	1	$9^{1/2}$	6.07	8	$3/4$
8	$13^{1/2}$	$1^{1/8}$	$11^{3/4}$	7.98	8	$3/4$
10	16	$1^{3/16}$	$14^{1/4}$	10.02	12	$7/8$
12	19	$1^{1/4}$	17	12.00	12	$7/8$
14 OD	21	$1^{3/8}$	$18^{3/4}$	†	12	1
16 OD	$23^{1/2}$	$1^{7/16}$	$21^{1/4}$	†	16	1
18 OD	25	$1^{9/16}$	$22^{3/4}$	†	16	$1^{1/8}$
20 OD	$27^{1/2}$	$1^{11/16}$	25	†	20	$1^{1/8}$
24 OD	32	$1^{7/8}$	$29^{1/2}$	†	20	$1^{1/4}$

For footnotes, see next page.

ANSI STANDARD STEEL PIPE FLANGES (Continued)

Nominal pipe size	Flange OD	Flange thickness	Bolt circle dia	Bore weld neck socket weld‡	No. of bolts	Bolt dia
			300-lb Standard°			
1/2	3 3/4	9/16	2 5/8	0.62	4	1/2
3/4	4 5/8	5/8	3 1/4	0.82	4	5/8
1	4 7/8	11/16	3 1/2	1.05	4	5/8
1 1/4	5 1/4	3/4	3 7/8	1.38	4	5/8
1 1/2	6 1/8	13/16	4 1/2	1.61	4	3/4
2	6 1/2	7/8	5	2.07	8	5/8
2 1/2	7 1/2	1	5 7/8	2.47	8	3/4
3	8 1/4	1 1/8	6 5/8	3.07	8	3/4
3 1/2	9	1 3/16	7 1/4	3.55	8	3/4
4	10	1 1/4	7 7/8	4.03	8	3/4
5	11	1 3/8	9 1/4	5.05	8	3/4
6	12 1/2	1 7/16	10 5/8	6.07	12	3/4
8	15	1 5/8	13	7.98	12	7/8
10	17 1/2	1 7/8	15 1/4	10.02	16	1
12	20 1/2	2	17 3/4	12.00	16	1 1/8
14 OD	23	2 1/8	20 1/4	†	20	1 1/8
16 OD	25 1/2	2 1/4	22 1/2	†	20	1 1/4
18 OD	28	2 3/8	24 3/4	†	24	1 1/4
20 OD	30 1/2	2 1/2	27	†	24	1 1/4
24 OD	36	2 3/4	32	†	24	1 1/2
			400-lb Standard§			
1/2	3 3/4	9/16	2 5/8	†	4	1/2
3/4	4 5/8	5/8	3 1/4	†	4	5/8
1	4 7/8	11/16	3 1/2	†	4	5/8
1 1/4	5 1/4	13/16	3 7/8	†	4	5/8
1 1/2	6 1/8	7/8	4 1/2	†	4	3/4
2	6 1/2	1	5	†	8	5/8
2 1/2	7 1/2	1 1/8	5 7/8	†	8	3/4
3	8 1/4	1 1/4	6 5/8	†	8	3/4
3 1/2	9	1 3/8	7 1/4	†	8	7/8
4	10	1 3/8	7 7/8	†	8	7/8
5	11	1 1/2	9 1/4	†	8	7/8
6	12 1/2	1 5/8	10 5/8	†	12	7/8
8	15	1 7/8	13	†	12	1
10	17 1/2	2 1/8	15 1/4	†	16	1 1/8
12	20 1/2	2 1/4	17 3/4	†	16	1 1/4
14 OD	23	2 3/8	20 1/4	†	20	1 1/4
16 OD	25 1/2	2 1/2	22 1/2	†	20	1 3/8
18 OD	28	2 5/8	24 3/4	†	24	1 3/8
20 OD	30 1/2	2 3/4	27	†	24	1 1/2
24 OD	36	3	32	†	24	1 3/4

From ANSI Standard, Steel Pipe Flanges and Flanged Fittings, B16.5–1968.
° Flange thickness includes 1/16-in. raised face.
† To be specified by purchaser.
‡ Socket-weld flanges not available at 400-lb rating.
§ Flange thickness does not include 1/4-in. raised face.

ANSI STANDARD STEEL PIPE FLANGES (Continued)

Nominal pipe size	Flange OD	Flange thickness	Bolt circle dia	Bore weld neck socket weld‡	No. of bolts	Bolt dia
			600-lb Standard§			
1/2	3 3/4	9/16	2 5/8	†	4	1/2
3/4	4 5/8	5/8	3 1/4	†	4	5/8
1	4 7/8	11/16	3 1/2	†	4	5/8
1 1/4	5 1/4	13/16	3 7/8	†	4	5/8
1 1/2	6 1/8	7/8	4 1/2	†	4	3/4
2	6 1/2	1	5	†	8	5/8
2 1/2	7 1/2	1 1/8	5 7/8	†	8	3/4
3	8 1/4	1 1/4	6 5/8	†	8	3/4
3 1/2	9	1 3/8	7 1/4	†	8	7/8
4	10 3/4	1 1/2	8 1/2	†	8	7/8
5	13	1 3/4	10 1/2	†	8	1
6	14	1 7/8	11 1/2	†	12	1
8	16 1/2	2 3/16	13 3/4	†	12	1 1/8
10	20	2 1/2	17	†	16	1 1/4
12	22	2 5/8	19 1/4	†	20	1 1/4
14 OD	23 3/4	2 3/4	20 3/4	†	20	1 3/8
16 OD	27	3	23 3/4	†	20	1 1/2
18 OD	29 1/4	3 1/4	25 3/4	†	20	1 5/8
20 OD	32	3 1/2	28 1/2	†	24	1 5/8
24 OD	37	4	33	†	24	1 7/8
			900-lb Standard§			
1/2	4 3/4	7/8	3 1/4	†	4	3/4
3/4	5 1/8	1	3 1/2	†	4	3/4
1	5 7/8	1 1/8	4	†	4	7/8
1 1/4	6 1/4	1 1/8	4 3/8	†	4	7/8
1 1/2	7	1 1/4	4 7/8	†	4	1
2	8 1/2	1 1/2	6 1/2	†	8	7/8
2 1/2	9 5/8	1 5/8	7 1/2	†	8	1
3	9 1/2	1 1/2	7 1/2	†	8	7/8
4	11 1/2	1 3/4	9 1/4	†	8	1 1/8
5	13 3/4	2	11	†	8	1 1/4
6	15	2 3/16	12 1/2	†	12	1 1/8
8	18 1/2	2 1/2	15 1/2	†	12	1 3/8
10	21 1/2	2 3/4	18 1/2	†	16	1 3/8
12	24	3 1/8	21	†	20	1 3/8
14 OD	25 1/4	3 3/8	22	†	20	1 1/2
16 OD	27 3/4	3 1/2	24 1/4	†	20	1 5/8
18 OD	31	4	27	†	20	1 7/8
20 OD	33 3/4	4 1/4	29 1/2	†	20	2
24 OD	41	5 1/2	35 1/2	†	20	2 1/2

From ANSI Standard, Steel Pipe Flanges and Flanged Fittings, B16.5–1968.

° Flange thickness includes 1/16-in. raised face.

† To be specified by purchaser.

‡ Socket-weld flanges not available at 400-lb rating.

§ Flange thickness does not include 1/4-in. raised face.

ANSI STANDARD STEEL PIPE FLANGES (Continued)

Nominal pipe size	Flange OD	Flange thickness	Bolt circle dia	Bore weld neck socket weld	No. of bolts	Bolt dia
			1,500-lb Standard§			
$^1/_2$	$4^3/_4$	$^7/_8$	$3^1/_4$	†	4	$^3/_4$
$^3/_4$	$5^1/_8$	1	$3^1/_2$	†	4	$^3/_4$
1	$5^7/_8$	$1^1/_8$	4	†	4	$^7/_8$
$1^1/_4$	$6^1/_4$	$1^1/_8$	$4^3/_8$	†	4	$^7/_8$
$1^1/_2$	7	$1^1/_4$	$4^7/_8$	†	4	1
2	$8^1/_2$	$1^1/_2$	$6^1/_2$	†	8	$^7/_8$
$2^1/_2$	$9^5/_8$	$1^5/_8$	$7^1/_2$	†	8	1
3	$10^1/_2$	$1^7/_8$	8	†	8	$1^1/_8$
4	$12^1/_4$	$2^1/_8$	$9^1/_2$	†	8	$1^1/_4$
5	$14^3/_4$	$2^7/_8$	$11^1/_2$	†	8	$1^1/_2$
6	$15^1/_2$	$3^1/_4$	$12^1/_2$	†	12	$1^3/_8$
8	19	$3^5/_8$	$15^1/_2$	†	12	$1^5/_8$
10	23	$4^1/_4$	19	†	12	$1^7/_8$
12	$26^1/_2$	$4^7/_8$	$22^1/_2$	†	16	2
14 OD	$29^1/_2$	$5^1/_4$	25	†	16	$2^1/_4$
16 OD	$32^1/_2$	$5^3/_4$	$27^3/_4$	†	16	$2^1/_2$
18 OD	36	$6^3/_8$	$30^1/_2$	†	16	$2^3/_4$
20 OD	$38^3/_4$	7	$32^3/_4$	†	16	3
24 OD	46	8	39	†	16	$3^1/_2$
			2,500-lb Standard§			
$^1/_2$	$5^1/_4$	$1^3/_{16}$	$3^1/_2$	†	4	$^3/_4$
$^3/_4$	$5^1/_2$	$1^1/_4$	$3^3/_4$	†	4	$^3/_4$
1	$6^1/_4$	$1^3/_8$	$4^1/_4$	†	4	$^7/_8$
$1^1/_4$	$7^1/_4$	$1^1/_2$	$5^1/_8$	†	4	1
$1^1/_2$	8	$1^3/_4$	$5^3/_4$	†	4	$1^1/_8$
2	$9^1/_4$	2	$6^3/_4$	†	8	1
$2^1/_2$	$10^1/_2$	$2^1/_4$	$7^3/_4$	†	8	$1^1/_8$
3	12	$2^5/_8$	9	†	8	$1^1/_4$
4	14	3	$10^3/_4$	†	8	$1^1/_2$
5	$16^1/_2$	$3^5/_8$	$12^3/_4$	†	8	$1^3/_4$
6	19	$4^1/_4$	$14^1/_2$	†	8	2
8	$21^3/_4$	5	$17^1/_4$	†	12	2
10	$26^1/_2$	$6^1/_2$	$21^1/_4$	†	12	$2^1/_2$
12	30	$7^1/_4$	$24^3/_8$	†	12	$2^3/_4$

From ANSI Standard, Steel Pipe Flanges and Flanged Fittings, B16.5–1968.
° Flange thickness includes $^1/_{16}$-in. raised face.
† To be specified by purchaser.
‡ Socket-weld flanges not available at 400-lb rating.
§ Flange thickness does not include $^1/_4$-in. raised face.

ANSI STANDARD CAST-IRON PIPE FLANGES

Nominal pipe size	Flange OD	Flange thickness	Bolt circle dia	No. of bolts	Bolt dia
125-lb Standard					
1	$4\frac{1}{4}$	$\frac{7}{16}$	$3\frac{1}{8}$	4	$\frac{1}{2}$
$1\frac{1}{4}$	$4\frac{5}{8}$	$\frac{1}{2}$	$3\frac{1}{2}$	4	$\frac{1}{2}$
$1\frac{1}{2}$	5	$\frac{9}{16}$	$3\frac{7}{8}$	4	$\frac{1}{2}$
2	6	$\frac{5}{8}$	$4\frac{3}{4}$	4	$\frac{5}{8}$
$2\frac{1}{2}$	7	$\frac{11}{16}$	$5\frac{1}{2}$	4	$\frac{5}{8}$
3	$7\frac{1}{2}$	$\frac{3}{4}$	6	4	$\frac{5}{8}$
$3\frac{1}{2}$	$8\frac{1}{2}$	$\frac{13}{16}$	7	8	$\frac{5}{8}$
4	9	$\frac{15}{16}$	$7\frac{1}{2}$	8	$\frac{5}{8}$
5	10	$\frac{15}{16}$	$8\frac{1}{2}$	8	$\frac{3}{4}$
6	11	1	$9\frac{1}{2}$	8	$\frac{3}{4}$
8	$13\frac{1}{2}$	$1\frac{1}{8}$	$11\frac{3}{4}$	8	$\frac{3}{4}$
10	16	$1\frac{3}{16}$	$14\frac{1}{4}$	12	$\frac{7}{8}$
12	19	$1\frac{1}{4}$	17	12	$\frac{7}{8}$
14 OD	21	$1\frac{3}{8}$	$18\frac{3}{4}$	12	1
16 OD	$23\frac{1}{2}$	$1\frac{7}{16}$	$21\frac{1}{4}$	16	1
18 OD	25	$1\frac{9}{16}$	$22\frac{3}{4}$	16	$1\frac{1}{8}$
20 OD	$27\frac{1}{2}$	$1\frac{11}{16}$	25	20	$1\frac{1}{8}$
24 OD	32	$1\frac{7}{8}$	$29\frac{1}{2}$	20	$1\frac{1}{4}$
30 OD	$38\frac{3}{4}$	$2\frac{1}{8}$	36	28	$1\frac{1}{4}$
36 OD	46	$2\frac{3}{8}$	$42\frac{3}{4}$	32	$1\frac{1}{2}$
42 OD	53	$2\frac{5}{8}$	$49\frac{1}{2}$	36	$1\frac{1}{2}$
48 OD	$59\frac{1}{2}$	$2\frac{3}{4}$	56	44	$1\frac{1}{2}$
54 OD	$66\frac{1}{4}$	3	$62\frac{3}{4}$	44	$1\frac{3}{4}$
60 OD	73	$3\frac{1}{8}$	$69\frac{1}{4}$	52	$1\frac{3}{4}$
250-lb Standard°					
1	$4\frac{7}{8}$	$\frac{11}{16}$	$3\frac{1}{2}$	4	$\frac{5}{8}$
$1\frac{1}{4}$	$5\frac{1}{4}$	$\frac{3}{4}$	$3\frac{7}{8}$	4	$\frac{5}{8}$
$1\frac{1}{2}$	$6\frac{1}{8}$	$\frac{13}{16}$	$4\frac{1}{2}$	4	$\frac{3}{4}$
2	$6\frac{1}{2}$	$\frac{7}{8}$	5	8	$\frac{5}{8}$
$2\frac{1}{2}$	$7\frac{1}{2}$	1	$5\frac{7}{8}$	8	$\frac{3}{4}$
3	$8\frac{1}{4}$	$1\frac{1}{8}$	$6\frac{5}{8}$	8	$\frac{3}{4}$
$3\frac{1}{2}$	9	$1\frac{3}{16}$	$7\frac{1}{4}$	8	$\frac{3}{4}$
4	10	$1\frac{1}{4}$	$7\frac{7}{8}$	8	$\frac{3}{4}$
5	11	$1\frac{3}{8}$	$9\frac{1}{4}$	8	$\frac{3}{4}$
6	$12\frac{1}{2}$	$1\frac{7}{16}$	$10\frac{5}{8}$	12	$\frac{3}{4}$
8	15	$1\frac{5}{8}$	13	12	$\frac{7}{8}$
10	$17\frac{1}{2}$	$1\frac{7}{8}$	$15\frac{1}{4}$	16	1
12	$20\frac{1}{2}$	2	$17\frac{3}{4}$	16	$1\frac{1}{8}$
14 OD	23	$2\frac{1}{8}$	$20\frac{1}{4}$	20	$1\frac{1}{8}$
16 OD	$25\frac{1}{2}$	$2\frac{1}{4}$	$22\frac{1}{2}$	20	$1\frac{1}{4}$
18 OD	28	$2\frac{3}{8}$	$24\frac{3}{4}$	24	$1\frac{1}{4}$
20 OD	$30\frac{1}{2}$	$2\frac{1}{2}$	27	24	$1\frac{1}{4}$
24 OD	36	$2\frac{3}{4}$	32	24	$1\frac{1}{2}$
30 OD	43	3	$39\frac{1}{4}$	28	$1\frac{3}{4}$
36 OD	50	$3\frac{3}{8}$	46	32	2
42 OD	57	$3\frac{11}{16}$	$52\frac{3}{4}$	36	2
48 OD	65	4	$60\frac{3}{4}$	40	2

From ANSI Standard, Cast Iron Pipe Flanges and Flange Fittings, B16.1–1967.

° Flange thickness includes $\frac{1}{16}$-in. raised face.

CAST-IRON PIPE DIMENSIONS

Internal pressure, psi

Pipe size, in.	OD, in.	50			100			150			200			250			300			350		
		Thickness class	Wall thickness, in.	ID, in.	Thickness class	Wall thickness, in.	ID, in.	Thickness class	Wall thickness, in.	ID, in.	Thickness class	Wall thickness, in.	ID, in.	Thickness class	Wall thickness, in.	ID, in.	Thickness class	Wall thickness, in.	ID, in.	Thickness class	Wall thickness, in.	ID, in.
3	3.96	22	0.32	3.32	22	0.32	3.32	22	0.32	3.32	22	0.32	3.32	22	0.32	3.32	22	0.32	3.32	22	0.32	3.32
4	4.80	22	0.35	4.10	22	0.35	4.10	22	0.35	4.10	22	0.35	4.10	22	0.35	4.10	22	0.35	4.10	22	0.35	4.10
6	6.90	22	0.38	6.14	22	0.38	6.14	22	0.38	6.14	22	0.38	6.14	22	0.38	6.14	22	0.38	6.14	22	0.38	6.14
8	9.05	22	0.41	8.23	22	0.41	8.23	22	0.41	8.23	22	0.41	8.23	22	0.41	8.23	22	0.41	8.23	22	0.41	8.23
10	11.10	22	0.44	10.22	22	0.44	10.22	22	0.44	10.22	22	0.44	10.22	22	0.44	10.22	23	0.48	10.14	24	0.52	10.06
12	13.20	22	0.48	12.24	22	0.48	12.24	22	0.48	12.24	22	0.48	12.24	23	0.52	12.16	23	0.52	12.16	24	0.56	12.08
14	15.30	21	0.48	14.39	22	0.51	14.28	22	0.51	14.28	23	0.55	14.20	24	0.59	14.12	24	0.59	14.12	25	0.64	14.02
16	17.40	22	0.54	16.32	22	0.54	16.32	22	0.54	16.32	23	0.58	16.24	24	0.63	16.14	25	0.68	16.04	25	0.68	16.04
18	19.50	21	0.54	18.42	22	0.58	18.34	22	0.58	18.34	23	0.63	18.24	24	0.68	18.14	25	0.73	18.04	26	0.79	17.92
20	21.60	21	0.57	20.46	22	0.62	20.36	22	0.62	20.36	23	0.67	20.26	24	0.72	20.16	25	0.78	20.04	26	0.84	19.92
24	25.80	21	0.63	24.54	22	0.68	24.44	23	0.73	24.34	24	0.79	24.22	24	0.79	24.22	25	0.85	24.10	26	0.92	23.96
30	32.00	22	0.79	30.42	22	0.79	30.42	23	0.85	30.30	24	0.92	30.16	25	0.99	30.02	26	1.07	29.86	27	1.16	29.68
36	38.30	22	0.87	36.56	22	0.87	36.56	23	0.94	36.42	24	1.02	36.26	25	1.10	36.10	26	1.19	35.92	27	1.29	35.72
42	44.50	22	0.97	42.56	22	0.97	42.56	23	1.05	42.40	24	1.13	42.24	25	1.22	42.06	26	1.32	41.86	27	1.43	41.64
48	50.80	22	1.06	48.68	22	1.06	48.68	23	1.14	48.52	24	1.23	48.34	25	1.33	48.14	27	1.56	47.68	28	1.68	47.44

This table gives the dimensions of cast-iron pipe, suitable for pressures from 50 to 350 psi, taken from specification ANSI A21.6-1967 (AWWA H1-67) and applying to the following specific conditions:

1. Pipe laid in flat-bottom trench, backfill tamped
2. Depth of cover, 5 ft
3. Iron strength of 18/40, or iron having a bursting strength of 18,000 psi and a ring modulus of rupture of 40,000 psi, centrifugally cast

The thickness class given in the table is a manufacturer's designation for standard wall thickness.
For other conditions of installation than those outlined above, the subject specification must be consulted.

Section **3**

Fluids Engineering Data

PROPERTIES OF WATER AT VARIOUS TEMPERATURES*

Temp, °F	Temp, °C	Specific volume, cu ft/lb	Specific weight, lb/cu ft	Specific gravity†	Vapor pressure, psia	Vapor pressure, in. Hg abs
32	0.0	0.01602	62.420	1.0016	0.0886	0.1804
33	0.6	0.01602	62.423	1.0017	0.0922	0.1878
34	1.1	0.01602	62.423	1.0017	0.0960	0.1955
35	1.7	0.01602	62.423	1.0017	0.0999	0.2034
36	2.2	0.01602	62.423	1.0017	0.1040	0.2118
37	2.8	0.01602	62.428	1.0018	0.1082	0.2203
38	3.3	0.01602	62.428	1.0018	0.1125	0.2290
39	3.9	0.01602	62.428	1.0018	0.1170	0.2382
40	4.4	0.01602	62.428	1.0018	0.1216	0.2476
41	5.0	0.01602	62.428	1.0018	0.1264	0.2574
42	5.6	0.01602	62.427	1.0018	0.1314	0.2675
43	6.1	0.01602	62.426	1.0017	0.1366	0.2781
44	6.7	0.01602	62.424	1.0017	0.1419	0.2889
45	7.2	0.01602	62.423	1.0017	0.1474	0.3001
46	7.8	0.01602	62.422	1.0017	0.1531	0.3117
47	8.3	0.01602	62.417	1.0016	0.1590	0.3237
48	8.9	0.01602	62.417	1.0016	0.1651	0.3361
49	9.4	0.01602	62.415	1.0016	0.1714	0.3490
50	10.0	0.01602	62.412	1.0015	0.1780	0.3624
51	10.6	0.01602	62.408	1.0014	0.1847	0.3760
52	11.1	0.01602	62.405	1.0014	0.1916	0.3900
53	11.7	0.01602	62.400	1.0013	0.1988	0.4048
54	12.2	0.01603	62.397	1.0013	0.2062	0.4196
55	12.8	0.01603	62.392	1.0012	0.2139	0.4355
56	13.3	0.01603	62.389	1.0011	0.2218	0.4516
57	13.9	0.01603	62.383	1.0010	0.2300	0.4682
58	14.4	0.01603	62.379	1.0010	0.2384	0.4853
59	15.0	0.01603	62.374	1.0009	0.2471	0.5031
60	15.6	0.01603	62.368	1.0008	0.2561	0.5214
62	16.7	0.01604	62.357	1.0006	0.2749	0.5517
64	17.8	0.01604	62.345	1.0004	0.2950	0.6006
66	18.9	0.01604	62.331	1.0002	0.3163	0.6439
68	20.0	0.01605	62.318	1.0000	0.3389	0.6900
70	21.1	0.01605	62.304	0.9998	0.3629	0.7388
75	23.9	0.01606	62.263	0.9991	0.4296	0.8747
80	26.7	0.01607	62.217	0.9984	0.5068	1.0318
85	29.4	0.01608	62.169	0.9976	0.5958	1.2130
90	32.2	0.01610	62.116	0.9968	0.6981	1.4213
95	35.0	0.01611	62.058	0.9958	0.8153	1.6600
100	37.8	0.01613	62.00	0.9949	0.9492	1.9325
110	43.3	0.01616	61.86	0.9927	1.2750	2.5959
120	48.9	0.01620	61.71	0.9903	1.6927	3.4463
130	54.4	0.01625	61.56	0.9878	2.2230	4.5260
140	60.0	0.01629	61.38	0.9850	2.8892	5.8824
150	65.6	0.01634	61.20	0.9821	3.7184	7.570
160	71.1	0.01640	61.01	0.9790	4.7414	9.653
170	76.7	0.01645	60.79	0.9755	5.9926	12.200
180	82.2	0.01651	60.57	0.9720	7.5110	15.292
190	87.8	0.01657	60.35	0.9684	9.3400	19.016
200	93.3	0.01664	60.13	0.9649	11.526	23.467

PROPERTIES OF WATER AT VARIOUS TEMPERATURES (Continued)

Temp, °F	Temp, °C	Specific volume, cu ft/lb	Specific weight, lb/cu ft	Specific gravity†	Vapor pressure, psia	Vapor pressure, in. Hg abs
210	98.9	0.01670	59.88	0.9609	14.123	
220	104.4	0.01678	59.63	0.9569	17.186	
230	110.0	0.01685	59.38	0.9529 .	20.779	
240	115.6	0.01693	59.10	0.9484	24.968	
250	121.1	0.01701	58.82	0.9439	29.825	
260	126.7	0.01709	58.51	0.9389	35.427	
270	132.2	0.01718	58.24	0.9346	41.856	
280	137.8	0.01726	57.94	0.9297	49.200	
290	143.3	0.01736	57.64	0.9249	57.550	
300	148.9	0.01745	57.31	0.9196	67.005	
310	154.4	0.01755	56.98	0.9143	77.667	
320	160.0	0.01766	56.66	0.9092	89.643	
330	165.6	0.01776	56.31	0.9036	103.045	
340	171.1	0.01787	55.96	0.8980	117.992	
350	176.7	0.01799	55.59	0.8920	134.604	
360	182.2	0.01811	55.22	0.8861	153.010	
370	187.8	0.01823	54.85	0.8802	173.339	
380	193.3	0.01836	54.47	0.8741	195.729	
390	198.9	0.01850	54.05	0.8673	220.321	
400	204.4	0.01864	53.65	0.8609	247.259	
410	210.0	0.01878	53.25	0.8545	276.694	
420	215.6	0.01894	52.80	0.8473	308.780	
430	221.1	0.01909	52.36	0.8402	343.674	
440	226.7	0.01926	51.92	0.8332	381.54	
450	232.2	0.01943	51.5	0.826	422.55	
460	237.8	0.01961	51.0	0.818	466.87	
470	243.3	0.01980	50.5	0.810	514.67	
480	249.9	0.02000	50.0	0.802	566.15	
490	254.4	0.02021	49.5	0.794	621.48	
500	260.0	0.02043	49.0	0.786	680.86	
510	265.6	0.02067	48.3	0.775	744.47	
520	271.1	0.02091	47.8	0.767	812.53	
530	276.7	0.02118	47.2	0.757	885.23	
540	282.2	0.02146	46.5	0.746	962.79	
550	287.8	0.02176	45.9	0.737	1,045.43	
560	293.3	0.02207	45.2	0.725	1,133.38	
570	298.9	0.02242	44.6	0.716	1,226.88	
580	304.4	0.02279	43.9	0.704	1,326.17	
590	310.0	0.02319	43.1	0.692	1,431.5	
600	315.6	0.02364	42.4	0.680	1,543.2	
610	321.1	0.02412	41.5	0.666	1,661.6	
620	326.7	0.02466	40.5	0.650	1,786.9	
630	332.2	0.02526	39.5	0.634	1,919.5	
640	337.8	0.02595	38.5	0.618	2,059.9	
650	343.3	0.02674	37.3	0.599	2,208.4	
660	348.9	0.02768	36.0	0.578	2,365.7	
670	354.4	0.02884	34.5	0.554	2,532.2	
680	360.0	0.03037	32.8	0.526	2,708.6	
690	365.6	0.03256	30.5	0.489	2,895.7	
705.47	374.1	0.05078	19.9	0.319	3,208.2	

° Computed by permission from "1967 ASME Steam Tables," The American Society of Mechanical Engineers.

† Referred to water at 68°F. Weighing 62.318 lb/cu ft.

CONVERSION OF POUNDS PER SQUARE INCH TO HEAD IN FEET OF WATER AT 68°F, WEIGHING 62.318 LB/CU FT

Psi	Head in Feet	Psi	Head in Feet	Psi	Head in Feet	Psi	Head in Feet
		50	115.55	100	231.1	500	1156
1	2.311	51	117.86	105	242.7	525	1213
2	4.622	52	120.17	110	254.2	550	1271
3	6.933	53	122.48	115	265.8	575	1329
4	9.244	54	124.79	120	277.3	600	1387
5	11.555	55	127.11	125	288.9	625	1444
6	13.866	56	129.42	130	300.4	650	1502
7	16.177	57	131.73	135	312.0	675	1560
8	18.488	58	134.04	140	323.5	700	1618
9	20.799	59	136.35	145	335.1	725	1675
10	23.110	60	138.66	150	346.7	750	1733
11	25.421	61	140.97	155	358.2	775	1791
12	27.732	62	143.28	160	369.8	800	1849
13	30.043	63	145.59	165	381.3	825	1907
14	32.354	64	147.90	170	392.9	850	1964
15	34.665	65	150.22	175	404.4	875	2022
16	36.976	66	152.53	180	416.0	900	2080
17	39.287	67	154.84	185	427.5	925	2138
18	41.598	68	157.15	190	439.1	950	2196
19	43.909	69	159.46	195	450.6	975	2253
20	46.220	70	161.77	200	462.2	1000	2311
21	48.531	71	164.08	210	485.3	1050	2427
22	50.842	72	166.39	220	508.4	1100	2542
23	53.153	73	168.70	230	531.5	1150	2658
24	55.464	74	171.01	240	554.6	1200	2773
25	57.775	75	173.33	250	577.8	1250	2889
26	60.086	76	175.64	260	600.9	1300	3004
27	62.397	77	177.95	270	624.0	1350	3120
28	64.708	78	180.26	280	647.1	1400	3235
29	67.019	79	182.57	290	670.2	1450	3351
30	69.330	80	184.88	300	693.3	1500	3467
31	71.641	81	187.19	310	716.4	1550	3582
32	73.952	82	189.50	320	739.5	1600	3698
33	76.263	83	191.81	330	762.6	1650	3813
34	78.574	84	194.12	340	785.7	1700	3929
35	80.885	85	196.44	350	808.9	1750	4044
36	83.196	86	198.75	360	832.0	1800	4160
37	85.507	87	201.06	370	855.1	1850	4275
38	87.818	88	203.37	380	878.2	1900	4391
39	90.129	89	205.68	390	901.3	1950	4506
40	92.440	90	207.99	400	924.4	2000	4622
41	94.751	91	210.30	410	947.5	2050	4738
42	97.062	92	212.61	420	970.6	2100	4853
43	99.373	93	214.92	430	993.7	2150	4969
44	101.68	94	217.23	440	1017	2200	5084
45	104.00	95	219.55	450	1040	2250	5200
46	106.31	96	221.86	460	1063	2300	5315
47	108.62	97	224.17	470	1086	2350	5431
48	110.93	98	226.48	480	1109	2400	5546
49	113.24	99	228.79	490	1132	2450	5662

At other temperatures correction must be made for specific gravity.

CONVERSION OF INCHES OF MERCURY (AT 68°F)* TO FEET OF WATER (AT 68°F)*

1 in. Hg = 1.131 ft water

Inches of Mercury	INCHES OF MERCURY IN FRACTIONS							
	0	1/8	1/4	3/8	1/2	5/8	3/4	7/8
	FEET OF WATER							
0	0.000	0.141	0.283	0.424	0.566	0.707	0.848	0.990
1	1.131	1.272	1.414	1.555	1.697	1.838	1.979	2.121
2	2.262	2.403	2.545	2.686	2.828	2.969	3.110	3.252
3	3.393	3.534	3.676	3.817	3.959	4.100	4.241	4.383
4	4.524	4.665	4.807	4.948	5.090	5.231	5.372	5.514
5	5.655	5.796	5.938	6.079	6.221	6.362	6.503	6.645
6	6.786	6.927	7.069	7.210	7.352	7.493	7.634	7.776
7	7.917	8.058	8.200	8.341	8.483	8.624	8.765	8.907
8	9.048	9.189	9.331	9.472	9.614	9.755	9.896	10.038
9	10.179	10.320	10.462	10.603	10.745	10.886	11.027	11.169
10	11.310	11.451	11.593	11.734	11.876	12.017	12.158	12.300
11	12.441	12.582	12.724	12.865	13.007	13.148	13.289	13.431
12	13.572	13.713	13.855	13.996	14.138	14.279	14.420	14.562
13	14.703	14.844	14.986	15.127	15.269	15.410	15.551	15.693
14	15.834	15.975	16.117	16.258	16.400	16.541	16.682	16.824
15	16.965	17.106	17.248	17.389	17.531	17.672	17.813	17.955
16	18.096	18.237	18.379	18.520	18.662	18.803	18.944	19.086
17	19.227	19.368	19.510	19.651	19.793	19.934	20.075	20.217
18	20.358	20.499	20.641	20.782	20.924	21.065	21.206	21.348
19	21.489	21.630	21.772	21.913	22.055	22.196	22.337	22.479
20	22.620	22.761	22.903	23.044	23.186	23.327	23.468	23.610
21	23.751	23.892	24.034	24.175	24.317	24.458	24.599	24.741
22	24.882	25.023	25.165	25.306	25.448	25.589	25.730	25.872
23	26.013	26.154	26.296	26.437	26.579	26.720	26.861	27.003
24	27.144	27.285	27.427	27.568	27.710	27.851	27.992	28.134
25	28.275	28.416	28.558	28.699	28.841	28.982	29.123	29.265
26	29.406	29.547	29.689	29.830	29.972	30.113	30.254	30.396
27	30.537	30.678	30.820	30.961	31.103	31.244	31.385	31.527
28	31.668	31.809	31.951	32.092	32.234	32.375	32.516	32.658
29	32.799	32.940	33.082	33.223	33.365	33.506	33.647	33.789
30	33.930	34.071	34.213	34.354	34.496	34.637	34.778	34.920

Temp. °F	Correction *	Temp. °F	Correction *	Temp. °F	Correction *
32	1.00199	65	0.99997	100	1.00196
35	1.00160	70	1.00004	105	1.00251
40	1.00105	75	1.00018	110	1.00313
45	1.00063	80	1.00040	115	1.00380
50	1.00032	85	1.00069	120	1.00451
55	1.00011	90	1.00105	125	1.00529
60	1.00000	95	1.00148	130	1.00612

* Correct tabular values to other temperatures by multiplying by correction. To use this table with a mercury and water differential manometer, subtract the number of inches of mercury divided by 12 from the corrected tabular value to obtain the equivalent number of feet of water.

VELOCITY HEAD $V^2/2g$ FOR VARIOUS VELOCITIES

VELOC-ITY fps	VELOCITY IN TENTHS									
	0	0.1	0.2	0.3	0.4	0.5	0.6	0.7	0.8	0.9
	VELOCITY HEAD (FEET)									
0	0	0	0	0	0	0	0	0	0.01	0.01
1	0.02	0.02	0.02	0.03	0.03	0.04	0.04	0.05	0.05	0.06
2	0.06	0.07	0.08	0.08	0.09	0.10	0.11	0.11	0.12	0.13
3	0.14	0.15	0.16	0.17	0.18	0.19	0.20	0.21	0.22	0.24
4	0.25	0.26	0.27	0.29	0.30	0.32	0.33	0.34	0.36	0.37
5	0.39	0.40	0.42	0.44	0.45	0.47	0.49	0.51	0.52	0.54
6	0.56	0.58	0.60	0.62	0.64	0.66	0.68	0.70	0.72	0.74
7	0.76	0.78	0.81	0.83	0.85	0.88	0.90	0.92	0.95	0.97
8	0.99	1.00	1.05	1.07	1.10	1.12	1.15	1.18	1.20	1.23
9	1.26	1.29	1.32	1.35	1.37	1.40	1.43	1.46	1.49	1.52
10	1.56	1.59	1.62	1.65	1.68	1.71	1.75	1.78	1.81	1.85
11	1.88	1.92	1.95	1.99	2.02	2.06	2.09	2.13	2.17	2.20
12	2.24	2.28	2.31	2.35	2.39	2.43	2.47	2.51	2.55	2.59
13	2.63	2.67	2.71	2.75	2.79	2.83	2.88	2.92	2.96	3.00
14	3.05	3.09	3.14	3.18	3.22	3.27	3.31	3.36	3.41	3.45
15	3.50	3.55	3.59	3.64	3.69	3.74	3.78	3.83	3.88	3.93
16	3.98	4.03	4.08	4.13	4.18	4.23	4.28	4.34	4.39	4.44
17	4.49	4.55	4.60	4.65	4.71	4.76	4.82	4.87	4.93	4.98
18	5.04	5.10	5.15	5.21	5.25	5.32	5.38	5.44	5.50	5.55
19	5.61	5.67	5.73	5.79	5.85	5.91	5.97	6.03	6.10	6.16
20	6.22	6.28	6.34	6.41	6.47	6.53	6.60	6.66	6.73	6.79
21	6.86	6.92	6.99	7.05	7.12	7.19	7.25	7.32	7.39	7.46
22	7.53	7.59	7.66	7.73	7.80	7.87	7.94	8.01	8.08	8.15
23	8.22	8.30	8.37	8.44	8.51	8.59	8.66	8.73	8.81	8.88
24	8.96	9.03	9.11	9.18	9.26	9.33	9.41	9.49	9.56	9.64
25	9.72	9.80	9.87	9.95	10.03	10.11	10.19	10.27	10.35	10.43
26	10.51	10.59	10.67	10.75	10.84	10.92	11.00	11.08	11.17	11.25
27	11.33	11.42	11.50	11.59	11.67	11.76	11.84	11.93	12.02	12.10
28	12.19	12.28	12.36	12.45	12.54	12.63	12.72	12.81	12.90	12.99
29	13.08	13.17	13.26	13.35	13.44	13.53	13.62	13.71	13.81	13.90
30	13.99	14.09	14.18	14.27	14.37	14.46	14.56	14.65	14.75	14.84

CONVERSION OF INCHES OF MERCURY TO POUNDS PER SQUARE INCH

Multiply inches of mercury by conversion factor to obtain pounds per square inch

Temperature °F	Conversion Factor	Temperature °F	Conversion Factor
0	0.49276	70	0.48929
5	0.49251	75	0.48905
10	0.49226	80	0.48880
15	0.49201	85	0.48855
20	0.49176	90	0.48831
25	0.49152	95	0.48806
30	0.49127	100	0.48782
35	0.49102	105	0.48757
40	0.49077	110	0.48733
45	0.49053	115	0.48708
50	0.49028	120	0.48684
55	0.49003	125	0.48660
60	0.48979	130	0.48635
65	0.48954	135	0.48611

VISCOSITY OF FLUIDS

Viscosity is that property of any fluid (liquid or gas) which tends to resist a shearing force. It is important to fluid flow because nearly all fluid motion is accompanied by shearing forces.

The two basic viscosity parameters are the *dynamic* (or *absolute*) *viscosity* μ, having the dimension force × time/(length)^2, and the *kinematic viscosity* ν, having the dimension (length)^2/time. The parameters are related through the mass density ρ of the fluid, such that $\nu = \mu/\rho = \mu g/\gamma$, where γ is the specific weight and g is the acceleration of gravity.

The unit of dynamic viscosity in English measure is the *pound-second per square foot*, which is numerically identical with the *slug per foot-second*. The unit of dynamic viscosity in metric measure is the *dyne-second per square centimeter*, called the *poise*, which is numerically identical with the *gram per centimeter-second*. Numerical values generally are expressed in *centipoises*, a unit which is one-hundredth of a poise. A unit called the *reyn*, equal to 1 *pound-second per square inch*, is used in lubrication problems.

The unit of kinematic viscosity in English measure is the *square foot per second*. The unit of kinematic viscosity in metric measure is the *square centimeter per second*, called the *stoke*. Numerical values generally are expressed in *centistokes*, a unit which is one-hundredth of a stoke.

Widespread use of the Saybolt viscosimeter has led to the use of the time of efflux in seconds, for 60 cu cm of liquid, as an arbitrary unit of kinematic viscosity. The term SSU (Seconds Saybolt Universal) refers to the smaller, and the term SSF (Seconds Saybolt Furol) refers to the larger of two orifices with which the instrument may be equipped. Other empirical measures of kinematic viscosity may be converted to basic units by the chart on page 3-11 and the table on page 3-12.

The dynamic viscosity of any fluid is a function of temperature and pressure. The dynamic viscosity of most liquids increases with increase of pressure, but fortunately the changes may be neglected for the ranges of pressure usually encountered in engineering problems. The dynamic viscosity of gases is virtually independent of pressure except at extremely high or low pressures. Pressure is very important in determining the kinematic viscosity of a gas because of its influence on the mass density. The kinematic viscosities of many fluids are shown in the charts on pages 3-14 to 3-18, inclusive.

Viscosities of air and water at 68°F and atmospheric pressure are as follows:

Fluid	Dynamic viscosity μ		Kinematic viscosity ν		
	Poises	lb-sec/sq ft	Stokes	sq ft/sec	SSU
Air	180.8×10^{-6}	0.3369×10^{-6}	0.1501	161.6×10^{-6}	
Water.	0.010087	21.067×10^{-6}	0.010105	10.877×10^{-6}	30.1

Newtonian Materials

Newton deduced that the viscosity of a given liquid should be constant at any particular temperature and pressure and independent of the rate of shear, as illustrated in Fig. 3-1. In such "Newtonian fluids," shear stress is directly proportional to rate of shear. At temperatures above their cloud points most mineral oils are Newtonian fluids.

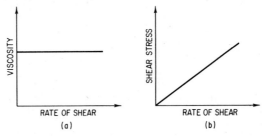

Fig. 3-1 Characteristics of Newtonian liquids. (a) Viscosity is independent of rate of shear. (b) Shear stress is directly proportional to rate of shear.

Non-Newtonian Materials

The viscosities of some materials, such as greases and polymer-thickened mineral oils, are affected by shearing effects, and these materials are termed *non-Newtonian*. In other words, the viscosity of a non-Newtonian fluid will depend on the rate of shear at which it is measured. Since a non-Newtonian fluid can have an unlimited number of viscosity values (as the shear rate is varied) the term *apparent viscosity* is used to describe its viscous properties. Apparent viscosity is expressed in absolute units and is a measure of the resistance to flow at a given rate of shear. It has meaning only if the rate of shear used in the measurement is also given and is obtained experimentally by measuring and dividing the shear stress by the rate of shear. A "rheogram" or "flow curve" relating shear stress to rate of shear is frequently used to describe completely the viscous properties of a non-Newtonian material.

Non-Newtonian materials may be divided into five types: plastic, pseudo-plastic, dilatant, thixotropic, and rheopectic. Figure 3-2 presents characteristic rheograms in which shear stress (e.g., pressure in a steady-flow system) is plotted against rate of shear (e.g., flow velocity). The curves at the left in Fig. 3-3 illustrate how the apparent viscosities of non-Newtonian materials vary with changing rates of shear.

As illustrated in curve 1 of Fig. 3-2, a *plastic* material, such as a grease, putty, or molding clay, is characterized by a "yield point" or "yield value." This means that a definite minimum stress or force must be applied to the material before any flow takes place. From a rheological standpoint,[1] tomato catsup is a common example of a plastic material. If a bottle is shaken only gently, its contents may not flow out because the "yield point" has not been exceeded. However, if the bottle is struck or shaken more vigorously, the yield point is exceeded, the viscosity is reduced, and the catsup gushes forth.

While a pseudo-plastic fluid has no yield point, its apparent viscosity also decreases

---

[1] Rheology: the science treating of deformation and flow of matter.

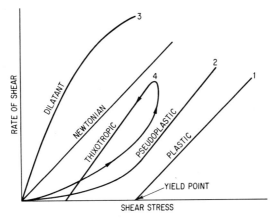

Fig. 3-2   Flow curves illustrating shear characteristics of various types of materials.

with increasing shear rates but stabilizes only at very high rates of shear. Many emulsions such as water-base fluids and resinous materials show this type of behavior.

Oppositely, the apparent viscosity of a dilatant fluid increases as the rate of shear increases. Such a fluid often solidifies at high rates of shear. Examples are pigment-vehicle suspensions such as paints and printing inks, and some starches.

The three fluids described above—plastic, pseudo-plastic, and dilatant—are also known as time-independent non-Newtonian fluids, since their rheological or flow properties are independent of time. The rate of shear at any point in the fluid is a simple function of the shear stress at that point.

On the other hand, the flow properties of two other non-Newtonian materials—thixotropic and rheopectic—are dependent on time. The apparent viscosity of these more complex fluids depends not only on the magnitude of the shear rate but also on the length of time during which shear has been applied, as illustrated in Fig. 3-3.

If a thixotropic fluid is subjected to a constant rate of shear for some time, its structure is gradually broken down and its apparent viscosity decreases to some minimum value. When the shear effect is removed and the fluid is at rest, the structure rebuilds gradually and apparent viscosity increases with time to the original value. This is called *reversible thixotropy*. If, however, upon removing the shear stress, a value less than the original viscosity is obtained with time, the phenomenon is known as *irreversible thixotropy*. Some oils containing high-molecular-weight polymers and mineral oils at temperatures below their cloud point show this latter effect.

During rotary drilling of deep oil wells, a very special "drilling mud" with thixotropic properties is pumped down the hollow drill stem to force cuttings back to the surface. As long as the mud is agitated by rotation of the drill stem and by pumping, it remains fluid and removes drilling debris. However, whenever drilling is stopped, the drilling

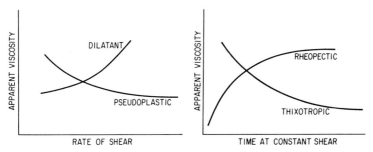

Fig. 3-3   Different types of non-Newtonian behavior.

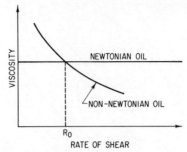

Fig. 3-4 Viscosity vs. rate of shear for Newtonian and non-Newtonian oils.

mud solidifies to a gel, holds the cuttings in suspension, and thereby prevents them from settling and interfering with subsequent drilling.

Quicksand is also thixotropic, since it becomes more and more fluid when agitated; therefore anyone caught in this water-and-sand mixture improves his chance of survival by remaining as motionless as possible.

If a rheopectic fluid is subjected to a constant rate of shear for a given period of time, its apparent viscosity increases to some maximum value. Upon cessation of shearing and resting for a time, its apparent viscosity decreases again.

Some greases are intentionally manufactured to have partial rheopectic properties, which facilitate pumping from a drum or central grease storage in which the grease is in a relatively fluid condition. Upon shearing in a bearing, however, the grease builds up to a higher apparent viscosity or consistency and stays in place. Such a grease does not have full rheopectic characteristics, however, since after shearing and resting, it still retains a higher consistency.

Since the viscosity of a non-Newtonian lubricant is dependent upon the rate of shear acting on it, the importance of measuring viscosity at various shear rates that will be encountered in the use of such a lubricant can be readily seen. In some machine elements, shear rates up to 3 million reciprocal seconds may be encountered, while in other applications only a few reciprocal seconds or a few tenths are the order of magnitude. In dispensing greases, shear rates as low as 0.1 reciprocal second are sometimes encountered, while leakage from housings during periods of shutdown involves an even lower range.

As illustrated by Fig. 3-4, the determination of viscosity of a non-Newtonian liquid at only one shear rate is not usually sufficient. Incorrect conclusions would be drawn and application difficulties would be invited if the viscosities of a Newtonian and a non-Newtonian oil were measured at some specific shear rate R_0, where the two curves happened to cross each other. While both oils have the same apparent viscosity at this one point, the remainders of their viscosity-shear curves are entirely different.

VISCOSITY CONVERSION FACTORS

Multiply	by	to obtain
poises	100	centipoises
pound-seconds/sq ft	47,880.1	centipoises
reyns	6.89473×10^6	centipoises
centipoises	2.08855×10^{-5}	pound-seconds/sq ft
centipoises	1.45038×10^{-7}	reyns
stokes	100	centistokes
sq ft/second	92,903.4	centistokes
centistokes	1.07639×10^{-5}	sq ft/second
sq ft/second	$1488.16 \times \gamma$ in pounds/cu ft	centipoises
centipoises	$6.71970 \times 10^{-4}/\gamma$ in pounds/cu ft	sq ft/second

Saybolt Viscosimeter Conversion Formulas

$$\mu, \text{ in centistokes} = 0.226 \times \text{SSU} - 195/\text{SSU} \quad \text{for SSU} \leq 100$$
$$\mu, \text{ in centistokes} = 0.220 \times \text{SSU} - 130/\text{SSU} \quad \text{for SSU} > 100$$
$$\mu, \text{ in centistokes} = 2.24 \times \text{SSF} - 184/\text{SSF} \quad \text{for } 25 \leq \text{SSF} \leq 40$$
$$\mu, \text{ in centistokes} = 2.16 \times \text{SSF} - 60/\text{SSF} \quad \text{for SSF} > 40$$

VISCOSITY CONVERSION CHART

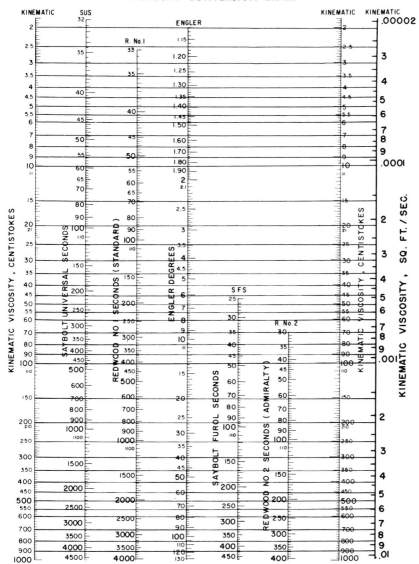

Viscosities at the *same temperature* on all scales are equivalent.   To extend the range of only the kinematic, Saybolt Universal, Redwood No. 1, and Engler scales: Multiply by 10 the viscosities on these scales between 100 and 1,000 centistokes on the kinematic scale and the corresponding viscosities on the other three scales.   For further extension, multiply these scales as above by 100 or a higher power of 10.   Example: 1,500 centistokes = 150 × 10 centistokes ≅ 695 × 10 SSU = 6,950 SSU.   (*Courtesy of Texaco, Inc.*)

VISCOSITY CONVERSION TABLE

The following table will give a comparison of various viscosity ratings, so that if the viscosity is given in terms other than Saybolt Universal, it can be translated quickly by following horizontally to the Saybolt Universal column.

Seconds Saybolt Universal SSU	Kinematic viscosity, centistokes °	Seconds Saybolt Furol SSF	Seconds Redwood 1 (Standard)	Seconds Redwood 2 (Admiralty)	Degrees Engler	Degrees Barbey	Seconds Parlin Cup No. 7	Seconds Parlin Cup No. 10	Seconds Parlin Cup No. 15	Seconds Parlin Cup No. 20	Seconds Ford Cup No. 3	Seconds Ford Cup No. 4
31	1.00		29	.....	1.00	6,200						
35	2.56		32.1	.....	1.16	2,420						
40	4.30		36.2	5.10	1.31	1,440						
50	7.40		44.3	5.83	1.58	838						
60	10.3		52.3	6.77	1.88	618						
70	13.1	12.95	60.9	7.60	2.17	483						
80	15.7	13.70	69.2	8.44	2.45	404						
90	18.2	14.44	77.6	9.30	2.73	348						
100	20.6	15.24	85.6	10.12	3.02	307						
150	32.1	19.30	128	14.48	4.48	195						
200	43.2	23.5	170	18.90	5.92	144	40					
250	54.0	28.0	212	23.45	7.35	114	46					
300	65.0	32.5	254	28.0	8.79	95	52.5	15	6.0	3.0	30	20
400	87.60	41.9	338	37.1	11.70	70.8	66	21	7.2	3.2	42	28
500	110.0	51.6	423	46.2	14.60	56.4	79	25	7.8	3.4	50	34
600	132	61.4	508	55.4	17.50	47.0	92	30	8.5	3.6	58	40
700	154	71.1	592	64.6	20.45	40.3	106	35	9.0	3.9	67	45
800	176	81.0	677	73.8	23.35	35.2	120	39	9.8	4.1	74	50
900	198	91.0	762	83.0	26.30	31.3	135	41	10.7	4.3	82	57
1,000	220	100.7	896	92.1	29.20	28.2	149	43	11.5	4.5	90	62
1,500	330	150	1,270	138.2	43.80	18.7	.....	65	15.2	6.3	132	90
2,000	440	200	1,690	184.2	58.40	14.1	.....	86	19.5	7.5	172	118
2,500	550	250	2,120	230	73.0	11.3	.....	108	24	9	218	147
3,000	660	300	2,540	276	87.60	9.4	.....	129	28.5	11	258	172
4,000	880	400	3,380	368	117.0	7.05	.....	172	37	14	337	230
5,000	1,100	500	4,230	461	146	5.64	.....	215	47	18	425	290
6,000	1,320	600	5,080	553	175	4.70	.....	258	57	22	520	350
7,000	1,540	700	5,920	645	204.5	4.03	.....	300	67	25	600	410

8,000	1,760	800	6,770	737	233.5	3.52	344	76	29	680	465
9,000	1,980	900	7,620	829	263	3.13	387	86	32	780	520
10,000	2,200	1,000	8,460	921	292	2.82	430	96	35	850	575
15,000	3,300	1,500	13,700	. . . . . .	438	2.50	650	147	53	1,280	860
20,000	4,400	2,000	18,400	. . . . . .	584	1.40	860	203	70	1,715	1,150

Reprinted from Standards of the Hydraulic Institute, 11th ed., Copyright 1965.

* Kinematic viscosity (in centistokes) = $\dfrac{\text{absolute viscosity (in centipoises)}}{\text{specific gravity}}$. Above 300 SSU, use the following approximate conversion: SSU = centistokes × 4.635. Above the range of this table and within the range of the viscosimeter, multiply their rating by the following factors to convert to SSU:

Viscosimeter	Factor
Saybolt Furol	10
Redwood Standard. . . .	1.095
Redwood Admiralty . . .	10.87
Engler, degrees	34.5

Viscosimeter	Factor
Parlin cup No. 15	98.2
Parlin cup No. 20	187.0
Ford cup No. 4	17.4

VISCOSITY OF FLUIDS

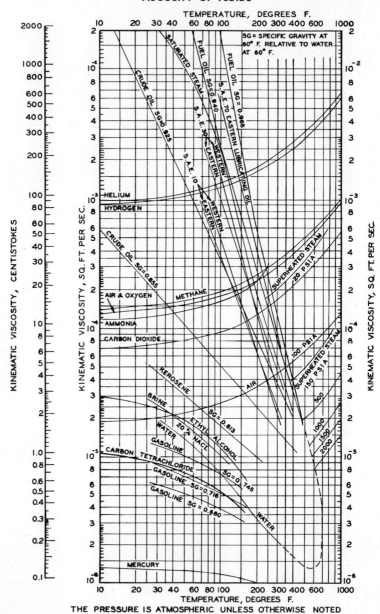

THE PRESSURE IS ATMOSPHERIC UNLESS OTHERWISE NOTED

EFFECT OF TEMPERATURE ON FUEL-OIL VISCOSITY*

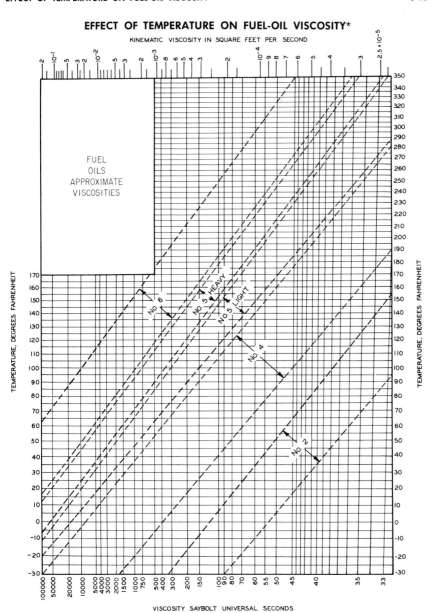

° Courtesy of Texaco, Inc.

EFFECT OF TEMPERATURE ON TURBINE-OIL VISCOSITY*

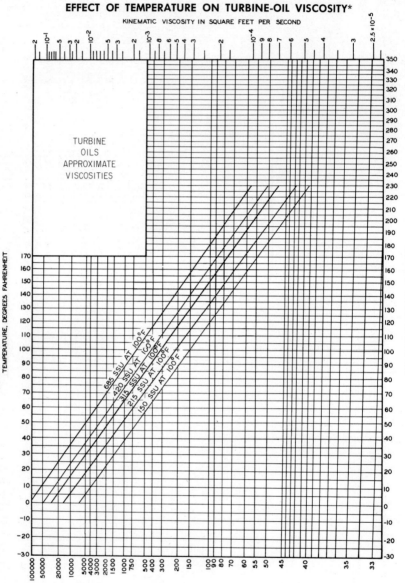

VISCOSITY SAYBOLT UNIVERSAL SECONDS

° Courtesy of Texaco, Inc.

CRANKCASE-OIL CLASSIFICATION

SAE Recommended Practice[1]

The SAE viscosity numbers constitute a classification for crankcase lubricating oils in terms of viscosity only. Other factors of oil character or quality are not considered. Viscosity numbers without an additional symbol are based on the viscosity at 210°F. Viscosity numbers with the additional symbol W are based on the viscosity at 0°F. Viscosity values are given in the following table:

SAE viscosity No.	Viscosity range, SSU			
	At 0°F		At 210°F	
	Min	Max	Min	Max
5W	. . . .	6,000		
10W	6,000°	Less than 12,000		
20W	12,000†	48,000		
20	. . . .	. . . . . .	45	Less than 58
30	. . . .	. . . . . .	58	Less than 70
40	. . . .	. . . . . .	70	Less than 85
50	. . . .	. . . . . .	85	110

NOTE: SAE crankcase oils should not be used in lubrication systems for which turbine oils are recommended.

° Minimum viscosity at 0°F can be waived, provided viscosity at 210°F is not below 40 SSU.

† Minimum viscosity at 0°F can be waived, provided viscosity at 210°F is not below 45 SSU.

A multiviscosity numbered oil is one whose 0°F viscosity falls within the prescribed range of one of the W-number classifications and whose 210°F viscosity falls within the prescribed range of one of the non-W-number classifications.

For the effect of temperature on SAE crankcase-oil viscosity, see page 3-18.

[1] Taken from the "Society of Automotive Engineers Handbook," 1969, by permission.

EFFECT OF TEMPERATURE ON SAE CRANKCASE-OIL VISCOSITY*

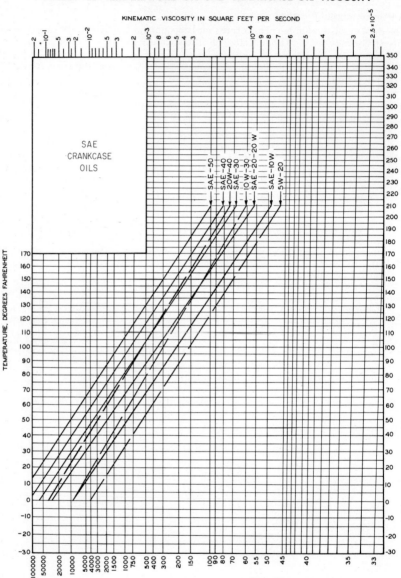

° Courtesy of Texaco, Inc.

FRICTION LOSSES IN PIPES

Pipe Friction

The resistance to the incompressible flow of any fluid in any pipe may be computed from the equation

$$h_f = f \frac{L}{D} \frac{V^2}{2g} \tag{1}$$

where h_f = frictional resistance, ft of fluid

L = length of pipe, ft, including the centerline length of all valves and fittings plus the allowance from pages 3-30 to 3-33, inclusive

D = average internal diameter of pipe, ft. For noncircular cross sections, replace D by four times the cross-sectional area in square feet divided by the wetted perimeter in feet

V = average velocity in pipe, fps

g = acceleration due to gravity = 32.17 ft/sec² at sea level and approximately 45° latitude

f = friction factor to be taken from the chart on page 3-21 according to the diameter, kind of pipe, and the *Reynolds number*

The Reynolds number R is a dimensionless flow parameter defined by

$$R = \frac{VD}{v} \tag{2}$$

where V and D are as defined above

v = kinematic viscosity, sq ft/sec

The flow in most commercial pipe systems may be assumed to be turbulent for all values of Reynolds number greater than 3,000. A critical state of flow usually occurs between $R = 2,000$ and $R = 3,000$ in which the frictional resistance is difficult to predict. For all values of the Reynolds number less than 2,000, the flow is laminar and the friction factor for any kind and size of pipe is given by

$$f = \frac{64}{R} \qquad R \lessgtr 2,000 \text{ only} \tag{3}$$

The chart shown on page 3-21 may be used to compute the friction loss due to the turbulent flow of any fluid, liquid or gas, in pipes of any material.

If the fluid is fresh water at 60°F or atmospheric air at 60°F, the two respective scales at the bottom may be used in lieu of the Reynolds number, the scale reading being the product of the average velocity in feet per second and the internal diameter in inches (VD'').

Tables for Water

The tables on pages 3-22 to 3-28, inclusive, show the average velocity and the friction loss per 100 ft of new clean pipe for fresh water at 60°F. Page 3-22 is for schedule 40 steel or wrought-iron pipe, ANSI Specification B36.10. Pages 3-23 to 3-28 are for asphalt-dipped cast-iron pipe. Asphalt-dipped pipe should not be confused with pipes lined with asphalt bitumen, for which the friction losses are considerably smaller. The allowance to be made for valves and fittings is given on pages 3-30 to 3-33, inclusive.

Charts for Viscous Fluids

The charts on pages 3-34 to 3-46, inclusive, are useful to determine the friction losses for various fluids flowing through schedule 40 new steel or wrought-iron pipes, ANSI Specification B36.10. Fluid viscosities are given in Seconds Saybolt Universal (SSU) and centistokes.

Friction-loss moduli for *laminar flow* are shown by the 45° lines in the upper left-hand portion of each chart. Moduli for *turbulent flow* are shown by the steeper curves in the lower right-hand portion.

The horizontal scale at the bottom of each chart shows the rate of flow in gallons per minute and, at the top, the corresponding average velocity in the pipe in feet per second. The vertical scales of friction-loss modulus are converted to pressure loss in pounds per square inch or to head loss in feet of liquid as described on the charts. The allowance to be made for valves and fittings is given on pages 3-30 to 3-33.

Construction of Charts and Tables

The friction factor f has been determined by the Colebrook equation

$$\frac{1}{\sqrt{f}} = -2 \log_{10} \left(\frac{\epsilon}{3.7D} + \frac{2.51}{R \sqrt{f}} \right) \tag{4}$$

where ϵ = absolute roughness of pipe wall, ft
  ϵ/D = relative roughness of pipe wall, dimensionless
  R = Reynolds number defined by Eq. (2)

Friction factors determined from Eq. (2) are within 10 percent of measured values for most new pipes. Insufficient data are available to establish reliable values of ϵ/D for old or deteriorated pipes. Equations (1) to (4), together with appropriate values of ϵ, have been used to construct all the charts and tables of fluid friction given in this section. The tables are based on $\nu = 0.00001216$ sq ft/sec, equivalent to 1.130 centistokes, which is the value for pure fresh water at 60°F. The absolute roughness $\epsilon = 0.00015$ ft has been used for new steel or wrought-iron pipe, and $\epsilon = 0.0004$ ft has been used for asphalt-dipped cast-iron pipe.

FRICTION FACTORS FOR ANY KIND AND SIZE OF PIPE°

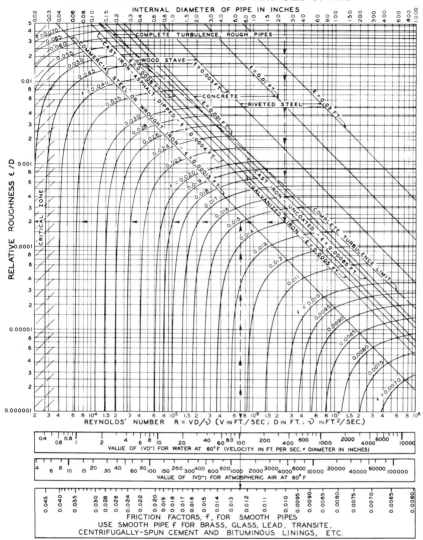

° For additional explanation of this chart, see page 3-19.

Example: Given a 24-in. ID asphalt-dipped cast-iron pipe handling 6,500 gpm of water. From the table on page 3-26 find $V = 4.61$ fps, $VD'' = 4.61 \times 24 = 110.6$. This is equivalent to a Reynolds number $R = 7 \times 10^5$. Find $f = 0.015$ and $\epsilon/D = 0.0002$ by following dotted lines shown on chart. From Eq. (1) on page 3-19 find $h_f = 0.246$ ft per 100 ft. Given any smooth pipe such as brass with $R = 7 \times 10^5$, find $f = 0.0124$.

FRICTION OF WATER IN NEW STEEL OR WROUGHT-IRON PIPE—SCHEDULE 40°

Friction is in feet of water at 60°F per 100 ft of pipe

gpm	Velocity fps	Friction ft./100 ft.	gpm	Velocity fps	Friction ft./100 ft.	gpm	Velocity fps	Friction ft./100 ft.
1-Inch Pipe (1.049" I.D.)			**1½-Inch Pipe (1.610" I.D.)**			**2½-Inch Pipe (2.469" I.D.)**		
2	0.742	0.379	4	0.630	0.164	8	0.536	0.0712
3	1.114	0.772	5	0.788	0.242	10	0.670	0.105
4	1.48	1.295	6	0.946	0.333	12	0.804	0.145
5	1.86	1.93	8	1.26	0.558	14	0.938	0.1⸱1
6	2.23	2.68	10	1.58	0.829	16	1.07	0.243
8	2.97	4.54	15	2.36	1.74	18	1.21	0.300
10	3.71	6.86	20	3.15	2.94	20	1.34	0.362
12	4.45	9.62	25	3.94	4.46	22	1.47	0.430
14	5.20	12.8	30	4.73	6.26	24	1.61	0.502
16	5.94	16.5	35	5.52	8.37	26	1.74	0.580
18	6.68	20.6	40	6.30	10.79	28	1.88	0.663
20	7.42	25.1	45	7.10	13.5	30	2.01	0.753
22	8.17	30.2	50	7.88	16.4	35	2.35	1.00
24	8.91	35.6	60	9.46	23.2	40	2.68	1.28
26	9.65	41.6	70	11.03	31.3	45	3.02	1.60
28	10.39	47.9	80	12.6	40.5	50	3.35	1.94
30	11.1	54.6	90	14.2	51.0	55	3.69	2.32
35	13.0	73.3	100	15.8	62.2	60	4.02	2.72
40	14.8	95.0	125	19.7	95.5	65	4.36	3.16
45	16.7	119.	150	23.6	137.	70	4.69	3.63
1¼-Inch Pipe (1.380" I.D.)			**2-Inch Pipe (2.067" I.D.)**					
4	0.858	0.342	5	0.478	0.0731	75	5.03	4.13
5	1.073	0.508	10	0.956	0.248	80	5.36	4.66
6	1.29	0.704	15	1.44	0.513	85	5.70	5.22
7	1.50	0.930	20	1.91	0.868	90	6.03	5.82
8	1.72	1.18	25	2.38	1.30	95	6.37	6.45
10	2.15	1.77	30	2.87	1.82	100	6.70	7.11
12	2.57	2.48	35	3.35	2.42	110	7.37	8.51
14	3.00	3.28	40	3.82	3.10	120	8.04	10.0
16	3.43	4.20	45	4.30	3.85	130	8.71	11.7
18	3.86	5.22	50	4.78	4.67	140	9.38	13.5
20	4.29	6.34	60	5.74	6.59	150	10.05	15.4
25	5.36	9.61	70	6.69	8.86	160	10.7	17.4
30	6.44	13.6	80	7.65	11.4	170	11.4	19.6
35	7.51	18.2	90	8.60	14.2	180	12.1	21.9
40	8.58	23.5	100	9.56	17.4	190	12.7	24.2
45	9.65	29.4	125	11.96	26.8	200	13.4	26.7
50	10.7	36.0	150	14.3	38.0	220	14.7	32.2
60	12.9	51.0	175	16.8	51.2	240	16.1	38.1
70	15.0	68.8	200	19.1	66.3	260	17.4	44.5
80	17.2	89.2	225	21.5	83.7	280	18.8	51.3
						300	20.1	58.5
						350	23.5	79.2
						400	26.8	103.

NOTE: No allowance has been made for age, differences in diameter, or any abnormal condition of interior surface. Any factor of safety must be estimated from the local conditions and the requirements of each particular installation.

° For explanation of these tables see page 3-19.

FRICTION OF WATER IN NEW ASPHALT-DIPPED CAST-IRON PIPE*

Friction is in feet of water at 60°F per 100 ft of pipe

gpm	Velocity fps	Friction ft./100 ft.	gpm	Velocity fps	Friction ft./100 ft.	gpm	Velocity fps	Friction ft./100 ft.
	3-Inch Pipe			4-Inch Pipe			6-Inch Pipe	
10	0.454	0.0435	20	0.511	0.03700	70	0.794	0.0496
15	0.681	0.0900	30	0.766	0.0770	80	0.908	0.0635
20	0.908	0.1510	40	1.02	0.131	90	1.02	0.0789
25	1.13	0.2280	50	1.28	0.199	100	1.13	0.0958
30	1.36	0.320	60	1.53	0.278	120	1.36	0.130
35	1.59	0.427	70	1.79	0.370	140	1.59	0.178
40	1.82	0.549	80	2.04	0.476	160	1.82	0.229
45	2.04	0.683	90	2.30	0.594	180	2.04	0.282
50	2.27	0.830	100	2.55	0.725	200	2.27	0.346
55	2.50	0.993	110	2.81	0.869	220	2.50	0.415
60	2.72	1.170	120	3.06	1.03	240	2.72	0.490
65	2.95	1.36	130	3.32	1.19	260	2.95	0.570
70	3.18	1.56	140	3.57	1.38	280	3.18	0.655
75	3.40	1.78	150	3.83	1.58	300	3.40	0.745
80	3.63	2.02	160	4.08	1.78	320	3.63	0.846
85	3.86	2.28	170	4.34	2.00	340	3.86	0.952
90	4.08	2.55	180	4.60	2.24	360	4.08	1.06
95	4.31	2.82	190	4.85	2.49	380	4.31	1.18
100	4.54	3.10	200	5.11	2.74	400	4.54	1.30
110	4.99	3.73	220	5.62	3.28	420	4.76	1.43
120	5.45	4.40	240	6.13	3.88	440	4.99	1.57
130	5.90	5.13	260	6.64	4.54	460	5.22	1.71
140	6.35	5.93	280	7.15	5.25	480	5.45	1.86
150	6.81	6.80	300	7.66	6.03	500	5.67	2.02
160	7.26	7.71	320	8.17	6.87	550	6.24	2.42
170	7.72	8.70	340	8.68	7.75	600	6.81	2.84
180	8.17	9.73	360	9.19	8.68	650	7.37	3.33
190	8.62	10.80	380	9.70	9.66	700	7.94	3.87
200	9.08	11.9	400	10.2	10.7	750	8.51	4.45
220	9.98	14.3	420	10.7	11.7	800	9.08	5.06
240	10.9	17.0	440	11.2	12.8	850	9.64	5.69
260	11.8	19.8	460	11.7	14.0	900	10.2	6.34
280	12.7	22.8	480	12.3	15.3	950	10.8	7.02
300	13.6	26.1	500	12.8	16.6	1,000	11.3	7.73
320	14.5	29.7	550	14.0	19.9	1,100	12.5	9.80
340	15.4	33.6	600	15.3	23.6	1,200	13.6	11.2
360	16.3	37.8	650	16.6	27.7	1,300	14.7	13.0
380	17.2	42.2	700	17.9	32.1	1,400	15.9	15.1
400	18.2	46.8	750	19.1	36.7	1,500	17.0	17.4
420	19.1	51.5	800	20.4	41.6	1,600	18.2	19.8
440	20.0	56.4	850	21.7	46.8	1,700	19.3	22.3
460	20.9	61.5	900	23.0	52.3	1,800	20.4	24.8
480	21.8	66.8	950	24.3	58.1	1,900	21.6	27.6
500	22.7	72.3	1,000	25.5	64.2	2,000	22.7	30.5

NOTE: No allowance has been made for age, differences in diameter, or any abnormal condition of interior surface. Any factor of safety must be estimated from the local conditions and the requirements of each particular installation.

* For explanation of these tables see page 3-19.

FRICTION OF WATER IN NEW ASPHALT-DIPPED
CAST-IRON PIPE (Continued)
Friction is in feet of water at 60°F per 100 ft of pipe

gpm	Velocity fps	Friction ft./100 ft.	gpm	Velocity fps	Friction ft./100 ft.	gpm	Velocity fps	Friction ft./100 ft.
8-Inch Pipe			**10-Inch Pipe**			**12-Inch Pipe**		
200	1.28	0.0828	200	0.817	0.0276	300	0.851	0.0236
220	1.40	0.0989	220	0.899	0.0329	350	0.993	0.0316
240	1.53	0.1163	240	0.980	0.0387	400	1.13	0.0404
260	1.66	0.135	260	1.06	0.0449	450	1.28	0.0500
280	1.79	0.155	280	1.14	0.0514	500	1.42	0.0604
300	1.91	0.176	300	1.23	0.0583	550	1.56	0.0718
320	2.04	0.198	350	1.43	0.0778	600	1.70	0.0845
340	2.17	0.222	400	1.63	0.0990	650	1.84	0.0990
360	2.30	0.248	450	1.84	0.1235	700	1.99	0.115
380	2.43	0.275	500	2.04	0.151	750	2.13	0.131
400	2.55	0.304	550	2.25	0.181	800	2.27	0.148
450	2.87	0.380	600	2.45	0.214	850	2.41	0.166
500	3.19	0.464	650	2.66	0.250	900	2.55	0.184
550	3.51	0.557	700	2.86	0.288	950	2.69	0.203
600	3.83	0.658	750	3.06	0.328	1,000	2.84	0.224
650	4.15	0.767	800	3.27	0.370	1,100	3.12	0.272
700	4.47	0.884	850	3.47	0.415	1,200	3.40	0.321
750	4.79	1.01	900	3.68	0.462	1,300	3.69	0.372
800	5.11	1.14	950	3.88	0.512	1,400	3.97	0.428
850	5.42	1.29	1,000	4.09	0.565	1,500	4.26	0.488
900	5.74	1.44	1,100	4.49	0.680	1,600	4.54	0.552
950	6.06	1.60	1,200	4.90	0.805	1,700	4.82	0.621
1,000	6.38	1.76	1,300	5.31	0.945	1,800	5.11	0.695
1,100	7.02	2.14	1,400	5.72	1.09	1,900	5.39	0.774
1,200	7.66	2.53	1,500	6.13	1.25	2,000	5.67	0.858
1,300	8.30	2.94	1,600	6.54	1.42	2,200	6.24	1.03
1,400	8.93	3.40	1,700	6.94	1.60	2,400	6.81	1.22
1,500	9.57	3.91	1,800	7.35	1.78	2,600	7.38	1.43
1,600	10.2	4.45	1,900	7.76	1.97	2,800	7.94	1.65
1,700	10.8	5.00	2,000	8.17	2.17	3,000	8.51	1.88
1,800	11.5	5.58	2,200	8.99	2.64	3,500	9.93	2.55
1,900	12.1	6.19	2,400	9.80	3.12	4,000	11.3	3.31
2,000	12.8	6.84	2,600	10.6	3.63	4,500	12.8	4.18
2,200	14.0	8.26	2,800	11.4	4.18	5,000	14.2	5.13
2,400	15.3	9.80	3,000	12.3	4.79	5,500	15.6	6.17
2,600	16.6	11.47	3,200	13.1	5.47	6,000	17.0	7.30
2,800	17.9	13.3	3,400	13.9	6.18	6,500	18.4	8.55
3,000	19.1	15.2	3,600	14.7	6.91	7,000	19.9	9.92
3,200	20.4	17.3	3,800	15.5	7.68	7,500	21.3	11.4
3,400	21.7	19.5	4,000	16.3	8.50	8,000	22.7	13.0
3,600	23.0	21.9	4,500	18.4	10.7	8,500	24.1	14.7
3,800	24.3	24.4	5,000	20.4	13.2	9,000	25.5	16.4
4,000	25.5	27.0	5,500	22.5	15.9	9,500	26.9	18.2
4,500	28.7	34.0	6,000	24.5	18.9	10,000	28.4	20.2

NOTE: No allowance has been made for age, differences in diameter, or any abnormal condition of interior surface. Any factor of safety must be estimated from the local conditions and the requirements of each particular installation.

FRICTION OF WATER IN NEW ASPHALT-DIPPED
CAST-IRON PIPE (Continued)

Friction is in feet of water at 60°F per 100 ft of pipe

gpm	Velocity fps	Friction ft./100 ft.	gpm	Velocity fps	Friction ft./100 ft.	gpm	Velocity fps	Friction ft./100 ft.
14-Inch Pipe			16-Inch Pipe			18-Inch Pipe		
400	0.834	0.0190	500	0.798	0.0148	700	0.883	0.0154
500	1.04	0.0284	600	0.957	0.0207	800	1.01	0.0197
600	1.25	0.0400	700	1.12	0.0276	900	1.13	0.0245
700	1.46	0.0533	800	1.28	0.0354	1,000	1.26	0.0298
800	1.67	0.0686	900	1.44	0.0441	1,100	1.39	0.0357
900	1.88	0.0859	1,000	1.60	0.0537	1,200	1.51	0.0420
1,000	2.08	0.1050	1,100	1.76	0.0642	1,300	1.64	0.0488
1,100	2.29	0.1256	1,200	1.91	0.0760	1,400	1.77	0.0560
1,200	2.50	0.148	1,300	2.07	0.0878	1,500	1.89	0.0639
1,300	2.71	0.172	1,400	2.23	0.101	1,600	2.02	0.0723
1,400	2.92	0.198	1,500	2.39	0.115	1,700	2.14	0.0812
1,500	3.13	0.225	1,600	2.55	0.130	1,800	2.27	0.0905
1,600	3.33	0.254	1,700	2.71	0.146	1,900	2.40	0.1001
1,700	3.54	0.285	1,800	2.87	0.163	2,000	2.52	0.110
1,800	3.75	0.318	1,900	3.03	0.180	2,500	3.15	0.170
1,900	3.96	0.353	2,000	3.19	0.200	3,000	3.78	0.240
2,000	4.17	0.391	2,200	3.51	0.240	3,500	4.41	0.320
2,200	4.59	0.470	2,400	3.83	0.282	4,000	5.04	0.415
2,400	5.00	0.554	2,600	4.15	0.329	4,500	5.67	0.525
2,600	5.42	0.648	2,800	4.47	0.379	5,000	6.30	0.645
2,800	5.84	0.749	3,000	4.79	0.433	5,500	6.93	0.775
3,000	6.25	0.858	3,200	5.11	0.490	6,000	7.56	0.920
3,200	6.67	0.971	3,400	5.43	0.553	6,500	8.20	1.07
3,400	7.09	1.095	3,600	5.74	0.618	7,000	8.83	1.24
3,600	7.50	1.22	3,800	6.06	0.684	7,500	9.46	1.42
3,800	7.92	1.36	4,000	6.38	0.754	8,000	10.09	1.61
4,000	8.34	1.50	4,500	7.18	0.948	8,500	10.7	1.81
4,500	9.38	1.89	5,000	7.98	1.17	9,000	11.3	2.02
5,000	10.4	2.31	5,500	8.78	1.41	10,000	12.6	2.48
5,500	11.5	2.79	6,000	9.57	1.66	11,000	13.9	3.01
6,000	12.5	3.31	7,000	11.2	2.26	12,000	15.1	3.56
6,500	13.5	3.88	8,000	12.8	2.96	13,000	16.4	4.19
7,000	14.6	4.50	9,000	14.4	3.73	14,000	17.7	4.85
7,500	15.6	5.16	10,000	16.0	4.57	15,000	18.9	5.56
8,000	16.7	5.87	11,000	17.6	5.50	16,000	20.2	6.31
8,500	17.7	6.60	12,000	19.1	6.52	17,000	21.4	7.11
9,000	18.8	7.42	13,000	20.7	7.63	18,000	22.7	7.95
9,500	19.8	8.27	14,000	22.3	8.81	19,000	24.0	8.85
10,000	20.8	9.15	15,000	23.9	10.1	20,000	25.2	9.79
11,000	22.9	11.05	16,000	25.5	11.5	21,000	26.5	10.78
12,000	25.0	13.0	17,000	27.1	13.0	22,000	27.7	11.9
13,000	27.1	15.2	18,000	28.7	14.6	23,000	29.0	12.9
14,000	29.2	17.6	19,000	30.3	16.3	24,000	30.3	14.1
15,000	31.3	20.2	20,000	31.9	18.1	25,000	31.5	15.3

NOTE: No allowance has been made for age, differences in diameter, or any abnormal condition of interior surface. Any factor of safety must be estimated from the local conditions and the requirements of each particular installation.

FRICTION OF WATER IN NEW ASPHALT-DIPPED
CAST-IRON PIPE (Continued)
Friction is in feet of water at 60°F per 100 ft of pipe

gpm	Velocity fps	Friction ft./100 ft.	gpm	Velocity fps	Friction ft./100 ft.	gpm	Velocity fps	Friction ft./100 ft.
20-Inch Pipe			24-Inch Pipe			30-Inch Pipe		
800	0.817	0.0117	1,400	0.993	0.0135	2,000	0.908	0.00876
900	0.919	0.0146	1,600	1.135	0.0173	2,500	1.13	0.0132
1,000	1.02	0.0177	1,800	1.276	0.0216	3,000	1.36	0.0186
1,100	1.12	0.0212	2,000	1.42	0.0262	3,500	1.59	0.0248
1,200	1.23	0.0249	2,200	1.56	0.0313	4,000	1.82	0.0320
1,300	1.33	0.0289	2,400	1.70	0.0369	4,500	2.04	0.0400
1,400	1.43	0.0332	2,600	1.84	0.0429	5,000	2.27	0.0488
1,500	1.53	0.0378	2,800	1.99	0.0494	5,500	2.50	0.0585
1,600	1.63	0.0427	3,000	2.13	0.0563	6,000	2.72	0.0690
1,700	1.74	0.0478	3,500	2.48	0.0759	6,500	2.95	0.0803
1,800	1.84	0.0533	4,000	2.84	0.098	7,000	3.18	0.0923
1,900	1.94	0.0590	4,500	3.19	0.122	8,000	3.63	0.119
2,000	2.04	0.0650	5,000	3.55	0.149	9,000	4.08	0.149
2,500	2.55	0.0998	5,500	3.90	0.179	10,000	4.54	0.183
3,000	3.06	0.140	6,000	4.26	0.211	12,000	5.45	0.260
3,500	3.57	0.188	6,500	4.61	0.246	14,000	6.35	0.351
4,000	4.08	0.243	7,000	4.96	0.284	16,000	7.26	0.455
4,500	4.59	0.306	7,500	5.32	0.326	18,000	8.17	0.572
5,000	5.11	0.376	8,000	5.67	0.369	20,000	9.08	0.703
6,000	6.13	0.533	8,500	6.03	0.416	22,000	9.98	0.850
7,000	7.15	0.721	9,000	6.38	0.464	24,000	10.89	1.006
8,000	8.17	0.935	10,000	7.09	0.571	26,000	11.80	1.18
9,000	9.19	1.18	11,000	7.80	0.688	28,000	12.7	1.36
10,000	10.2	1.45	12,000	8.51	0.817	30,000	13.6	1.57
11,000	11.2	1.74	13,000	9.22	0.952	32,000	14.5	1.78
12,000	12.3	2.07	14,000	9.93	1.11	34,000	15.4	2.01
13,000	13.3	2.43	15,000	10.64	1.26	36,000	16.3	2.25
14,000	14.3	2.80	16,000	11.35	1.43	38,000	17.2	2.50
15,000	15.3	3.22	17,000	12.06	1.61	40,000	18.2	2.77
16,000	16.3	3.66	18,000	12.76	1.80	42,000	19.1	3.05
17,000	17.4	4.11	19,000	13.5	2.00	44,000	20.0	3.34
18,000	18.4	4.60	20,000	14.2	2.21	46,000	20.9	3.65
19,000	19.4	5.12	22,000	15.6	2.67	48,000	21.8	3.97
20,000	20.4	5.66	24,000	17.0	3.16	50,000	22.7	4.30
21,000	21.4	6.24	26,000	18.4	3.71	52,000	23.6	4.66
22,000	22.5	6.84	28,000	19.9	4.32	54,000	24.5	5.02
23,000	23.5	7.47	30,000	21.3	4.97	56,000	25.4	5.40
24,000	24.5	8.13	32,000	22.7	5.65	58,000	26.3	5.78
25,000	25.5	8.83	34,000	24.1	6.35	60,000	27.2	6.18
26,000	26.5	9.54	36,000	25.5	7.10	62,000	28.1	6.60
27,000	27.6	10.3	38,000	26.9	7.90	64,000	29.0	7.03
28,000	28.6	11.1	40,000	28.4	8.75	66,000	30.0	7.47
29,000	29.6	11.9	42,000	29.8	9.63	68,000	30.9	7.92
30,000	30.6	12.7	44,000	31.2	10.5	70,000	31.8	8.39

NOTE: No allowance has been made for age, differences in diameter, or any abnormal condition of interior surface. Any factor of safety must be estimated from the local conditions and the requirements of each particular installation.

FRICTION OF WATER IN NEW ASPHALT-DIPPED
CAST-IRON PIPE (Continued)

Friction is in feet of water at 60°F per 100 ft of pipe

gpm	Velocity fps	Friction ft./100 ft.	gpm	Velocity fps	Friction ft./100 ft.	gpm	Velocity fps	Friction ft./100 ft.
36-Inch Pipe			42-Inch Pipe			48-Inch Pipe		
3,000	0.946	0.00751	4,000	0.926	0.00602	5,000	0.887	0.00474
3,500	1.103	0.0101	5,000	1.16	0.00915	6,000	1.064	0.00667
4,000	1.26	0.0129	6,000	1.39	0.0128	7,000	1.24	0.00890
4,500	1.41	0.0161	7,000	1.62	0.0172	8,000	1.42	0.0114
5,000	1.58	0.0196	8,000	1.85	0.0222	9,000	1.60	0.0142
5,500	1.73	0.0234	9,000	2.08	0.0276	10,000	1.77	0.0173
6,000	1.89	0.0276	10,000	2.32	0.0337	11,000	1.95	0.0207
7,000	2.21	0.0369	11,000	2.55	0.0405	12,000	2.13	0.0244
8,000	2.52	0.0475	12,000	2.78	0.0478	13,000	2.30	0.0284
9,000	2.84	0.0593	13,000	3.01	0.0557	14,000	2.48	0.0327
10,000	3.15	0.0724	14,000	3.24	0.0641	15,000	2.66	0.0373
11,000	3.47	0.0868	15,000	3.47	0.0732	16,000	2.84	0.0422
12,000	3.78	0.103	16,000	3.71	0.0829	17,000	3.01	0.0474
13,000	4.10	0.120	17,000	3.94	0.0931	18,000	3.19	0.0529
14,000	4.41	0.139	18,000	4.17	0.104	19,000	3.37	0.0587
15,000	4.73	0.159	19,000	4.40	0.115	20,000	3.55	0.0648
16,000	5.04	0.180	20,000	4.63	0.127	22,000	3.90	0.0778
17,000	5.36	0.203	22,000	5.09	0.153	24,000	4.26	0.0920
18,000	5.67	0.227	24,000	5.56	0.181	26,000	4.61	0.1073
19,000	5.99	0.252	26,000	6.02	0.211	28,000	4.96	0.124
20,000	6.30	0.279	28,000	6.48	0.244	30,000	5.32	0.142
22,000	6.93	0.335	30,000	6.95	0.279	35,000	6.21	0.192
24,000	7.56	0.397	32,000	7.41	0.317	40,000	7.09	0.248
26,000	8.19	0.465	34,000	7.87	0.357	45,000	7.98	0.314
28,000	8.83	0.538	36,000	8.34	0.399	50,000	8.87	0.384
30,000	9.46	0.617	38,000	8.80	0.444	55,000	9.75	0.463
32,000	10.09	0.699	40,000	9.26	0.490	60,000	10.64	0.548
34,000	10.72	0.787	45,000	10.42	0.620	65,000	11.5	0.641
36,000	11.3	0.880	50,000	11.6	0.760	70,000	12.4	0.742
38,000	12.0	0.979	55,000	12.7	0.918	75,000	13.3	0.850
40,000	12.6	1.08	60,000	13.9	1.09	80,000	14.2	0.966
45,000	14.1	1.36	65,000	15.1	1.28	85,000	15.1	1.09
50,000	15.8	1.68	70,000	16.2	1.48	90,000	16.0	1.22
55,000	17.3	2.02	75,000	17.4	1.70	95,000	16.8	1.35
60,000	18.9	2.40	80,000	18.5	1.92	100,000	17.7	1.50
65,000	20.5	2.81	85,000	19.7	2.17	110,000	19.5	2.805
70,000	22.1	3.25	90,000	20.8	2.44	120,000	21.3	2.15
75,000	23.6	3.72	95,000	22.0	2.71	130,000	23.0	2.52
80,000	25.2	4.23	100,000	23.2	2.98	140,000	24.8	2.92
85,000	26.8	4.77	110,000	25.5	3.63	150,000	26.6	3.34
90,000	28.4	5.35	120,000	27.8	4.30	160,000	28.4	3.80
95,000	29.9	5.96	130,000	30.1	5.03	170,000	30.1	4.29
100,000	31.5	6.60	140,000	32.4	5.82	180,000	31.9	4.82

NOTE: No allowance has been made for age, differences in diameter, or any abnormal condition of interior surface. Any factor of safety must be estimated from the local conditions and the requirements of each particular installation.

FRICTION OF WATER IN NEW ASPHALT-DIPPED
CAST-IRON PIPE (Continued)
Friction is in feet of water at 60°F per 100 ft of pipe

gpm	Velocity fps	Friction ft./100 ft.	gpm	Velocity fps	Friction ft./100 ft.	gpm	Velocity fps	Friction ft./100 ft.
54-Inch Pipe			60-Inch Pipe			72-Inch Pipe		
7,000	0.981	0.00499	8,000	0.908	0.00382	12,000	0.947	0.00329
8,000	1.121	0.00642	9,000	1.021	0.00476	13,000	1.025	0.00383
9,000	1.26	0.00800	10,000	1.13	0.00579	14,000	1.104	0.00438
10,000	1.40	0.00970	11,000	1.25	0.00691	15,000	1.18	0.00498
11,000	1.54	0.0116	12,000	1.36	0.00813	16,000	1.26	0.00563
12,000	1.68	0.0137	13,000	1.48	0.00945	17,000	1.34	0.00631
13,000	1.82	0.0159	14,000	1.59	0.01082	18,000	1.42	0.00703
14,000	1.96	0.0182	15,000	1.70	0.0123	19,000	1.50	0.00780
15,000	2.10	0.0207	16,000	1.82	0.0140	20,000	1.58	0.00859
16,000	2.24	0.0234	17,000	1.93	0.0156	25,000	1.97	0.0131
17,000	2.38	0.0263	18,000	2.04	0.0174	30,000	2.37	0.0184
18,000	2.52	0.0294	19,000	2.16	0.0195	35,000	2.76	0.0248
19,000	2.66	0.0326	20,000	2.27	0.0212	40,000	3.16	0.0320
20,000	2.80	0.0360	25,000	2.84	0.0325	45,000	3.55	0.0402
25,000	3.50	0.0550	30,000	3.40	0.0460	50,000	3.94	0.0493
30,000	4.20	0.0782	35,000	3.97	0.0618	55,000	4.34	0.0592
35,000	4.90	0.106	40,000	4.54	0.0800	60,000	4.73	0.0700
40,000	5.60	0.137	45,000	5.11	0.100	65,000	5.13	0.0816
45,000	6.30	0.172	50,000	5.67	0.124	70,000	5.52	0.0940
50,000	7.00	0.211	55,000	6.24	0.149	75,000	5.92	0.1074
55,000	7.70	0.254	60,000	6.81	0.176	80,000	6.31	0.122
60,000	8.40	0.301	70,000	7.94	0.237	90,000	7.10	0.154
65,000	9.11	0.352	80,000	9.08	0.307	100,000	7.89	0.189
70,000	9.81	0.408	90,000	10.21	0.387	110,000	8.68	0.228
75,000	10.51	0.467	100,000	11.3	0.478	120,000	9.47	0.271
80,000	11.21	0.530	110,000	12.5	0.578	130,000	10.25	0.317
85,000	11.91	0.597	120,000	13.6	0.688	140,000	11.04	0.365
90,000	12.6	0.668	130,000	14.8	0.805	150,000	11.8	0.418
95,000	13.3	0.743	140,000	15.9	0.930	160,000	12.6	0.475
100,000	14.0	0.820	150,000	17.0	1.062	170,000	13.4	0.534
110,000	15.4	0.982	160,000	18.2	1.20	180,000	14.2	0.598
120,000	16.8	1.18	170,000	19.3	1.36	190,000	15.0	0.665
130,000	18.2	1.38	180,000	20.4	1.52	200,000	15.8	0.736
140,000	19.6	1.59	190,000	21.6	1.69	220,000	17.4	0.887
150,000	21.0	1.82	200,000	22.7	1.87	240,000	18.9	1.050
160,000	22.4	2.07	210,000	23.8	2.06	260,000	20.5	1.237
170,000	23.8	2.34	220,000	25.0	2.26	280,000	22.1	1.43
180,000	25.2	2.62	230,000	26.1	2.47	300,000	23.7	1.64
190,000	26.6	2.91	240,000	27.2	2.69	320,000	25.2	1.86
200,000	28.0	3.22	250,000	28.4	2.92	340,000	26.8	2.10
210,000	29.4	3.55	260,000	29.5	3.16	360,000	28.4	2.35
220,000	30.8	3.89	270,000	30.6	3.40	380,000	30.0	2.62
230,000	32.2	4.25	280,000	31.8	3.66	400,000	31.6	2.90

NOTE: No allowance has been made for age, differences in diameter, or any abnormal condition of interior surface. Any factor of safety must be estimated from the local conditions and the requirements of each particular installation.

RESISTANCE COEFFICIENTS FOR INCREASERS AND DIFFUSERS

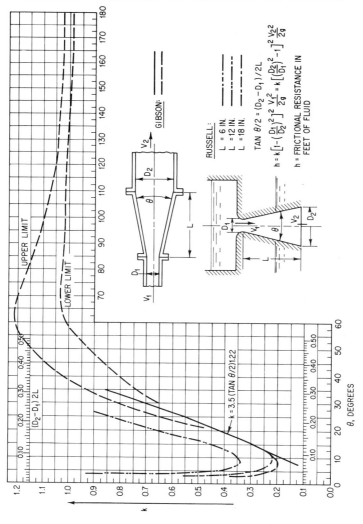

RESISTANCE COEFFICIENTS FOR REDUCERS

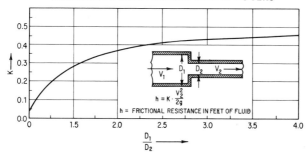

RESISTANCE OF VALVES AND FITTINGS TO FLOW

Equivalent Length of New Straight Pipe

Equivalent length is in *feet* and applies to *turbulent flow* only

FITTINGS			NOMINAL PIPE SIZE IN INCHES										
			¼	⅜	½	¾	1	1¼	1½	2	2½	3	4
REGULAR 90° ELBOW	SCREWED	STEEL	2.3	3.1	3.6	4.4	5.2	6.6	7.4	8.5	9.3	11	13
		C. I.										9.0	11
	FLANGED	STEEL			0.9	1.2	1.6	2.1	2.4	3.1	3.6	4.4	5.9
		C. I.										3.6	4.8
LONG RADIUS 90° ELBOW	SCREWED	STEEL	1.5	2.0	2.2	2.3	2.7	3.2	3.4	3.6	3.6	4.0	4.6
		C. I.										3.3	3.7
	FLANGED	STEEL			1.1	1.3	1.6	2.0	2.3	2.7	2.9	3.4	4.2
		C. I.										2.8	3.4
REGULAR 45° ELBOW	SCREWED	STEEL	0.3	0.5	0.7	0.9	1.3	1.7	2.1	2.7	3.2	4.0	5.5
		C. I.										3.3	4.5
	FLANGED	STEEL			0.5	0.6	0.8	1.1	1.3	1.7	2.0	2.6	3.5
		C. I.										2.1	2.9
TEE WITH LINE FLOW	SCREWED	STEEL	0.8	1.2	1.7	2.4	3.2	4.6	5.6	7.7	9.3	12	17
		C. I.										9.9	14
	FLANGED	STEEL			0.7	0.8	1.0	1.3	1.5	1.8	1.9	2.2	2.8
		C. I.										1.9	2.2
TEE WITH BRANCH FLOW	SCREWED	STEEL	2.4	3.5	4.2	5.3	6.6	8.7	9.9	12	13	17	21
		C. I.										14	17
	FLANGED	STEEL			2.0	2.6	3.3	4.4	5.2	6.6	7.5	9.4	12
		C. I.										7.7	10
180° RETURN BEND	SCREWED	STEEL	2.3	3.1	3.6	4.4	5.2	6.6	7.4	8.5	9.3	11	13
		C. I.										9.0	11
	REGULAR FLANGED	STEEL			0.9	1.2	1.6	2.1	2.4	3.1	3.6	4.4	5.9
		C. I.										3.6	4.8
	LONG RADIUS FLANGED	STEEL			1.1	1.3	1.6	2.0	2.3	2.7	2.9	3.4	4.2
		C. I.										2.8	3.4

RESISTANCE OF VALVES AND FITTINGS TO FLOW (Continued)

Equivalent Length of New Straight Pipe

Equivalent length is in *feet* and applies to *turbulent flow* only

5	6	8	10	12	14	16	18	20	24	30	36	42	48	54	60	72	84
7.3	8.9	12	14	17	18	21	23	25	31	40	50	58	65	72	79	94	108
	7.2	9.8	12	15	17	19	22	24	28	36	43	50	57	64	69	82	95
5.0	5.7	7.0	7.7	9.0	9.4	10	11	12	14	16	19	21	23	25	28	31	34
	4.7	5.7	6.8	7.8	8.6	9.6	11	11	13	14	16	19	22	22	24	27	30
4.5	5.6	7.7	9.0	11	13	15	16	18	22								
	4.5	6.3	8.1	9.7	12	13	15	17	20								
3.3	3.8	4.7	5.2	6.0	6.4	7.2	7.6	8.2	9.7	12	14	16	18	19	21	24	27
	3.1	3.9	4.6	5.2	5.9	6.5	7.2	7.7	8.9	11	12	14	16	17	18	21	24
15	18	24	28	34	37	43	47	52	62	78	96	108	123	137	150	178	202
	15	20	25	30	35	39	44	49	57	70	82	95	110	120	131	155	178
7.3	8.9	12	14	17	18	21	23	25	30								
	7.2	9.8	12	15	17	19	22	24	28								
5.0	5.7	7.0	7.7	9.0	9.4	10	11	12	14								
	4.7	5.7	6.8	7.8	8.6	9.6	11	11	13								

RESISTANCE OF VALVES AND FITTINGS TO FLOW (Continued)

Equivalent Length of New Straight Pipe

Equivalent length is in *feet* and applies to *turbulent flow* only

FITTINGS			NOMINAL PIPE SIZE IN INCHES										
			1/4	3/8	1/2	3/4	1	1 1/4	1 1/2	2	2 1/2	3	4
GLOBE VALVE	SCREWED	STEEL	21	22	22	24	29	37	42	54	62	79	110
		C. I.										65	86
	FLANGED	STEEL			38	40	45	54	59	70	77	94	120
		C. I.										77	99
GATE VALVE	SCREWED	STEEL	0.3	0.5	0.6	0.7	0.8	1.1	1.2	1.5	1.7	1.9	2.5
		C. I.										1.6	2.0
	FLANGED	STEEL								2.8	2.7	2.8	2.9
		C. I.										2.3	2.4
ANGLE VALVE	SCREWED	STEEL	13	15	15	15	17	18	18	18	18	18	18
		C. I.										15	15
	FLANGED	STEEL			15	15	17	18	18	21	22	28	38
		C. I.										23	31
SWING CHECK VALVE	SCREWED	STEEL	7.2	7.3	8.0	8.8	11	13	15	19	22	27	38
		C. I.										22	31
	FLANGED	STEEL			3.8	5.3	7.2	10	12	17	21	27	38
		C. I.										22	31
COUPLING OR UNION	SCREWED	STEEL	.14	.18	.21	.24	.29	.36	.39	.45	.47	.53	.65
		C. I.										.44	.52
BELL MOUTH INLET		STEEL	.04	.07	.10	.13	.18	.26	.31	.43	.52	.67	.95
		C. I.										.55	.77
SQUARE EDGE INLET		STEEL	.44	.68	.96	1.3	1.8	2.6	3.1	4.3	5.2	6.7	9.5
		C. I.										5.5	7.7
RE-ENTRANT PIPE		STEEL	0.9	1.4	1.9	2.6	3.6	5.1	6.2	8.5	10	13	19
		C. I.										11	15
SUDDEN ENLARGE-MENT		LOSS OF HEAD = h = $(V_1 - V_2)^2/2g$ FEET OF FLUID;												

RESISTANCE OF VALVES AND FITTINGS TO FLOW (Continued)

Equivalent Length of New Straight Pipe

Equivalent length is in *feet* and applies to *turbulent flow* only

NOMINAL PIPE SIZE IN INCHES																	
5	6	8	10	12	14	16	18	20	24	30	36	42	48	54	60	72	84
150	190	260	310	390													
	150	210	270	330													
3.1	3.2	3.2	3.2	3.2	3.2	3.2	3.2	3.2	3.3	3.5	3.5	3.7	3.7	3.6	3.7	3.9	3.8
	2.6	2.7	2.8	2.9	2.9	3.0	3.0	3.0	3.0	3.1	3.0	3.2	3.2	3.2	3.2	3.5	3.4
50	63	90	110	140	160	190	210	240	300								
	52	74	98	120	150	170	200	230	280								
50	63	90	110	140													
	52	74	98	120														
1.3	1.6	2.3	2.7	3.5	4.0	4.7	5.3	6.1	7.7	10	13	16	19	21	24	30	36
	1.3	1.9	2.4	3.0	3.6	4.3	5.0	5.7	7.1	9.2	11	14	16	19	21	26	32
13	16	23	27	35	40	47	53	61	77	103	133	159	186	214	242	301	360
	13	19	24	30	36	43	50	57	71	92	114	139	162	188	212	263	318
25	32	45	55	70	80	95	110	120	154	206	265	318	372	428	484	602	720
	26	37	49	61	73	86	100	110	142	184	227	278	324	376	424	526	635

IF $V_2 = 0$, $h = V_1^2/2g$ FEET OF FLUID.

Where V_1 is velocity in smaller pipe and V_2 is the velocity in larger pipe.

FRICTION LOSS FOR VISCOUS FLUIDS

Friction-loss Modulus for 100 feet of Pipe°

Loss, psi = modulus × specific gravity
Loss, ft of liquid = modulus × 2.31

Pipe Velocity Ft. Per Sec.

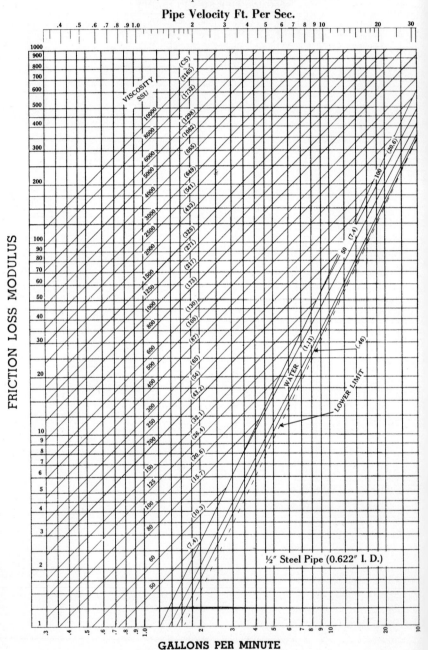

FRICTION LOSS MODULUS

GALLONS PER MINUTE

½″ Steel Pipe (0.622″ I. D.)

° For explanation of these charts see page 3-19.

FRICTION LOSS FOR VISCOUS FLUIDS (Continued)

Friction-loss Modulus for 100 feet of Pipe

Loss, psi = modulus × specific gravity
Loss, ft of liquid = modulus × 2.31

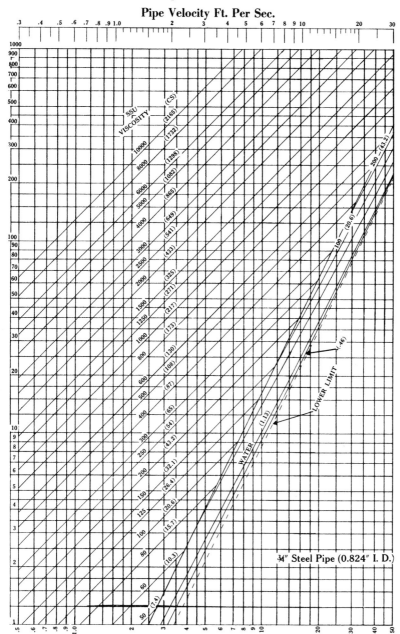

34″ Steel Pipe (0.824″ I. D.)

FRICTION LOSS FOR VISCOUS FLUIDS (Continued)

Friction-loss Modulus for 100 feet of Pipe

Loss, psi = modulus × specific gravity
Loss, ft of liquid = modulus × 2.31

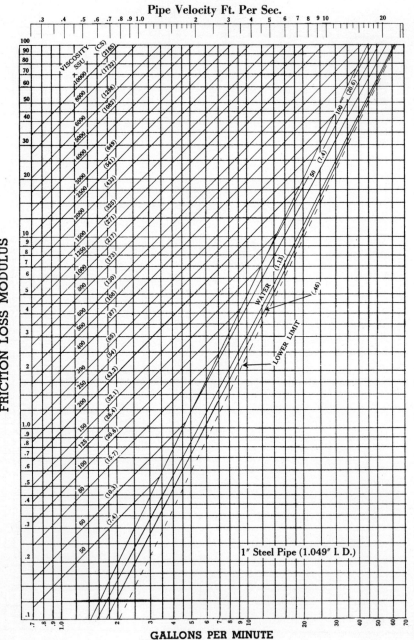

Pipe Velocity Ft. Per Sec.

FRICTION LOSS MODULUS

GALLONS PER MINUTE

1″ Steel Pipe (1.049″ I. D.)

FRICTION LOSS FOR VISCOUS FLUIDS (Continued)

Friction-loss Modulus for 100 feet of Pipe

Loss, psi = modulus × specific gravity
Loss, ft of liquid = modulus × 2.31

PIPE VELOCITY FT. PER SEC.

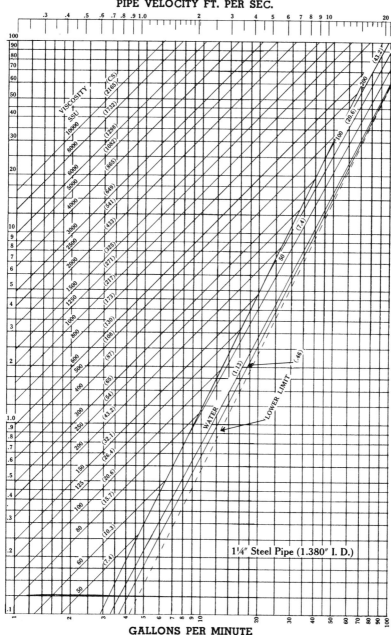

FRICTION LOSS MODULUS

GALLONS PER MINUTE

FRICTION LOSS FOR VISCOUS FLUIDS (Continued)

Friction-loss Modulus for 100 feet of Pipe

Loss, psi = modulus × specific gravity
Loss, ft of liquid = modulus × 2.31

PIPE VELOCITY FT. PER SEC.

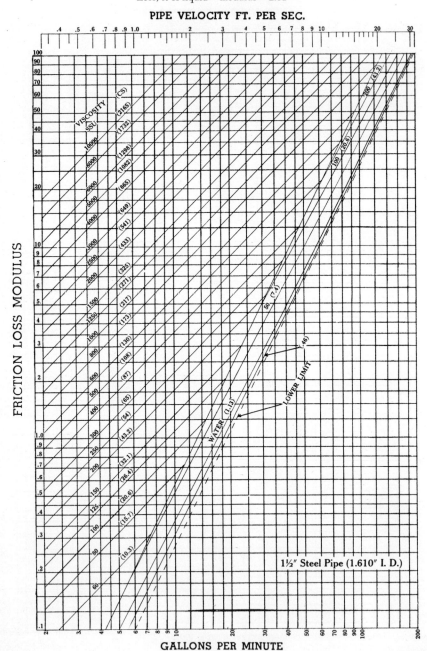

FRICTION LOSS MODULUS

GALLONS PER MINUTE

1½″ Steel Pipe (1.610″ I. D.)

FRICTION LOSS FOR VISCOUS FLUIDS (Continued)

Friction-loss Modulus for 100 feet of Pipe

Loss, psi = modulus × specific gravity
Loss, ft of liquid = modulus × 2.31

PIPE VELOCITY FT. PER SEC.

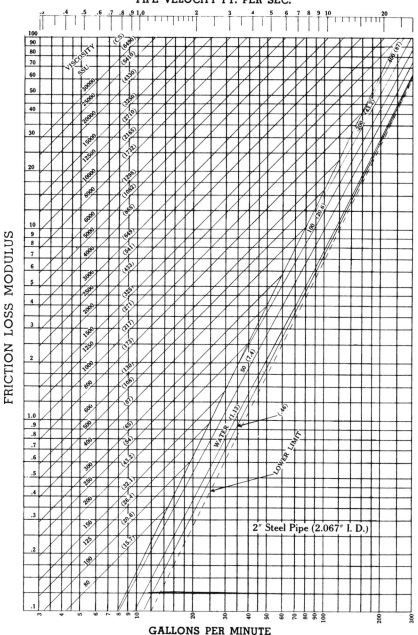

2" Steel Pipe (2.067" I. D.)

FRICTION LOSS MODULUS

GALLONS PER MINUTE

FRICTION LOSS FOR VISCOUS FLUIDS (Continued)

Friction-loss Modulus for 100 feet of Pipe

Loss, psi = modulus × specific gravity
Loss, ft of liquid = modulus × 2.31

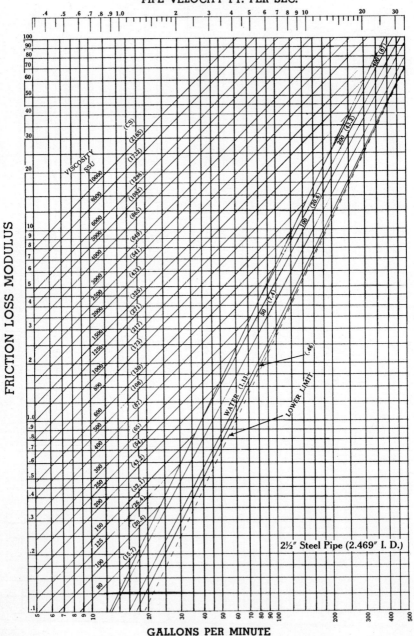

PIPE VELOCITY FT. PER SEC.

FRICTION LOSS MODULUS

GALLONS PER MINUTE

2½" Steel Pipe (2.469" I. D.)

FRICTION LOSS FOR VISCOUS FLUIDS (Continued)

Friction-loss Modulus for 100 feet of Pipe

Loss, psi = modulus × specific gravity
Loss, ft of liquid = modulus × 2.31

PIPE VELOCITY FT. PER SEC.

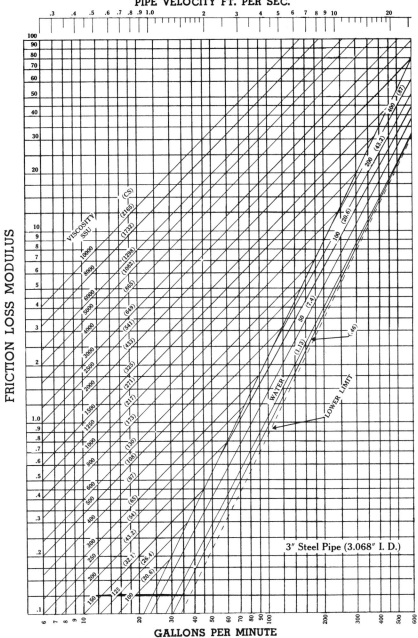

FRICTION LOSS MODULUS

3″ Steel Pipe (3.068″ I. D.)

GALLONS PER MINUTE

FRICTION LOSS FOR VISCOUS FLUIDS (Continued)

Friction-loss Modulus for 100 feet of Pipe

Loss, psi = modulus × specific gravity
Loss, ft of liquid = modulus × 2.31

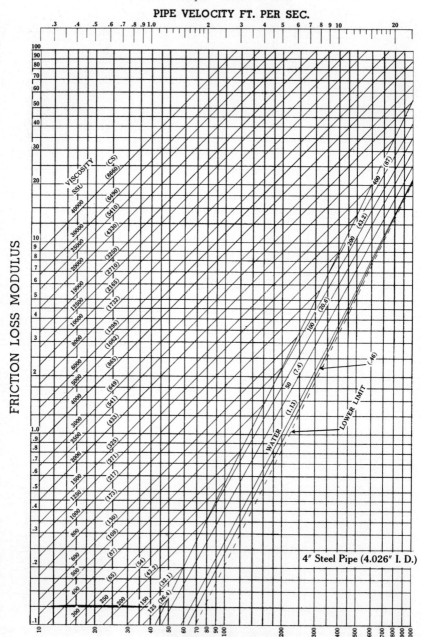

PIPE VELOCITY FT. PER SEC.

FRICTION LOSS MODULUS

4″ Steel Pipe (4.026″ I. D.)

GALLONS PER MINUTE

FRICTION LOSS FOR VISCOUS FLUIDS (Continued)

Friction-loss Modulus for 100 feet of Pipe

Loss, psi = modulus × specific gravity
Loss, ft of liquid = modulus × 2.31

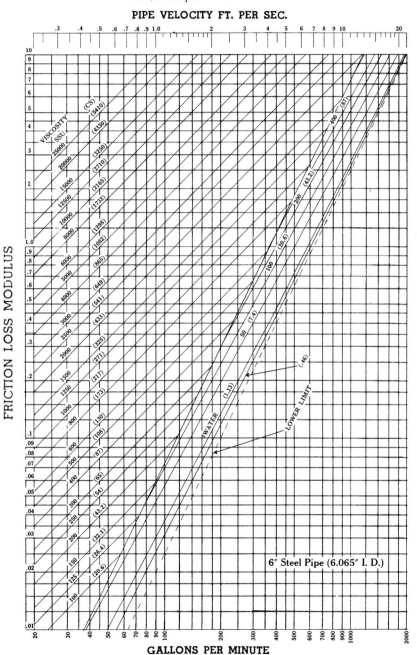

FRICTION LOSS FOR VISCOUS FLUIDS (Continued)

Friction-loss Modulus for 100 feet of Pipe

Loss, psi = modulus × specific gravity
Loss, ft of liquid = modulus × 2.31

PIPE VELOCITY FT. PER SEC.

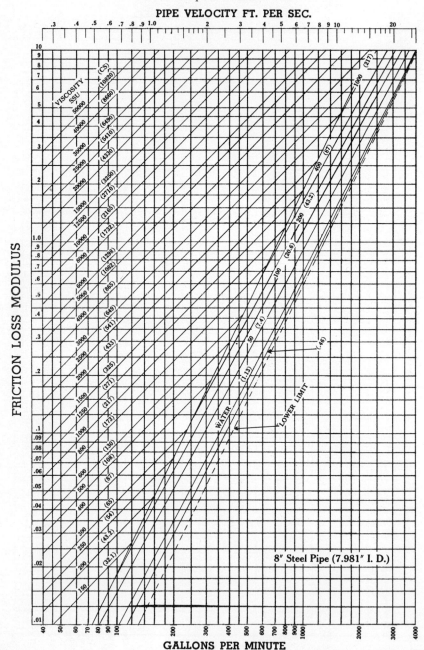

FRICTION LOSS MODULUS

GALLONS PER MINUTE

8″ Steel Pipe (7.981″ I. D.)

FRICTION LOSS FOR VISCOUS FLUIDS (Continued)

Friction-loss Modulus for 100 feet of Pipe

Loss, psi = modulus × specific gravity
Loss, ft of liquid = modulus × 2.31

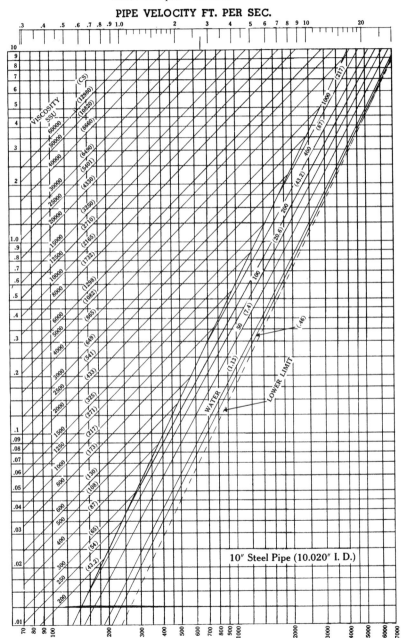

PIPE VELOCITY FT. PER SEC.

FRICTION LOSS MODULUS

10″ Steel Pipe (10.020″ I. D.)

GALLONS PER MINUTE

FRICTION LOSS FOR VISCOUS FLUIDS (Continued)

Friction-loss Modulus for 100 feet of Pipe

Loss, psi = modulus × specific gravity
Loss, ft of liquid = modulus × 2.31

PIPE VELOCITY FT. PER SEC.

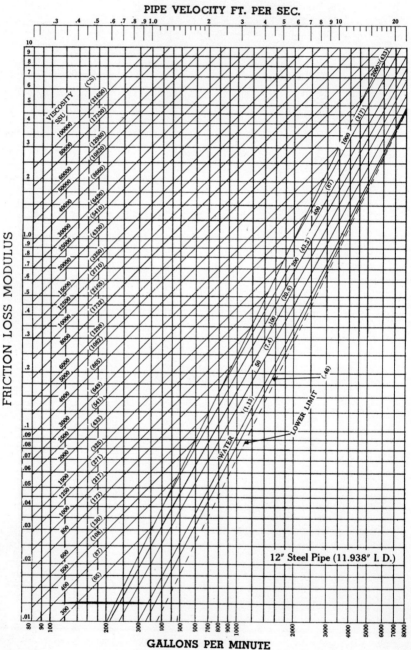

FRICTION LOSS MODULUS

GALLONS PER MINUTE

12" Steel Pipe (11.938" I. D.)

PROPERTIES OF SATURATED STEAM*

Abs pressure, psi	Temp, °F	Specific volume		Enthalpy			Entropy			Internal energy, evap
		Liquid	Vapor	Liquid	Evap	Vapor	Liquid	Evap	Vapor	
1.0	101.74	0.01614	333.60	69.73	1,036.1	1,105.8	0.1326	1.8455	1.9781	976.4
1.2	107.91	0.01616	280.96	75.90	1,032.6	1,108.5	0.1436	1.8192	1.9628	970.2
1.4	113.26	0.01618	243.02	81.23	1,029.5	1,110.7	0.1529	1.7969	1.9498	966.6
1.6	117.98	0.01620	214.33	85.95	1,026.8	1,112.7	0.1611	1.7775	1.9386	963.4
1.8	122.22	0.01621	191.85	90.18	1,024.3	1,114.5	0.1684	1.7604	1.9288	960.4
2.0	126.07	0.01623	173.76	94.03	1,022.1	1,116.2	0.1750	1.7450	1.9200	957.8
2.2	129.61	0.01624	158.87	97.57	1,020.1	1,117.6	0.1810	1.7311	1.9121	955.4
2.4	132.88	0.01626	146.40	100.84	1,018.2	1,119.0	0.1865	1.7183	1.9048	953.2
2.6	135.93	0.01627	135.80	103.88	1,016.4	1,120.3	0.1917	1.7065	1.8982	951.0
2.8	138.78	0.01629	126.67	106.73	1,014.7	1,121.5	0.1964	1.6956	1.8921	949.1
3.0	141.47	0.01630	118.73	109.42	1,013.2	1,122.6	0.2009	1.6854	1.8864	947.3
4.0	152.96	0.01636	90.64	120.92	1,006.4	1,127.3	0.2199	1.6428	1.8626	939.3
5.0	162.24	0.01640	73.53	130.20	1,000.9	1,131.1	0.2349	1.6094	1.8443	932.9
6.0	170.05	0.01645	61.98	138.03	996.2	1,134.2	0.2474	1.5820	1.8294	927.4
7.0	176.84	0.01649	53.65	144.83	992.1	1,136.9	0.2581	1.5587	1.8168	922.6
8.0	182.86	0.01653	47.34	150.87	988.5	1,139.3	0.2676	1.5384	1.8060	918.4
9.0	188.27	0.01656	42.40	156.30	985.1	1,141.4	0.2760	1.5204	1.7964	914.5
10	193.21	0.01659	38.42	161.26	982.1	1,143.3	0.2836	1.5043	1.7879	911.1
11	197.75	0.01662	35.14	165.82	979.3	1,145.1	0.2906	1.4896	1.7802	907.8
12	201.96	0.01665	32.39	170.05	976.6	1,146.7	0.2970	1.4763	1.7731	904.8
13	205.88	0.01668	30.05	174.00	974.2	1,148.2	0.3029	1.4638	1.7667	901.9
14	209.56	0.01670	28.04	177.71	971.9	1,149.5	0.3085	1.4522	1.7607	899.2
14.696	212.00	0.01672	26.79	180.17	970.3	1,150.5	0.3121	1.4447	1.7568	897.5
15	213.03	0.01673	26.29	181.21	969.7	1,150.9	0.3137	1.4415	1.7552	896.7
16	216.32	0.01675	24.75	184.52	967.6	1,152.1	0.3186	1.4314	1.7500	984.3
17	219.44	0.01677	23.38	187.66	965.6	1,153.2	0.3232	1.4219	1.7451	892.1
18	222.41	0.01679	22.17	190.66	963.7	1,154.3	0.3276	1.4129	1.7405	889.9
19	225.24	0.01681	21.07	193.52	961.8	1,155.3	0.3318	1.4043	1.7361	887.7
20	227.96	0.01683	20.087	196.27	960.1	1,156.3	0.3358	1.3962	1.7320	885.8
21	230.57	0.01685	19.190	198.90	958.4	1,157.3	0.3396	1.3885	1.7281	883.9
22	233.07	0.01687	18.373	201.44	956.7	1,158.1	0.3433	1.3811	1.7244	882.0
23	235.49	0.01689	17.624	203.88	955.1	1,159.0	0.3468	1.3740	1.7208	880.2
24	237.82	0.01691	16.936	206.24	953.6	1,159.8	0.3502	1.3672	1.7174	878.4
25	240.07	0.01693	16.301	208.5	952.1	1,160.6	0.3535	1.3607	1.7141	876.8
26	242.25	0.01694	15.714	210.7	950.6	1,161.4	0.3566	1.3544	1.7110	875.2
27	244.36	0.01696	15.168	212.9	949.2	1,162.1	0.3596	1.3483	1.7080	873.5
28	246.41	0.01698	14.661	214.9	947.9	1,162.8	0.3626	1.3425	1.7050	871.9
29	248.40	0.01699	14.181	217.0	946.5	1,163.5	0.3654	1.3368	1.7022	870.5
30	250.34	0.01701	13.744	218.9	945.2	1,164.1	0.3682	1.3313	1.6995	869.1
31	252.22	0.01702	13.328	220.8	943.9	1,164.8	0.3709	1.3260	1.6969	867.6
32	254.05	0.01704	12.938	222.7	942.7	1,165.4	0.3735	1.3209	1.6944	866.2
33	255.84	0.01705	12.570	224.5	941.5	1,166.0	0.3760	1.3159	1.6919	864.8
34	257.58	0.01707	12.223	226.3	940.3	1,166.6	0.3785	1.3110	1.6895	863.5
35	259.29	0.01708	11.896	228.0	939.1	1,167.1	0.3809	1.3063	1.6872	862.2
36	260.95	0.01709	11.586	229.7	938.0	1,167.7	0.3833	1.3017	1.6849	860.9
37	262.58	0.01711	11.292	231.4	936.9	1,168.2	0.3856	1.2972	1.6827	659.6
38	264.17	0.01712	11.014	233.0	935.8	1,168.8	0.3878	1.2928	1.6806	858.4
39	265.72	0.01714	10.749	234.6	934.7	1,169.3	0.3900	1.2885	1.6785	857.2
40	267.25	0.01715	10.496	236.1	933.6	1,169.8	0.3921	1.2844	1.6765	856.1
41	268.74	0.01716	10.256	237.7	932.6	1,170.2	0.3942	1.2803	1.6745	854.9
42	270.21	0.01718	10.027	239.2	931.5	1,170.7	0.3962	1.2763	1.6726	853.8
43	271.65	0.01719	9.808	240.6	930.5	1,171.2	0.3983	1.2724	1.6707	852.6
44	273.06	0.01720	9.599	242.1	929.5	1,171.6	0.4002	1.2686	1.6689	851.6
45	274.44	0.01721	9.399	243.5	928.6	1,172.0	0.4021	1.2649	1.6671	850.5
46	275.80	0.01723	9.207	244.9	927.6	1,172.5	0.4040	1.2613	1.6653	849.4
47	277.14	0.01724	9.023	246.2	926.6	1,172.9	0.4059	1.2577	1.6636	848.3
48	278.45	0.01725	8.846	247.6	925.7	1,173.3	0.4077	1.2542	1.6619	847.3
49	279.74	0.01726	8.677	248.9	924.8	1,173.7	0.4095	1.2507	1.6602	846.2

For footnotes, see end of table on p. 3-50.

PROPERTIES OF SATURATED STEAM* (Continued)

Abs pressure, psi	Temp, °F	Specific volume		Enthalpy			Entropy			Internal energy, evap
		Liquid	Vapor	Liquid	Evap	Vapor	Liquid	Evap	Vapor	
50	281.02	0.01727	8.514	250.2	923.9	1,174.1	0.4112	1.2474	1.6586	845.2
51	282.27	0.01728	8.357	251.5	923.0	1,174.5	0.4130	1.2441	1.6570	844.3
52	283.50	0.01730	8.206	252.8	922.1	1,174.9	0.4147	1.2408	1.6555	843.3
53	284.71	0.01731	8.060	254.0	921.2	1,175.2	0.4163	1.2376	1.6539	842.4
54	285.90	0.01732	7.920	255.2	920.4	1,175.6	0.4180	1.2345	1.6524	841.4
55	287.08	0.01733	7.785	256.4	919.5	1,175.9	0.4196	1.2314	1.6510	840.5
56	288.24	0.01734	7.654	257.6	918.7	1,176.3	0.4212	1.2284	1.6495	839.6
57	289.38	0.01735	7.528	258.8	917.8	1,176.6	0.4227	1.2254	1.6481	838.6
58	290.50	0.01736	7.406	259.9	917.0	1,177.0	0.4243	1.2224	1.6467	837.7
59	291.62	0.01737	7.288	261.1	916.2	1,177.3	0.4258	1.2196	1.6453	836.8
60	292.71	0.01738	7.174	262.2	915.4	1,177.6	0.4273	1.2167	1.6440	836.0
61	293.79	0.01739	7.063	263.3	914.6	1,177.9	0.4287	1.2139	1.6427	835.1
62	294.86	0.01740	6.956	264.4	913.8	1,178.2	0.4302	1.2112	1.6413	834.2
63	295.91	0.01741	6.852	265.5	913.0	1,178.6	0.4316	1.2084	1.6401	833.4
64	296.95	0.01742	6.751	266.6	912.3	1,178.8	0.4330	1.2058	1.6388	832.5
65	297.98	0.01743	6.653	267.6	911.5	1,179.1	0.4344	1.2031	1.6375	831.7
66	298.99	0.01744	6.558	268.7	910.8	1,179.4	0.4358	1.2005	1.6363	830.8
67	299.99	0.01745	6.466	269.7	910.0	1,179.7	0.4372	1.1979	1.6351	830.1
68	300.99	0.01746	6.376	270.7	909.3	1,180.0	0.4385	1.1954	1.6339	829.3
69	301.96	0.01747	6.290	271.7	908.5	1,180.3	0.4398	1.1929	1.6327	828.5
70	302.93	0.01748	6.205	272.7	907.8	1,180.6	0.4411	1.1905	1.6316	827.7
71	303.89	0.01749	6.123	273.7	907.1	1,180.8	0.4424	1.1880	1.6304	826.9
72	304.83	0.01750	6.042	274.7	906.4	1,181.1	0.4437	1.1856	1.6293	826.1
73	305.77	0.01751	5.964	275.7	905.7	1,181.3	0.4449	1.1833	1.6282	825.4
74	306.69	0.01752	5.888	276.6	905.0	1,181.6	0.4462	1.1809	1.6271	824.6
75	307.61	0.01753	5.814	277.6	904.3	1,181.9	0.4474	1.1786	1.6260	823.9
76	308.51	0.01754	5.742	278.5	903.6	1,182.1	0.4486	1.1763	1.6250	823.1
77	309.41	0.01755	5.672	279.4	902.9	1,182.4	0.4498	1.1741	1.6239	822.3
78	310.29	0.01756	5.603	280.3	902.3	1,182.6	0.4510	1.1718	1.6229	821.6
79	311.17	0.01756	5.536	281.3	901.6	1,182.8	0.4522	1.1696	1.6218	820.9
80	312.04	0.01757	5.471	282.1	900.9	1,183.1	0.4534	1.1675	1.6207	820.2
81	312.90	0.01758	5.407	283.0	900.3	1,183.3	0.4545	1.1653	1.6197	819.5
82	313.75	0.01759	5.345	283.9	899.6	1,183.5	0.4556	1.1632	1.6187	818.7
83	314.60	0.01760	5.284	284.8	899.0	1,183.8	0.4568	1.1611	1.6177	818.1
84	315.43	0.01761	5.225	285.7	898.3	1,184.0	0.4579	1.1590	1.6168	817.4
85	316.26	0.01762	5.167	286.5	897.7	1,184.2	0.4590	1.1569	1.6158	816.7
86	317.08	0.01762	5.110	287.4	897.0	1,184.4	0.4601	1.1549	1.6149	816.0
87	317.89	0.01763	5.055	288.2	896.4	1,184.6	0.4611	1.1529	1.6139	815.4
88	318.69	0.01764	5.000	288.0	895.8	1,184.8	0.4622	1.1509	1.6130	814.6
89	319.49	0.01765	4.947	289.9	895.2	1,185.0	0.4633	1.1489	1.6121	814.0
90	320.28	0.01766	4.895	290.7	894.6	1,185.3	0.4643	1.1470	1.6113	813.3
91	321.06	0.01767	4.844	291.5	893.9	1,185.5	0.4654	1.1450	1.6104	812.7
92	321.84	0.01768	4.795	292.3	893.3	1,185.7	0.4664	1.1431	1.6095	812.0
93	322.61	0.01768	4.746	293.18	892.7	1,185.9	0.4674	1.1412	1.6086	811.4
94	323.37	0.01769	4.698	293.9	892.1	1,186.0	0.4684	1.1393	1.6078	810.7
95	324.13	0.01770	4.651	294.7	891.5	1,186.2	0.4694	1.1375	1.6069	810.1
96	324.88	0.01771	4.606	295.5	891.0	1,186.4	0.4704	1.1356	1.6061	809.4
97	325.63	0.01772	4.560	296.3	890.4	1,186.6	0.4714	1.1338	1.6052	808.9
98	326.36	0.01772	4.517	297.0	889.8	1,186.8	0.4724	1.1320	1.6044	808.2
99	327.10	0.01773	4.473	297.8	889.2	1,187.0	0.4733	1.1302	1.6036	807.5
100	327.82	0.01774	4.431	298.5	888.6	1,187.2	0.4743	1.1284	1.6027	807.0
102	329.26	0.01776	4.349	300.0	887.5	1,187.5	0.4762	1.1249	1.6011	805.7
104	330.67	0.01777	4.270	301.5	886.4	1,187.9	0.4780	1.1215	1.5995	804.5
106	332.06	0.01779	4.193	303.0	885.2	1,188.2	0.4799	1.1181	1.5980	803.4
108	333.44	0.01780	4.120	304.4	884.1	1,188.5	0.4817	1.1148	1.5965	802.2
110	334.79	0.01782	4.048	305.8	883.1	1,188.9	0.4834	1.1115	1.5950	801.1
112	336.12	0.01783	3.980	307.2	882.0	1,189.2	0.4852	1.1083	1.5935	799.9
114	337.43	0.01785	3.914	308.6	880.9	1,189.5	0.4869	1.1052	1.5921	798.7
116	338.73	0.01786	3.850	309.9	879.9	1,189.8	0.4886	1.1021	1.5906	797.7
118	340.01	0.01787	3.788	311.3	878.8	1,190.1	0.4903	1.0990	1.5892	796.5
120	341.27	0.01789	3.728	312.6	877.8	1,190.4	0.4919	1.0960	1.5879	795.4
122	342.51	0.01790	3.670	313.9	876.8	1,190.7	0.4935	1.0930	1.5865	794.3

For footnotes, see end of table on p. 3-50.

PROPERTIES OF SATURATED STEAM* (Continued)

Abs pressure, psi	Temp, °F	Specific volume		Enthalpy			Entropy			Internal energy, evap
		Liquid	Vapor	Liquid	Evap	Vapor	Liquid	Evap	Vapor	
124	343.74	0.01792	3.613	315.2	875.8	1,190.9	0.4951	1.0901	1.5852	793.2
126	344.95	0.01793	3.559	316.4	874.8	1,191.2	0.4967	1.0872	1.5839	792.2
128	346.15	0.01794	3.506	317.7	873.8	1,191.5	0.4982	1.0843	1.5826	791.1
130	347.33	0.01796	3.454	319.0	872.8	1,191.7	0.4998	1.0815	1.5813	790.1
132	348.50	0.01797	3.405	320.2	871.3	1,192.0	0.5013	1.0788	1.5800	789.1
134	349.65	0.01799	3.356	321.4	870.8	1,192.2	0.5028	1.0760	1.5788	788.1
136	350.79	0.01800	3.309	322.6	869.9	1,192.5	0.5043	1.0733	1.5776	787.1
138	351.92	0.01801	3.263	323.8	869.9	1,192.7	0.5057	1.0707	1.5764	786.1
140	353.04	0.01803	3.219	325.0	868.0	1,193.0	0.5071	1.0681	1.5752	785.1
142	354.14	0.01804	3.176	326.1	867.1	1,193.2	0.5086	1.0655	1.5740	784.1
144	355.23	0.01805	3.134	327.3	866.2	1,193.4	0.5100	1.0629	1.5729	783.1
146	356.31	0.01806	3.093	328.4	865.2	1,193.6	0.5114	1.0604	1.5717	782.2
148	357.38	0.01808	3.053	329.5	864.3	1,193.9	0.5127	1.0579	1.5706	781.3
150	358.43	0.01809	3.014	330.6	863.4	1,194.1	0.5141	1.0554	1.5695	780.3
152	359.48	0.01810	2.976	331.8	862.5	1,194.3	0.5154	1.0530	1.5684	779.4
154	360.51	0.01812	2.939	332.8	861.6	1,194.5	0.5168	1.0506	1.5673	778.4
156	361.53	0.01813	2.903	333.9	860.8	1,194.7	0.5181	1.0482	1.5662	777.5
158	362.55	0.01814	2.868	335.0	859.9	1,194.9	0.5194	1.0458	1.5652	776.5
160	363.55	0.01815	2.834	336.1	859.0	1,195.1	0.5206	1.0435	1.5641	775.7
162	364.54	0.01817	2.800	337.1	858.2	1,195.3	0.5219	1.0412	1.5631	774.7
164	365.53	0.01818	2.767	338.2	857.3	1,195.5	0.5232	1.0389	1.5621	773.9
166	366.50	0.01819	2.736	339.2	856.5	1,195.7	0.5244	1.0367	1.5611	773.0
168	367.47	0.01820	2.704	340.2	855.6	1,195.8	0.5256	1.0344	1.5601	772.1
170	368.42	0.01821	2.674	341.2	854.8	1,196.0	0.5269	1.0322	1.5591	771.2
172	369.37	0.01823	2.644	342.2	853.9	1,196.2	0.5281	1.0300	1.5581	770.3
174	370.31	0.01824	2.615	343.2	853.1	1,196.4	0.5293	1.0279	1.5571	769.5
176	371.24	0.01825	2.586	344.2	852.3	1,196.5	0.5305	1.0257	1.5562	768.7
178	372.16	0.01826	2.558	345.2	851.5	1,196.7	0.5316	1.0236	1.5552	767.8
180	373.08	0.01827	2.531	346.2	850.7	1,196.9	0.5328	1.0215	1.5543	766.9
182	373.98	0.01828	2.504	347.2	849.9	1,197.0	0.5330	1.0194	1.5534	766.2
184	374.88	0.01830	2.478	348.1	849.1	1,197.2	0.5351	1.0174	1.5525	765.3
186	375.77	0.01831	2.453	349.1	848.3	1,197.3	0.5362	1.0153	1.5516	764.5
188	376.65	0.01832	2.428	350.0	847.5	1,197.5	0.5373	1.0133	1.5507	763.6
190	377.53	0.01833	2.403	350.9	846.7	1,197.6	0.5384	1.0113	1.5498	762.8
192	378.40	0.01834	2.379	351.9	845.9	1,197.8	0.5395	1.0094	1.5489	762.0
194	379.26	0.01835	2.355	352.8	845.1	1,197.9	0.5406	1.0074	1.5480	761.3
196	380.12	0.01836	2.332	353.7	844.4	1,198.1	0.5417	1.0054	1.5471	760.5
198	380.96	0.01838	2.310	354.6	843.6	1,198.2	0.5428	1.0035	1.5463	759.7
200	381.80	0.01839	2.287	355.5	842.8	1,198.3	0.5438	1.0016	1.5454	758.9
205	383.88	0.01841	2.233	357.7	840.9	1,198.7	0.5465	0.9969	1.5434	756.9
210	385.91	0.01844	2.182	359.9	839.1	1,199.0	0.5490	0.9923	1.5413	755.0
215	387.91	0.01847	2.133	362.1	837.2	1,199.3	0.5515	0.9878	1.5393	753.1
220	389.88	0.01850	2.086	364.2	835.4	1,199.6	0.5540	0.9834	1.5374	751.2
225	391.80	0.01852	2.0414	366.2	833.6	1,199.9	0.5564	0.9790	1.5354	749.4
230	393.70	0.01855	1.9985	368.3	831.8	1,200.1	0.5588	0.9748	1.5336	747.6
235	395.56	0.01857	1.9572	370.3	830.1	1,200.4	0.5611	0.9706	1.5317	745.8
240	397.39	0.01860	1.9177	372.3	828.4	1,200.6	0.5634	0.9665	1.5299	744.1
245	399.19	0.01863	1.8797	374.2	826.6	1,200.9	0.5657	0.9625	1.5281	742.2
250	400.97	0.01865	1.8432	376.1	825.0	1,201.1	0.5679	0.9585	1.5264	740.5
260	404.44	0.01870	1.7742	379.9	821.6	1,201.5	0.5722	0.9508	1.5230	737.2
270	407.80	0.01875	1.7101	383.6	818.3	1,201.9	0.5764	0.9433	1.5197	733.9
280	411.07	0.01880	1.6505	387.1	815.1	1,202.3	0.5805	0.9361	1.5166	730.6
290	414.25	0.01885	1.5948	390.6	812.0	1,202.6	0.5844	0.9291	1.5135	727.4
300	417.35	0.01889	1.5427	394.0	808.9	1,202.9	0.5882	0.9223	1.5105	724.3
320	423.31	0.01899	1.4480	400.5	802.9	1,203.4	0.5956	0.9092	1.5048	718.3
340	428.99	0.01908	1.3640	406.8	797.0	1,203.8	0.6026	0.8969	1.4994	712.4
360	434.41	0.01917	1.2891	412.8	791.3	1,204.1	0.6092	0.8851	1.4943	706.8
380	439.61	0.01925	1.2218	418.6	785.8	1,204.4	0.6156	0.8738	1.4894	701.3
400	444.60	0.01934	1.1610	424.2	780.4	1,204.6	0.6217	0.8630	1.4847	696.0
420	449.40	0.01942	1.1057	429.6	775.2	1,204.7	0.6276	0.8527	1.4802	690.8
440	454.03	0.01950	1.0557	434.8	770.0	1,204.8	0.6332	0.8427	1.4759	685.6
460	458.50	0.01959	1.0092	439.8	765.0	1,204.8	0.6387	0.8331	1.4718	680.7
480	462.82	0.01967	0.9668	444.7	760.9	1,204.8	0.6439	0.8238	1.4677	675.9

For footnotes, see end of table on p. 3-50.

PROPERTIES OF SATURATED STEAM* (Continued)

Abs pressure, psi	Temp, °F	Specific volume		Enthalpy			Entropy			Internal energy
		Liquid	Vapor	Liquid	Evap	Vapor	Liquid	Evap	Vapor	Vapor
500	467.01	0.0198	0.9276	449.5	755.1	1,204.7	0.6490	0.8148	1.4639	1,118.8
520	471.07	0.0198	0.8914	454.2	750.4	1,204.5	0.6540	0.8062	1.4601	1,118.8
540	475.01	0.0199	0.8577	458.7	745.7	1,204.4	0.6587	0.7977	1.4565	1,118.7
560	478.84	0.0200	0.8264	463.1	741.0	1,204.2	0.6634	0.7895	1.4529	1,118.5
580	482.57	0.0201	0.7971	467.5	736.5	1,203.9	0.6679	0.7816	1.4495	1,118.4
600	486.20	0.0201	0.7698	471.7	732.0	1,203.7	0.6723	0.7738	1.4461	1,118.2
620	489.74	0.0202	0.7441	475.8	727.5	1,203.4	0.6766	0.7662	1.4428	1,118.0
640	493.19	0.0203	0.7199	479.9	723.1	1,203.0	0.6808	0.7588	1.4396	1,117.8
660	496.57	0.0204	0.6972	483.9	718.8	1,202.7	0.6849	0.7516	1.4365	1,117.5
680	499.86	0.0204	0.6758	487.8	714.5	1,202.3	0.6889	0.7446	1.4334	1,117.2
700	503.08	0.0205	0.6556	491.6	710.2	1,201.8	0.6928	0.7377	1.4304	1,116.9
720	506.23	0.0206	0.6364	495.4	706.0	1,201.4	0.6966	0.7309	1.4275	1,116.6
740	509.32	0.0206	0.6182	499.1	701.9	1,200.9	0.7003	0.7243	1.4246	1,116.3
760	512.34	0.0207	0.6010	502.7	697.7	1,200.4	0.7040	0.7178	1.4218	1,115.9
780	515.30	0.0208	0.5846	506.3	693.6	1,199.9	0.7076	0.7114	1.4190	1,115.5
800	518.21	0.0209	0.5690	509.8	689.6	1,199.4	0.7111	0.7051	1.4163	1,115.2
820	521.06	0.0209	0.5541	513.3	685.5	1,198.8	0.7146	0.6990	1.4136	1,114.8
840	523.86	0.0210	0.5399	516.7	681.5	1,198.2	0.7180	0.6929	1.4109	1,114.3
860	526.60	0.0211	0.5263	520.1	677.6	1,197.7	0.7214	0.6869	1.4083	1,113.9
880	529.30	0.0212	0.5133	523.4	673.6	1,197.0	0.7247	0.6811	1.4057	1,113.4
900	531.95	0.0212	0.5009	526.7	669.7	1,196.4	0.7279	0.6753	1.4032	1,113.0
920	534.56	0.0213	0.4890	530.0	665.8	1,195.7	0.7311	0.6696	1.4007	1,112.5
940	537.13	0.0214	0.4776	533.2	661.9	1,195.1	0.7342	0.6640	1.3982	1,112.0
960	539.65	0.0214	0.4666	536.3	658.0	1,194.4	0.7373	0.6584	1.3958	1,111.5
980	542.14	0.0215	0.4561	539.5	654.2	1,193.7	0.7404	0.6530	1.3934	1,111.0
1,000	544.58	0.0216	0.4460	542.6	650.4	1,192.9	0.7434	0.6476	1.3910	1,110.4
1,050	550.53	0.0218	0.4222	550.1	640.9	1,191.0	0.7507	0.6344	1.3851	1,109.0
1,100	556.28	0.0220	0.4006	557.5	631.5	1,189.1	0.7578	0.6216	1.3794	1,107.4
1,150	561.82	0.0221	0.3807	564.8	622.2	1,187.0	0.7647	0.6091	1.3738	1,106.7
1,200	567.19	0.0223	0.3624	571.9	613.0	1,184.8	0.7714	0.5966	1.3683	1,104.0
1,250	572.38	0.0225	0.3456	578.8	603.8	1,182.6	0.7780	0.5850	1.3630	1,102.6
1,300	577.42	0.0227	0.3299	585.6	594.6	1,180.2	0.7843	0.5733	1.3577	1,000.9
1,350	582.35	0.0229	0.3148	592.1	584.0	1,176.1	0.7902	0.5604	1.3506	1,099.0
1,400	587.07	0.0231	0.3018	598.8	576.5	1,175.3	0.7966	0.5507	1.3474	1,097.1
1,450	591.73	0.0233	0.2884	605.2	565.5	1,170.7	0.8023	0.5379	1.3402	1,095.2
1,500	596.20	0.0235	0.2772	611.7	558.4	1,170.1	0.8085	0.5288	1.3373	1,093.1
1,600	604.87	0.0239	0.2554	624.2	540.3	1,164.5	0.8199	0.5076	1.3274	1,088.9
1,700	613.13	0.0243	0.2361	636.5	522.2	1,158.6	0.8309	0.4867	1.3176	1,084.4
1,800	621.02	0.0247	0.2186	648.5	503.8	1,153.3	0.8417	0.4662	1.3079	1,079.5
1,900	628.56	0.0252	0.2028	660.4	485.2	1,145.6	0.8522	0.4459	1.2981	1,074.3
2,000	635.80	0.0256	0.1883	672.1	466.2	1,138.3	0.8625	0.4256	1.2881	1,068.6
2,200	649.45	0.0267	0.1627	695.5	426.7	1,122.2	0.8828	0.3848	1.2676	1,055.9
2,400	662.11	0.0279	0.1408	719.0	384.8	1,103.7	0.9031	0.3430	1.2460	1,041.2
2,600	673.91	0.0294	0.1211	744.5	337.6	1,082.0	0.9247	0.2977	1.2225	1,023.8
2,800	684.96	0.0313	0.1031	770.7	285.1	1,055.8	0.9468	0.2491	1.1958	1,002.4
3,000	695.33	0.0343	0.0850	801.8	218.4	1,020.3	0.9728	0.1891	1.1619	973.1
3,200	705.08	0.0447	0.0566	875.5	56.1	931.6	1.0351	0.0482	1.0832	898.1
3,208.2	705.47	0.0508	0.0508	906.0	0.0	906.0	1.0612	0.0000	1.0612	875.9

Computed by permission from "1967 ASME Steam Tables," The American Society of Mechanical Engineers.

* See also Mollier diagram on p. 5-4.

STEAM TABLE FOR USE IN CONDENSER CALCULATIONS

Temp, °F t	Abs pressure p		Specific volume sat vapor v_g	Enthalpy			Entropy	
	psi	in. Hg		Sat liquid h_f	Evap h_{fg}	Sat vapor H_g	Sat liquid s_f	Sat vapor s_g
50	0.17796	0.3623	1,704.8	18.05	1,065.3	1,083.4	0.0361	2.1262
52	0.19165	0.3901	1,589.2	20.06	1,064.2	1,084.2	0.0400	2.1197
54	0.20625	0.4199	1,482.2	22.06	1,063.1	1,085.1	0.0439	2.1134
56	0.22183	0.4516	1,383.6	24.06	1,061.9	1,086.0	0.0478	2.1070
58	0.23843	0.4854	1,292.2	26.06	1,060.8	1,086.9	0.0516	2.1008
60	0.25611	0.5214	1,207.6	28.06	1,059.7	1,087.7	0.0555	2.0946
62	0.27494	0.5597	1,129.2	30.06	1,058.5	1,088.6	0.0595	2.0885
64	0.29497	0.6005	1,056.5	32.06	1,057.4	1,089.5	0.0632	2.0824
66	0.31626	0.6439	989.1	34.06	1,056.3	1,090.4	0.0670	2.0764
68	0.33889	0.6899	926.5	36.05	1,055.2	1,091.2	0.0708	2.0704
70	0.36292	0.7389	868.4	38.05	1,054.0	1,092.1	0.0745	2.0645
72	0.38844	0.7908	814.3	40.05	1,052.9	1,093.0	0.0783	2.0587
74	0.41550	0.8459	764.1	42.05	1,051.8	1,093.8	0.0821	2.0529
76	0.44420	0.9044	717.4	44.04	1,050.7	1,094.7	0.0858	2.0472
78	0.47461	0.9663	673.9	46.04	1,049.5	1,095.6	0.0895	2.0415
80	0.50683	1.0319	633.3	48.04	1,048.4	1,096.4	0.0932	2.0359
82	0.54093	1.1013	595.6	50.03	1,047.3	1,097.3	0.0969	2.0303
84	0.57702	1.1748	560.3	52.03	1,046.1	1,098.2	0.1006	2.0248
86	0.61518	1.2525	527.5	54.03	1,045.0	1,099.0	0.1043	2.0193
88	0.65551	1.3346	496.8	56.02	1,043.9	1,099.9	0.1079	2.0139
90	0.69813	1.4214	468.1	58.02	1,042.7	1,100.8	0.1115	2.0086
92	0.74313	1.5130	441.3	60.01	1,041.6	1,101.6	0.1152	2.0033
94	0.79062	1.6097	416.3	62.01	1,040.5	1,102.5	0.1188	1.9980
96	0.84072	1.7117	392.9	64.01	1,039.3	1,103.3	0.1224	1.9928
98	0.89356	1.8193	370.9	66.00	1,038.2	1,104.2	0.1260	1.9876
100	0.94924	1.9326	350.4	68.00	1,037.1	1,105.1	0.1295	1.9825
102	1.00789	2.0520	331.1	70.00	1,035.9	1,105.9	0.1331	1.9775
104	1.06965	2.1778	313.1	71.99	1,034.8	1,106.8	0.1366	1.9725
106	1.1347	2.3102	296.2	73.99	1,033.6	1,107.6	0.1402	1.9675
108	1.2030	2.4493	280.3	75.98	1,032.5	1,108.5	0.1437	1.9626
110	1.2750	2.5956	265.4	77.98	1,031.4	1,109.3	0.1472	1.9577
112	1.3505	2.7496	251.4	79.98	1,030.2	1,110.2	0.1507	1.9528
114	1.4299	2.9112	238.2	81.97	1,029.1	1,111.0	0.1542	1.9480
116	1.5133	3.0810	225.8	83.97	1,027.9	1,111.9	0.1577	1.9433
118	1.6009	3.2594	214.2	85.97	1,026.8	1,112.7	0.1611	1.9386
120	1.6927	3.4463	203.26	87.97	1,025.6	1,113.6	0.1646	1.9339
122	1.7891	3.6423	192.95	89.96	1,024.5	1,114.4	0.1680	1.9293
124	1.8901	3.8482	183.24	91.96	1,023.3	1,115.3	0.1715	1.9247
126	1.9959	4.0636	174.09	93.96	1,022.2	1,116.1	0.1749	1.9202
128	2.1068	4.2894	165.47	95.96	1,021.0	1,117.0	0.1783	1.9157

Computed by permission from "1967 ASME Steam Tables," The American Society of Mechanical Engineers.

SUPERHEATED-STEAM TABLES

v = specific volume, cu ft/lb; h = enthalpy, Btu/lb; s = entropy

Pressure, psi (saturation temp, °F)		340	380	420	450	500	550	600	650	700
20 (227.96)	v	23.59	24.82	26.04	27.25	28.46	29.96	31.47	32.97	34.46
	h	1,210.6	1,229.7	1,248.7	1,267.8	1,286.7	1,310.8	1,334.9	1,359.1	1,383.5
	s	1.8052	1.8285	1.8506	1.8718	1.8921	1.9164	1.9397	1.9621	1.9836
40 (267.25)	v	11.679	12.311	12.934	13.552	14.165	14.927	15.685	16.441	17.195
	h	1,206.8	1,226.6	1,246.2	1,265.6	1,285.0	1,309.3	1,333.6	1,358.0	1,382.5
	s	1.7250	1.7492	1.7720	1.7936	1.8143	1.8389	1.8624	1.8849	1.906
60 (292.71)	v	7.705	8.140	8.566	8.985	9.400	9.914	10.425	10.932	11.438
	h	1,202.8	1,223.3	1,243.5	1,263.4	1,283.2	1,307.7	1,332.3	1,356.8	1,381.5
	s	1.6764	1.7015	1.7250	1.7471	1.7681	1.7931	1.8168	1.8395	1.861
80 (312.03)	v	5.715	6.053	6.381	6.702	7.018	7.408	7.794	8.178	8.560
	h	1,198.6	1,220.0	1,240.8	1,261.2	1,281.3	1,306.2	1,330.9	1,355.7	1,380.5
	s	1.6405	1.6667	1.6909	1.7136	1.7349	1.7602	1.7842	1.8070	1.828
100 (327.81)	v	4.519	4.799	5.068	5.331	5.588	5.904	6.216	6.525	6.833
	h	1,194.2	1,216.5	1,238.0	1,258.9	1,279.3	1,304.6	1,329.6	1,354.5	1,379.5
	s	1.6116	1.6389	1.6638	1.6870	1.7088	1.7344	1.7586	1.7816	1.803
120 (341.25)	v	.....	3.962	4.193	4.416	4.634	4.901	5.163	5.424	5.681
	h	.....	1,212.9	1,235.1	1,256.5	1,277.4	1,302.9	1,328.2	1,353.3	1,378.4
	s	.....	1.6154	1.6412	1.6650	1.6872	1.7132	1.7376	1.7608	1.782
140 (353.02)	v	.....	3.363	3.567	3.763	3.953	4.184	4.412	4.636	4.858
	h	.....	1,209.2	1,232.1	1,254.1	1,275.3	1,301.3	1,326.8	1,352.2	1,377.4
	s	.....	1.5948	1.6215	1.6459	1.6686	1.6949	1.7196	1.7430	1.7652
160 (363.53)	v	.....	2.913	3.097	3.272	3.441	3.647	3.848	4.046	4.242
	h	.....	1,205.3	1,229.1	1,251.6	1,273.3	1,299.6	1,325.4	1,351.0	1,376.4
	s	.....	1.5764	1.6041	1.6291	1.6522	1.6790	1.7039	1.7275	1.7499
180 (373.06)	v	.....	2.562	2.730	2.890	3.043	3.229	3.409	3.587	3.762
	h	.....	1,201.3	1,225.9	1,249.0	1,271.2	1,297.9	1,324.0	1,349.8	1,375.3
	s	.....	1.5596	1.5882	1.6140	1.6376	1.6647	1.6900	1.7137	1.7362

200 (381.79)	v	· · · ·	· · · ·	2.437	2.584	2.725	2.894	3.058	3.219	3.378
	h	· · · ·	· · · ·	1,222.6	1,246.4	1,269.0	1,296.2	1,322.6	1,348.6	1,374.3
	s	· · · ·	· · · ·	1.5737	1.6001	1.6242	1.6518	1.6773	1.7013	1.7239
220 (389.86)	v	· · · ·	· · · ·	2.196	2.334	2.464	2.620	2.771	2.919	3.064
	h	· · · ·	· · · ·	1,219.3	1,243.7	1,266.9	1,294.5	1,321.2	1,347.3	1,373.2
	s	· · · ·	· · · ·	1.5601	1.5873	1.6120	1.6400	1.6658	1.6900	1.7128
260 (404.42)	v	· · · ·	· · · ·	1.8246	1.9471	2.062	2.198	2.329	2.456	2.581
	h	· · · ·	· · · ·	1,212.2	1,238.2	1,262.4	1,290.9	1,318.2	1,344.9	1,371.1
	s	· · · ·	· · · ·	1.5353	1.5642	1.5899	1.6189	1.6453	1.6699	1.6930
300 (417.33)	v	· · · ·	· · · ·	1.5506	1.6627	1.7665	1.8833	2.004	2.117	2.226
	h	· · · ·	· · · ·	1,204.8	1,232.3	1,257.7	1,287.2	1,315.2	1,342.4	1,368.9
	s	· · · ·	· · · ·	1.5127	1.5433	1.5703	1.6003	1.6274	1.6524	1.6758
350 (431.72)	v	· · · ·	· · · ·	· · · ·	1.3973	1.4913	1.6002	1.7028	1.8013	1.8970
	h	· · · ·	· · · ·	· · · ·	1,224.7	1,251.5	1,282.4	1,311.4	1,339.2	1,366.2
	s	· · · ·	· · · ·	· · · ·	1.5197	1.5483	1.5797	1.6077	1.6333	1.6571
400 (444.59)	v	· · · ·	· · · ·	· · · ·	1.1970	1.2841	1.3836	1.4763	1.5646	1.6499
	h	· · · ·	· · · ·	· · · ·	1,216.5	1,245.1	1,277.5	1,307.4	1,335.9	1,363.4
	s	· · · ·	· · · ·	· · · ·	1.4978	1.5282	1.5611	1.5901	1.6163	1.6406

SUPERHEATED-STEAM TABLES (Continued)

Pressure, psi (saturation temp, °F)		Temp of steam, °F								
		500	550	600	650	700	750	800	900	1000
450 (456.28)	v	1.1231	1.2154	1.3005	1.3810	1.4584	1.5337	1.6074	1.7516	1.8928
	h	1,238.4	1,272.0	1,302.8	1,331.9	1,359.9	1,387.3	1,414.3	1,467.7	1,521.0
	s	1.5095	1.5437	1.5735	1.6003	1.6250	1.6481	1.6699	1.7108	1.7486
500 (467.01)	v	0.9919	1.0791	1.1584	1.2327	1.3037	1.3725	1.4397	1.5708	1.6992
	h	1,231.2	1,267.0	1,299.1	1,329.1	1,357.7	1,385.4	1,412.7	1,466.6	1,520.3
	s	1.4921	1.5284	1.5595	1.5871	1.6123	1.6357	1.6578	1.6990	1.7371
550 (476.94)	v	0.8852	0.9686	1.0431	1.1124	1.1783	1.2419	1.3038	1.4241	1.5414
	h	1,223.7	1,261.2	1,294.3	1,324.9	1,354.0	1,382.3	1,409.9	1,464.3	1,518.2
	s	1.4751	1.5131	1.5451	1.5734	1.5991	1.6228	1.6452	1.6868	1.7250
600 (486.21)	v	0.7944	0.8746	0.9456	1.0109	1.0726	1.1318	1.1892	1.3008	1.4093
	h	1,215.9	1,255.6	1,290.3	1,322.0	1,351.8	1,380.4	1,408.3	1,463.0	1,517.4
	s	1.4590	1.4993	1.5329	1.5621	1.5884	1.6125	1.6351	1.6769	1.7155
700 (503.10)	v		0.7271	0.7928	0.8520	0.9072	0.9596	1.0102	1.1078	1.2023
	h		1,243.4	1,281.0	1,314.6	1,345.6	1,375.2	1,403.7	1,459.4	1,514.4
	s		1.4726	1.5090	1.5509	1.5673	1.5923	1.6154	1.6580	1.6970
800 (518.23)	v		0.6151	0.6774	0.7323	0.7828	0.8303	0.8759	0.9631	1.0470
	h		1,230.1	1,271.1	1,306.8	1,339.3	1,369.8	1,399.1	1,455.8	1,511.4
	s		1.4472	1.4869	1.5198	1.5484	1.5742	1.5980	1.6413	1.6807
900 (531.98)	v		0.5263	0.5869	0.6388	0.6858	0.7296	0.7713	0.8504	0.9262
	h		1,215.5	1,260.6	1,298.6	1,332.7	1,364.3	1,394.4	1,452.2	1,508.5
	s		1.4223	1.4659	1.5010	1.5311	1.5578	1.5822	1.6263	1.6662
1,000 (544.61)	v		0.4535	0.5137	0.5636	0.6080	0.6489	0.6875	0.7603	0.8295
	h		1,199.3	1,249.3	1,290.1	1,325.9	1,358.7	1,389.6	1,448.5	1,505.4
	s		1.3973	1.4457	1.4833	1.5149	1.5426	1.5677	1.6126	1.6530
1,100 (556.31)	v			0.4531	0.5017	0.5440	0.5826	0.6188	0.6865	0.7505
	h			1,237.3	1,281.2	1,318.8	1,352.9	1,384.7	1,444.7	1,502.4
	s			1.4259	1.4664	1.4996	1.5284	1.5542	1.6000	1.6410
1,200 (567.22)	v			0.4016	0.4497	0.4905	0.5273	0.5615	0.6250	0.6845
	h			1,224.2	1,271.8	1,311.5	1,346.9	1,379.7	1,440.9	1,499.4
	s			1.4061	1.4501	1.4851	1.5150	1.5415	1.5883	1.6298

Abs. Press. (Sat. Temp.)								
1,400 (587.10)	v	· · · · ·	0.3176	0.3667	0.4059	0.4400	0.4712	0.5282	0.5809
	h	· · · · ·	1,194.1	1,251.4	1,296.1	1,334.5	1,369.3	1,433.2	1,493.2
	s	· · · · ·	1.3652	1.4181	1.4575	1.4900	1.5182	1.5670	1.6096
1,600 (604.90)	v	· · · · ·	· · · · ·	0.3026	0.3415	0.3741	0.4032	0.4555	0.5031
	h	· · · · ·	· · · · ·	1,228.3	1,279.4	1,321.4	1,358.5	1,425.2	1,486.9
	s	· · · · ·	· · · · ·	1.3861	1.4312	1.4667	1.4968	1.5478	1.5916
1,800 (621.03)	v	· · · · ·	· · · · ·	0.2505	0.2906	0.3223	0.3500	0.3988	0.4426
	h	· · · · ·	· · · · ·	1,201.2	1,261.1	1,307.4	1,347.2	1,417.1	1,480.6
	s	· · · · ·	· · · · ·	1.3526	1.405	1.4446	1.4768	1.5302	1.5753
2,000 (635.82)	v	· · · · ·	· · · · ·	0.2056	0.2488	0.2805	0.3072	0.3534	0.3942
	h	· · · · ·	· · · · ·	1,168.3	1,240.9	1,292.6	1,335.4	1,408.7	1,474.1
	s	· · · · ·	· · · · ·	1.3154	1.3794	1.4231	1.4578	1.5138	1.5603
2,200 (649.46)	v	· · · · ·	· · · · ·	0.1636	0.2134	0.2458	0.2720	0.3161	0.3545
	h	· · · · ·	· · · · ·	1,123.9	1,218.0	1,276.8	1,323.1	1,400.0	1,467.6
	s	· · · · ·	· · · · ·	1.2691	1.3523	1.4020	1.4395	1.4984	1.5463

PROPERTIES OF THE LOWER ATMOSPHERE

Altitude, ft	Pressure, psia	Pressure, in. Hg at 32°F	Specific wt, lb/cu ft	Temp, °F
0	14.696	29.921	0.07648	59.0
100	14.64	29.81	0.0763	58.6
200	14.59	29.71	0.0760	58.3
300	14.54	29.60	0.0758	57.9
400	14.48	29.49	0.0756	57.6
500	14.43	29.38	0.0754	57.2
600	14.38	29.28	0.0751	56.9
700	14.33	29.17	0.0749	56.5
800	14.28	29.07	0.0747	56.1
900	14.22	28.96	0.0745	55.8
1,000	14.17	28.86	0.0743	55.4
1,100	14.12	28.75	0.0740	55.1
1,200	14.07	28.65	0.0738	54.7
1,300	14.02	28.54	0.0736	54.4
1,400	13.97	28.44	0.0734	54.0
1,500	13.92	28.33	0.0732	53.7
1,600	13.87	28.23	0.0730	53.3
1,700	13.82	28.13	0.0727	52.9
1,800	13.76	28.02	0.0725	52.6
1,900	13.71	27.92	0.0723	52.2
2,000	13.66	27.82	0.0721	51.9
2,200	13.56	27.62	0.0717	51.2
2,400	13.47	27.42	0.0712	50.4
2,600	13.37	27.21	0.0708	49.7
2,800	13.27	27.02	0.0704	49.0
3,000	13.17	26.82	0.0700	48.3
3,500	12.93	26.33	0.0689	46.5
4,000	12.69	25.84	0.0679	44.7
4,500	12.46	25.37	0.0669	43.0
5,000	12.23	24.90	0.0659	41.2
6,000	11.78	23.98	0.0639	37.6
7,000	11.34	23.09	0.0620	34.0
8,000	10.92	22.22	0.0601	30.5
9,000	10.50	21.39	0.0583	26.9
10,000	10.11	20.58	0.0565	23.3
12,000	9.346	19.03	0.0530	16.2
14,000	8.633	17.58	0.0497	9.1
15,000	8.293	16.89	0.0481	5.5
16,000	7.965	16.21	0.0466	1.9
18,000	7.339	14.94	0.0436	− 5.2
20,000	6.753	13.75	0.0407	−12.3
25,000	5.453	11.10	0.0343	−30.2
30,000	4.364	8.885	0.0286	−48.0
35,000	3.458	7.041	0.0237	−65.8
40,000	2.720	5.538	0.0188	−69.7
45,000	2.139	4.355	0.0148	−69.7
50,000	1.682	3.425	0.0116	−69.7
55,000	1.323	2.693	0.00915	−69.7
60,000	1.040	2.118	0.00720	−69.7
65,000	0.8180	1.665	0.00566	−69.7

Data from NASA Standard Atmosphere (1962).

SONIC VELOCITY

As the speed of rotating machinery such as turbines and centrifugal compressors is continually being increased, the velocity of sound is the fluid becomes increasingly important. If the velocity of the fluid equals or exceeds that of sound in the fluid, shock waves are set up, and the actions which take place are vastly different from those when the fluid velocities are below that of sound.

The ratio of the fluid velocity to that of sound in the fluid is called the *Mach number.* For a Mach number of 1 the fluid velocity equals that of sound; for a Mach number of 2 the fluid velocity is twice that of sound, and so on.

The velocity of sound in air at 68°F is 1,126 fps. The value for any gas may be calculated from the equation $V = \sqrt{kgp/\gamma}$ in fps, where k is the ratio of the specific heats, g is the acceleration due to gravity $= 32.2$ ft/sec², p is the absolute pressure of the gas in psf, and γ is the specific weight of the gas in lb/cu ft. The equation may also be written as follows:

$$V = \sqrt{kgpv} = \sqrt{kgRT}$$

where v is the specific volume in cu ft/lb, R is the gas constant, and T is the absolute temperature in °F.

If a supercompressibility factor is used in the calculation, the equation for sonic velocity changes to

$$V = \sqrt{kgZRT}$$

where Z is the compressibility factor.

An analysis of the equations shows that the sonic velocity is independent of the pressure of the gas, but that it is directly proportional to the square root of the absolute temperature.

AVERAGE CALORIC VALUES OF FUELS

The table below gives the average caloric value of various fuels for use in heat-balance calculations. For more accurate values of individual fuels obtained from different sources, consult the references given.

Fuels	High heat value, Btu/lb
Solid fuels:	. . . .
Wood (with 12% moisture) . . .	. . . .
Oak	15,000
Pine, yellow	13,000
Coal (as delivered):	. . . .
Anthracite	12,000–14,000
Bituminous A	12,000–14,000
Bituminous C	9,000–11,000
Coke	12,000–14,000
Liquid fuels:	
Petroleums:	
Crude oil	18,000–19,500
Gasoline	20,750
Kerosene	19,800
Fuel oil	18,500–19,300

Gases	High heat value per cu ft of dry gas at 60°F and 30 in. Hg pressure	Avg specific gravity (air = 1.0 weighing 0.0750 lb/cu ft)
Natural gas	1,000–1,100	0.60
Producer gas	150–160	0.86
Blast-furnace gas . . .	90–92	1.02
Coke-oven gas	510–575	0.40
Carbureted water gas . .	500–550	0.60
Coal gas	480–530	0.50

For references see ASTM Standards on Coal and Coke, ASTM Symposium on Industrial Fuels 1936, Marks' "Standard Handbook for Mechanical Engineers," 7th ed., McGraw-Hill Book Company, New York, 1967.

Basic Engineering Concepts

MECHANICS

Nomenclature

Symbol	Name	Definition	Dimensions
a	(linear) acceleration	$\dfrac{dv}{dt}$	in./sec², ft/sec²
a, b, c	vectors	. . . .	according to use
A	area	. . . .	sq in., sq ft
E	work done	$F \times S$	in.-lb, ft-lb
E_K	kinetic energy	$\dfrac{mv^2}{2}$	in.-lb, ft-lb
F	force	fundamental	lb
g	acceleration of gravity	. . . .	32.16 ft/sec², 386 in./sec²
h, H	hydrostatic head	$\dfrac{p}{\gamma}$	in., ft (of liquid)
hp	horsepower	550 ft-lb/sec	hp
I	area moment of inertia	$\int y^2\, dA$	in.⁴
J	polar mass moment of inertia	$\int r^2\, dm$	in.-lb-sec², ft-lb-sec²
k	area radius of gyration	$I = k^2 A$	in., ft

MECHANICS (Continued)

Nomenclature

Symbol	Name	Definition	Dimensions
k_0	polar radius of gyration	$J = k_0^2 m$	in., ft
K	spring rate (or modulus)	$\dfrac{F}{S}$	lb/in.
kw	kilowatt	737.6 ft-lb/sec	kw
m	mass	$\dfrac{W}{g}$	lb-sec²/in., lb-sec²/ft
M	moment, torque	$F \times r$	in.-lb, ft-lb
N	rotating speed	revolutions per minute	rpm
N_0	initial rotating speed	. . . .	rpm
p	hydrostatic pressure	$\dfrac{F}{A}$	psi, psf
P	power	$\dfrac{FS}{T}$	ft-lb/sec, hp
q	flow rate	. . . .	cu ft/sec
r, R	radius	. . . .	in., ft
$\vec{R}$	vector force	. . . .	lb
S	displacement	. . . .	in., ft
S_0	initial displacement	. . . .	in., ft
t	time, as a variable	fundamental	sec
T	period of time	. . . .	sec
v	velocity	$\dfrac{ds}{dt}$	in./sec, fps
v_0	initial velocity	. . . .	in./sec, fps
V	volume	. . . .	cu in., cu ft
w	weight flow	. . . .	lb/sec
W	weight	fundamental	lb
$x, X; y, Y; z, Z$	spatial coordinates	. . . .	in., ft
α	angular acceleration	$\dfrac{d\omega}{dt}$	1/sec²
γ	specific weight	$\dfrac{W}{v}$	lb/cu in., lb/cu ft
θ	angle of rotation	. . . .	radians, in./in.
μ	coefficient of friction		
ω	angular velocity	$\dfrac{d\theta}{dt}$	radians/sec, 1/sec
ω_0	initial angular velocity	. . . .	1/sec

NOTE: Every mechanical relationship must be written in consistent dimensions, except where expressly noted otherwise. Also, the two sides of an equation must have the same dimensions.

Example: In the formula

$$E_K = \frac{m}{2} v^2$$

m must be in lb-sec²/in., v in in./sec, and then E_K will be obtained in in.-lb; or m is in lb-sec²/ft, v in fps and then E_K is in ft-lb.

Fundamental Laws of Engineering Mechanics

1. In a closed system, the sum of all masses remains constant throughout any process.
2. In a closed system, the sum of all energies remains constant throughout any process. (But one form of energy may transform into another.)
3. The momentum of a closed system remains constant throughout any mechanical process.

4. In a closed system, the sum of all energies at the end of any process is always at a lower potential than at the beginning.   In any transformation of energy some *usable* energy is lost.

5. Of all conceivable modes of energy transformation under a set of conditions, the actually occurring process requires the least amount of work.

Basic Mechanical Relations (Kinematics)

Uniform motion

Linear motion	Rotary motion
$S = vt$	$\theta = \omega t$
$v = \text{const}$	$\omega = \dfrac{\pi N}{30} = \text{const}$
$a = 0$	$\alpha = 0$

Uniform acceleration.   Initial velocity and displacement zero

Linear motion	Rotary motion
$S = \dfrac{a}{2} t^2 = \dfrac{v}{2} t$	$\theta = \dfrac{\alpha}{2} t^2 = \dfrac{\omega}{2} t$
$v = at = \sqrt{2as}$	$\omega = \alpha t = \sqrt{2\alpha\theta}$

Free fall

$$S = \frac{g}{2} t^2$$

Example: How long does an object take to reach the ground in free fall if it has been released from a height of 100 ft?

$$t = \sqrt{\frac{2S}{g}} = \sqrt{\frac{200}{32.16}} = 2.5 \text{ sec}$$

Uniform acceleration or deceleration

Linear motion Initial velocity v_0	Rotary motion Initial angular velocity ω_0
$S = v_0 t \pm \dfrac{a}{2} t^2$	$\theta = \omega_0 t \pm \dfrac{\alpha}{2} t^2$
$v = v_0 \pm at$	$\omega = \omega_0 \pm \alpha t$

NOTE: Use + sign for acceleration, − sign for deceleration.

Action of a Force or Moment on a Mass (Dynamics)

No resistance.   The force produces only acceleration or deceleration of the mass.

Linear motion	Rotary motion
$F = am = \dfrac{W}{g} a$	$M = \alpha J$
$v = v_0 \pm \dfrac{F}{m} t$	$\omega = \omega_0 \pm \dfrac{M}{J} t$
$S = v_0 t \pm \dfrac{F}{2m} t^2$	$\theta = \omega_0 t \pm \dfrac{M}{2J} t^2$
$E = FS$	$E = M\theta$
$E_K = \dfrac{m}{2} (v^2 - v_0^2)$	$E_K = \dfrac{J}{2} (\omega^2 - \omega_0^2)$
$E_K = \dfrac{m}{2} v^2$	$E_K = \dfrac{J}{2} \omega^2 = \dfrac{J\pi^2 N^2}{1,800}$

Example 1:   If a force equal to its weight $(F = W)$ acts on a free body, what will be its acceleration?

Answer: $a = \dfrac{F}{m} = \dfrac{W}{W/g} = g$

Example 2: If a retarding moment (torque) of 1,200 ft-lb is applied to a turbine rotor of $J = 300$ in.-lb-sec² rotating at 3,600 rpm, what is the time to standstill ($\omega = 0$)?

Answer: $t = (\omega_0 - \omega)\dfrac{J}{M} = \left(\dfrac{3,600\pi}{30} - 0\right)\dfrac{300}{1,200 \times 12} = 7.86$ sec

NOTE: Use + sign for acceleration, − sign for deceleration.

Constant resistance F_R, $M_R =$ const. The force overcomes the resistance, and the excess force results in acceleration.

Linear motion	Rotary motion
$F = am + F_R$	$M = \alpha J + M_R$
$v = v_0 \pm \dfrac{F - F_R}{m}\,t$	$\omega = \omega_0 \pm \dfrac{M - M_R}{J}$
$S = v_0 t \pm \dfrac{F - F_R}{2m}\,t^2$	$\theta = \omega_0 t \pm \dfrac{M - M_R}{2J}\,t^2$
$E = FS$	$E = M\theta$
$E_K = \dfrac{m}{2}\,v^2$	$E_K = \dfrac{J}{2}\,\omega^2 = \dfrac{J\pi^2 N^2}{1,800}$

Example: How far will a weight of 100 lb travel from standstill in 60 sec against a constant friction force of 25 lb, if it is pulled by a force of 40 lb (Fig. 4-1)?

Answer: $S = \dfrac{40 - 25}{2(100/32.16)} \times 60^2 = 8,680$ ft

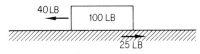

40 LB ← | 100 LB |

25 LB

Fig. 4-1

No excess force—no acceleration

Linear motion	Rotary motion
$v = v_0 = $ const	$\omega = \omega_0 = \dfrac{\pi N}{30} = $ const
$S = v_0 t$	$\theta = \omega_0 t = \dfrac{\pi N}{30}\,t$
$E = Fv_0 t$	$E = M\theta$
$E_K = \dfrac{m}{2}\,v_0^2$	$E_K = \dfrac{J}{2}\,\omega_0^2 = \dfrac{\pi^2}{1,800}JN^2$
$P = Fv_0$ (ft-lb/sec, in.-lb/sec)	$P = M\omega_0$ (ft-lb/sec, in.-lb/sec)
or $P = \dfrac{F(\text{lb})v_0(\text{fps})}{550}$ (hp)	$P = \dfrac{M(\text{in.-lb})N(\text{rpm})}{63,025}$ (hp)

Example 1: What is the torque at the coupling that the shaft of a 2,500-kw 1,200-rpm steam turbine must carry?

Answer: $M = 1.34 \times 2,500 \times \dfrac{63,025}{1,200} = 175,945$ in.-lb

Example 2: What is the power absorbed by a water brake rotating at 3,000 rpm and registering a moment of 5,040 in.-lb (Fig. 4-2)?

Answer: $P = \dfrac{5,040 \times 3,000}{63,025} = 240$ hp

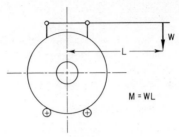

$M = WL$

Fig. 4-2

Viscous resistance. Dragging a body through water, oil, air, etc.

Linear motion	*Rotary motion*
$F_R = Cv^2$	$M_R = C'\omega^2$
$F = am + Cv^2$	$M = \alpha J + C'\omega^2$

Expressions for the calculation of velocities, displacements, and energy are beyond the scope of this section; however, the case of $M = 0$ (no external torque), $\omega_0 = \pi N_0/30$ is of special interest, because it can be used to determine the mechanical resistance of a rotating machine.

Rotary motion

$$C' = \frac{30J}{\pi T}\left(\frac{1}{N_T} - \frac{1}{N_0}\right) \qquad \text{in.-lb-sec}^2$$

$$M_R = \frac{\pi J N^2}{30T}\left(\frac{1}{N_T} - \frac{1}{N_0}\right) \qquad \text{in.-lb}$$

$$P_R = \frac{J N^3}{601,843T}\left(\frac{1}{N_T} - \frac{1}{N_0}\right) \qquad \text{hp}$$

where N_T is the speed in rpm after time T

Example: A turbine running at 7,200 rpm develops 3,000 hp. After power is shut off, the turbine slows down to 3,600 rpm in 6 min. What is the mechanical efficiency of the turbine-and-load combination? The WR^2 of turbine and connected load is 75,000 lb-in.^{2}.

Answer: $P_R = \dfrac{75,000/386 \times 7,200^3}{601,843 \times 6 \times 60}\left(\dfrac{1}{3,600} - \dfrac{1}{7,200}\right) = 46.5 \text{ hp}$

Mechanical efficiency $= \dfrac{3,000 - 46.5}{3,000} = 0.984$

Dynamic Forces and Moments
Gravitational attraction of masses

Magnitude

$$F = 3.44 \times 10^{-8}\,\frac{m_1 m_2}{r^2} \qquad \text{lb}$$

(m_1, m_2 are lb-sec^2/ft, r is ft)

Electrodynamic attraction of two parallel conductors

Magnitude

$$F = 4.50 \times 10^{-8}\,\frac{I_1 I_2}{r} \qquad \text{lb/ft}$$

(I_1, I_2 are amperes, r is ft)

Vertical impact $v = \sqrt{2gh}$; *the energy of the fall is completely converted into distortion of both bodies, and of the foundation K* (Fig. 4-3).

Magnitude (plastic impact, spring depressed initially)

$$F = W + W' + \sqrt{W^2 + \left(\frac{2W^2 Kh}{W + W'}\right)}$$

Magnitude (energy conserved, spring relaxed initially)

$$F = (W + W') + \sqrt{(W + W')^2 + 2WKh} \qquad \text{if } W' = 0$$
$$F = W + \sqrt{W^2 + 2WKh}$$

Horizontal impact; the energy of the impact is wholly absorbed by the elastic distortions of the impacting bodies (Fig. 4-4).

$$F = v \sqrt{\frac{W}{g} K}$$

Example: An automobile of 2,300 lb, traveling at 60 mph, strikes a guardrail; the elasticity of the guardrail is expressed by $K = 0.05 \times 10^6$ lb/in. What is the force F_a felt by the driver, who weighs 180 lb and is rigidly attached to the vehicle?

$$F = \frac{2,300}{32.16} a = \frac{60 \times 5,280}{3,600} \sqrt{\frac{2,300}{32.16} \times 0.05 \times 12 \times 10^6} = 577,600 \text{ lb}$$

$$F_a = \frac{180}{2,300} \times F = 45,160 \text{ lb}$$

Torsional impact

$$M = \frac{\pi N}{30} \sqrt{JK}$$

Example: A turbine running at 1,200 rpm seizes in a journal bearing and stops suddenly. The WR^2 of its rotor and connected load are 350,000 in.^{2}-lb. What is the shock torque in the shaft next to the failed bearing? $K = 15 \times 10^6$ in.-lb/rad.

Answer: $M = \dfrac{\pi \times 1,200}{30} \dfrac{350,000}{386} \times 15 \times 10^6 = 14,695,000$ in.-lb

Hydraulic impact of a flowing fluid (water, air, etc.) on a plate under an angle δ to the direction of flow (Fig. 4-5).

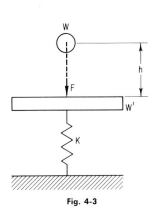

Fig. 4-3

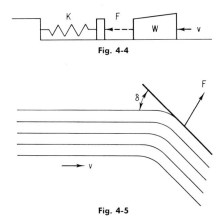

Fig. 4-4

Fig. 4-5

$$F = 2 \frac{w}{g} v \sin\left(\frac{\delta}{2}\right)$$

where w is the flow in lb/sec.

Sudden load (as a weight placed on a table, without drop; or sudden pressure increase)

$$F = 2(F_{\text{static}})$$

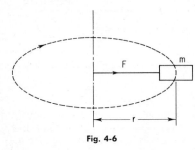

Example: A pump casing, which is filled with water, but not under pressure, is suddenly connected to a main at 2,400 psig. What is the instantaneous pressure rise that all parts of the casing must withstand?

Answer: $P = 2 \times 2,400 = 4,800$ psig

Centrifugal force of a mass rotating about an axis (Fig. 4-6)

Fig. 4-6

$$F = \frac{mv^2}{r} = \frac{W}{g} \times \frac{v^2}{r} = \frac{W}{g} r \left(\frac{\pi N}{30}\right)^2$$

where r is the distance from the axis to the center of gravity of m.

Example: A turbine disk has an unbalance of 1.5 oz at a radius of 14 in. What is the resulting unbalancing force on the shaft at 3,600 rpm?

Answer: $F = \dfrac{1.5}{16 \times 386} \times 14 \times \left(\dfrac{\pi \times 3,600}{30}\right)^2 = 483$ lb

Moments of Inertia of Bodies

Polar (mass) moment of inertia of a body about a given axis

$$J = r_1^2 m_1 + r_2^2 m_2 + r_3^2 m_3 + \cdots$$

For a (turbine-compressor-pump) rotor about its centerline,

$$J = \frac{1}{g} \sum W r^2$$

Definition of WR²

The expression WR^2 as used in industry for defining the moment of inertia of a symmetrical body about a given axis (turbine rotors, etc.) is the product of the rotor weight W in pounds times the polar radius of gyration squared, k_0^2, in feet squared.

For some simple bodies the radius of gyration and the corresponding WR^2 are given below:

	k_0, ft	WR^2, lb-ft²
Uniform disk . . .	$\dfrac{D_0}{24\sqrt{2}} \cong \dfrac{D_0}{34}$	$W\dfrac{D_0^2}{1,152}$
Ring	$\dfrac{\sqrt{D_0^2 + D_1^2}}{24\sqrt{2}} \cong \dfrac{\sqrt{D_0^2 + D_1^2}}{34}$	$W\dfrac{D_0^2 + D_1^2}{1,152}$
Solid cone	$\dfrac{D_0}{24\sqrt{10/3}} \cong \dfrac{D_0}{44}$	$W\dfrac{D_0^2}{1,920}$

where $D_0 = $ OD, in.
$\quad\quad D_1 = $ ID, in.

For a composite system, as, for instance, a motor-driven compressor connected through a speed-up gear, the equivalent WR^2 as referred to the motor shaft will be

$$WR^2_{\text{motor equivalent}} = WR^2_{\text{motor and gear wheel}} + \left(\frac{N_{\text{compressor}}}{N_{\text{motor}}}\right)^2 WR^2_{\text{compressor and pinion}}$$

Combining and Resolving Vectors (Statics of Solids)

Displacements, velocities, forces, and moments can be represented as vectors, that is, by a straight arrow in a specified direction and of a length equal to the scaled value of the magnitude it represents. Addition and subtraction of vectors may be handled either graphically or analytically, depending upon convenience.

The vector of a moment is perpendicular to the plane of the moment and is oriented so that the moment turns counterclockwise when sighting in the direction of the arrow. A moment vector may be moved parallel to itself without changing the system.

In this paragraph we shall deal only with vectors in the same plane.

Addition of two vectors through one point (Fig. 4-7)

$$\overline{(a+b)} = \sqrt{a^2 + b^2 + 2ab \cos \alpha}$$

$$\sin \beta = \frac{b \sin \alpha}{\sqrt{a^2 + b^2 + 2ab \cos \alpha}}$$

Example: What is the tangential friction force on a pinion of 20° tooth form when driving a rack with 3,500-lb pitch-line force (Fig. 4-8)? The friction coefficient = 0.05.

Answer: $F = 3,500 \cos 20° \times 0.05 = 164.5$ lb

Addition of several parallel forces acting on a mass (Fig. 4-9)

$$R = a + b - c + d + e$$

$$X_R = \frac{1}{R} (ax_a + bx_b - cx_c + dx_d + ex_e)$$

Resolution of a force into two forces through two given points and intersecting in a third point (Fig. 4-10)

Graphically: Construct a vector diagram by drawing lines through the end points of vector F and parallel to F_1 and F_2. The sides of the triangle yield the values of F_1 and F_2 to the same scale as the scale of F.

Example: A turbine casing of 24,000 lb is lifted by two chains 4 ft long from a crane hook; the chains are attached to two eyebolts which are 54 in. apart and one of which

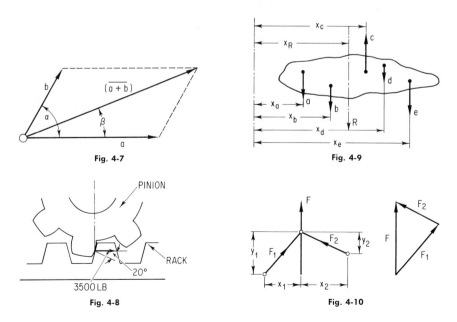

Fig. 4-7

Fig. 4-9

PINION

RACK

20°

3500 LB

Fig. 4-8

Fig. 4-10

is 11 in. higher from the horizontal joint than the other. What must be the rating of the chains, assuming that the center of gravity of the load is directly under C in Fig. 4-11?

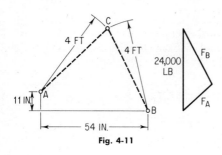

Fig. 4-11

Answer: The graphic approach is the most convenient.

1. Lay out the positions of eyebolts A and B to some scale.

2. To the same scale draw two circles 4 ft in diameter out of the eyebolts and intersect them; this fixes the position of crane hook C.

3. Draw the force polygon to a force scale so that the directions of the components are parallel to AC and BC.

4. Scale F_A and F_B. F_A scales 10,200 lb. F_B scales 18,500 lb. The rating of the chains should be at least 18,500 lb or more.

Hydrostatics

Force due to the weight of a column of liquid. Hydrostatic head (Fig. 4-12)

$$F = AH\gamma$$
$$p = \frac{F}{A} = H\gamma$$

Note that pressure depends only upon the height of the column of liquid and its density, but not upon its shape. Therefore, the head H is frequently used to express pressure.

Lateral pressure force (Fig. 4-13)

$$p = H\gamma$$

Hydrostatic pressure at a point is the same in all directions.

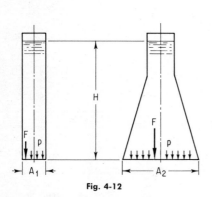

Fig. 4-12

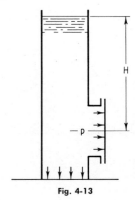

Fig. 4-13

Hydrodynamics

Hydrodynamic reaction (Fig. 4-14)

$$F_x = \frac{w}{g}\,(v_2 \sin \alpha_2 - v_1 \sin \alpha_1)$$

$$F_y = \frac{w}{g}\,(v_1 \cos \alpha_1 + v_2 \cos \alpha_2)$$

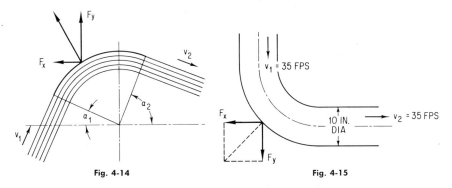

Fig. 4-14   **Fig. 4-15**

Example: What are the reactions along the two legs of a 10-in.-diameter 90° elbow through which water is flowing with a velocity of 35 fps (Fig. 4-15)?

$$w = \left(\frac{10}{12}\right)^2 \frac{\pi}{4} \times 35 \times 62.4 = 1,348 \qquad \text{lb/sec}$$

$$F_x = \frac{w}{g}\,(v_2 \sin 90° - v_1 \sin 0°) = \frac{w}{g}\, v_2$$

$$= \frac{1,348}{32.2} \times 35 = 1,470 \text{ lb}$$

$$F_y = \frac{w}{g}\,(v_1 \cos 0 + v_2 \cos 90°) = \frac{w}{g}\, v_1$$

$$= \frac{1,348}{32.2} \times 35 = 1,470 \text{ lb}$$

Forced vortex (fluid has same angular velocity as rotor) (Fig. 4-16)

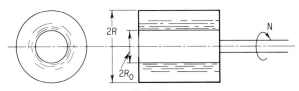

Fig. 4-16

Centrifugal pressure

$$p_R = \frac{\gamma}{2g}\left(\frac{\pi N}{30}\right)^2 (R^2 - R_0^2)$$

HEAT TRANSFER

Introduction and Definitions (Steady State, Unsteady State)

Heat transfer is an important engineering topic and has many industrial applications. Any problem involving objects of different temperatures may require heat-transfer analysis. Some of the basic concepts involved are:

Heat is energy which is transferred from a high-temperature region to a low-temperature region because of the temperature difference which is acting as the "driving force."

The three fundamental modes in which heat is transferred are conduction, convection, and radiation.

Conduction is heat transfer due to molecular action only, and involves no visible motion.   For gases, conduction takes place by elastic impact; for solid nonconductors, longitudinal movements take place; for metals, electronic movements.

Convection is heat transfer by means of mass motion of a fluid.   The laws of fluid dynamics govern convection, which involves transportation and exchange of heat due to mixing motion of different parts of a fluid.

Radiation is heat transfer due to electromagnetic waves (as in the case of sunshine). It is a part of optics in its geometry and dynamics.

We say that a high-temperature region giving off heat is a "heat source," and the cold region receiving heat is a "heat sink."

Heat energy is usually measured in "British thermal units," or Btu.   A Btu is the energy required to raise the temperature of 1 lb of water from 63 to 64°F.

Conduction

When heat flows from a region of higher temperature to a region of lower temperature within a medium (solid, liquid, or gaseous) or between different media in direct

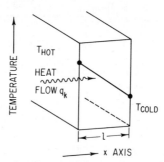

Fig. 4-17   Steady-state conduction through plain wall.

physical contact, then we talk about heat transfer by conduction.   The energy is transmitted by direct molecular communication without appreciable displacement of molecules.   (See Fig. 4-17.)

The basic equation for conduction is the Fourier law (1828), which can be stated for the one-dimensional case in the steady state as follows:

$$q_k = -kA \frac{dT}{dx}$$

where q_k = rate of heat flow, Btu/hr
k = thermal conductivity of material through which heat flows, Btu/(hr)(ft)(°F)
A = area of section through which heat flows by conduction, to be measured perpendicular to the direction of heat flow, sq ft

$-\dfrac{dT}{dx}$ = rate of change of temperature T with respect to distance x in the direction of heat flow.   The negative sign is due to our sign convention specifying that the direction of increasing distance x is to be the direction of positive heat flow.   Thus, the heat flows in the direction of decreasing temperature in accordance with the second law of thermodynamics.   (°F/ft)

This condition is satisfied when the gradient is taken negative.

Materials having a high thermal conductivity are called *conductors*, and those of low thermal conductivity are referred to as *insulators*.   The value of k varies somewhat with temperature, but in most engineering applications this variation can be neglected and a constant average value for k used.   In the case of composite structures the above simple analysis applies to each layer separately.   Taking in consideration the convection coefficient on both sidewalls, the various "heat resistances" can be treated analytically in the same fashion as electrical resistances.   This analogy has become a standard tool in solving the more complicated heat-transfer problems.

Some commonly used values of k are given in Table 4-1.

TABLE 4-1   Thermal Conductivity k of Insulating Materials
Values of k are to be regarded as rough average values for the temperature range indicated

Material	Bulk density, lb/cu ft	Temp, °F	k	Material	Bulk density, lb/cu ft	Temp, °F	k
Asbestos board, compressed				Sand, dry	94.8	68	0.188
asbestos and cement . . .	123	86	0.225	Sawdust, dry	13.4	68	0.042
Asbestos millboard	60.5	86	0.070	Soil, dry.	. . .	68	0.075
Asbestos wool	25	212	0.058	Soil, dry, including stones .	127	68	0.30
Concrete, sand, and gravel.	142	75	1.05	Snow.	7–31	32	0.34–1.3
Concrete, cinder.	97	75	0.41	Wool, pure	5.6	86	0.021
Cork, granulated.	5.4	23	0.028	Woods, ovendry, across			
Cotton wool.	5.0	100	0.035	grain:°			
Earth plus 42% water,				Douglas fir.	29	85	0.063
frozen	108	0	0.62	Fir, white.	26	85	0.069
Glass, pyrex.	139	200	0.59	Maple, sugar.	43	85	0.094
Gypsum board	51	99	0.062	Oak, red	42	85	0.099
Ice	57.5	. . .	1.26	Pine, southern yellow . .	35	85	0.078
Mica	122	. . .	0.25	Pine, white.	25	85	0.060
Rubber, hard	74.3	100	0.092	Redwood	25	85	0.062
Rubber, soft, vulcanized . .	68.6	86	0.08	Spruce	21	85	0.052

Thermal Conductivity k, Specific Heat c, Density ρ, and Thermal Diffusivity a of Metals and Alloys

Material	k, Btu/(hr)(ft)(°F)				c, Btu/(lb$_m$)(°F), 32°F	ρ, lb$_m$/cu ft, 32°F	a, sq ft/hr, 32°F
	32°F	212°F	572°F	932°F			
Metals:							
Aluminum	117	119	133	155	0.208	169	3.33
Copper, pure	224	218	212	207	0.091	558	4.42
Gold	169	170	. . .	. . .	0.030	1203	4.68
Iron, pure	35.8	36.6	. . .	. . .	0.104	491	0.70
Lead	20.1	19	18	. . .	0.030	705	0.95
Magnesium	91	92	. . .	. . .	0.232	109	3.60
Nickel	34.5	34	32	. . .	0.103	555	0.60
Silver.	242	238	. . .	. . .	0.056	655	6.6
Tin	36	34	. . .	. . .	0.054	456	1.46
Zinc.	65	64	59	. . .	0.091	446	1.60
Alloys:							
Admiralty metal.	65	64					
Brass, 70 Cu, 30 Zn. . . .	56	60	66	. . .	0.092	532	1.14
Bronze, 75 Cu, 25 Sn. . .	15	. . .	. . .	. . .	0.082	540	0.34
Cast iron:							
Plain	33	31.8	27.7	24.8	0.11	474	0.63
Alloy	30	28.3	27	. . .	0.10	455	0.66
Steel, mild 0.1% C	26.5	26	25	22	0.11	490	0.49
18–8 stainless steel:							
Type 304.	8.0	9.4	10.9	12.4	0.11	488	0.15
Type 347.	8.0	9.3	11.0	12.8	0.11	488	0.15

The thermal conductivity of different materials varies greatly.   For metals and alloys k is high, while for certain insulating materials, such as glass wool, cork, and kapok, it is very low.   In general, k varies with the temperature, but in the case of metals, the variation is relatively small.   With most other substances, k increases with rising temperatures, but in the case of many crystalline materials, the reverse is true.
° With heat flow parallel to the grain, k may be two to three times that with heat flow perpendicular to the grain.

The following equations are derived assuming 1 sq ft of wall using the simple Fourier law and the electrical analogy (see Fig. 4-18):

$$T_{hot} - T_{cold} = q(R_1 + R_2 + R_3 + R_4 + R_5)$$

or, generally,

$$q = \frac{T_{hot} - T_{cold}}{\sum\limits_{n=1}^{n=5} R_n}$$

where R_1 and R_5 represent the convection at the respective walls.

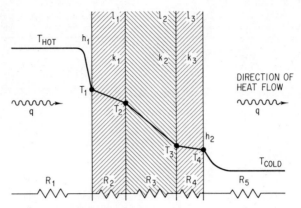

Fig. 4-18 Steady-state conduction through composite wall.

Thus the heat flow through five sections in series is equal to the overall temperature potential divided by the sum of the thermal resistances in the path of the heat flow. This analysis can also be applied to radial heat flow through concentric cylinders, such as the case of an insulated pipe with fluid flowing inside at a temperature lower or higher than that of the outside.

Convection (Free, Forced)

Convection is defined as the heat transfer between a surface and a fluid. The rate of heat transfer is determined by the relation, also called the "law of cooling," established by Newton (1701) as follows:

$$q_c = h_c A_s \, \Delta T$$

where q_c = time rate of heat transfer by convection, Btu/hr
$\quad h_c$ = average convective heat-transfer film coefficient or surface coefficient of heat transfer, Btu/(hr)(sq ft)(°F)
$\quad A_s$ = heat-transfer area, sq ft
$\quad \Delta T$ = temperature difference between surface and fluid at a location away from the boundary layer, °F

Convection is in itself a rather complex process. The coefficient h_c of a system depends on the geometry of the surface, the velocity of the fluid, the physical properties of the fluid, and the level and magnitude of the temperature difference ΔT. Because of the often wide variations in these parameters, one must distinguish between the local surface coefficient and the *average* surface coefficient, which is in most cases sufficient for engineering calculations and applications. The commonly used values of h_c are to be found in the references listed below.

Free convection is present when the mixing motion takes place merely as a result of density differences caused by existing temperature gradients. Under these conditions, the values for coefficient h_c are low and the actual heat-transfer rate is small.

Forced convection is obtained when the mixing motion is induced by some external agency, such as a pump or a blower. The rate of heat transfer can be increased very substantially in this manner. Most modern heat-transfer devices such as boilers, condensers, and cooling towers are based on forced convection.

Boundary layer in heat transfer by convection plays an important role. Basically two types are recognized: laminar and turbulent. In both cases the fluid particles in the vicinity of the surface are slowed down by virtue of viscous forces. Those adjacent to the surface stick to it and have zero velocity relative to the boundary. In laminar flow, the particle interaction, or viscous shear, takes place between molecules on a submicroscopic scale. In turbulent flow, an interaction between lumps of fluid on a macroscopic scale called turbulent shear is superimposed on this viscous shear. The fluid contained in the region of substantial velocity change is called the hydrodynamic boundary layer, the quality of which has a large influence on the energy-transport mechanism in both free and forced convections.

The effect of heat transfer on the velocity profiles in fully developed laminar flow can be seen in Fig. 4-19, where a is isothermal flow (constant temperature), b is heating of liquid or cooling of gas, and c is cooling of liquid or heating of gas.

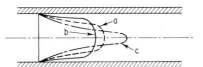

Extended surfaces are being used for increasing the rate of heat transfer or cooling. Generally, the problem is that of a solid fin of relatively small cross-sectional area protruding from a large body into a fluid of a different temperature.

Fig. 4-19 Effect of heat transfer on laminar velocity profile.

It can be successfully solved by means of one-dimensional analysis and a few simplifying assumptions. Extended surfaces are presently used in many different forms such as straight rectangular fins, tapered fins, and circumferential fins with various cross-sectional shapes. All the common configurations have been thoroughly analyzed, and accurate heat-transfer data are available in the literature.

Flow over tubes is perhaps the most common application for heat transfer by convection over exterior surfaces. The determination of the overall convective conductance between a bank of tubes and a fluid flowing at right angles to the tubes has been performed for various tube diameters, pitches in-line or stagger, ligaments, etc., and experimental results are available in the literature. These are of great importance in the design and performance analyses of many types of commercial heat exchangers. The rate of heat transfer in flow over tube bundles depends largely on the flow pattern and the degree of turbulence, which both in turn are functions of the fluid velocity and the size and arrangement of the tubes. In the transition zone between laminar- and turbulent-flow regions, the performance of a closely spaced, staggered tube arrangement is somewhat superior to that of a similar in-line arrangement.

Radiation

The quantity of energy leaving any surface as radiant heat depends upon the absolute temperature and the nature of the surface. This relation is governed by the Stefan-Boltzmann law (1884), which states that a perfect radiator (blackbody) emits radiant energy from its surface at the following rate:

$$q_r = \sigma A_1 T_1^4$$

where q_r = time rate of heat emitted by radiation, Btu/hr
A_1 = surface area, sq ft
T_1 = surface absolute temperature, °R
σ = the dimensional Stefan-Boltzmann constant
= 0.1714×10^{-8}, Btu/(hr)(sq ft)(°R^4)

Thus any blackbody surface above the temperature of absolute zero radiates at a rate proportional to the fourth power of its absolute temperature. The rate of emission is independent of conditions of the surroundings, and a net transfer of radiant heat requires a difference in surface temperature of any two bodies between which the exchange is taking place.

Real bodies do not meet the specifications of an ideal radiator but emit radiation at a lower rate than blackbodies. A gray body emits, at a temperature equal to that of a blackbody, a constant fraction of blackbody emission at each wavelength. The net rate of heat transfer from a gray body at a temperature T_1 to a black surrounding body at temperature T_2 is

$$q_r = \sigma A_1 \epsilon_1 (T_1^4 - T_2^4)$$

where ϵ_1 = emissivity of the gray surface, equal to the ratio of emission from the gray surface to the emission from a perfect radiator at the same temperature

Representative values of the normal total emissivity of various surfaces are given in Table 4-2.

TABLE 4-2 Total Emissivities for Various Surfaces

Surface	t, °F	Emissivity
Metals and Their Oxides		
Aluminum:		
Highly polished plate, 98.3% pure.	440–1070	0.039–0.057
Polished plate.	73	0.040
Rough plate	78	0.055
Oxidized at 1110°F	390–1110	0.11–0.19
Al-surfaced roofing	100	0.216
Calorized surfaces, heated at 1110°F:		
Copper.	390–1110	0.18–0.19
Steel	390–1110	0.52–0.57
Brass:		
Highly polished:		
73.2 Cu, 26.7 Zn	476–674	0.028–0.031
62.4 Cu, 36.8 Zn, 0.4 Pb, 0.3 Al	494–710	0.033–0.037
82.9 Cu, 17.0 Zn	530	0.030
Polished	100–600	0.096
Rolled plate, natural surface	72	0.06
Rolled plate, rubbed with coarse emery	72	0.20
Dull plate	120–660	0.22
Oxidized by heating at 1110°F	390–1110	0.61–0.59
Chromium (see nickel alloys for Ni-Cr steels)	100–1000	0.08–0.26
Copper:		
Carefully polished electrolytic	176	0.018
Plate, heated long time, covered with thick oxide layer	77	0.78
Plate heated at 1110°F	390–1110	0.57
Cuprous oxide.	1470–2010	0.66–0.54
Molten copper	1970–2330	0.16–0.13
Iron and steel:		
Metallic surfaces (or very thin oxide layer):		
Electrolytic iron, highly polished	350–440	0.052–0.064
Polished iron	800–1880	0.144–0.377
Oxidized surfaces:		
Iron plate, pickled, then rusted red.	68	0.612
Iron plate, pickled, then completely rusted	67	0.685
Rolled sheet steel	70	0.657
Oxidized iron.	212	0.736
Cast iron, oxidized at 1100°F.	390–1110	0.64–0.78
Steel, oxidized at 1100°F	390–1110	0.79
Smooth oxidized electrolytic iron	260–980	0.78–0.82
Iron oxide.	930–2190	0.85–0.89
Rough ingot iron.	1700–2040	0.87–0.95
Wrought iron, dull oxidized	70–680	0.94
Steel plate, rough	100–700	0.94–0.97
High-temp alloy steels (see nickel alloys)		
Molten metal:		
Cast iron.	2370–2550	0.29
Mild steel	2910–3270	0.28
Lead:		
Pure (99.96%), unoxidized.	260–440	0.057–0.075
Gray oxidized.	75	0.281
Oxidized at 390°F.	390	0.63
Molybdenum filament	1340–4700	0.096–0.292
Monel metal, oxidized at 1110°F	390–1110	0.41–0.46
Nickel:		
Electroplated on polished iron, then polished.	74	0.045
Technically pure (98.9 Ni + Mn), polished.	440–710	0.07–0.087

TABLE 4-2   Total Emissivities for Various Surfaces (Continued)

Surface	t, °F	Emissivity
Nickel (continued):		
Electroplated on pickled iron, not polished	68	0.11
Wire	368–1844	0.096–0.186
Plate, oxidized by heating at 1110°F.	390–1110	0.37–0.48
Nickel oxide.	1200–2290	0.59–0.86
Nickel alloys:		
Chromnickel.	125–1894	0.64–0.76
Nickelin (18–32 Ni, 55–68 Cu, 20 Zn), gray oxidized	70	0.262
Tin, bright tinned iron sheet	76	0.043 and 0.064
Tungsten:		
Filament, aged	80–6000	0.032–0.35
Filament.	6000	0.39
Zinc:		
Commercial, 99.1%, polished.	440–620	0.045–0.053
Oxidized by heating at 750°F	750	0.11
Galvanized sheet iron, fairly bright	82	0.228
Galvanized sheet iron, gray oxidized	75	0.276

Refractories, Building Materials, Paints, and Miscellaneous

Surface	t, °F	Emissivity
Asbestos:		
Board.	74	0.96
Paper.	100–700	0.93–0.945
Brick:		
Red, rough, but no gross irregularities	70	0.93
Silica, unglazed, rough	1832	0.80
Silica, glazed, rough	2012	0.85
Grog brick, glazed	2012	0.75
See also refractory materials		
Carbon:		
T carbon (Gebr. Siemens) 0.9% ash. This started with emissivity		
at 260°F of 0.72, but on heating changed to values given	260–1160	0.81–0.79
Carbon filament.	1900–2560	0.526
Enamel, white fused, on iron	66	0.897
Glass, smooth	72	0.937
Gypsum, 0.02 in. thick on smooth or blackened plate.	70	0.903
Marble, light gray, polished.	72	0.931
Oak, planed	70	0.895
Oil layers on polished nickel (lub. oil):		
Polished surface, alone	68	0.045
+0.001-in. oil	. . . . . .	0.27
+0.002-in. oil	. . . . . .	0.46
+0.005-in. oil	. . . . . .	0.72
∞ thick oil layer.	. . . . . .	0.82
Oil layers on aluminum foil (linseed oil):		
Aluminum foil.	212	0.087
+ 1 coat oil.	212	0.561
+ 2 coats oil	212	0.574
Paints, lacquers, varnishes:		
Snow-white enamel varnish on rough iron plate	73	0.906
Black shiny lacquer, sprayed on iron	76	0.875
Oil paints, 16 different, all colors	212	0.92–0.96
Aluminum paints and lacquers:		
10% Al, 22% lacquer body, on rough or smooth surface	212	0.52
Paper, thin:		
Pasted on tinned iron plate	66	0.924
Pasted on rough iron plate	66	0.929
Pasted on black lacquered plate	66	0.944

At thermal equilibrium the ratio of the emissive power of a surface to its absorptivity is the same for all bodies. This is Kirchhoff's law and can be written as follows:

$$\frac{W_1}{\alpha_1} = \frac{W_2}{\alpha_2} = \frac{W_x}{\alpha_x} \qquad (x \text{ is any body})$$

where $W_{1,2,\ldots,x}$ = total emissive power or energy per unit time per unit area of the surface emitted throughout the hemisphere above each element of the surface, Btu/(hr)(sq ft)

$\alpha_{1,2,\ldots,x}$ = absorptivity of the body, the fraction of incident radiation which is absorbed

The emissivities of metallic conductors are low and proportional to absolute temperature. The proportionality constant of different metals varies as the square root of electrical resistance at a standard base temperature.

The emissivities of nonconductors are much higher and generally decrease with increase in temperature. The emissivities for iron and steel vary widely with degree of oxidation and roughness. Clean metallic surfaces have an emissivity range of 0.05 to 0.45 at low temperatures and 0.40 to 0.70 at high temperatures, and oxidized and rough metallic surfaces have values of 0.60 to 0.95 at low temperatures and 0.90 to 0.95 at high temperatures.

The absorptivity α of a surface depends on the factors affecting emissivity but in addition also on the quality of the incident radiation, measured by its distribution in the spectrum.

Radiation from Gases, Vapors, and Flames Many of the common gases and gas mixtures such as oxygen, nitrogen, hydrogen, and dry air have symmetrical molecules and are practically transparent to thermal radiation. They neither emit nor absorb appreciable amounts of radiant energy at temperatures of practical interest. However, other gases such as H_2O, CO_2, SO_2, CO, and various hydrocarbons and alcohols exhibit quite a different behavior and are important in calculation of furnaces and heat exchangers of various kinds. Whereas solids radiate at all wavelengths over the entire spectrum, these gases emit and absorb radiation only between narrow regions of wavelengths or bands.

Generally, the intensity of gas radiation increases less rapidly with temperature than the intensity of blackbody radiation. The emission and absorption of radiant energy are essentially surface phenomena for a solid body, but for a body of gas its thickness, pressure, shape, and surface area must be considered in determining radiation emitted or absorbed by it. Tables have been worked out for pertinent data in various engineering applications such as heating of boilers and are available in the references listed.

If blackbody radiation passes through a gas body, for example, carbon monoxide (CO), then absorption occurs in certain bands of the infrared spectrum. If the gas body is then heated, it radiates in these same wavelength bands.

Radiation from a luminous flame can be analyzed with standard methods, but several factors make the results exceedingly uncertain. Such variable factors are changes in soot concentration, burner design, shape of combustion chamber, fuel-gas composition, and draft regulation. Valuable experimental information in this area can be found in recent literature.

Solar radiation through our atmosphere plays an important role in man's life, and nearly all sources of energy for heating and power generation have been derived from the sun. Present applications of solar radiation include, for example, heating homes and distilling seawater. Solar energy plays a great role in evaluation of heating and cooling requirements for aircraft, space capsules, and buildings. Solar radiation can, in general, be calculated with a good degree of accuracy, and specific information can be found in the literature.

Heat Exchangers

Transfer of heat from one fluid to another is accomplished by a heat exchanger, which is based on the three modes of heat transmission: conduction, convection, and radiation. A heat exchanger can be direct or indirect, fired or unfired, and is most commonly used for liquids and gases. The design of a heat exchanger requires considerable engineering skill. Three phases can be separated: thermal analysis, conceptual design, and final mechanical design for manufacture. With the purpose of achieving maximum economy, most manufacturers have standard lines of heat exchangers. This fact will, to some extent, limit the freedom for optimum design. Codes and standards for heat exchangers have been established by the American Society of Mechanical Engineers (ASME), the Tubular Exchanger Manufacturers Association (TEMA), and the Heat Exchanger Institute (HEI).

Shell-and-tube Heat Exchanger A simple example of a shell-and-tube heat exchanger is of the parallel-flow type. If they flow in opposite directions, it is of the counterflow As shown in Fig. 4-20, it could have both the tube-side fluid and the shell-side fluid, neither condensing nor evaporating. If one of the fluids condenses, the exchanger becomes a condenser or a heater, depending upon whether the primary purpose of the equipment is to condense the one fluid or to heat the other. Similarly, if one of the fluids evaporates, the equipment is designed either as an evaporator or as a cooler, depending upon whether the primary purpose is to evaporate the one fluid or to cool the other.

When both fluid streams traverse the exchanger only once, the arrangement is called a single-pass heat exchanger. If both fluids flow in the same direction, the exchanger is of the parallel-flow type. If they flow in opposite directions, it is of the counterflow type. If the two fluids flow along the heat-transfer surface at right angles to each other, the exchanger is of the cross-flow type. The temperature difference between the hot and cold fluid is, in general, not constant along the tube. The rate of heat transfer will vary from section to section, and therefore, to determine figures suitable for analysis, one must use an appropriate mean-temperature difference. The temperature distribution for a single-pass parallel-flow heat exchanger is shown in Fig. 4-20b and that for a single-pass counterflow exchanger in Fig. 4-20c.

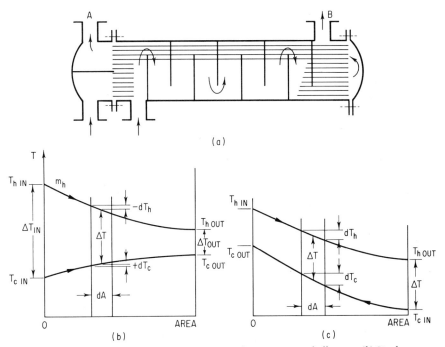

Fig. 4-20 Shell-and-tube heat exchanger. (a) Two tube passes, one shell pass. (b) Single pass, parallel flow. (c) Single pass, counterflow.

The rate of heat transfer in any of these types of heat exchanger must satisfy the following equation:

$$dq = U \, dA \, \Delta T$$

where dq = heat transferred from one fluid to another, Btu/hr
U = overall unit heat conductance, Btu/(hr)(sq ft)(°F)
dA = heat-transfer area, sq ft
ΔT = temperature difference across heat-transfer surface

This expression must be integrated over the total heat-transfer area A along the entire exchanger for the correct result. Making simplifying assumptions of U being constant and the exchanger being insulated, and neglecting the kinetic energy, the integration can be accomplished with relative ease. Striking the proper heat balances, it is possible to arrive at the following expression for the heat-transfer rate:

$$q = UA \, \frac{\Delta T_a - \Delta T_b}{\ln \, (\Delta T_a/\Delta T_b)}$$

where subscripts a and b refer to the two ends of the heat exchanger.

For engineering thermal analysis we define the average effective temperature difference $\Delta \bar{T}$ for the entire heat exchanger as follows:

$$q = UA \, \Delta \bar{T}$$

LMTD and Thermal Effectiveness Using this definition, thus, for a parallel- or counterflow heat exchanger:

$$\Delta \bar{T} = \frac{\Delta T_a - \Delta T_b}{\ln \, (\Delta T_a/\Delta T_b)} = \text{LMTD}$$

or the *logarithmic mean overall temperature difference*. The use of it in practice is only an approximation, because U is mostly not constant. Correction factors are available for the LMTD values according to the number of shell passes and tube passes.

Another characteristic of a heat exchanger is the *thermal effectiveness* ϵ, which is defined as the ratio of the actual rate of heat transfer in a given heat exchanger to the minimum possible rate of heat exchange. The latter would be obtained in a counterflow heat exchanger of infinite heat-transfer area. The effectiveness measures the actual heat-transfer rate vs. the maximum rate, limited only by the second law of thermodynamics. The effectiveness of a heat exchanger can be written as

$$\epsilon = \frac{C_c(T_{c \, \text{out}} - T_{c \, \text{in}})}{C_{\min}(T_{h \, \text{in}} - T_{c \, \text{in}})}$$

where $C_{\min}$ is the smaller of products $(m_h c_{ph})$ and $(m_c c_{pc})$ and C_c equals $m_c c_{pc}$ and where c_p is the specific heat at constant pressure, m is the mass flow, subscript c means cold, and subscript h means hot.

With the effectiveness known, the heat-transfer rate is obtained from the following:

$$q = \epsilon C_{\min}(T_{h \, \text{in}} - T_{c \, \text{in}})$$

The parameters in this equation are the effectiveness, the smaller hourly heat capacity, and the difference between the inlet temperatures. No outlet temperatures are used, and as such, this approach is often simpler to use than that using the LMTD. A large number of curves for various heat-exchanger types have been plotted, based on experimental data, and are available in the literature.

The LMTD is often tedious to compute because it involves the ratio of small differences in large quantities. Also, the effects of configurations other than pure counterflow or parallel flow cause correction factors that are very difficult to evaluate. Correction curves are also available for calculations with thermal effectiveness which can in certain cases be closely related to the LMTD.

Fouling The process of fouling occurs with usage of a heat exchanger, and in some applications this takes place rapidly. With most liquids and gases a dirt film gradually builds up on the heat-transfer surface. This deposit could be rust, boiler scale, silt, or some other particles that are attracted to the surface for one reason or another. The effect of fouling is to increase the thermal resistance. It is almost impossible to predict accurately the nature of the deposit or the time rate of fouling. Thus only a clean heat exchanger can be guaranteed as far as initial performance goes.

By sufficient testing of the deposit effects on heat-transfer rates, a fouling scale and fouling factor can be determined for each particular case. The TEMA has published normal fouling factors to be applied to specific cases of heat-exchanger installations.

References

1. W. H. McAdams, "Heat Transmission," 3d ed., McGraw-Hill Book Company, New York, 1954.
2. M. Jakob and G. A. Hawkins, "Elements of Heat Transfer," John Wiley & Sons, Inc., New York, 1957.
3. E. R. G. Eckert and R. M. Drake, "Heat and Mass Transfer," 2d ed., McGraw-Hill Book Company, New York, 1959.
4. F. Kreith, "Principles of Heat Transfer," 2d ed., International Textbook Company, Scranton, Pa., 1965.
5. D. Q. Kern, "Process Heat Transfer," McGraw-Hill Book Company, New York, 1950.
6. W. M. Kays and A. L. London, "Compact Heat Exchangers," 2d ed., McGraw-Hill Book Company, New York, 1964.
7. B. E. Lauer, "Heat Transfer Calculations, A Technical Manual," Oil and Gas Journal, Tulsa, Okla., 1953.
8. P. Buthod and B. W. Whiteley, "Heat Transfer, A Manual for Refinery Technologists and Operating Men," Oil and Gas Journal, Tulsa, Okla., 1944.

THERMODYNAMICS

General Energy Equation

The general energy equation for a fluid moving through a system represents the energy balance for a steady-state device. It ties together the various forms of energy and is based on the fact that mechanical work and heat are equivalent. Steady state means that the fluid going to and from the device is moving across any section continuously and at a constant rate. It is also assumed that thermal equilibrium exists and that there is no accumulation or diminution of energy within the device; in other words, the law of conservation of energy holds. All parts are at constant operating temperatures, and heat-transfer rates to and from are constant. One additional assumption is that there is no accumulation or diminution of fluid within the device; thus the law of the continuity of mass prevails.

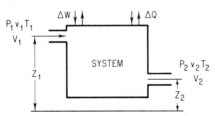

Fig. 4-21 General energy-system diagram. V = velocity, P = pressure, v = volume, T = temperature, Z = elevational energy, ΔW = work done on or by fluid, ΔQ = heat added or subtracted.

The general energy-system diagram for a steady-state machine that could be a boiler, engine, turbine, compressor, pump, nozzle, or throttle valve is shown in Fig. 4-21, and the general energy equation is written as follows:

$$Z_1 + \frac{\bar{V}_1^2}{2g_c} + P_1 v_1 + u_1 J = Z_2 + \frac{\bar{V}_2^2}{2g_c} + P_2 v_2 + u_2 J \pm \Delta W \pm \Delta Q J$$

Each term must be taken in a consistent system of units, and in engineering the Btu is mostly used. One pound of fluid is assumed. The various parts of the general energy equation are identified as follows:

Z = mechanical potential energy by virtue of elevation above a datum line (elevational energy)

$\dfrac{\bar{V}^2}{2g_c}$ = kinetic energy of fluid in approaching or leaving the device (g_c = conversion factor 32.2)

Pv = flow work energy due to motion of substance moving toward and away from the device

u = internal energy due to molecular activity in the fluid as measured above a convenient datum state

ΔW = work done on or by the fluid

ΔQ = transferred heat, added or abstracted

J = energy conversion factor, 778.16 ft-lb/Btu

Subscripts 1 and 2 refer to entering (or initial) and leaving (or final) conditions.

In most heat engines the change in potential energy from Z_1 to Z_2 is negligible because of the small difference in elevations of inlet and exit openings. The magnitudes of kinetic energy and the flow work are independent of the nature of the working fluid and the process involved. However, the internal-energy change depends on the nature of the substance, and the transferred heat and work depend as well upon the kind of process which the substance is undergoing.

According to sign convention used, W and Q, as solved in the equation, obey the following:

Positive W means net work is done by the fluid.

Negative W means net work is done on the fluid.

Positive Q means net heat is added to the fluid.

Negative Q means net heat is abstracted from the fluid.

This equation may also be applied to reciprocating engines, even though admission of the working fluid is intermittent and not steady.

The energy Q represents heat passing into or out of the fluid. It is not a quantity that exists by virture of a property or characteristic state of the fluid such as velocity, pressure, or volume. Transferred heat is energy in transition as opposed to stored energy. In a similar sense, work is energy in transition. It may occur because of a change in stored energy, but it is not inherent in the fluid.

Laws of Thermodynamics

First Law of Thermodynamics This is the law of conservation of energy that states that energy can be neither created nor destroyed. In equation form it can be written as follows:

$$\Delta E = Q - W + \sum_i (h_i + e_{xi}) m_i$$

where ΔE = change in energy content of system

Q = heat transferred to system

W = work transferred from system

h_i = enthalpy

e_{xi} = extrinsic energy, dependent on frame of reference

m_i = mass

The summation term represents energy convected into or out of the system by mass m_i. For a fluid system, e_{xi} = kinetic energy + potential energy = $V^2/2g_c + Z$, where V is fluid velocity and Z potential energy due to elevation.

This equation applies equally well to processes and cycles, steady and transient flow situations. In such cases where changes in kinetic energy and elevation of fluid stream can be neglected, the above equation reduces to the simple form

$$W \cong m(h_{in} - h_{out})$$

Thus work from a system approximately equals the decrease in enthalpy. This holds for the steady-state adiabatic expansion in a turbine, for example.

Second Law of Thermodynamics This law states that it is impossible to bring about any change or series of changes resulting in transfer of energy as heat from a low to a high temperature. In other words, heat will not by itself flow from low to high temperatures. It is advantageous, especially for direct quantitative-loss analysis in processes and systems, to express this law in the form of an equation as follows:

$$\Delta S = \frac{Q}{T} + I + \sum_i S_i$$

where ΔS = change in entropy of system

$\dfrac{Q}{T} = \sum_i \dfrac{Q_i}{T_i}$ = sum of heat transferred over system boundaries Q_i

T_i = local temperature at boundary

I = irreversibility (≥ 0); for a reversible process or cycle $I = 0$, for an irreversible $I > 0$

$\sum_i S_i$ = entropy flow into and out of system with mass flow m_i

For example, a steady-flow adiabatic expansion through a turbine would reduce the above equation to the following form:

$$I = - \sum_i m_i S_i = -m(S_{in} - S_{out})$$

$$= m(S_{out} - S_{in})$$

The second law in the above equation form can be used for qualitative examination of all power-plant processes regardless of the fluids used or the specific cycles employed.

Gas Laws of Thermodynamics These laws represent fundamental rules for the behavior of gases. The imaginary ideal or perfect gas is defined as having the desired properties to obey the gas laws exactly and to change from one state to another in a reversible fashion. This means that both the system and the surroundings may be returned to their original states. No actual gas conforms exactly to the ideal concept, but many gases such as air, oxygen, and nitrogen can, for engineering purposes, be considered as perfect gases. Gas laws of thermodynamics are discussed in Sec. 6 under Centrifugal and Axial Compressors.

Basic Heat-engine Cycles—Steam

General The essential elements for a thermodynamic cycle are (1) a working fluid or substance for receiving and rejecting heat and to do work, (2) a source of heat by means of which heat can be added to the working fluid, (3) a heat sink to which heat can be rejected by the working fluid, and (4) the engine itself. During every cycle operating in a steady state, the working substance goes through the same series of events or processes and always returns to its initial condition, which may be chosen at any point of the cycle.

Thermal efficiency of a cycle, in its simplest form as shown in Fig. 4-22, is the output divided by the input. In the case of a power cycle, the output is represented by the produced power or net work; the input consists of heat added to the working substance from an external source of heat. The thermal efficiency can be written as follows:

$$\eta = \frac{W}{Q_A} = \frac{Q_A - Q_R}{Q_A} = \frac{\Sigma Q}{Q_A}$$

where W = net work, $W_{out} - W_{in}$

Q_A = heat added from external source

Q_R = heat rejected by the cycle

If the cycle is performed entirely within an engine, the above thermal efficiency represents that of the engine itself.

For any heat engine utilizing steam as a fluid, the Mollier enthalpy-entropy diagram is useful in following the changes in state (see Fig. 5-1 in Sec. 5).

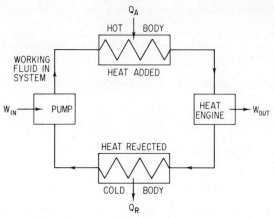

Fig. 4-22 Simple power cycle.

The Carnot Cycle The three important contributions by Frenchman Sadi Carnot (1824) were the concept of reversibility, the concept of the cycle, and the definition of a heat engine producing maximum work when operating cyclically between two fixed reservoirs at given temperatures. The knowledge of the ideal cycle in each application is useful and often essential in judging the performance of the actual cycle.

The components of the Carnot cycle are two isothermal and two isentropic processes as shown in Fig. 4-23. The TS diagram of a Carnot cycle for an ideal gas is shown together with the pv diagram. Both a nonflow and a flow device can be considered.

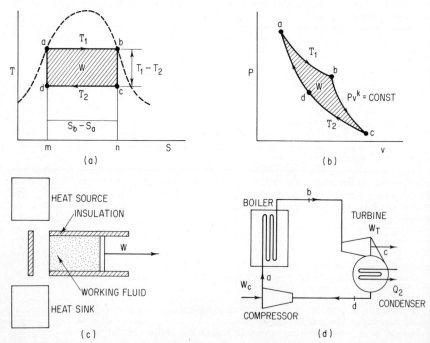

Fig. 4-23 The Carnot cycle. (*a*) TS diagram. (*b*) pv diagram, ideal gas. (*c*) Nonflow system. (*d*) Flow system.

It can be shown that work derived from this cycle is represented by the enclosed area in the TS plane.   The thermal efficiency is

$$\eta = \frac{T_1 - T_2}{T_1}$$

In practice the Carnot cycle faces irreversibilities in the form of finite temperature differences during heat-transfer processes and fluid friction during work-transfer processes.   Also, a two-phase compression causes difficulties in many applications. In overcoming these difficulties and others, the cost of the needed equipment increases rapidly, and therefore, other cycles provide a far more practical approach as shown in the following.

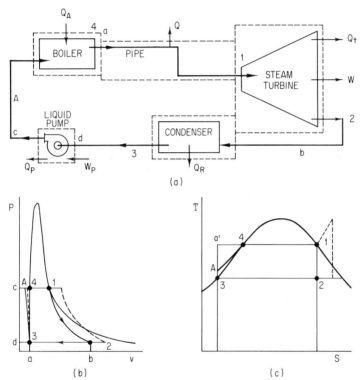

Fig. 4-24   The Rankine cycle.   (a) Rankine steam-power-plant cycle. Q_A = added heat, Q_R = rejected heat.   (b) pv diagram.   (c) TS diagram.

The Rankine Cycle   Rankine (1859) established a sound thermodynamic basis for steam-power-plant practice by replacing the Carnot two-phase compression with a simple liquid pump.   This closely reproduced the actual case where the condensation process, inherent in the heat rejection, continues until the saturated-liquid state is reached.   The Rankine steam-power-plant cycle and corresponding state changes are shown in Fig. 4-24.   The volumes of liquid and the temperature rise are indicated in the diagrams.

The loss of cycle work due to irreversible heating of the compressed liquid from state a to saturated liquid can be identified in the Rankine cycle.   The lower pressure of state a as compared with a' makes possible a much smaller work of compression between d and a.   In actual cases this amounts to perhaps 1 percent of turbine output. The Rankine cycle then follows the line 1-2-3-A-4-1.   The dashed line is used in case of superheated steam

The Rankine modification as compared with the Carnot cycle eliminates the two-phase vapor-compression process, reduces compression work to a negligible amount, and makes the Rankine cycle less sensitive than the Carnot cycle to the irreversibilities bound to occur in the actual steam power plant. Because of the above reasons, the Rankine cycle has a larger net work output per unit mass of fluid circulated than the Carnot cycle. Also, it requires smaller-size and lower-cost equipment and has operating-plant thermal efficiencies exceeding those of the Carnot cycle.

The *regenerative* version of the Rankine cycle is a recent modification aimed at increased thermal efficiency of the basic cycle. The working vapor is reheated after partial expansion, followed by continued expansion to the final sink temperature. In the regenerative cycle the heat is transferred from one part of the cycle to another in order to eliminate or reduce external irreversibilities. The number of extraction steam heaters varies from 2 to 10 according to size and design of the power plant. The temperatures of these heat sources are always slightly above those of the compressed liquid being heated. The regenerative Rankine cycle is shown in Fig. 4-25.

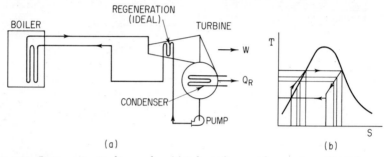

Fig. 4-25   Regenerative Rankine cycle.   (*a*) Reheat after partial expansion.   (*b*) *TS* diagram.

Using *reheat*, the Rankine-cycle thermal efficiency can be still further improved and the moisture content reduced to more acceptable levels in the last several stages of the turbine. Erosion damage by water droplets to rotating blading is limited by this means. Reheating is done by interrupting the expansion process and removing the vapor for reheat on the outside at constant pressure. It is thereafter returned for continued expansion down to condenser pressure. Reheating can be done in a special section of the boiler, in a separately fired heat exchanger, or even in a steam-to-steam heat exchanger. In a large power plant reheat permits an improvement of some 5 percentage points in thermal efficiency. It also substantially reduces the heat rejected to the condenser cooling water. Normally only one stage, or a maximum of two stages of reheat is encountered in large power-plant installations.

The *supercritical-pressure* steam-power cycle has been made possible by advances in metallurgy. Optimum cycle economy is obtained at a steam temperature of 1200°F and pressure of 5,000 psia. Both the regenerative cycle and reheat cycle are effectively used for maximum thermal efficiency, which lately has reached values better than 40 percent. The supercritical cycle puts very severe demands on all cycle components but perhaps most on the boiler-feed pump, which must pump the heated water against extremely high heads. To do this successfully requires very special design features and experience with high-pressure water pumps with shaft input of up to 40,000 shp and more.

Many modifications to the original supercritical-pressure steam-power cycle have appeared recently, and changes are expected to continue in the future when more actual experience in these power plants has been gained.

In the *back-pressure* power cycle steam is admitted into a turbine at a suitable initial pressure and emerges from there usually in a superheated state. A desuperheater, including a pressure water spray, is used for constant-temperature control. This can be achieved automatically. Saturated steam then enters the heater and is completely

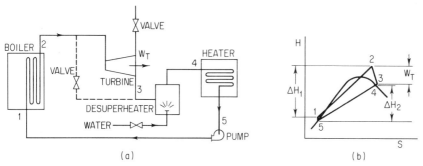

Fig. 4-26 Back-pressure steam-power cycle. (*a*) Flow diagram. (*b*) HS diagram.

condensed. The steam demands for power, process work, or heating can vary widely, and controls of pressure must be included in the cycle. Also, additional fresh steam can be supplied to the desuperheater when needed. In some versions the heating is done by hot water under high pressure, which is supplied by steam contained in an expansion drum.

The basic back-pressure steam-power cycle is shown in Fig. 4-26.

The Nuclear Cycle Most of the principles used in nuclear cycles are those also used in connection with the conventional steam power plant, but there are major differences in their application. For example, there is relative freedom in the selection of initial steam pressure for a conventional boiler plant but not so in the case of a nuclear plant. Any type of nuclear reactor represents, on the one hand, a remarkable concentration of heat output which, on the other hand, must be suppressed in temperature because of the several limitations imposed by materials of construction. The method of heat transfer from reactor to steam plant is therefore the foremost problem.

The *gas-cooled* nuclear plant uses a single-pressure or dual-pressure steam cycle as shown in Figs. 4-27 and 4-28. In the first, steam evaporation takes place at constant pressure, for example, 340 psia, to the saturation line at a temperature of 429°F and is then superheated to 30°F below the temperature of the gas cooling the reactor. This state is called the pinch point and is most important for operation of the power plant. If the feedwater is preheated, less added heat is required and the pinch point occurs at a lower gas temperature. Also, the saturation temperature is lower and so is the steam pressure. Various curves can be plotted for the steam-cycle temperatures and pressures which permit estimates of efficiencies and costs.

The dual-pressure steam cycle is essentially a high-pressure boiler in series with a low-pressure boiler. The high-pressure steam enters the turbine steam path at the

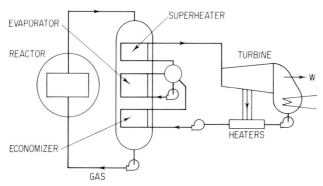

Fig. 4-27 Single-pressure nuclear steam cycle (gas-cooled).

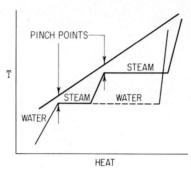

Fig. 4-28   Dual-pressure temperature-heat diagram.

beginning; the low-pressure steam at a point farther down in the expansion.   The temperature of the gas leaving the HP boiler can be much higher than could be tolerated on the grounds of blower power requirements.   The LP boiler is now given the task of cooling the gas to the required blower temperature.   Therefore, substantial amounts of steam can be produced at four to five times the pressure otherwise obtainable. There are now two pinch points apart from those at the outlets of the superheaters. There are, again, definite relationships between the gas temperatures, the temperature approaches, the feed temperature, and the obtainable steam pressures.   Also, there is a relation between these parameters and the relative proportions of HP and LP steam.   The advantage of the dual-pressure steam cycle is likely to decrease in the future when the simple single-pressure cycle attains increasingly higher steam pressures.

As was the case with conventional power plants, reheating is beneficially used in the nuclear steam cycles.   Steam is generated in the heat exchanger at a single pressure, expanded in part of the turbine, returned to the heat exchanger, resuperheated, and then expanded in the remainder of the turbine, as shown in Fig. 4-29.   The optimum reheat pressure is about one-fourth of the initial steam pressure.   A tolerable moisture content at turbine exhaust is taken at 13 percent.   The steam pressure obtainable in the reheat cycle, for any given inlet- and outlet-gas temperatures, is lower than it is in the nonreheat cycle.   This and the pressure losses in pipes between turbine and reheater are two reasons why expected advantages from application of reheat to the nuclear cycle do not fully materialize.   Adopting the supercritical-pressure concept and utilizing the once-through boiler having no steam drum, further improvements to the nuclear cycle are to be expected, and overall net thermal efficiencies of 40 percent and beyond can be contemplated.

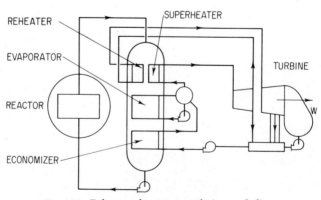

Fig. 4-29   Reheat nuclear steam cycle (gas-cooled).

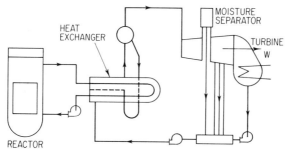

Fig. 4-30   Pressurized-water-cooled nuclear steam cycle.

The *water-cooled* water-monitored nuclear power plant is becoming popular because of the comparatively high density and good heat-transfer properties of the coolant, making heat removal from the reactor core relatively simple.   Coolant circulators are used to raise the mean temperature of the coolant.   However, available temperatures are limited by the pressure-temperature characteristics of saturated water.   A margin is needed to suppress any tendency for boiling in the reactor core.

In the pressurized-water reactor, cycle water is circulated through the reactor under high pressure and then through one or several heat exchangers which produce saturated steam.   Moisture extraction and separation are used along the turbine steam path to control wetness of the steam at turbine exhaust.   The amount of coolant circulating through the reactor is selected as high as possible for attaining highest mean coolant temperature, leading to highest-quality steam being produced by the heat exchangers. The pressurized-water reactor steam cycle is shown in Fig. 4-30.

Separate superheating using fossil fuels can be added to the above cycle, thus eliminating the difficulties caused by wetness of the steam and improving the net output of the cycle by about 45 percent.   When the attainable steam temperatures in nuclear power plants become higher, as they already have done in gas-cooled reactors, the attraction of separate superheating diminishes.

The boiling-water reactor allows steam to form in the reactor core itself.   The steam-water mixture is then separated within the reactor or in separate steam-water drums. The saturated steam goes directly to the turbine, as shown in Fig. 4-31.   Steam pressures as high as 6,000 psia are used, and relatively good cycle efficiencies of 36 percent and above can be obtained.   The level of auxiliary power consumption, including the feed pump, becomes increasingly larger at the higher pressures and may well limit the selection of pressure level for the cycle.

The dual-pressure concept can be combined with the boiling-water cycle to com-

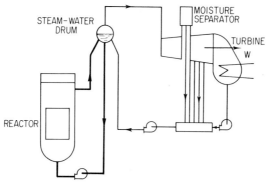

Fig. 4-31   Boiling-water-cooled nuclear steam cycle.

bat the voidage in the reactor core. Coolant temperature at the inlet to the reactor is lower after passing through a heat exchanger of the pressurized-water reactor type. In this system low-pressure steam is generated and taken to the turbine at an appropriate point of its steam path.

The *liquid-metal-cooled* reactor presents difficulties in heat transfer because of the violent reaction between suitable metals, such as molten sodium and potassium, and water. Any possible leakage must be eliminated; therefore, barrier liquids such as mercury are used, and the cycle becomes complicated.

The above brief review of the various steam cycles for nuclear-power-plant application shows the various possibilities available for the designer. It can be said that the nuclear steam cycle, as such, is here to stay, and only drastic improvements in attainable coolant temperatures from the nuclear reactor, based on some new technology, can change the status of steam as the basic fluid in the nuclear power cycle. However, recently, closed gas turbine–nuclear reactor cycles, with helium as working medium, have shown promise in the solution of heat-transfer–power problems without the use of water or steam.

Basic Heat-engine Cycles—Combustion

Internal Combustion—Reciprocating Principle

In the internal-combustion type of heat engine the working fluid consists of the products of combustion of the fuel-air mixture itself. The two main advantages of the reciprocating internal-combustion engine are (1) the absence of heat exchangers in the working fluid stream, leading to simplicity of the engine; and (2) that all its parts can work at temperatures well below the maximum cyclic temperature, which fact allows very high cyclic temperatures to be used, leading to high cyclic efficiencies. A third advantage is the low weight per horsepower ratio, which allows suitable applications where no other engine system can compete.

The automotive engine represents a common highly developed internal-combustion engine based on the reciprocating principle. The basis of its operation is the indicated pv diagram composed of an expansion and a compression of the working fluid, as shown in Fig. 4-32. Based on the diagram, the mean effective pressure (MEP) and induced horsepower (IHP) can be determined. The common processes of the cycle can be reviewed as follows:

Adiabatic process, one in which no heat is transferred

Isentropic process, one of constant entropy

Polytropic process, one internally reversible which conforms to the relation $pv = $ const or $p_1 v_1^n = p_2 v_2^n$ where n is the polytropic exponent, which in practice has a value near to k, the specific heat ratio c_p/c_v.

Work can be expressed for all three processes with suitable formulas.

Internal-combustion engines fall basically into two classifications: the spark-ignition (SI) engine and the compression-ignition (CI) engine. The former represents lightweight and higher-rpm applications, the latter heavier and slow-speed applications. As the name indicates, the basic difference is in method of igniting the compressed combustile fuel-air mixture. The thermodynamic cycles applicable are as follows:

The *Otto cycle* (1876) represents the ideal spark-ignition condition, where the combustion process takes place instantaneously at top dead center to give a constant-volume combustion of the fuel. This ideal cycle is shown in Fig. 4-33. Based on this principle, the reciprocating engine can have a four-stroke cycle (suction, compression, expansion of power, and exhaust) or a two-stroke cycle (scavenging by blowing air into cylinder).

The actual cycle in a SI engine differs from the ideal fuel-air cycle because of leakage, incomplete combustion, progressive burning, time and heat losses, and exhaust losses due to opening the exhaust valve before bottom dead center.

The *Diesel cycle* by Rudolf Diesel (1893) was originally developed to operate on coal as fuel. The present four-stroke-cycle diesel engine takes in only air during the suction stroke, and the liquid fuel is injected at the end of the compression stroke. Injection continues at such a rate that burning proceeds at constant pressure. The ideal diesel cycle is shown in Fig. 4-34. The diesel engine can also be built on the two-cycle principle, and many of the low-speed marine diesel engines are of this variety.

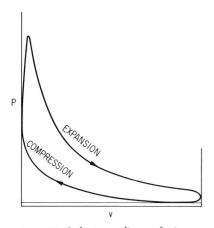

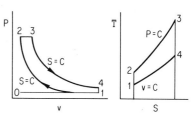

Fig. 4-34   Diesel cycle—ideal.

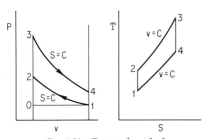

Fig. 4-32   Indicator pv diagram for ice.

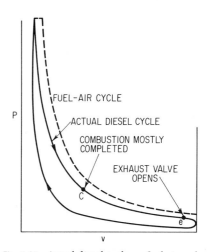

Fig. 4-33   Otto cycle—ideal.

Fig. 4-35   Actual diesel cycle vs. fuel-air cycle.

The actual diesel cycle differs from the ideal because (1) there is always a delay period between the start of injection and the appearance of a flame or measurable pressure rise due to combustion, (2) most of the fuel tends to burn during the period of the very rapid rise in pressure, (3) the rise is followed by relatively slow combustion during the expansion stroke as the remaining unburned fuel finds the necessary oxygen, and (4) the crank angles for these three periods vary with design and operating conditions.

At any given engine rpm the crank angles are subject to a certain amount of control by means of injection timing, fuel-spray characteristics, and fuel composition. The actual diesel (compression-ignition) cycle differs from the ideal fuel-air cycle because of leakage, heat losses, time losses, and exhaust losses, as shown in Fig. 4-35.

The *Brayton cycle* was originally invented for a reciprocating engine (1906), but the cycle today is mainly applied to gas-turbine installations.   The ideal Brayton cycle is shown in Fig. 4-36.   A Carnot cycle operating through the same temperature limits

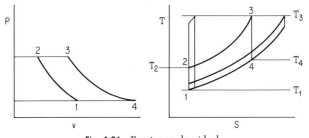

Fig. 4-36   Brayton cycle—ideal.

T_3 and T_1 has a greater efficiency $(T_3 - T_1)/T_3$. The thermal efficiency for the Brayton cycle is $(T_3 - T_4)/T_3$. It increases as T_2 increases and as T_4 decreases.

The efficiency of an actual Brayton cycle is the actual net work delivered, divided by the actual energy chargeable against the cycle. In the case of a gas-turbine application, each of the three or more pieces of equipment must be evaluated separately for maximum efficiency. The fluid friction takes an increasingly significant part in such a cycle. The actual Brayton-cycle gas-turbine diagram with its four parts is shown in Fig. 4-37. Using entropies for the various state points, the separate irreversible-loss effects of the cycle can be conveniently evaluated and examined independently with superposition of loss to determine the overall effect on the actual cycle.

Other gas-turbine cycles and turbochargers are discussed in Sec. 5 under Gas Turbines, Turbochargers, and Expanders.

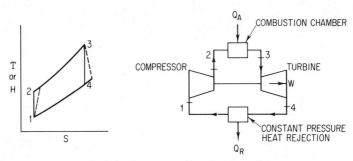

Fig. 4-37   Basic gas-turbine Brayton cycle.

Measuring Engine Performance

The heat-engine performance is measured after a steady-state condition has been reached, and the *heat balance* constitutes an important tool in this procedure. It is a tabulation based on test results obtained and includes all pertinent thermodynamic parameters. Basically, the heat supplied to the system in one form or other must equal the heat being taken away. For mechanical work the Joule equivalent should be used. The conventional dimension in heat-balance investigations is Btu per pound mass of fluid.

The heat-balance tabulation itemizes each energy transfer. The heat drops, both adiabatic and estimated, for the various losses are enumerated. Experimental results as well as previous tests and theoretical calculations are made available for loss calculations. When the energy tabulation has been completed, the efficiency of the heat engine can be obtained by a simple division. Also, other parameters such as heat rate and specific fuel consumption are then available from heat-balance data compiled similarly by simple mathematical means.

For *reciprocating engines* special measures must be made to obtain a yardstick for their performance. The indicator card is the most important measuring device and represents a picture record of the variation of pressure and volume of the working substance in a cylinder as the piston reciprocates. The record obtained by an indicator gives the indicated MEP (mean effective pressure) for the engine. The indicated horsepower can then be calculated. Based on this information, a heat balance can be set up for any reciprocating heat engine. As measured on a dynamometer, the brake or shaft horsepower can be determined and brake mean pressure calculated. The mechanical efficiency is defined as the ratio of brake horsepower over indicated horsepower.

For *gas turbines* the setting up of a heat balance is difficult and hinges on accurate measurements in various locations of the open or closed loop. Many of the temperatures are highly elevated and, because of high fluid velocities, difficult to measure accurately. Also, factors such as combustion efficiency can often be only roughly estimated.

The two most important performance parameters for gas turbines are the SFC (specific fuel consumption) and thermodynamic efficiency. In addition, such parameters as engine weight per horsepower or space occupied per horsepower are important, depending on the particular application.

References

1. J. H. Keenan, "Thermodynamics," John Wiley & Sons, Inc., New York, 1941.
2. V. M. Faires, "Thermodynamics," 4th ed., The Macmillan Company, New York, 1962.
3. J. B. Jones and G. A. Hawkins, "Engineering Thermodynamics," John Wiley & Sons, Inc., New York, 1960.
4. J. S. Doolittle and A. H. Zerban, "Engineering Thermodynamics," 3d ed., International Textbook Company, Scranton, Pa., 1964.
5. J. F. Lee and F. W. Sears, "Thermodynamics," 2d ed., Addison-Wesley Publishing Company, Inc., Reading, Mass., 1963.
6. J. W. Sawyer, "Gas Turbine Engineering Handbook," Gas Turbine Publications, Inc., Stamford, Conn., 1966.
7. C. F. Taylor, "The Internal Combustion Engine in Theory and Practice," 2d ed., The M.I.T. Press, Cambridge, Mass., 1966.

FLUID MECHANICS

Introduction

This section deals with selected topics in the field of fluid dynamics. The descriptions have been kept simple.

A system of measurements based on the pound force as a fundamental unit has been used in order to conform with the section on mechanics.

Other topics of fluid mechanics have been treated in other sections. Such topics are hydrostatics, hydrodynamics, and pipe friction. The various fields are related to each other. It is interesting to note that Bernoulli's simple theorem has evolved into the general energy equation of thermodynamics, of which Bernoulli's theorem is now a special case.

It may also be interesting to discover that the thrust of a jet engine or a rocket motor leads back to the same formula as the axial force on a section of reducing pipe.

Bernoulli's Theorem

The theorem of Daniel Bernoulli (1738) is a most important law of fluid dynamics for many engineering applications. In its original form, the law expresses the conservation of mechanical energy in an ideal (frictionless, nonviscous) and incompressible fluid in steady motion. Mechanical energy appears as kinetic energy, pressure energy, and potential energy or energy of elevation. These are interchangeable, and their sum must remain constant.

Bernoulli's theorem is applicable to fluid-flow problems where changes of energy other than mechanical are considered to be negligible. This includes many problems in liquid flow and low-speed aerodynamics.

Consider the motion of a small particle in a flowing ideal fluid. It generally follows a three-dimensional curve called a streamline. If the shape of the streamlines and the velocity at any point do not change with time, the fluid is in steady motion.

Consider the motion of a somewhat larger particle of a fluid in steady motion. Its boundary is a surface of streamlines called a stream tube. No fluid crosses the surface and no mechanical work is exchanged with an adjacent stream tube.

Consider the stream tube to be sufficiently thin so that constant conditions prevail over any cross section. Generally, the area, the fluid velocity, the pressure, and the elevation will change from cross section to cross section. Such a stream tube between area 1 and area 2 is shown in Fig. 4-38.

The flow in the stream tube is constant. The same amount of fluid enters through

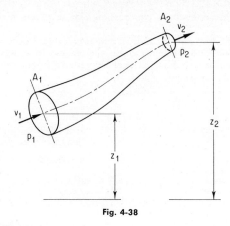

Fig. 4-38

area 1 as leaves through area 2 in any time interval, which may be expressed by the following continuity equation:

$$w = A_1 v_1 \gamma_1 = A_2 v_2 \gamma_2$$

where w = weight flow, lb/sec
A = cross-sectional area, sq ft
v = velocity, fps
γ = specific weight, lb/cu ft
p = pressure, psf
Av = volume flow, cfs

If the specific weight remains constant, the velocity is inversely proportional to the area. This condition is approximately met by the flow of a liquid through a pipe, the pipe being represented by a stream tube.

Bernoulli's theorem expresses that, for any point along a stream tube as described above, the total mechanical energy or the sum of the mechanical-energy components must remain constant. This may be written as the following equation:

$$\frac{Wv^2}{2g} + \frac{Wp}{\gamma} + Wz = \text{const} \qquad \text{(see note below)}$$

where W = fluid weight, lb
$\dfrac{Wv^2}{2g}$ = kinetic energy, ft-lb
$\dfrac{Wp}{\gamma}$ = pressure energy, ft-lb
Wz = potential energy, ft-lb
v = velocity, fps
γ = specific weight, lb/cu ft
p = pressure, psf
z = elevation, ft
g = 32.174 ft/sec²

Canceling W, the equation may be conveniently written as follows:

$$\frac{v^2}{2g} + \frac{p}{\gamma} + z = \text{const}$$

where the terms are expressed as head, ft (energy per pound weight).

The equation is used only to compare the conditions at different points, such as the conditions at areas 1 and 2 of the stream-tube section shown above. The absolute magnitude of the total mechanical energy is of no significance, and the elevation may be referenced to any arbitrary datum.

Example: Consider the section of a pipe between area 1 and area 2 as shown by the stream tube above. What is the fluid pressure at area 2 under the absence of losses (cross-sectional velocities uniform)? The Bernoulli theorem tells that

$$\frac{v_1^2}{2g} + \frac{p_1}{\gamma_1} + z_1 = \frac{v_2^2}{2g} + \frac{p_2}{\gamma_2} + z_2$$

or

$$\frac{p_2}{\gamma_2} = \frac{p_1}{\gamma_1} - \Delta \frac{v^2}{2g} - \Delta z$$

where $\Delta \dfrac{v^2}{2g} = \dfrac{v_2^2}{2g} - \dfrac{v_1^2}{2g} =$ increase in velocity head

$\Delta z = z_2 - z_1 =$ increase in elevation

The velocities may be calculated by the continuity equation shown previously.

The relationship may be expressed in different words: When velocity and elevation increase, the pressure (pressure head) decreases.

The pressure-energy term may require some explanation. Consider the section of a stream tube shown above. Work is required to push weight W into the section at area 1. This work is force times length of path or

$$p_1 A_1 \frac{W}{\gamma_1 A_1} = \frac{W p_1}{\gamma_1}$$

In the same time interval (steady flow), an equivalent weight W leaves the section at area 2 and does the amount of work

$$\frac{W p_2}{\gamma_2}$$

The net amount of work or energy supplied to the section

$$\frac{W p_1}{\gamma_1} - \frac{W p_2}{\gamma_2}$$

compensates for the change in elevation and the change in kinetic energy. The term

$$\frac{W p}{\gamma}$$

may be considered as a form of mechanical energy contained in fluid weight W.

For many engineering problems, a change in elevation has a negligible effect, resulting in the following simplified equation:

$$\frac{v^2}{2g} + \frac{p}{\gamma} = \text{const}$$

This equation may readily be modified as follows:

$$\frac{\rho v^2}{2} + p = \text{const}$$

where $\rho =$ specific mass or density $= \gamma/g$, the form mostly used in aerodynamics

The first term is usually called velocity pressure or dynamic pressure.

The Bernoulli theorem may be expanded to cover cases where the losses are not negligible and where part of the mechanical energy is lost by friction. The equation may then be used as follows:

$$\frac{v_1^2}{2g} + \frac{p_1}{\gamma_1} + z_1 = \frac{v_2^2}{2g} + \frac{p_2}{\gamma_2} + z_2 + h_f$$

where $h_f =$ friction head, ft, mechanical energy per pound of fluid lost by friction

In order to calculate pressure p_2 in the previous example, the friction head must also be subtracted, resulting in a lower pressure than obtained without losses.

NOTE: Precisely, the equation should be written as follows:

$$\frac{Wv^2}{2g_c} + \frac{Wp}{\gamma} + \frac{Wg}{g_c}z = \text{const}$$

where g_c = standard acceleration of gravity, which is a constant of proportionality for the system
   of measurements used
   = 32.174 ft/sec²
   g = local acceleration of gravity, ft/sec²

For simplicity, it has been assumed that the local acceleration of gravity is equal to the standard acceleration of gravity.

Dynamic Similarity

For the design and development of fluid-flow machinery and components, test and experimental data are required.   It is often economical to gather the desired information from the test of a scaled-down model.

In order for a model test to be valid, the fluid flow should be similar.   The flow is similar when the ratio between the various fluid forces is maintained.   For instance, consider a fluid-flow problem where the inertia and the viscous forces are the only fluid forces of significance.   Flow similarity would be obtained when the ratio of these two forces is the same in the model as in the full-scale case.   It may be shown that this ratio is expressed by the Reynolds number, which is a dimensionless group of variables entering the problem as defined above.   Flow similarity would then be obtained when the Reynolds numbers are equal.

Fluid friction and pressure drop in a pipe are the classic example for such a problem. Fluid flow in two similar pipes (equal shape and equal relative roughness in turbulent flow) is similar when the Reynolds numbers are equal, resulting in equal pipe-friction factors as shown by the Moody diagram.   Reynolds number is defined as follows:

$$\text{Re} = \frac{\rho v d}{\mu}$$

where ρ = specific mass or density = γ/g
   γ = specific weight, lb/cu ft
   g = 32.174 ft/sec²
   v = velocity, fps
   d = characteristic length dimension, i.e., inside diameter for a circular pipe, ft
   μ = absolute viscosity, lb-sec/sq ft

The Moody diagram is a plot made from experimental results (model test).   It makes it possible to calculate the pressure drop in a pipe by looking up the friction factor for a similar flow case (equal Reynolds number) which has been tested.

Many practical fluid-flow problems require an equal Reynolds number for similarity. This includes machinery-casing tests to study flow distribution, tests for flow resistance of bodies, and losses in passages due to friction.   It is important that compressibility effects remain negligible, as will be explained below.

In order to maintain an equal Reynolds number for the model test, it is required to change the value of some of the variables in order to compensate for the decrease in length dimension.   This may be achieved in many different ways.   The velocity may be increased to the limit imposed by consideration of compressibility effects; the test may be made at a higher pressure level or density, at a different temperature level (viscosity); or a different test fluid may be used.

In general, many variables enter a fluid-flow problem.   The variables contained in the Reynolds number such as density and viscosity are not the only ones.   Dimensional analysis shows how the variables may be arranged in dimensionless groups. The Reynolds number is one of these dimensionless groups.   The theory tells that the value of these groups which represent ratios of fluid forces should all be maintained for the model to have strict similarity.   This is not possible to achieve in practice, and consideration is concentrated on those groups which represent the forces of significance to a particular flow problem.

For instance, in the model testing of ship hulls, it is important to maintain the value of the Froude number, which expresses the ratio of inertia force and gravitational force. Gravitational effects are an important factor in the motion of free surface waves (water surface waves). Froude number is defined as follows:

$$Fr = \frac{v^2}{gL}$$

where v = velocity, fps
g = acceleration of gravity, ft/sec²
L = characteristic length dimension, ft

Equal Froude number means that a ship model having a smaller length would have to be tested in a water tank at a lower speed.

Another dimensionless group of variables is the Mach number, which represents the (square root of the) ratio of inertia and elastic forces in an ideal gas, such as air. Model tests of aerodynamic shapes at high speed where the compressibility effects become most important should take place at the same Mach number. Mach number is defined as follows:

$$M = \frac{v}{a}$$

where v = velocity, fps
a = sound velocity, fps

The principle of dynamic similarity is applied in the performance test of a gas turbine or a centrifugal compressor, where test data are corrected (reduced) to a reference temperature, which is different from the temperature under which the test was made. Fluid velocities are proportional to the rotor-tip speed, and sound velocity is proportional to the square root of the temperature. The standard correction factors are such that the Mach number is maintained between a test point and a corrected point.

Resistance and Lift

A body immersed in a fluid, and moving relative to it with a steady motion, experiences forces transmitted from the fluid. The resultant force on the body may have two components. One component is in the direction of fluid motion, called resistance or drag. There may be a component at a right angle to the fluid motion, called lift.

The steady flow of fluid, air or water, past a *sphere* may serve as an example (see Fig. 4-39). The sphere is symmetrical to the direction of motion. The resultant force is the resistance, or drag. Drag is expressed as follows:

$$D = \frac{1}{2}\rho v^2 A C_D$$

where ρ = specific mass or density = γ/g
γ = specific weight, lb/cu ft
g = 32.174 ft/sec²
v = velocity, fps
A = projected body area, sq ft
C_D = drag coefficient

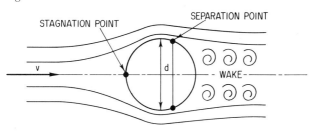

Fig. 4-39

Drag is referred to the dynamic pressure $\frac{1}{2}\rho v^2$ (see Bernoulli's theorem). The projected area in this case is the frontal area of the sphere, or $\pi d^2/4$. The drag coefficient is determined experimentally and expresses the drag as a fraction of the total dynamic-pressure force.

As the fluid flows around the sphere, the velocity will change in the vicinity of the surface. The fluid will come to a halt in front center, the so-called "stagnation point," and it will reach maximum velocity at the diameter d. According to Bernoulli's theorem, there is a corresponding change in static pressure. The pressure buildup at the stagnation point is equal to the dynamic pressure.

With an ideal nonviscous fluid there would be no drag in this case. The velocity and pressure distribution would be the same on the back of the sphere as in front, and there would also be a stagnation point in back center. The drag is due to the direct and indirect effects of the fluid viscosity. The direct effect is the skin friction or shear in the boundary layer, and the indirect effect is the pressure distribution caused by boundary-layer separation. The pressure will be less on the downstream side of the sphere than in front, because of the formation of eddies in the wake.

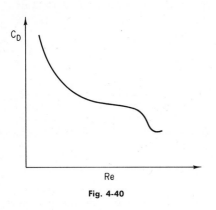

Fig. 4-40

If the changes in pressure are small compared with the total pressure, or if the Mach number is small, the drag coefficient depends only on the Reynolds number Re having the diameter d as a characteristic length dimension. The drag coefficient may then be found from an experimentally determined plot in function of the Reynolds number (Fig. 4-40). The steady flow of fluid past an *airfoil section* may serve as another example (Fig. 4-41). The airfoil section may be the section of an airplane wing or the section of a turbomachinery blade. Profiles of this sort are designed to yield maximum lift and minimum drag. The profile may or may not be symmetrical with respect to its chord line, but a certain angle of attack is required in order to obtain lift.

It has been explained previously that the fluid is subject to velocity and pressure changes when flowing around a body. The pressure distribution around an airfoil section is such that the resultant pressure force is larger for the bottom surface than for the top surface, yielding a net resultant force with a large lift component.

Similar to the previous example, lift and drag are expressed as follows:

$$L = \frac{1}{2}\rho v^2 A C_L$$
$$D = \frac{1}{2}\rho v^2 A C_D$$

Again, A is the projected body area, but in this case, the "wing" area or, for the airfoil section, chord times unit length of span.

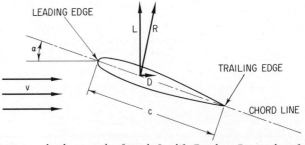

Fig. 4-41 c = chord, α = angle of attack, L = lift, D = drag, R = resultant force.

As explained previously, the drag is due to the direct and indirect effects of the fluid viscosity. It is called profile drag in order to distinguish it from the induced drag. Induced drag is due to the end effects of a three-dimensional case such as a complete airplane wing. The airfoil section is considered to be part of a very long span, a two-dimensional case. The published airfoil-section data contain profile drag only.

The lift and drag coefficients have been determined experimentally for many different airfoil sections by NASA and other research institutes. The data are plotted in function of the angle of attack in a range of Reynolds numbers. Applications for the data include the design of airplane wings and turbomachinery blading, specifically the blading of axial-flow compressors.

Propulsion

The thrust produced by various propulsion devices may readily be calculated as an application of the momentum theory of fluids reduced to a one-dimensional case.

The force exerted on a *section of reducing pipe* may serve as an introduction. The fluid is assumed to be in steady motion (Fig. 4-42).

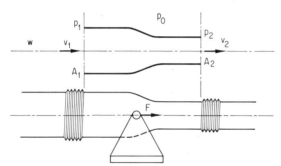

Fig. 4-42 p_0 = outside pressure, psf; p_1 = pressure at area A_1, psf; p_2 = pressure at area A_2, psf; v_1 = velocity at area A_1, fps; v_2 = velocity at area A_2, fps; w = weight flow, lb/sec; F = axial force on pipe, lb.

The section of reducing pipe is considered to be detached from adjoining pipes. For a practical case it may be assumed that the pipe section is connected to adjoining pipes through very flexible expansion joints. The pipe section has to have its own support. The support has to hold the axial force, which will be determined below.

The force exerted on the pipe by the fluid is equal in magnitude to the force exerted on the fluid by the pipe but acts in the opposite direction (reaction principle).

The momentum theory of fluids says that the rate of change of momentum is equal to the force acting on the fluid. For the present case, the force acting on the fluid consists of the pressure forces at areas A_1 and A_2 in addition to the force F' exerted on the fluid by the pipe in the direction toward the larger end. Considered is the amount of fluid contained in the pipe section. The following force acts on the fluid in the direction toward the smaller end:

$$-F' + p_1A_1 - p_2A_2$$

This force must be equal to the rate of change of momentum. Considering the amount of fluid leaving at area A_2 and entering at area A_1 in unit time, the rate of change of momentum is

$$\frac{w}{g}(v_2 - v_1)$$

Equating the two expressions, the following equation is obtained:

$$F' = p_1A_1 - p_2A_2 - \frac{w}{g}(v_2 - v_1)$$

A force of equal magnitude is exerted on the pipe by the fluid but in the direction toward the smaller end. This force is transmitted at the inside surface of the pipe. There is also a pressure force on the outside surface. The total force on the pipe in the direction toward the smaller end is

$$F = F' - p_0(A_1 - A_2)$$

or

$$F = (p_1 - p_0)A_1 - (p_2 - p_0)A_2 - \frac{w}{g}(v_2 - v_1)$$

The first terms of the equation may be called gage pressure forces, and the last term is the rate of change of fluid momentum. The equation is valid for viscous flow as well as for frictionless flow and for compressible flow as well as for incompressible flow (assuming constant velocity over area A_1 and area A_2). The mechanism under which the force is transmitted between the fluid and the pipe does not have to be specified. For the case of frictionless flow, the force is transmitted by pressure only. It is left to the reader to verify the equation by integrating the pressure forces on the pipe wall in the axial direction under the simplifying assumption of an incompressible, frictionless fluid and using Bernoulli's theorem.

It should be recognized that the equation is valid irrespective of the losses which the fluid may incur inside the pipe section. The equation is not an energy balance. For instance, the pipe section may contain a restriction such as the globe valve sketched in Fig. 4-43. The pressure p_2 would be lower than without restriction, and the force would be larger, as expected.

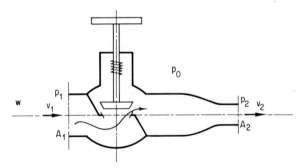

Fig. 4-43

The fluid may even be transformed and heat energy may be added without restricting the validity of the equation. Suppose the fluid entering the pipe section is compressed air and a fuel (of negligible weight flow) is burned in it. The velocity v_2 would be higher than without combustion and may cause the force to change direction, again as expected (Fig. 4-44).

The thrust of a *jet engine* may now be calculated. Velocities are considered to be relative to the engine. Any air resistance acting on the outside will not be included (Fig. 4-45).

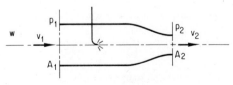

Fig. 4-44

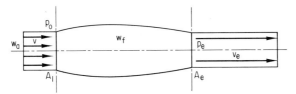

Fig. 4-45 p_0 = atmospheric pressure, psf; p_e = pressure at area A_e, psf; A_1 = inlet area, sq ft; A_e = nozzle exit area, sq ft; v = flight speed, fps; v_e = jet velocity, fps; w_a = airflow, lb/sec; w_f = fuel flow, lb/sec; F = thrust, lb.

The thrust of the jet engine is (see Fig. 4-45):

$$F = \frac{w_a + w_f}{g}\, v_e - \frac{w_a}{g}\, v + (p_e - p_0)A_e$$

Note that the formula is basically the same as for the section of reducing pipe. The momentum force is much larger than the pressure force because the high jet velocity is created by means of combustion and does not penalize the pressure, as is the case with the section of reducing pipe. The net thrust is in the direction opposite to the fluid flow, and the sign has been reversed for convenience. The pressure at the inlet is equal to the atmospheric pressure, and the gage-pressure term for the inlet is zero.

The equation may be simplified by combining the pressure thrust with the jet thrust and introducing a so-called effective jet velocity v_j as follows:

$$F = \frac{w_a + w_f}{g}\, v_j - \frac{w_a}{g}\, v$$

Neglecting the fuel flow, which is small compared with the airflow, the equation may be simplified further:

$$F = \frac{w}{g}\, (v_j - v)$$

It is evident that the jet engine cannot fly faster than its effective jet velocity. If the effective jet velocity is equal to the flight speed, the thrust becomes zero. The exhaust gases would be standing still relative to the atmosphere and no change of fluid momentum would take place. Without leaving loss, the propulsive efficiency would reach a maximum, however.

The ideal *propulsive efficiency* is defined as follows:

$$\eta_P = \frac{P_F}{P_F + P_L}$$

where P_F = thrust power, ft-lb/sec
$\quad\quad\; P_L$ = leaving loss power, ft-lb/sec

with $$P_F = Fv = \frac{w}{g}\, (v_j - v)v$$

and $$P_L = \frac{1}{2}\frac{w}{g}\, (v_j - v)^2$$

$$P_F + P_L = \frac{1}{2}\frac{w}{g}\, (v_j^2 - v^2)$$

$$\eta_P = \frac{2v/v_j}{1 + v/v_j}$$

The ideal propulsive efficiency expresses the fraction of the available power which is utilized, the available power being based on the kinetic energy of the exhaust gas relative to the atmosphere.

The thrust of a *rocket motor* may be calculated in a similar way (Fig. 4-46).

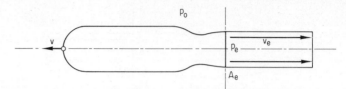

Fig. 4-46 p_0 = atmospheric pressure (if any), psf; p_e = pressure at area A_e, psf; A_e = nozzle exit area, sq ft; v_e = jet velocity, fps; v = flight speed, fps; w = weight flow, lb/sec; F = thrust, lb.

The thrust of the rocket motor is (see Fig. 4-46):

$$F = \frac{w}{g} v_e + (p_e - p_0)A_e$$

The two terms may be combined into one term by the introduction of the effective jet velocity v_j. The thrust may then be expressed as follows:

$$F = \frac{w}{g} v_j$$

The thrust is independent of the flight speed. As opposed to the jet engine, it is very well possible for the rocket motor to fly faster than its effective jet velocity.

The ideal propulsive efficiency becomes

$$\eta_P = \frac{2v/v_j}{1 + (v/v_j)^2}$$

MECHANICAL VIBRATIONS

In all rotating or reciprocating machinery, a condition of mechanical vibration will be present because of the force and energy levels inherent in the equipment. The question as to whether these vibrations prove to be harmful or not is dependent on several factors. These factors can best be expressed in terms of the dynamic motions of the simple harmonic oscillator when subjected to a sinusoidal, time-varying, external force. A typical representation of this system is shown in Fig. 4-47 with the standard nomenclature used in the vibration field.

$$\omega_N = \sqrt{\frac{Kg_0}{W}} = \text{undamped natural frequency}$$

$$\tau = \frac{2\pi}{\omega_N} = \text{period of free vibration}$$

$$\omega_d = \omega_N \sqrt{1 - \zeta^2} = \text{damped natural frequency}$$

$$c_c = 2 \sqrt{\frac{KW}{g_0}} = \text{critical damping}$$

$$\zeta = \frac{c}{c_c} = \text{damping ratio}$$

where W = weight of mass in Fig. 4-47, lb
K = spring constant in this system, lb/in.
g_0 = standard gravitational constant (386 in./sec²)
ω = frequency, rad/sec
c = damping coefficient, lb-sec/in.

Utilizing the above definitions, the equation of motion for this system is the following:

$$\frac{W}{g} \ddot{x} + c\dot{x} + Kx = P \sin \omega t$$

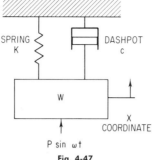

Fig. 4-47

where P is the maximum amplitude of the exciting force, lb, and t is time, sec. The dots represent differentiation with respect to time t. In general the damping ratio ζ is small and the steady-state response of the system is given by the usual equation:

$$x = \frac{P}{K} \frac{1}{\sqrt{[1 - (\omega/\omega_N)^2]^2 + [2\zeta(\omega/\omega_N)]^2}} \sin(\omega t - \phi)$$

$$\phi = \tan^{-1} \frac{2\zeta(\omega/\omega_N)}{1 - (\omega/\omega_N)^2} = \text{phase angle}$$

The second fraction in the expression for x above is frequently referred to as the *magnification factor* for the system. A plot of this parameter and of the phase angle as functions of the frequency ratio ω/ω_N is given in Fig. 4-48.

The successive peaks of the curves for the magnification factor (often termed the response curve) located at or near the condition of forcing frequency ω equal to natural

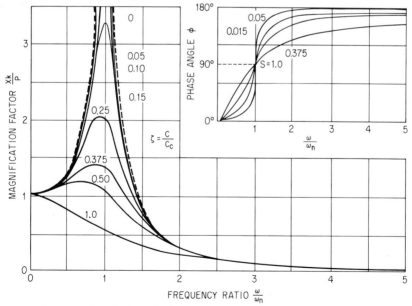

Fig. 4-48 (*Courtesy of Marks, "Standard Handbook for Mechanical Engineers," 7th ed., McGraw-Hill Book Company, New York, 1967.*)

system frequency ω_N are termed a condition of "resonance." This phenomenon of resonance explains the critical nature of vibration in the design of mechanical systems, since the deformation and stress of a member may be multiplied by a considerable factor (5 to 10) above the static reaction to a steady load of intensity P, thus inducing an eventual fatigue failure. The associated concept of tuning the system also stems from consideration of the response curves. By adjusting either the exciting frequencies or the system natural frequency so the ratio ω/ω_N is significantly removed from the unity value, the system is said to be detuned. In the case $\omega/\omega_N > 1.5$, the response to the forcing function will, in reality, be an attenuation of the input motions.

A final useful parameter, in discussing the characteristics of the single-degree-of-freedom system, is the logarithmic decrement of damping and is a measure of the energy-absorption capability of the system. This quantity is defined as the logarithm ratio of successive peaks of the free-vibration response of the system to a step input. It also may be defined by means of the response curve in terms of the half-power points. Thus the decrement δ is given by either of the following:

$$\delta = \ln \frac{x_i}{x_{i+1}} = \frac{\pi(\omega_2 - \omega_1)}{\omega_N} \cong 2\pi\zeta$$

where ω_2 = frequency above ω_N where the magnification factor is 0.707 times the value at ω_N
ω_1 = frequency below ω_N where the magnification factor is also 0.707 times the value at ω_N

Many of the above concepts carry over into linear multiple-degree-of freedom systems and into continuously elastic systems in the neighborhood of resonance. It is clearly evident that for lightly damped systems the number of resonant peaks of the response curve will coincide with the number of discrete lumped masses in the system. To investigate response near resonance, the use of equivalent viscous damping as an energy absorption device is frequently justified.

The case of torsional vibration (Fig. 4-49) is analogous to that of lateral vibration, wherein the free vibration is governed by the equation

$$I\theta + c\ddot{\theta} + K\dot{\theta} = 0$$

The natural frequency of this system in cycles per second (the term hertz, Hz, is now replacing cps in common usage) is

$$f_N = \frac{1}{2\pi} \sqrt{\frac{K}{I}} = \frac{1}{2\pi} \sqrt{\frac{GI_p}{Il}}$$

where I = mass moment of inertia of disk
I_p = polar moment of inertia of shaft
G = shear modulus of shaft

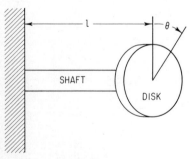

Fig. 4-49

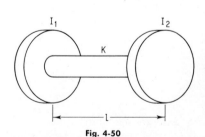

Fig. 4-50

For the system of two disks and a shaft (Fig. 4-50) the frequency is

$$f_N = \sqrt{\frac{(I_1 + I_2)GI_p}{I_1 I_2 l}}$$

For more complex torsional systems the tabular method due to Holzer is used to compute the several frequencies of the system.

NOISE AND NOISE MEASUREMENTS

Noise is generally defined in terms of undesirable sound. As such, it tends to interfere with the useful functions associated with operating heavy machinery. Noise may be either structure-borne or airborne. Structure-borne noise is usually closely associated with machine vibrations. Airborne noise principally affects personnel and hinders their activity in the vicinity of the noise source. Airborne noise is also frequently an adequate gage by which deterioration in performance of a machine may be detected. A distinct increase in noise level often indicates internal distress due to component failure or excessive wear with an operating unit.

Noise, like vibration, is characterized by frequency content and amplitude or intensity. The combination of these quantities over the entire spectrum constitutes the signature of the noise source. This signature is obtained by identifying the amplitude of each discrete frequency band (usually octave or one-third octave band) by means of a sound analyzer. The analyzer consists of a group of instruments performing the functions of gathering and decomposing the sound energy, i.e., a microphone, attenuator, amplifier, frequency analyzer, and an indicator or recorder. Although noise, or sound energy, is often expressed in terms of a sound-power level, the more usual practice is to utilize sound-pressure level, SPL. This quantity is defined in terms of decibels, db, which is the logarithmic ratio of the sound-pressure wave related to a standard value. Accepted international usage has a 20 micronewtons per meter squared (20 μN/m^2) reference standard. The older standard was 0.0002 microbar. Thus

$$SPL = 20 \log \frac{p}{p_{\text{ref}}} \quad db$$

The correlation between newtons per meter squared, microbars, and dynes per centimeter squared is

$$1.0 \text{ newton/meter}^2 = 10 \ \mu\text{bars} = 10 \text{ dynes/cm}^2$$

In terms of an average observer's reaction to sound-pressure levels in the center frequencies of the audible range, the following table is representative:

Decibels SPL re 0.00002 N/m^2	Description	Example
120	Discomfort threshold	Thunder
110	Deafening	Jet aircraft
		Factory noise
90	Very loud	Blaring radio
80	. . . .	Noisy office
70	Loud	City street noise
60	. . . .	Noisy home
50	Moderate	Conversational level
40	. . . .	Quiet radio
30	Faint	Quiet conversation
20	. . . .	Whisper

Objectionable noise is a very subjective term which is greatly dependent on the hearer. However, recently the Committee on Hearing, Bio-Acoustics and Bio-Mechanics of the National Academy of Science and National Research Council

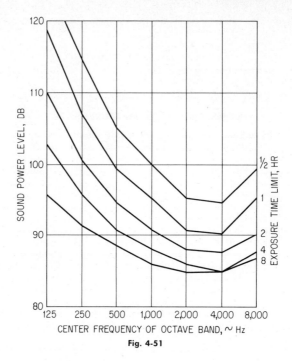

Fig. 4-51

(CHABA) has published hearing-damage-risk criteria curves[1] for guidance in this area. The curves in Fig. 4-51 refer to one exposure per day to steady noise and give the maximum exposure time limit per day. The shape of these curves indicates the pronounced effect frequency has on tolerance level. The human ear is more sensitive to the higher-frequency noise.

ROTATING MACHINERY

With the recent introduction of high-speed, heavily loaded rotating machinery, the problem of dynamic response of the rotors is becoming increasingly significant. The basic principles may be understood from consideration of the simple single-disk shaft as illustrated in Fig. 4-52.

By equating centrifugal forces acting on the disk with the elastic restoring forces of the shaft, the following is obtained (see Fig. 4-52):

$$\frac{W}{g}\omega^2(X + e) = kX$$

If the lateral vibration frequency of the rotor is introduced, $\omega_N^2 = kg_0/W$, the more usual form for the displacement is obtained:

$$X = \frac{(\omega/\omega_N)^2}{1 - (\omega/\omega_N)^2}e$$

For the case where ω approaches ω_N, the displacement increases drastically and a condition of resonance exists. This value of ω_N is often termed the "critical speed"

[1] K. D. Kryter, W. D. Ward, J. D. Miller, and D. H. Eldredge, Hazardous Exposure to Intermittent and Steady-state Noise, *Journal of Acoustical Society of America*, vol. 39, no. 3, pp. 451–464, March, 1966.

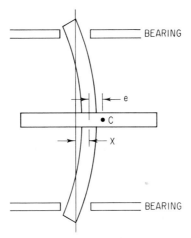

Fig. 4-52 W = weight of rotor, C = location of rotor center of gravity, e = distance between geometric center and C, X = displacement of rotor geometric center from bearing line, ω = rotating frequency of rotor, k = equivalent spring constant for shaft restoring force.

and, more accurately, induces a condition of synchronous whirl of the shaft. For the simple case where the mass of the rotor may be concentrated at the center of the span,

$$N_c = \frac{60}{2\pi}\sqrt{\frac{g_0}{\delta_{st}}} = \frac{187.8}{\sqrt{\delta_{st}}}$$

where N_c = critical speed, rpm

δ_{st} = static shaft deflection = W/k, in.

The variation between the geometric center and the center of gravity as measured by e gives rise to the concept of balancing rotating machinery. By proper addition or removal of weight on a rotor, the product We can be reduced to minimal limits. It should be noted, however, that each rotor retains some residual unbalance due to practical considerations and therefore will, at all times, exhibit a response phenomenon. The objective in balancing is to reduce this response to a tolerable minimum.

Balancing may be of the static or dynamic variety. For the case with all the rotor unbalance in a single plane and on one side of the geometric axis, a static balance in that plane is sufficient for corrective purposes. However, the general case consists of several planes of unbalance, randomly distributed around the geometric axis. This condition is illustrated in Fig. 4-53 for the case of two arbitrarily located unbalance weights.

Generally, the two planes in which balance correction will be accomplished are

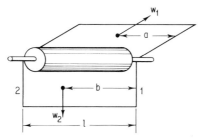

Fig. 4-53 a = distance between W_1 and right balance plane, b = distance between W_2 and right balance plane.

located toward the ends of the rotor, labeled (1) and (2) in Fig. 4-53. The two corrections at (1) will be $[-W_1(l - a)]/l$ and $[-W_2(l - b)]/l$ and will be coplanar with the respective unbalances W_1 and W_2, as indicated by the negative sign. Likewise, the correction at (2) will be $-W_1a/l$, $-W_2b/l$. In general, large high-speed rotors can be balanced within fractions of an ounce-inch.

To determine the critical speeds for actual turbomachine rotors which are more complex cases, where there are several weights W_1, W_2, . . . , W_i each concentrated on a single span, a Rayleigh-type energy approach yields, as an estimate of the lowest frequency,

$$N_c = 187.7 \sqrt{\frac{W_1y_1 + W_2y_2 + \cdots + W_iy_i}{W_1y_1^2 + W_2y_2^2 + \cdots + W_iy_i^2}} \quad \text{rpm}$$

where the y_i are the static deflections of each disk or plane which weighs W_i.

To improve the accuracy of the estimate, the deflection y_i can be computed from dynamic loading, which is initially evaluated on a basis of static deflections. This iterative procedure of improving the accuracy of the y_i by recalculating dynamic loads based on the previous estimate of the shaft-deflection shape is the basis for the modern Prohl-Myklestad approach to critical-speed calculation. The higher critical speeds can be obtained by substituting the second, third, etc., mode shapes in the basic Rayleigh equation.

A second useful tool in obtaining an estimate of the first critical speed of a shaft with several concentrated weights is that given by Dunkerley,

$$\frac{1}{N_c^2} = \frac{1}{N_0^2} + \frac{1}{N_1^2} + \frac{1}{N_2^2} + \frac{1}{N_3^2} + \cdots$$

where N_0 = critical speed of shaft only
N_1 = critical speed of shaft with W_1 only, located at its proper position on shaft
N_2 = critical speed of shaft with W_2 only, etc.

Utilization of the fact that resonance for synchronous whirl will occur at the same frequency as lateral vibration enables the computation of critical speeds of uniform shafts by means of the formula

$$N_c = a_n \sqrt{\frac{EIg_0}{Wl^4}}$$

where EI = flexural stiffness of the shaft
W = weight per unit length of shaft
l = length of shaft
a_n = constant based on shaft-fixity conditions and the mode number as tabulated below

Shaft fixity	a_1	a_2	a_3
Simply supported	94.2	376.8	846.0
Clamped-free	33.6	214.2	589.2
Free-free or clamped-clamped . . .	214.2	589.2	1,152.0
Clamped-hinged or hinged-free. . .	147.0	477.6	996.0

Modern computational methods for rotor-response evaluations introduce the concepts of bearing-oil-film flexibility and bearing-pedestal stiffness and damping. Thus the physical idealization of the system involved in dynamic response is depicted in Fig. 4-54.

The dashpots in Fig. 4-54 imply energy absorption of the resultant dynamic motions and provide a means of evaluation of the rotor's displacement, since the input rotational energy must be equated to the energy removed from the system by means of the dashpots. In general, the bearing-oil-film characteristics are linearized, using an assumption of small oscillations in order to facilitate the computation. The addition of the

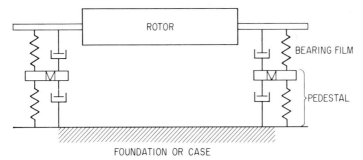

Fig. 4-54 Idealized structure for rotor-response calculation.

bearing flexibility usually depresses the lowest frequency of rotor response below that computed for the rigid-bearing critical speed. However, since the additional freedoms introduced greatly affect the normal mode shapes, no general statement can be made for higher modes, and each machine system must be evaluated independently.

These rotor-response computational methods for obtaining dynamic motions also yield dynamic stresses throughout the system since, in general, the deflection curve and/or its derivatives are proportional to the internal-stress patterns of the various components, i.e., for the shaft,

$$\sigma \alpha M = EIy''$$

In practical operation of machinery the dynamics of the equipment is affected not only by the design but also by the physical condition of the hardware and the variables related to the installation. Thus items such as unbalance caused by wear or dirt accumulations, misalignment of couplings, bent shafts, and eccentric journals or bearings often cause unsatisfactory conditions. In the final analysis all factors must be evaluated in terms of machinery operation in field service. A useful criterion for evaluating the dynamic characteristics of a machine is the measurement of the vibration levels on the shaft in the vicinity of the bearing caps.

The Compressed Air and Gas Institute (CAGI) has proposed a specification for shaft-vibration levels as follows:

$$\text{Peak-to-peak mils} = \sqrt{\frac{12,000}{\text{rpm}}}$$

Figure 4-55 shows a plot of this relation. (See also Vibration Limits for Pumps in Sec. 6, pages 6-38 to 6-40.)

BEARINGS AND LUBRICATION

Bearings

Introduction Bearings permit relative motion to occur between two machine elements. Two types of relative motion are possible, rolling or sliding. The existing type of relative motion is dependent on the design of the mechanical bearing element. Thus bearings are classified into two general types: the rolling-contact type (rolling) and the sliding-contact bearing design in which the bearing elements are separated by a film of oil (sliding). Both can be designed to accommodate axial and/or radial loads. Each has a wide variation of types and designs to fit a wide variation in uses. The selection of a bearing type involves a performance evaluation and cost consideration with application to a particular situation.

There is ample literature available to the inquisitive person to determine the relative merits of each. It will be our purpose here to provide generally a résumé of the types of bearings presently encountered in the equipment covered in this edition. Changes take place frequently because many scientists and engineers work constantly to improve the state of the art in bearing design.

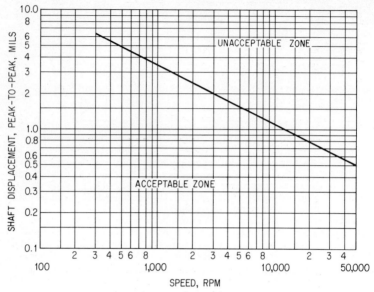

Fig. 4-55 Vibration limits.

Rolling-contact Bearings Rolling-contact bearings include ball bearings, roller bearings, and needle bearings. Within each category several variations exist which have been developed for specific application. Variations in the amounts of radial and thrust load capabilities also exist between specific types. Self-aligning ball or roller bearings, by virtue of their spherically ground outer race, can tolerate misalignment of the shaft or housing.

Rolling-contact bearings consist of four principal components: an outer race, an inner race, rolling elements, and a separator or spacer for the rolling elements. The inner ring is mounted on the shaft. The outer ring securely fits in a stationary housing. Both the inner surface of the outer ring and the outer surface of the inner ring conform to the rolling-element shape. The rolling elements (with separator) accurately space the inner and outer races and thus enable smooth relative motion to occur (see Fig. 4-56).

Sliding-contact Bearings Sliding-contact bearings are classified into two general types: journal bearings and thrust bearings. Journal bearings support radial loads imparted by the rotating shaft and may also be required to arrest or eliminate hydraulic instabilities which may be encountered in lightly loaded, high-speed, present-day machinery. The thrust bearings are used for loads parallel to the shaft and may be required to support the full weight of the rotor in cases of vertical machinery.

Journal Bearings The common types of journal bearings are:

Plain journal bearings
Three-lobe journal bearings
Tilting-pad journal bearings

The *plain journal bearing* may be either force-fed from a pressure-lubrication system or ring-oiled by means of a free ring which rests on and rotates with the shaft to serve as a pumping medium, as shown in Fig. 4-57. A section of a typical force-fed journal bearing is shown in Fig. 4-58. This shows a babbitt-lined split-type bearing. Journal-bearing clearance for high-speed machinery, i.e., turbines, centrifugal compressors, pumps, etc., should be not less than 0.0015 in./in. of diameter for satisfactory operation.

The *three-lobe journal bearing* is applied on high-speed machinery, usually when the bearing is end-fed and used in combination with a face-contact seal or when the bearing

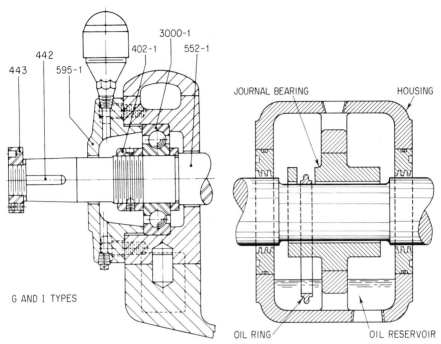

Fig. 4-56   Mounting of grease-lubricated ball bearing.

Fig. 4-57   Ring oil lubrication.

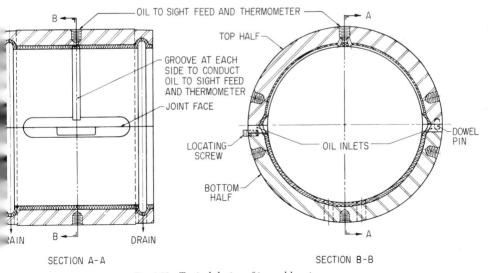

Fig. 4-58   Typical design of journal bearing.

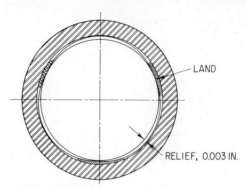

Fig. 4-59 Section through three-lobe journal bearing.

itself is a shaft seal.   The three-lobe design provides, intrinsically, a stable three-point support and is particularly adaptable to very light loads in either horizontal or vertical shafts.   Because of the small amount of additional clearance, the end-leakage effect of this bearing can be well controlled and provides good impurity tolerance from the oil system with a means for continuous flushing.   A typical bearing is shown in Fig. 4-59.

The *tilting-pad journal bearing* may be made with any number of multiple shoes, and its mechanical design and performance follow closely the theory of the tilting-pad thrust bearing.   A typical bearing of this kind utilizes five pads of which one pad is on the bottom, dead center for horizontal shafts, to provide a fixed means of supporting the shaft during alignment.   This bearing is considered to be the best design for attaining rotor stability.   It also is inherently more tolerant of impurities in the oil system without bearing failure.   A typical section of this bearing is shown in Fig. 4-60.   This bearing is pressure-fed from a circulation system, and the amount of oil passing through the bearing is controlled by a restriction at the inlet to the bearing shell.

Thrust Bearings   The simplest type of thrust bearing is the sliding-contact type with

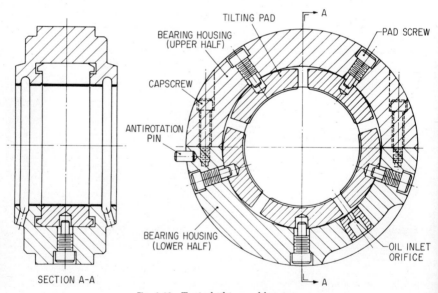

Fig. 4-60 Typical tilting-pad bearing.

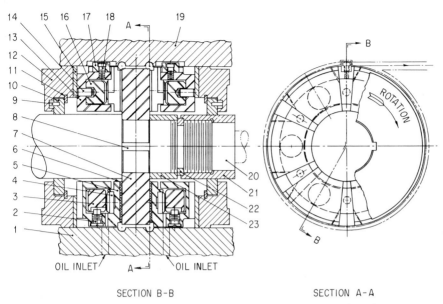

SECTION B-B   SECTION A-A

Fig. 4-61 Section of tilting-pad thrust bearing. (1) Bearing bracket. (2) Leveling-plate setscrew. (3) Upper leveling plate. (4) Shoe support. (5) Shoe. (6) Shoe babbitt (4, 5, and 6 assembled as a unit). (7) Collar. (8) Key. (9) Pin. (10) Oil guard. (11) Snap ring. (12) Thrust-bearing ring. (13) Base ring (in halves). (14) Leveling-plate dowel. (15) Shim. (16) Lower leveling plate. (17) Base-ring key. (18) Base-ring key screw. (19) Bearing-bracket cap. (20) Shaft. (21) Outer check nut. (22) Retaining ring. (23) Inner check nut.

plain babbitted face, which is used in lightly loaded thrust applications. The second, more complicated design for intermediate thrust loading is found in the tapered-land thrust bearing. This design has a multiple radial series of fixed lands having a tapered inlet edge in the direction of rotation to develop a hydrodynamic film to support the thrust load.

The most common thrust bearing found in high-speed machinery is the tilting-pad thrust bearing. This bearing contains independent-acting shoes with a hardened, pivoted pad backing. Each shoe acts to establish a hydrodynamic film proportional to the speed and loading of the shaft to support the thrust load. A typical bearing section of this type is shown in Fig. 4-61. This bearing may be single-sided in the case of turbines where unidirectional thrust is encountered, or double-sided in the case of compressors or pumps where the thrust loading may shift, depending on the operating conditions.

Lubrication

Introduction Lubricants derived from petroleum are a mixture of chemical compounds contained in the original crude from which the lubricant was extracted; additionally, the lubricant will contain materials resulting from the refining process as well as materials intentionally added to impart specific properties. Consequently, brands of lubricant, each generally suitable for a given type of application, probably have been treated differently in the course of their preparation and may produce somewhat different results when applied in any specific instance.

The choice of the proper lubricant not only is important to the manufacturer in order to enable him to meet his guarantees for performance and reliability but is, of course, of the utmost importance to the user of the equipment in keeping his maintenance cost to a minimum and safeguarding the machinery against abnormal wear, corrosion, and the effects of contamination.

It is generally recognized that a specification giving only physical and chemical properties does not guarantee satisfactory performance of any particular lubricant. The manufacturer and the user, therefore, have to rely on the experience, integrity, and reputation of the lubricant supplier and on the record of satisfactory past performance of the particular type of lubricant offered for a given purpose.

It is not the intention of this handbook to restrict the recommendations for lubricants to any particular brands, and any recommendations made are given only to serve as a guide in the selection of a suitable grade of lubricant for the service intended. Conformance to these recommendations, therefore, should not relieve the vendor of the lubricant from the responsibility of determining service requirements and supplying a satisfactory product. Furthermore, the vendor should furnish evidence of satisfactory past performance of the proposed lubricant in similar machinery installations and service over a reasonable period of time. The vendor should also guarantee that the proposed lubricant will be uniform and will be identical to the lubricant for which evidence of past satisfactory performance has been submitted.

The lubricant should be a first-grade branded product which has previously been used and proved to be satisfactory for the continuous lubrication of similar equipment in the same service. Such experience should have proved the lubricant to be satisfactory, particularly with respect to foaming, rusting, sludging, and separation from water and other impurities.

The brand of lubricant decided upon should be continued in use and should not be changed without compelling reason.

Oil Characteristics A lubricating oil should be a petroleum oil of high quality having guaranteed uniformity, high lubricating qualities, and adequate protection against rust and oxidation. It should be free from acids, alkali, asphaltum, pitch, soap, resin, and water. The oil must not have any solid matter or materials that will injure the oil itself or the parts it contacts or impair its lubricating properties. Lubricating oil should not foam, form permanent emulsions, oxidize rapidly, or form sludge. It may contain additives or inhibitors if their use supplements but does not adversely affect the desirable properties and characteristics of an oil.

No additive should be put in a lubricating oil without approval of the original lubricant supplier.

Grease Characteristics Greases should be high-grade high-temperature lubricants suitable for application by hand, pressure gun, or hand compression cup.

Greases should remain in the solid state at operating temperatures. They should not separate on standing or when heated below their dropping point. Grease components should not separate under the action of centrifugal force.

Greases should resist oxidation and must not gum, harden, or decompose. They must not contain dirt, fillers, abrasive matter, excessive moisture, free acid, or free lime.

Lubrication Methods Either splash lubrication or forced-feed oil lubrication is commonly used for rotating machinery such as turbines, pumps, compressors, reduction gears, and worm gears. Splash lubrication is used for relatively slow-speed machinery, while high-speed machinery always requires forced-feed lubrication.

The usual form of splash lubrication employs oil rings. In this arrangement a loose ring rides freely on the journal and dips into a sump in the bearing bracket containing oil. The ring rotates because of its contact with the journal, but at a slower speed. The oil adheres to the ring until it reaches the top of the journal, when it flows onto the shaft.

The predominate use of ring oiling for small machines is dictated by economic reasons, where the additional cost of a pumping system cannot be justified. The system enjoys the advantage of self-containment, needing no external motivation for its performance. Cooling coils are sometimes added when the sump temperature may become excessive.

The fully forced, or direct-pressure, system is used in the majority of large circulation systems, wherein the oil is forced into the bearing under pressure.

Grease lubrication is principally used for ball bearings and roller bearings at normal ambient temperatures and at shaft speeds not exceeding 3,600 rpm.

The selection charts on pages 4-56 to 4-58 give desirable viscosities and other specifications for oils and grease recommended for various applications, and may be used as a general guide in specifying lubricants for the types of machinery listed.

Oil Selection Turbine and compounded steam cylinder oils should pass rust test ASTM D 665-49T. Lubricating oil for marine installations should pass procedures A and B. Procedure B may be waived on oil for land installations if contamination by brackish water is improbable.

Turbine oils should have a minimum flash point of 350°F, as measured by ASTM D 92–46.

If high ambient temperatures, restricted ventilation, faulty bearing operation, etc., cause the temperature of a turbine oil leaving a bearing to exceed 180°F, consult the manufacturer or lubricant supplier for recommendations. Above 200°F the deterioration of the lubricating properties in most turbine oils is accelerated.

Horsepower losses, bearing exit temperatures, and oil-film thicknesses decrease with lower viscosity values and increase with higher viscosity values.

When cold starting is important, or a product has ring oiled bearings, a lubricating oil with a high viscosity index should be used. A high viscosity index means that the rate of change of viscosity of an oil with change of temperature is small.

Oil Maintenance The lubricating system must be kept clean and free from impurities at all times. The accumulation of impurities will cause lubricant failure and damage to the equipment.

Provision should be made for maximum protection against rust during idle periods. The main lubricating system should be operated at intervals to remove condensation from metal surfaces and coat these surfaces with a protective layer of lubricant. This should be done daily when the variation in day and night temperatures is great, and weekly when the variation in day and night temperatures is small. In addition, a unit idle for an extended period of time should, if possible, be operated from time to time at the reduced speeds specified under normal starting procedures.

The use of a suitable oil purifier is recommended. Since some purifiers can alter the properties of lubricating oils, especially inhibited oils, the manufacturer should be consulted before the purifier is selected.

Lubrication Piping Oil feed and oil drain piping is generally of low-carbon steel. Piping used should be pickled (a procedure of cleaning the internal surfaces). If low-carbon-steel piping has not been pickled the following procedure should be followed:

1. Sandblast pipe along the pipe run.
2. Deburr if necessary.
3. Wash all internal surfaces with a petroleum-base cleaning solvent.
4. Air-blast dry.
5. Visually inspect.
6. If piping is to be stored "in house," fog all internal surfaces progressively along the pipe run, through all openings, with an oil-soluble preservative compound.

Oil-selection Chart

Product					Type of oil	Viscosity, SSU ASTM D 88						Oil temp, °F	
						100°F		130°F		210°F		Min operating	Normal to bearings
						Min	Max	Min	Max	Min	Max		
Marine propulsion units													
Ships service turbine-generator sets					Turbine	375	525	180	230	54	min	90	110 130
Marine auxiliaries—direct or gear drive													
	Direct drive	Ring oiled bearings	With water cooling		Turbine	250	350	120	155	47	min	...	140 160
			Without water cooling	Liquids up to 130°F	Turbine	250	350	120	155	47	min	...	140 160
				Liquids 131°F and above	Turbine	375	525	180	230	54	min	...	140 180
		Forced circulation			Turbine	250	350	120	155	47	min	...	110 120
	Gear drive	Forced feed			Turbine	140	180	85	105	42	min	90	110 120
Centrifugal pumps		Forced feed			Turbine	250	350	120	155	47	min	90	110 120

Equipment	Sub-category	Driver					
Gears	Helical and planetary	Turbine	250 / 350	120 / 155	47 min	90	110 / 120
Gears	Herringbone		See Table 2, AGMA 250.02				
Gears	Worm		See Sec. 7, page 7-29				
	Ring oiled bearings — Direct drive — With water cooling	Turbine	250 / 350	120 / 155	47 min	…	140 / 160
	Ring oiled bearings — Direct drive — Without water cooling	Turbine	375 / 525	180 / 230	54 min	…	140 / 180
	Direct drive — Forced circulation	Turbine	250 / 350	120 / 155	47 min	…	110 / 120
	Direct drive — Forced feed	Turbine	140 / 180	85 / 105	42 min	90	110 / 120
	Gear drive — Forced feed	Turbine	250 / 350	120 / 155	47 min	90	110 / 120
Turbines	Direct drive	Turbine°	140 / 180	85 / 105	42 min	90	110 / 120
Turbines	Gear drive	Turbine°	250 / 350	120 / 155	47 min	90	110 / 120
Turbines	Lubricated independently	Turbine	375 / 525	180 / 230	54 min	…	120 / 160
Centrifugal compressors							
Turbo-chargers	Lubricated by engine	See engine manufacturer's specifications	SAE 20 or 30 preferred			…	120 / 160

° Compressors with oil seals, 190 minimum aniline point.

Grease-selection Chart

Component		Type	NLGI No.	Worked penetration Min ASTM D 217–52T	Drop point Min F ASTM D 566-42	Corrosion test
Ball bearings, roller bearings, oscillating or sliding plain bearings, sliding pedestal supports°		Sodium, lithium, or sodium-calcium soap base	2	265–295	350	Pass Federal Test Method Std. No. 791 Method 5309.2
Governor valve lifting gear	Steam temp 600°F max	Sodium or lithium soap base	2	265–295	350	Pass Federal Test Method Std. No. 791 Method 5309.2
	Steam temp 600–825°F	Nonsoap base	1 or 2	265–340	500	Pass Federal Test Method Std. No. 791 Method 5309.2
	Steam temp over 825°F	Silicone	1 or 2	265–340	520	Pass Military G-3278

° An alternate lubricant for sliding pedestal supports is a mixture of fine graphite and cylinder or turbine oil mixed to a paste consistency.

Grease Maintenance   New grease should be added only when the grease in service is found to be in good condition.

Any grease in service that has separated mechanically or has been contaminated with water, chemicals, or other impurities should be discarded.   The equipment should be cleaned thoroughly before the new charge of grease is used.

Use the proper amount of grease.   Excess grease can cause overheating of bearings.

Section 5

Prime Movers

STEAM TURBINES

General

The steam turbine is the most widely used prime mover on the market. In large capacities, it rules without competition; for smaller sizes, the gas turbine and the internal-combustion engine are its only competitors; but for the smallest sizes both the reciprocating steam engine and the internal-combustion engine compete with the steam turbine for the market.

Steam turbines have been designed and built for an output ranging from a few horse-power up to 1,000,000 kw; with speeds ranging from less than 1,000 rpm to more than 30,000 rpm; for inlet pressures from subatmospheric up to approximately the critical pressure of steam; with inlet temperatures from those corresponding to saturated steam up to 1050°F; and for exhaust vacuums up to 29½ in. Hg.

The turbine requires much less space than an internal-combustion engine or a reciprocating steam engine and much lighter foundations since the reciprocating forces on the foundations are eliminated.

Another major advantage of the turbine is its ability to extract power from the steam and then exhaust all the steam or part of it into a heating system or to a manufacturing process, entirely free from oil.

The simplicity, reliability, and low maintenance cost of the turbine and its ability to supply both power and heat are the main justifications for the industrial turbine. A small factory or a building complex cannot produce electric power as cheaply as a large central-station power plant; but if steam is needed for industrial purposes or for heating, the production of power can be combined with the utilization of extracted or exhaust steam and the power becomes a cheap by-product.

The small noncondensing turbine also occupies a large and important field in power plants and marine installations because it is particularly adapted to drive variable-speed auxiliaries and because its exhaust steam can be used to supply heat to the feed-water. A further advantage of the auxiliary turbine is its availability and convenience as a standby unit in case of interruptions to the power supply of motor-driven auxiliaries.

Steam Cycles

The Rankine Cycle Potential energy of steam is transformed into mechanical energy in a turbine. The number of Btu required to perform work at the rate of one horse-power for one hour is 2,544; for one kilowatt for one hour it is 3,413 Btu.

The enthalpy, or heat content, is expressed as Btu per pound of steam. This is, in effect, the potential energy contained in the steam measured above the conventionally accepted zero point (that of condensed steam at 32°F). Practically it is not possible to release all the energy, so that the end point of heat extraction in a condensing turbine is given by the temperature attainable in the condenser. The considerable amount of energy still contained in the steam at this point cannot be recovered and serves only to heat the cooling water.

The portion of the potential energy that can be used to produce power is called the "available energy" and is represented by the isentropic enthalpy difference between the initial steam condition h_1 and the final condition corresponding to the exhaust pressure h_2. If the condensate enthalpy is h_w, the "ideal Rankine cycle efficiency," or the "thermal efficiency," is

$$\eta_R = \frac{h_1 - h_2}{h_1 - h_w}$$

The available energy can be converted into mechanical (kinetic) energy only with certain losses due to steam friction and throttling, which increase the entropy of the steam. The end pressure is therefore attained at a higher steam enthalpy h_2' than with isentropic expansion. The "internal turbine efficiency" then is

$$\eta_i = \frac{h_1 - h_2'}{h_1 - h_2}$$

This efficiency may be reduced to the "external turbine efficiency" by including the mechanical and leakage losses not incident to the steam cycle.

Since one horsepower-hour is equivalent to 2,544 Btu/hr, the theoretical steam rate of the Rankine cycle in lb/hp-hr is obtained by dividing 2,544 by the available energy in Btu. The corresponding value on a lb/kwhr basis may be found by dividing 3,413 by the available energy. To obtain the actual steam rate at the coupling of the turbine, the theoretical steam rate is divided by the "external turbine efficiency," which includes the mechanical losses.

To facilitate steam-cycle calculations, standard tables of the thermodynamic properties of steam are reproduced in abstract on pages 3-47 to 3-55 of Sec. 3. The data contained in these tables are plotted on a "Mollier diagram" as Fig. 5-1, which is employed extensively to solve thermodynamic problems relating to steam turbines.

Example: Determine the performance of a condensing turbine operating on a Rankine cycle based on the following data:

Initial steam pressure.	200 psia
Initial steam temperature	600°F
Exhaust steam pressure	2 in. Hg
Moisture in exhaust steam	5%
Exhaust steam temperature	101°F
Measured steam rate	10.5 lb/hp-hr

From the Mollier diagram:

Enthalpy at inlet h_1.	1,322 Btu/lb
Entropy at inlet.	1.6767 Btu/°F
Enthalpy at 2 in. Hg and entropy of 1.6767 (h_2)	936 Btu/lb
Enthalpy at 2 in. Hg and 5% moisture (h_2')	1,054 Btu/lb
Enthalpy of saturated liquid at 2 in. Hg (h_w)	69 Btu/lb

Calculations:

Isentropic enthalpy drop $= h_1 - h_2 = 1,322 - 936 = 386$ Btu/lb
Actual enthalpy drop $= h_1 - h_2' = 1,322 - 1,054 = 268$ Btu/lb

$$\text{Ideal Rankine cycle efficiency} = \eta_R = \frac{h_1 - h_2}{h_1 - h_w}$$

$$= \frac{1,322 - 936}{1,322 - 69} = \frac{386}{1,253} = 30.8\%$$

$$\text{Internal turbine efficiency} = \eta_i = \frac{h_1 - h_2'}{h_1 - h_2}$$

$$= \frac{1,322 - 1,054}{1,322 - 936} = \frac{268}{386} = 69.5\%$$

$$\text{Rankine cycle steam rate} = \frac{2,544}{h_1 - h_2} = \frac{2,544}{386} = 6.6 \text{ lb/hp-hr}$$

$$\text{External turbine efficiency} = \frac{\text{Rankine cycle steam rate}}{\text{measured steam rate}}$$

$$= \frac{6.6}{10.5} = 63\%$$

Improvements in the Rankine cycle may be obtained by raising the initial pressure and temperature. However, to avoid excessive moisture in the low-pressure stages, the increase in pressure must be accompanied by a corresponding increase in temperature. With present alloy steels the upper limit of the cycle is about 1050°F. The

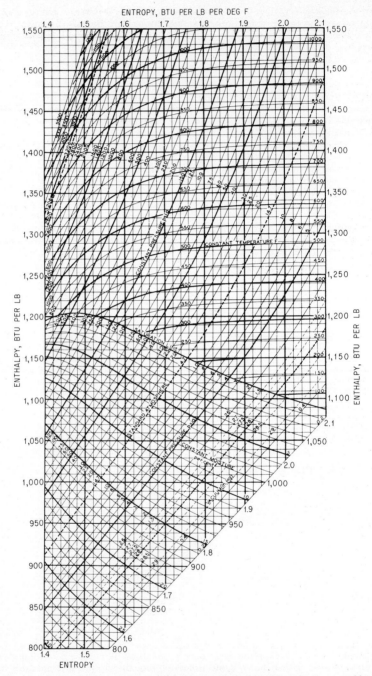

Fig. 5-1 Mollier diagram. *(Computed by permission from 1967 ASME Steam Tables.)*

lower limit of the cycle depends on the maximum vacuum obtainable with the available cooling water and rarely exceeds 29¼ to 29½ in. Hg. The economical limit of the cycle for a particular size of plant may be determined by a study of relative costs and savings.

The Reheat Cycle The reheat cycle, which is sometimes used for large units, is similar to the Rankine with the exception that the steam is reheated in one or more steps during its expansion.

The reheating may be accomplished by passing the partly expanded steam through a steam superheater, a special reheat boiler, or a heat exchanger using high-pressure live steam. The internal thermal efficiency of the cycle is calculated by totaling the available energy converted in each part of the expansion, as shown on the Mollier diagram, and dividing by the total heat supplied in the boiler, in the superheater, and in the reheat boiler or heat exchanger.

In a plant operating with a steam pressure of 1,000 psi, a steam temperature of 750°F and an exhaust pressure of 1 in. Hg with one stage of reheating to 750°F at 175 psi in a reheat boiler, the increase in thermal efficiency is about 7½ percent. With two reheating stages the improvement over the straight Rankine cycle becomes approximately 10½ percent.

The main advantage of the reheat cycle is that excessive moisture in the low-pressure stages is avoided without employing high initial steam temperature.

The Regenerative Cycle In the regenerative or feed-heating cycle, steam is withdrawn from the turbine at various points to supply heat to the feedwater. A considerable gain in economy may be obtained by using this cycle since the extracted steam has already given up part of its heat doing work in the turbine, and because the latent heat of the steam condensed in the feedwater heaters is conserved and returned to the boiler, thus reducing the heat loss to the condenser.

The cycle efficiency may be calculated using a method similar to that already mentioned, but, in connection with this cycle, it is customary to design a flow diagram and to prepare a complete heat balance of the plant. In small and medium-sized plants, one or two extraction heaters may be used in addition to the exhaust heater which serves the steam-driven auxiliaries, and in large plants up to four or five heaters may be employed.

Additional plant economies result from reduced size of the condenser. From the viewpoint of steam generation, however, the load on the boiler is slightly increased to compensate for the steam extracted to the feed heaters. Furthermore, the higher temperature of the feedwater, while reducing the size of the economizer, also decreases the boiler efficiency by raising the lower level of the combustion gas cycle. This conflict between turbine and boiler cycle efficiencies may be removed by installing an air heater, which restores this lower level and permits the full benefit of the more economic method of regenerative feed heating. On pages 5-23 to 5-25 a method of estimating gains from feedwater heating is given.

Classification of Turbines

To broaden the understanding of turbines and to assist in the preliminary selection of a type suitable for a proposed application, Table 5-1 has been prepared. In this table the general field of application is shown, with corresponding steam and operating conditions which may be provided for in the design of the turbine.

As an example, an industrial plant may use a moderate amount of power which can be obtained at low cost from the steam required for some chemical process; in this case a condensing, high-pressure turbine with single or double extraction would be selected, with steam pressure, temperature, and extraction corresponding to the desired conditions. As an alternative, a noncondensing, back-pressure turbine might be considered, particularly when power and steam requirements are nearly balanced. The advantage of this type of plant is a less expensive turbine and the elimination of condensing equipment.

In recent years, the superposed or topping turbine has found considerable favor in large power stations and industrial plants to provide additional power or process steam and, incidentally, to improve station economy. This turbine is usually of the high-

**TABLE 5-1   Classification of Steam Turbines with Reference to
Application and Operating Condition**

Basic type	Operating condition	Steam condition	Application
Condensing	High-pressure turbine (with or without extraction for feedwater heating)	100–2,400 psig, saturated, 1050°F, 1–5 in. Hg abs	Drivers for electric generators, blowers, compressors, pumps, marine propulsion, etc.
	Low-pressure turbine	0–100 psig, saturated, 750°F, 1–5 in Hg abs	Drivers for electric generators, blowers, compressors, pumps, etc.
	Reheat turbine	1,450–3,500 psig, 900–1050°F, 1–5 in. Hg abs	Electric-utility plants
	Automatic extraction turbine	100–2,400 psig, saturated, 1050°F, 1–5 in. Hg abs	Drivers for electric generators, blowers, compressors, pumps, etc.
	Mixed-pressure (induction) turbine	100–2,400 psig, saturated, 1050°F, 1–5 in. Hg abs	Drivers for electric generators, blowers, compressors, pumps, etc.
	Cross-compound turbine (with or without extraction for feedwater heating, with or without reheat)	400–1,450 psig, 750–1,050°F, 1–5 in Hg abs	Marine propulsion
Noncondensing	Straight-through turbine	600–3,500 psig, 600–1050°F, atmosphere, 1,000 psig	Drivers for electric generators, blowers, compressors, pumps, etc.
	Automatic extraction turbine	600–3,500 psig, 600–1050°F, atmosphere, 600 psig	

speed, multistage type.   Because of the small specific volume of the steam at high pressure, it becomes possible to concentrate a large amount of power in a turbine and boiler plant of relatively small physical dimensions; thus in many cases the plant capacity may be greatly increased without extensions to existing buildings.

Small turbines for auxiliary drives are usually of the single-stage, noncondensing type exhausting at atmospheric or slightly higher pressure into a deaerating feed heater or to a heating system.   In many cases small turbines are used as standby or quick-starting emergency units, or for variable-speed applications.

The final selection of a turbine type depends on its place and functions in the scheme of the complete steam plant.   When all pertinent information has been collected and the many factors bearing on the problem have been closely estimated, a tabulation of various alternatives may be prepared.

As a general principle, the investment and operating costs of a less complicated and less expansive turbine and boiler plant may be balanced against increments of savings anticipated with more elaborate equipment.   Thus, the selection of the turbine may be based on optimum economy.

Turbine Performance

The problem of determining tentative performance of steam turbines is frequently encountered in connection with preliminary estimates for proposed industrial steam plants, investigations pertaining to extensions and modernization of existing plants, or for the purpose of making comparisons between steam and electrically driven aux-iliaries as sometimes required in heat-balance calculations for power plants or for ship propulsion.

At this stage the available information usually is rather incomplete or based on as-sumptions; therefore, a "short method" yielding results sufficiently accurate to serve as a yardstick in comparing different alternatives may be justified. Following the same reasoning, the actual design of the turbine and its physical dimensions are as yet un-known. As a preliminary approach only the required horsepower, the approximate speed, and the steam conditions are available, or assumed; hence average turbine efficiencies may be employed.

In the final analysis it may be found that the turbine manufacturer will suggest alter-native performances depending on type of turbine, available standard frame sizes, and other considerations. Steam rates based on guaranteed performance, applying to the selected operating conditions, should be used for final calculations.

From a study of a number of tests and published reports relating to various sizes and types of steam turbines, it is possible to establish fairly consistent efficiency curves applying to groups of similar turbines operated at selected standard conditions. A simple classification may include, for instance, multistage turbines, condensing and noncondensing, in sizes from 200 to 100,000 rated horsepower, used as main units, as shown in Fig. 5-2, and single-stage turbines, noncondensing, in sizes from 25 to 500 rated horsepower, for auxiliary or mechanical drive, as illustrated in Fig. 5-3.

The curves refer to efficiencies at full load and are based on the assumption that a series of suitable frame sizes is available permitting the selection of wheel diameter, steam inlet and exhaust sizes, and other design features appropriate to the horse-power in question. Average correction factors for superheat and for vacuum applying to the efficiency curves of multistage turbines are inserted in Fig. 5-2; ordinary methods of interpolation for values between the curves may also be used, but a consistent pro-cedure should be employed to obtain true comparisons.

Partial load performance of a group of turbines is more difficult to standardize than the performance at rated or full load. However, for preliminary estimates a multiply-ing steam-rate factor for a given partial load (usually one-half load) as shown in the upper part of Fig. 5-2 for multistage and in Fig. 5-3 for single-stage turbines may be employed.

A general method of determining the steam rate at any load is based on the use of the so-called "Willan's line" (see Fig. 5-10). When a turbine is operating under throttle control at constant rpm, the relation between total steam flow (lb/hr) and horsepower output may be shown graphically by a nearly straight line which is called the Willan's line. Therefore, with the steam rates at full load and one-half load determined with the aid of Fig. 5-2 or 5-3 the total steam flow at these points can be calculated and the Willan's line for the turbine can be drawn; sometimes the steam flow at no load is known from tests of similar turbines, or can be estimated as a percentage of the full-load steam flow, in which case the no-load instead of the half-load point may be used for the Willan's line. Steam rates at any load may then be calculated by dividing the total steam flow obtained from the Willan's line by the corresponding horsepower.

Partial-load steam rates are improved by the use of so-called nozzle cutout with multi-port governor valves on larger turbines and by hand-operated nozzle valves on small single-stage turbines. Individual Willan's lines then apply to each nozzle combina-tion, and the steam-rate curve is "stepped" in relation to these lines; thus better partial-load steam rates result than may be obtained by simple throttle governing.

Other types such as high-pressure (topping) turbines and low-pressure condensing (exhaust) turbines are usually built to suit special requirements; efficiencies and performance estimates should therefore be obtained from the turbine manufacturers. Extraction or induction turbines also require special study based on anticipated power load and steam demand as illustrated by a typical case in a following section.

Marine turbines may be considered a special class of turbines, developed to meet conditions characteristic of ship propulsion. Elaborate heat-balance calculations are always made to determine the overall fuel consumption of the complete plant including its auxiliaries and ship's service requirements.

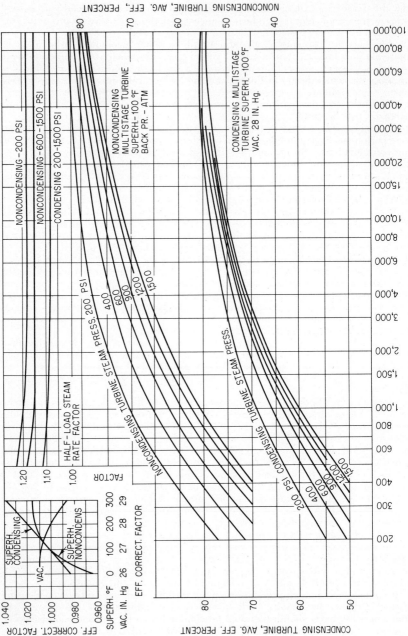

Fig. 5-2 Average efficiency of multistage turbines (gear loss not included).

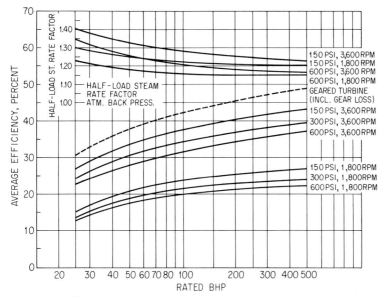

Fig. 5-3   Average efficiency of single-stage turbines (noncondensing, dry, and saturated steam).

To illustrate the method of using the curves, a few problems have been worked out pertaining to the selection of turbines.

Example 1:   Determine the steam rate and total steam per hour of a 500-hp turbine operating at an inlet steam pressure of 300 psi, 100°F superheat, exhaust pressure 10 psi, and a speed of 3,600 rpm.

The steam tables on pages 3-47 to 3-55 and also the Mollier diagram are based on absolute pressure; therefore, 15 lb (14.7) is added to the inlet and outlet steam pressures, which are given in pounds gage in the example.   Further, the steam temperature at 315 psia is 421.8°F; adding 100°F superheat, a total steam temperature of 522°F is obtained.

From the Mollier diagram the enthalpy at the turbine inlet is 1,269 Btu, and expanding the steam at a constant entropy of 1.577 the enthalpy at the exhaust condition is 1,064 Btu.   Thus the available energy is 205 Btu.   Dividing 2,544 by 205 gives the theoretical steam rate of 12.42 lb/hp-hr.

From the curves it appears that the required 500 hp would fall in the lower range of a multistage turbine, or if a single-stage turbine is considered it would be close to the upper limit covered by standard frame sizes, suggesting that both alternatives should be investigated.

Thus, in the case of the multistage, noncondensing turbine the average efficiency for the specified condition is about 61.5 percent, obtained from the curve in Fig. 5-2, by interpolation for 300 psi steam pressure.   Since the efficiency curves in Fig. 5-2 are based on 100°F, the superheat correction factor is 1.00.

The efficiency correction for back pressure is small in this case and may be neglected in preliminary calculations.   To obtain the actual steam rate, the theoretical steam rate of 12.42 lb is divided by the average efficiency 0.615.   A steam rate of 20.20 lb/hp-hr may thus be expected, referred to the output at the turbine coupling.   The total steam required at the rated load then becomes 10,100 lb/hr.

Referring to a single-stage noncondensing turbine of 500 rated horsepower operating at the same steam conditions and speed, the efficiency as indicated in the curve in Fig. 5-3 would be about 39.5 percent, resulting in a steam rate of 31.4 lb/hp-hr or a total steam requirement of about 15,700 lb/hr.

This curve also illustrates the advantage of geared turbines as compared with direct drive when the driven machine must be operated at low speed.   For instance, a pump used as an auxiliary in a power station may require 500 hp at 1,800 rpm, in which case a direct-connected single-stage turbine would have an efficiency of about 24 percent, while a geared turbine may show an efficiency of 49 percent at the gear output coupling. Assuming the same steam conditions as before, the direct-driven unit would require about 26,000 lb of steam per hour as compared with 12,700 lb, or about one-half, for the geared turbine.

In connection with turbines exhausting into feedwater heaters or when the exhaust steam is used for heating or for process steam, it may be necessary to determine the enthalpy and the superheat or moisture in the steam after it passes through the turbine.

The method usually employed is to subtract the heat actually converted to work in the turbine, as expressed by the average (or more correctly the internal) efficiency, from the enthalpy at the inlet condition; this gives the enthalpy available in the exhaust steam.   The superheat or moisture is then conveniently obtained from the Mollier diagram at the point of intersection between the remaining enthalpy and the appropriate absolute back pressure.

To illustrate this, in the case of the 500-hp multistage turbine operating at 315 psia, 522°F total steam temperature, and 25 psia exhaust pressure with an average efficiency of 61.5 percent, the calculations are made as follows: the available energy is 205 Btu and with an efficiency of 61.5 percent the work done in the turbine is 126 Btu; deducting this from the enthalpy at the inlet condition, which is 1,269 Btu, leaves 1,143 Btu in the steam at the turbine exhaust.   The intersection on the Mollier diagram at 25 psia and the enthalpy of 1,143 Btu is the approximate "end point" of the expansion in the turbine, and the exhaust steam contains about 1¾ percent moisture.   In this case, if dry steam is desired at the turbine exhaust, the initial steam temperature must be increased to about 550°F.

As a comparison, the single-stage direct-connected 500-hp turbine would convert to useful work 39.5 percent of the available energy; thus the enthalpy at the turbine exhaust would be 1,188 Btu, corresponding to about 55° of superheat, at 25 psia.   The interrelations between the various factors entering the problem are easily understood by referring to the Mollier diagram.

Applying this example to an actual case, approximately dry steam may be required at the point where the process steam is used; therefore, after an allowance has been made for radiation loss in the connecting steam pipe, the appropriate initial steam temperature can be selected.   If moisture is permissible at the exhaust, a corresponding correction in steam flow is made to ensure that an adequate supply of process heat is available.

Example 2:   In connection with a present and future plant, it may be desired to compare the steam rate of a straight condensing turbine driving a 2,500-kw generator at two different steam conditions, alternative A, 250 psi, 500°F, 28 in. Hg, and alternative B, 600 psi, 750°F, 28.5 in. Hg.   Assuming a generator efficiency of 94.5 percent, the required full-load output of the turbine is about 3,550 hp.   From the curve in Fig. 5-2, which is based on rated brake horsepower and applies to multistage condensing turbines, average efficiency of 74.25 and 71.3 percent, respectively, are obtained.

In the first case the vacuum is 28 in. Hg and the superheat 94°F, which is close to the standard conditions used as a basis for this curve; therefore, no correction factors are necessary.   The expected steam rate, obtained by dividing the theoretical rate, 6.77 lb/hp-hr, by the efficiency, 0.7425, is 9.12 lb/hp-hr and the total steam flow 32,350 lb/hr.

In the second case, a vacuum correction factor of about 0.993 is approximated from the insert on the curve for 28.5 in. Hg, and since the superheat is 260°F, the correction factor for superheat is about 1.029.   These are multiplying factors; thus the turbine efficiency is increased to 72.8 percent.   The steam rate then becomes 7.06 lb/hp-hr, and the total steam required is 25,100 lb/hr.   Referring to turbine-driven generators, the performance is usually expressed in terms of pounds of steam per kilowatthour, which transposition may conveniently be made by dividing the total steam per hour by the kilowatt output at the terminals.   Thus the respective steam rates are 12.93 and 10.02 lb/kwhr, including the generator loss.

The following tabulation will serve to illustrate the comparison:

Alternative	A	B
Output, kw	2,500	2,500
Output, bhp	3,550	3,550
Steam pressure, psi.	250	600
Steam temp, °F	500	750
Vacuum, in. Hg.	28	28.5
Available enthalpy drop, Btu	376	495
Theoretical steam rate, lb/hp-hr	6.77	5.14
Turbine efficiency from curve	74.25	71.3
Turbine efficiency corrected, %	74.25	72.8
Steam rate, lb/hp-hr.	9.12	7.06
Steam rate, lb/kwhr.	12.93	10.02
Total steam, lb/hr	32,350	25,100

It should be noted, however, that the saving of 7,250 lb steam/hr, or 22.4 percent as shown by this example, does not represent the actual fuel saving corresponding to alternative B. As mentioned in connection with turbine cycles, the heat supplied to the cycle must be considered. For the two examples the initial enthalpies are 1,263 and 1,380 Btu/lb, the condensate enthalpies 69 and 60 Btu/lb; so the Rankine-cycle efficiencies are 31.5 and 37.5 percent, and with the external turbine efficiencies of 74.25 and 72.8 percent the final external thermal efficiencies are 23.35 and 27.27 percent, respectively. So the increase in cycle efficiency is 16.8 percent and, with the same boiler efficiency, the saving in fuel 14.4 percent. Further improvement would result if the comparison were based on the regenerative cycle rather than on the straight condensing Rankine cycle.

Turbine Design

The steam turbine is a comparatively simple type of prime mover. It has only one major moving part, the rotor which carries the buckets or blades. These, with the stationary nozzles or blades, form the steam path through the turbine. The rotor is mounted on a shaft which is supported on journal bearings, and axially positioned by a thrust bearing. A housing with steam inlet and outlet connections surrounds the rotating parts and serves as a frame for the unit.

However, a great number of factors enter into the design of a modern turbine, and its present perfection is the result of many years of research and development. While the design procedure may be studied in books treating this particular subject, a short review of the main principles may serve to present a comparison between the various types. This will aid in the selection and evaluation of turbines suitable for specific requirements.

Considering the method of energy conversion, two main types of blading are employed, namely, impulse and reaction. An impulse stage consists of one or more stationary nozzles in which the steam expands, transforming heat energy into velocity or kinetic energy; and one or more rows of rotating buckets which transform the kinetic energy of the steam into power delivered by the shaft. In a true impulse stage the full expansion of the steam takes place in the nozzle. Hence, no pressure drop occurs while the steam passes through the buckets.

A reaction stage consists of two elements. There is a stationary row of blades in which part of the expansion of the steam takes place, and a moving row where the pressure drop of the stage is completed.

Many turbines employ both impulse and reaction stages to obtain the inherent advantages of each type.

Figure 5-4 illustrates some of the most common types of nozzle and blade combinations used in present turbines. Four of the diagrams, a, b, c, and d, apply to the impulse principle as noted in the text under each picture and the last one, e, shows a type of reaction blading. A constructional difference may also be pointed out; impulse

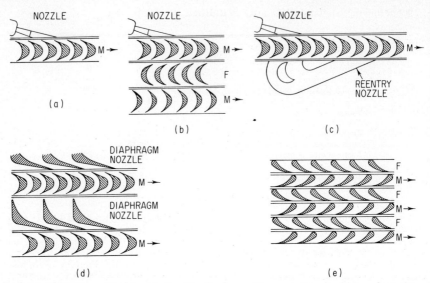

Fig. 5-4 Main types of turbine blading (F = fixed row, M = moving row). (*a*) Impulse turbine, single velocity stage. (*b*) Impulse turbine, two velocity stages. (*c*) Reentry impulse turbine, two velocity stages. (*d*) Impulse turbine, multistage. (*e*) Reaction turbine, multistage.

buckets are usually carried on separate disks with nozzles provided in stationary partitions called diaphragms while the moving reaction blades are generally supported on a rotor drum with the stationary blades mounted in a casing.

The impulse stage has a definite advantage over the reaction stage in handling steam with small specific volume as in the high-pressure end of a turbine or where the enthalpy drop per stage is great; thus small single-stage turbines are always of the impulse type. It may be designed for partial admission with the nozzles covering only a part of the full circumference; therefore, the diameter of the wheel may be chosen independently of the bucket height. Used as a first stage in a multistage turbine, the impulse stage with partial admission permits adjustment of the nozzle area by arranging the nozzles in separate groups under governor control, thus improving partial load performance.

The dominating principle in turbine design involves the expression of the efficiency of the energy conversion in nozzles and buckets or in reaction blades, usually referred to as stage efficiency, as a function of the ratio u/C. The blade speed u, fps, is calculated from the pitch diameter of the nozzle and thus determines the size of the wheel at a given rpm and C, also in fps, is the theoretical velocity of the steam corresponding to the isentropic enthalpy drop in the stage, expressed by the formula

$$C = 223.8 \sqrt{\text{Btu}}$$

Figure 5-5 illustrates average stage efficiencies which may be attained in various types of turbines operating at design conditions. The losses that are represented in the stage-efficiency curves are due to friction, eddies, and flow interruptions in the steam path, plus the kinetic energy of the steam as it leaves a row of blades.

Part of the latter loss can be recovered in the following stage. Additional losses not accounted for in the stage-efficiency curves are due to windage and friction of the rotating parts, and steam leakage from stage to stage. With the exception of the kinetic energy that may be recovered, all losses are converted to heat with a corresponding increase in the entropy of the steam.

From the group of curves of Fig. 5-5 it follows that the maximum combined efficiency for various types of stages is attained at different velocity ratios. This ratio is highest for reaction stages and lowest for three-row impulse wheels. This implies that for equal pitch-line speeds the theoretical steam velocity or the stage enthalpy drop must be lowest for reaction stages and highest for three-row wheels to maintain the maximum possible efficiency. At this maximum efficiency, the three-row wheel can work with many times the steam velocity and a correspondingly larger enthalpy drop compared with a reaction stage.

The maximum efficiency of reaction stages may exceed 90 percent at a velocity ratio of 0.85, as shown in Fig. 5-5. However, these values can be attained only with a great number of stages. Hence, they are normally not designed for a higher velocity ratio than 0.65. A section of reaction blading is shown in Fig. 5-4e.

Single-row impulse stages have a maximum efficiency of about 80 percent at a velocity ratio of 0.45. Figure 5-4a shows a combination of impulse buckets with a De Laval expanding nozzle; and Fig. 5-4d shows multistage impulse blading with nonexpanding nozzles.

Assuming, as an example, a blade speed of 500 fps, corresponding to a turbine wheel with 32 in. pitch diameter operating at a speed of 3,600 rpm, the optimum steam velocity would be $500/0.45 = 1,100$ fps. The kinetic energy of the steam may be expressed in Btu by the relation Btu $= (C/223.8)^2 = 1,100^2/50,000 = 24$; thus the enthalpy drop utilized per stage at the point of maximum efficiency is about 24 Btu for the above condition.

In the case of a turbine operating at high steam pressure and temperature, exhausting at low vacuum the available energy may be approximately 500 Btu; therefore, about 20 single-row impulse stages would be required for maximum efficiency. Obviously the pitch diameter of the wheels cannot be chosen arbitrarily, but this example illustrates the method of dividing the energy in a number of steps called pressure stages. The turbine would be classified as a multistage impulse turbine.

Figure 5-5 further shows one curve labeled two-row with an extension in broken line referring to small single-stage turbines and one curve marked three-row impulse wheel. These refer to so-called velocity-compounded stages as illustrated by Fig. 5-4b and c. The purpose of the two- and three-row and also the reentry stage is to utilize a much greater enthalpy drop per stage than that possible in a single-row impulse stage. When the enthalpy drop per stage is increased, the velocity ratio is reduced and the kinetic energy is only partly converted into work in the first row of revolving buckets; thus the steam leaves with high residual velocity. By means of stationary guide buckets the steam is then redirected into a second, and sometimes a third, row of moving buckets, where the energy conversion is completed.

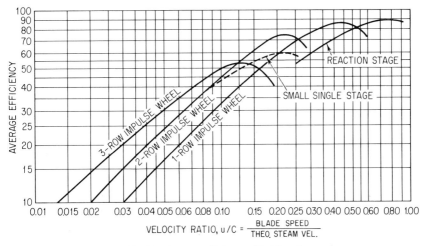

Fig. 5-5 Average efficiency of turbine stages.

In the so-called helical-flow stage, with semicircular buckets milled into the rim of the wheel, and also in the reentry stage shown in Fig. 5-4c, only one row of revolving buckets is used. This type of velocity compounding is sometimes employed in noncondensing single-stage auxiliary turbines.

The curve marked two-row impulse wheel indicates that a maximum stage efficiency of about 68 percent may be attained at a velocity ratio of approximately 0.225. At this condition, the two-row velocity-compounded stage will utilize about four times as much energy as a single-row impulse stage. Comparing the efficiencies on the basis of operating conditions as defined by the velocity ratio, it appears from the curves that the two-row wheel has a higher efficiency than a single row when the velocity ratio is less than 0.27.

Occasionally, in small auxiliary turbines operating at low speed ratio, a three-row stage may be used. The curve marked three-row indicates a maximum efficiency of about 53 percent at a speed ratio of about 0.125. Apparently, at this point the efficiency of a two-row wheel is almost as good, thus the three-row stage would be justified only at still lower speed ratios, that is, for low-speed applications.

The design of a turbine, especially of the multistage type, involves a great many factors which must be evaluated and considered. A detailed study of the steam path must be made, various frictional and leakage losses which tend to decrease the efficiency, as well as compensating factors such as reheat and carryover, must be computed and accounted for in the final analysis of the performance of the turbine. Stresses must be calculated to permit correct proportioning of the component parts of the turbine, and materials suitable for the various requirements must be selected.

Single-stage Turbines

Single-stage turbines, sometimes called mechanical-drive or general-purpose turbines, are usually designed to operate noncondensing or against a moderate back pressure. The principal use of these turbines is to drive power-plant and marine auxiliaries such as centrifugal pumps, fans, blowers, and small generator sets. They may also be applied as prime movers in industrial plants, and in many cases small turbines are installed as standby units to provide protection in case of interruption of the electric-power supply.

They are built in sizes up to 1,500 hp and may be obtained in standardized frames up to 1,000 hp with wheel diameters from 12 to 36 in. Rotational speeds vary from 600 to 7,200 rpm, or higher; the lower speeds apply to the larger wheel sizes used with direct-connected turbines and the higher speeds are favored in geared units. The bucket speed usually falls between 250 and 450 fps in direct-connected turbines operating at 3,600 rpm and may exceed 600 fps in geared turbines.

The efficiency of a turbine generally improves with increasing bucket speed as noted by referring to efficiency vs. velocity ratio curves in Fig. 5-5; thus it would seem that both high revolutions and large diameters might be desirable. However, for a constant rpm the rotation loss of the disk and the buckets varies roughly as the fifth power of the wheel diameter and for a constant bucket speed almost as the square of the diameter. Thus, in direct-connected turbines with the speed fixed by the driven unit, the rotation losses may become the dominating factor in selecting the wheel size for maximum efficiency. On the other hand, when reduction gears are adopted, the velocity ratio may be increased by means of higher revolutions, sometimes even with smaller wheel diameter; thus considerably higher efficiencies may be expected as shown by the dashed curve in Fig. 5-3. Since the rotation losses vary approximately in direct relation to the density of the steam surrounding the wheel, it follows that small wheel diameters should be used particularly for operation at high back pressure.

Turbine manufacturers have complete test data on standard sizes of small turbines on which steam-rate guarantees are based. Knowing the characteristics of different turbines, they are thus in a position to offer suggestions regarding the most suitable type and size to choose for specific requirements.

The single-stage turbine is simple and rugged and can be depended on to furnish many years of service with a minimum of maintenance expense. The few parts which may require renewal after long periods of operation, for instance, bearings, carbon

rings, and possibly valve parts, are inexpensive and easy to install. It is also comparatively simple to exchange the steam nozzles to suit different steam conditions as sometimes encountered in connection with modernization of old plants, or to adapt the
turbine to new conditions due to changes in process steam requirements.

Steam-rate Calculations Approximate steam rates of small single-stage turbines
(less than 500 hp) may be computed by the following general method:

1. The available energy, $h_1 - h_2 = H_a$, at the specified steam condition is obtained
from the Mollier diagram.

2. Deductions are made for pressure drop through the governor valve (12.5 Btu), loss
due to supersaturation C_s (about 0.95), and 2 percent margin (0.98). The remaining
enthalpy drop is called net available energy H_n.

3. The theoretical steam velocity C, fps, is calculated, based on net available energy
H_n. The formula for steam velocity is $C = 223.8 \times \sqrt{H_n}$.

4. The bucket speed u, fps, is calculated from the pitch diameter, in. (of the nozzles),
and the rpm.

5. The velocity ratio u/C is calculated and the "basic" turbine efficiency E is obtained from an actual test curve similar to those given in Fig. 5-5.

6. The "basic" steam rate for the turbine is calculated from the formula

$$\text{Basic steam rate} = \frac{2,544}{H_n E C_s \times 0.98} = \text{lb/hp-hr}$$

7. The loss horsepower for the specific turbine size is estimated from Fig. 5-6, corrected for back pressure as noted on the chart.

8. The actual steam rate of the turbine at the specified conditions is

$$\text{Basic steam rate} \times \frac{\text{rated hp} + \text{loss hp}}{\text{rated hp}} = \text{lb/hp-hr}$$

Example: As a matter of comparison with the "short method" of estimating turbine
performance, the same example (on page 5-9) of a 500-hp turbine with a steam condition of 300 psi, 100°F superheat, and 10 psi back pressure at a speed of 3,600 rpm may
be selected. It is further assumed that a frame size with a 24-in.-pitch-diameter two-
row wheel is used.

The available energy is 205 Btu; subtracting 12.5 Btu drop through the governor valve
leaves 192.5 net Btu, which corresponds to a theoretical steam velocity $C = 223.8 \times
\sqrt{192.5} = 3,104$ fps.

The bucket speed $u = 3,600 \times 24 \times \pi/60 \times 12 = 377$ fps. Thus the velocity ratio
$u/C = 377/3,104 = 0.12$. From Fig. 5-5 on page 5-13 the approximate efficiency 0.47
is obtained on the curve marked "two-row impulse wheel" at $u/C = 0.12$.

The supersaturation loss factor C_s (due to the expansion of the steam into supersaturation state) is a function increasing with the initial superheat and decreasing with the
available enthalpy, in this case about 0.96; a margin of 2 percent may also be included,
thus the

$$\text{Basic steam rate} = \frac{2,544}{192.5 \times 0.47 \times 0.96 \times 0.98} = 30.0 \text{ lb/hp-hr}$$

The rotational loss of a 24-in.-pitch-diameter wheel at 3,600 rpm, determined from
Fig. 5-6, is about 6.3 hp. This chart is based on atmospheric exhaust pressure; therefore, a correction factor must be applied as noted on the chart. At 10 lb back pressure
the specific volume of the steam is about 16.3 cu ft/lb. Thus

$$\text{Loss hp} = 6.3 \times \frac{22}{16.3} = 8.5$$

$$\text{Steam rate of turbine} = 30.0 \times \frac{500 + 8.5}{500} = 30.5 \text{ lb/hp-hr}$$

The use of the "short method" and Fig. 5-3 results in a steam rate of 31.4 lb/hp-hr in
this case, which is about 3 percent higher than that obtained by calculations applying

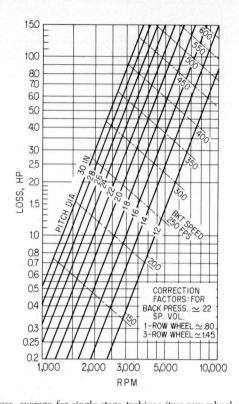

Fig. 5-6 Rotational loss, average for single-stage turbines (two-row wheel, atmosphere exhaust).

Figs. 5-5 and 5-6; both methods are consistent and may serve the purpose for which they are suggested.

Multistage Turbines

The most important application of the steam turbine is that of serving as prime mover to drive generators, blast-furnace blowers, air compressors, pumps, etc., and for ship propulsion. Since the economic production of power is the main objective, these turbines are generally of the multistage type, designed for condensing operation; i.e., the exhaust steam from the turbine passes into a condenser, in which a high vacuum is maintained.

The dominating factor affecting the economy, which may be expressed in terms of station heat rate or fuel consumption, is the selection of the steam cycle and its range of operating conditions, as previously discussed in connection with turbine cycles.   For smaller units the straight condensing Rankine cycle may be used; for medium and large turbines the feed-heating, regenerative cycle is preferred; and in large base-load stations a combination of a reheating, regenerative cycle may offer important advantages.

Assuming average economical considerations, such as capacity of the plant and size of the individual units, load characteristics, and amount of investment, the initial steam conditions may be found to vary approximately as follows:

Small units	150 to 400 psi; 500 to 750°F
Medium	400 to 600 psi; 750 to 825°F
Large.	600 to 900 psi; 750 to 900°F
Large.	900 to 2,000 psi; 825 to 1050°F

Similar conditions may prevail with reference to the vacuum; smaller units may operate at 26 to 28 in. Hg in connection with spray ponds or cooling towers, while larger turbines usually carry 28 to 29 in. Hg and require a large supply of cooling water.

These general specifications are equivalent to an available enthalpy drop varying from about 350 Btu to a maximum of about 600 Btu. Therefore, the modern condensing turbine must be built to handle a large enthalpy drop; hence a comparatively large number of stages is required to obtain a high velocity ratio consistent with high efficiency, as indicated in Fig. 5-5. Incidentally, the average efficiency curves of condensing, multistage turbines in the lower part of Fig. 5-2 cover a range from 363 Btu at 200 psi to 480 Btu at 1,500 psi.

As shown in Fig. 5-7, the overall efficiency of multistage turbines is sometimes expressed as a function of the so-called "quality factor," which serves as a convenient criterion of the whole turbine in the same manner as the velocity ratio applies to each stage separately. The quality factor is the sum of the squares of the pitch-line velocity of each revolving row divided by the total isentropic enthalpy drop. The pitch-line velocity is expressed in fps and the enthalpy drop in Btu.

The curve is empirical, determined from tests of fairly large turbines, and indicates average performance at the turbine coupling. It may be used to evaluate preliminary designs, assuming alternative values of speed, wheel diameters, and number of stages, or to compare actual turbines when pertinent information is available. To obtain consistent results the size and type of the turbine must be considered; generally, the internal efficiency improves appreciably with increased volume flow and the mechanical efficiency also improves slightly with increased capacity; thus a size factor should be applied to the efficiency curve to correlate units of different capacity, or individual efficiency curves based on tests may be used for each standard size.

Example: Determine provisional dimensions of a 3,000-hp 3,600-rpm condensing turbine operating at 400 psi, 750°F, and 28 in. Hg. A turbine efficiency of 73 percent is desired; thus, assuming a size factor of, say, 95 percent, the required efficiency is 77 percent, corresponding to a quality factor of about 7,500. The available enthalpy is 460 Btu; consequently the sum of velocity squares is $7,500 \times 460 = 3,450,000$. Various

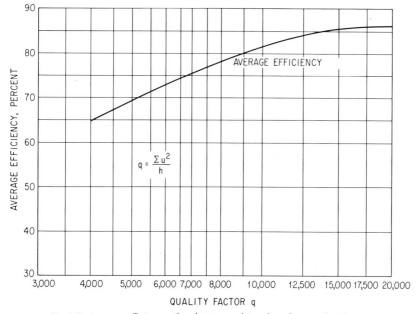

Fig. 5-7 Average efficiency of multistage turbines based on quality factor.

combinations of bucket speed and number of moving rows may be selected; for instance, a bucket speed of 500 fps corresponding to a pitch diameter of about 32 in. would require 14 rows of buckets; 475 fps equals 30¼ in. diameter with 15 rows, etc.

The pitch diameter usually increases gradually toward the exhaust end; therefore, the so-called "root mean square diameter" is used in these calculations. In this example the diameters would be adjusted in relation to the flow path through the turbine and the number of stages, perhaps 14, resulting in the most satisfactory bucket dimensions and in general compactness of design. This discussion illustrates the general principle of the interdependence of diameters and number of stages for a required turbine efficiency.

Analyzing the design of a condensing turbine as shown in Fig. 5-8, the first stages must be suitable for steam with comparatively high pressure, high temperature, and small specific volume. The last stage, on the other hand, presents the problem of providing sufficient area to accommodate a large volume flow of low-pressure steam. Taking a large enthalpy drop in the first stage by means of a two-row velocity stage as shown in this particular case results in a moderate first-stage pressure with low windage and gland leakage losses. Furthermore, the remaining enthalpy drop, allotted to the following stages, also becomes less; i.e., the velocity ratio improves and thus a good overall turbine efficiency results from this combination.

Extraction points for feed heating may be located in one or more stages as required, and provision may also be made to return leakage steam from the high-pressure gland to an appropriate stage, thus partly recovering this loss by work done in succeeding stages.

The bearings are of the sleeve-journal type with babbitt-lined steel shells. They are made in two halves and arranged for forced-feed lubrication. The oil pump and governor are driven from the main turbine shaft through a worm-gear reduction. The turbine-shaft seals are of the labyrinth type, with the labyrinths flexibly mounted.

The turbine casing is divided horizontally with the diaphragms also made in two halves, the upper ones being dismountable with the top casing.

The turbine support is arranged to maintain alignment at all times. The turbine is anchored at the exhaust end, and the casing is permitted to expand freely with changes in temperature.

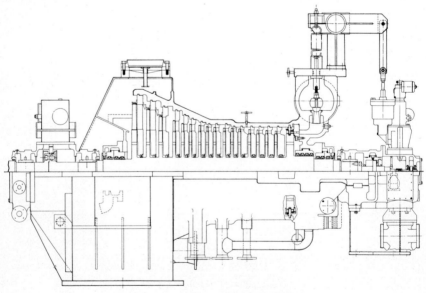

Fig. 5-8 Cross section of multistage turbine.

Group nozzle control, operated from a speed governor by a hydraulic servomotor, results in economic part-load performance combined with desirable speed-governing characteristics.

This condensing turbine represents a logical application of design principles to obtain the maximum efficiency by the proper selection of wheel diameters and number of stages and by proportioning the steam path to accommodate the volume flow of steam through the turbine.

Superposed and Back-pressure Turbines

Superposed and back-pressure turbines operate at exhaust pressures considerably higher than atmospheric and thus belong to the general classification of noncondensing turbines. Relatively high efficiency is required; therefore, these turbines are of the multistage type. The small single-stage auxiliary turbines previously described are also of the noncondensing type, but of a much simpler design, suitable for less exacting steam conditions.

The main application of superposed turbines, often referred to as "topping" turbines, is to furnish additional power and to improve the economy in electric power stations and sometimes in large industrial plants. Since boilers usually fail or become obsolete long before the turbines they serve, it has proved economically sound in many plants to replace the old boilers with modern high-pressure high-temperature boilers supplying steam to a new superposed turbine with its generator. The existing condensing turbines are retained and operated at the same inlet conditions as before with the exhaust steam from the superposed turbine. A considerable increase in plant capacity and improvement in station economy is thus obtained with a comparatively small additional investment.

Superposed turbines may be built in sizes from 500 kw for use in industrial plants to 65,000 kw or larger for installation in central stations. The initial steam conditions may vary from 600 to 2,000 psi with steam temperatures from 600 to 1050°F; the exhaust pressure may range from 200 to 600 psi and must correspond to the initial pressure of the existing plant. Topping units are usually arranged to serve a group of turbines but may also be proportioned for individual units.

Investigations in connection with proposed topping units may cover various aspects, for instance, determination of additional capacity obtainable with assumed initial steam conditions or, conversely, selection of initial steam conditions for a desired increase in power. Incidentally, the improvement in station heat rate is also calculated for use in evaluating the return on the proposed investment. However, this involves heat-balance calculations for the complete plant including the feed-heating cycle adjusted to the new conditions.

To indicate the possibilities of the superposed turbine the following example is suggested: An existing plant of 5,000 kw rated capacity is operating at 200 psi, 500°F, and 1½ in. Hg abs condenser pressure. Assuming a full-load steam rate of 13.0 lb/kwhr based on two 2,500-kw units the total steam flow is about 65,000 lb/hr. Determine the additional power to be expected from a topping unit operating at 850 psi, 750°F initial steam condition at the turbine throttle, and exhausting into the present steam main.

The available energy of the high-pressure steam is 147 Btu, corresponding to a theoretical steam rate of 23.2 lb/kwhr. Assuming a generator efficiency of about 94 percent and a "noncondensing" turbine efficiency of 63 percent, approximated from the curve sheet in Fig. 5-2, the steam rate becomes about 39 lb/kwhr. Incidentally, the enthalpy at the turbine exhaust, calculated from the efficiency, is about 1,272 Btu, referring to the Mollier diagram, this corresponds to about 508°F at 215 psia; thus the initial steam temperature of 750°F selected for the topping unit matches approximately the 500°F assumed at the existing steam header.

Based on a total steam flow of 65,000 lb/hr and a steam rate of 39 lb/kwhr, the increase in power is about 1,665 kw at the full-load condition. Thus the increase in capacity is 33.3 percent; likewise, the combined turbine steam rate is 9.75 lb/kwhr, an improvement of 25 percent. To calculate the corresponding fuel saving, additional data for the boiler and plant auxiliaries would be required.

The approximate size of the unit may be arrived at by the quality-factor method referred to on page 5-17. Applying an appropriate size factor, the topping turbine may in this case be designed for an efficiency of, say, 67 percent, corresponding to a quality factor of about 4,500. With an available enthalpy drop of 147 Btu the sum of the velocity squares is 660,000. Because of the comparatively small volume flow and the high density of the steam, small wheel diameters are used; thus the bucket speed is rather low. Assuming, for instance, 350 fps, corresponding to about 22½ in. pitch diameter at 3,600 rpm, the number of stages required would be about 5; and at 300 fps with 19 in. pitch diameter the number of stages would be 7, etc. Provisional inlet and outlet connections can be determined from Fig. 5-20, thus indicating the general overall dimensions of the turbine.

Back-pressure turbines, frequently of fairly large capacity, are often installed in industrial plants where a large amount of process steam may be required. In this case, the electric power required to operate the plant may be obtained from the process steam as a by-product at very low cost. Since good economy is important, these turbines are generally of the multistage type. The usual range of initial pressure is from 200 to 900 psi with corresponding steam temperatures from 500 to 900°F. The back pressure, which depends on the requirements of the process steam, may fall between the limits of 5 and 150 psi.

The approach to the problem is to estimate the amount of power that can be obtained from the process steam, assuming various initial steam conditions. In this manner a balance between available steam and power demand is determined, and as a preliminary step, the appropriate initial steam condition is selected. A check on the enthalpy at the turbine exhaust then indicates possible adjustment of the initial steam temperature to obtain approximately dry steam at the point where the process steam is used. Occasionally, heavy demands for steam in excess of the power load may be provided for by supplying the additional steam through a reducing valve directly from the boilers. Supplementary power for peak loads may be obtained from an outside source or from a condensing unit.

Extraction and Induction Turbines

Many industrial plants requiring various quantities of process steam combined with a certain electric-power load make use of extraction turbines. It is possible to adapt the extraction turbine to a great variety of plant conditions, and many different types are built, for instance, noncondensing and condensing extraction turbines with one or more extraction points; automatic and nonautomatic extraction, etc.

A related type of turbine, the so-called mixed flow or induction turbine, with provision for the use of high-pressure and low-pressure steam in proportion to the available supply, may also be mentioned in this connection. Generally, the low-pressure steam is expected to carry normal load, and high-pressure steam is admitted only in case of deficiency of the low-pressure steam. Even in case of complete failure of the low-pressure supply the turbine may be designed to carry the load with good economy on high-pressure steam alone.

The most frequently used extraction turbine is the single, automatic-extraction, condensing turbine as shown in Fig. 5-9. For design purposes it may be considered as a noncondensing and a condensing turbine, operating in series and built into a single casing. Because of the emphasis placed on compactness and comparatively simple construction, the number of stages is usually limited. The performance may therefore not be quite equal to the combined performance of a corresponding back pressure and a straight condensing turbine built in two separate units. On the other hand, the price of the extraction turbine is also less than the total price of two independent units would be.

Guarantees of steam rate for condensing and noncondensing automatic-extraction turbines are always made on a straight condensing or a straight noncondensing performance, respectively, obtained with no extraction but with the extraction valve wide open, that is, not functioning to maintain the extraction pressure. This nonextraction performance guaranteed for an automatic extraction turbine will not differ much from that for a straight condensing or a noncondensing unit of the same capacity and designed for the same steam conditions.

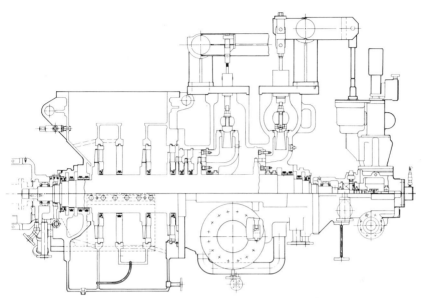

Fig. 5-9 Cross section of single, automatic-extraction turbine.

The complete performance of an extraction turbine can be represented by a chart such as Fig. 5-10, in which the output is expressed in percent of rated capacity and the throttle flow in percent of that at full load without extraction. The line labeled "0% Extraction at Const. Extr. Press." represents the performance of the turbine when no steam is extracted but with the extraction valve acting to hold extraction pressure at the bleed connection.

The guaranteed steam flow for nonextraction, with the pressure at the bleed point varying with the load, that is, with the extraction valve wide open, is also plotted as a broken line on Fig. 5-10. This line intersects the zero extraction line at full load, while at partial loads the throttle flow for nonextraction is less than for zero extraction. The reason for this is that the low-pressure end of the turbine has been designed for the steam flow which at full load, nonextraction, with the extraction valve wide open, will give the extraction pressure required. If the steam flow through the low-pressure end of the turbine is decreased, as at partial loads, the absolute pressure at the extraction point would decrease in proportion to the steam flow if it were not for the action of the extraction valve, which throttles the steam to maintain the required extraction pressure. This throttling loss occurs when operating with zero extraction, but not when operating nonextraction.

When steam is extracted from a turbine carrying a given load, the throttle flow must increase, but the increase is not equal to the amount extracted. For a given turbine and set of steam conditions, the increase in throttle steam over that required for zero extraction will bear nearly a constant ratio to the amount extracted. This ratio is called the extraction factor. As the extraction pressure is raised from exhaust pressure to inlet pressure by extracting at points of progressively higher pressure, the extraction factor increases from 0 to 1.

The line labeled "Operation at Maximum Extraction" represents the performance when all steam entering the throttle, except the cooling steam, is extracted. The line "Maximum Throttle Flow" represents the maximum flow which the high-pressure section can pass when the turbine is operated with its normal steam conditions. The corresponding limit for the low-pressure section is the one titled "Exr. Press. Rise." The turbine can operate in the region to the right of this limit but will not then main-

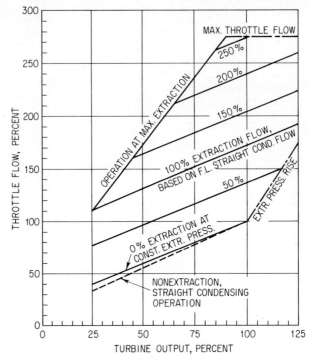

Fig. 5-10 Throttle flow vs. output of condensing automatic-extraction turbine.

tain normal extraction pressure.   For any given load the flow to exhaust is maximum at zero extraction, so that the maximum flow through the exhaust section for which the turbine must be proportioned is determined by the maximum load to be carried with minimum extraction.

Similar diagrams may be constructed applying to other combinations, such as double automatic and mixed-flow turbines.   As an example, lines of "Constant Induction Flow" would be located below and parallel to a line of "Zero Induction Flow" in the case of mixed-pressure or induction turbines.

Marine Propulsion Turbines

Marine propulsion turbines are multistage turbines of the condensing type specifically designed for shipboard application and are usually direct-connected to a marine-type reduction gear, which reduces the relatively high turbine speed to the ship propeller speed.

For the smaller powers up to about 10,000 hp output single-casing turbines may be used, but the majority of the modern units are of the cross-compound type.

They are further characterized by having a reversing turbine built into the unit, usually in the low-pressure turbine of the cross-compound unit.   The reversing turbine is designed to develop 75 to 100 percent of design torque at full-ahead-power steam flow and at 50 percent speed.

Figure 5-10a shows a cross section of the low-pressure turbine of a 32,000-hp cross-compound unit with a reversing element.

Control System   Modern De Laval marine turbines are provided with a control system that adapts the necessary features of remote and local control as used for steam power plants.   The position of the steam valves is controlled by hydraulic actuators, which may be operated remotely from the bridge by electrical means or from

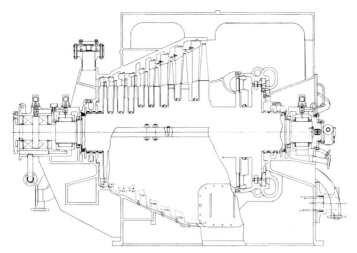

Fig. 5-10a Cross section of low-pressure marine turbine with reversing element.

the engine-room control console by either electrical or mechanical means. When operating in either mode, the actuator will respond to an overspeed signal from the speed-control system, limiting the maximum speed.

Regenerative Feedwater Heating

The basic principles of this cycle have been discussed on page 5-5. There is an optimum temperature to which the condensate can be heated. When this limit is exceeded, the amount of work delivered by the extracted steam is reduced and the benefit to the cycle gradually diminishes. Assuming, as an example, steam conditions of 400 psi and 750°F at the throttle and a 29 in. Hg vacuum, the most favorable feedwater temperature is about 240°F for one stage of feedwater heating, 290°F for two stages, 320°F for three stages, and 330°F for four stages, as shown in Fig. 5-11.

As the number of heating stages is increased, the savings become proportionately less, as illustrated by the curves. For the steam conditions noted above, the cycle is

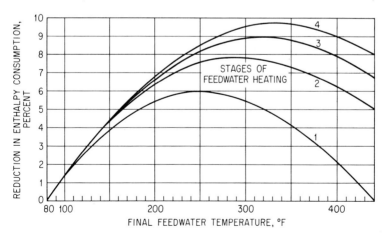

Fig. 5-11 Reduction in enthalpy consumption due to regenerative feedwater heating (steam conditions: 400 psi, 750°F, 29 in. Hg).

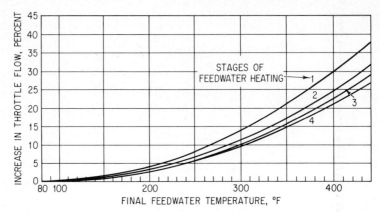

Fig. 5-12 Increase in steam flow to turbine due to regenerative feedwater heating (steam conditions: 400 psi, 750°F, 29 in. Hg).

improved a maximum of 6 percent with one stage, 7¾ percent with two stages, 9 percent with three stages, and 9¾ percent with four stages.   For this reason, it is not economically sound to install more than one or two heaters for a small-capacity turbine. Furthermore, the overall plant economy may limit the maximum feedwater temperature.   With the condensate heated to a higher temperature because of the increased number of feed-heating stages, the temperature difference available to the economizer, usually provided in the boiler, becomes less; therefore, less heat will be extracted from the flue gases by the economizer.   The resulting increase in stack loss and corresponding decrease in boiler efficiency may thus more than outweigh the improvement in the turbine cycle.   The use of air preheaters instead of economizers to recover the stock loss makes it possible to obtain the full benefit from the regenerative feed-heating cycle.

Regenerative feedwater heating affects the distribution of steam flow through the turbine.   The steam required to heat the feedwater is extracted from the turbine at various points, determined by the temperature in the corresponding feed-heating stage. The extracted steam does not complete its expansion to the vacuum at the turbine exhaust; thus somewhat less power is delivered than with straight condensing operation. To obtain equal output, the steam flow to the turbine must therefore be slightly increased, as shown in Fig. 5-12, which refers to the same steam conditions as the previous figure.   It may be noted from Fig. 5-12 that, for instance, with one stage of feedwater heating to the optimum temperature of 240°F, it is necessary to add about 7½ percent to the throttle flow, and that with two stages the increase is about 10½ percent, etc.

On the other hand, a certain percentage of the total steam flow is extracted; thus the flow to the condenser is reduced as shown on Fig. 5-13.   For one and two feed-heating stages in the above example the decrease in steam flow to the condenser is about 8 and 10½ percent, respectively, as compared with straight condensing operation. The tube surface and size of the condenser can therefore be reduced by similar amounts.

Furthermore, the redistribution of the flow benefits the turbine; the first stages, which usually operate with partial admission, can easily handle more steam efficiently, and the last stage in particular will gain in efficiency, mainly because of a decrease in leaving loss resulting from less flow to the condenser.

Fuel savings of 5 to 10 percent, increasing with steam pressure and number of heating stages, and decreasing with superheat, may be obtained by the use of regenerative feedwater heating.   The additional equipment is simple and inexpensive; therefore, this cycle is generally employed in preference to straight condensing operation.

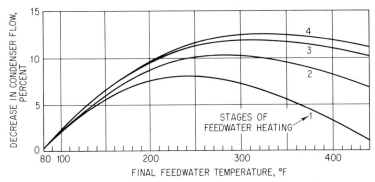

Fig. 5-13 Decrease in steam flow to condenser due to regenerative feedwater heating (steam conditions: 400 psi, 750°F, 29 in. Hg).

Turbine Governors

The governor is the "brains" behind the "brawn" of the turbine.   The governor may sense, or measure, a single quantity such as turbine speed, inlet, extraction, induction or exhaust pressure, or any combination of these quantities, and then control the turbine to regulate the quantities measured.   Shaft-speed governors are the most common. A simple speed governor will first be considered.

In the direct-acting mechanical governor shown in Fig. 5-14 speed is measured by spring-loaded rotating weights.   As the weights are rotated, they generate a force proportional to the product of their mass, the radius of their rotation, and the square of their speed of rotation.   Under steady-stage conditions the weight force is balanced by the opposing force of the weight spring, and the governor stem remains stationary.

If some load is removed from the turbine, the turbine would speed up, and the governor weights would move outward. As the governor weights move outward their force is further increased, but the force of the weight spring increases even faster and soon limits the travel of the weights.   The movement of the weights is transferred through the governor stem and connecting linkage to the turbine control valve to reduce the flow of steam to the turbine, limiting the turbine-speed increase.

If some load is added to the turbine, the turbine will slow down, and the governor weights will move inward.   As the governor weights move inward their force is further decreased, but the force of the weight spring decreases even faster and limits the travel of the weights.   The movement of the weights is transferred through the governor stem and connecting linkage to the turbine control valve to increase the flow of steam to the turbine, limiting the turbine speed decrease.

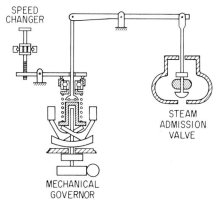

Fig. 5-14   Direct-acting mechanical speed governor.

For any constant setting of the weight spring a certain change in speed is required to provide a full travel of the governor weights.   This change in speed between the full-load and no-load speed of the governor is called either the governor droop or, when

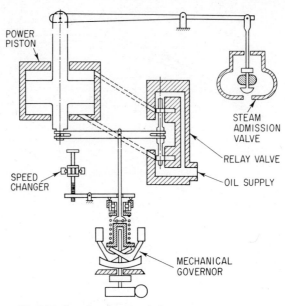

POWER
PISTON

STEAM
ADMISSION
VALVE

RELAY VALVE

SPEED
CHANGER

OIL SUPPLY

MECHANICAL
GOVERNOR

Fig. 5-15 Speed governor with direct-acting servomotor.

expressed as a percentage of the full-load speed, the governor regulation. When units are operated in parallel, any changes in the total load will be shared by the units in inverse proportion to their individual governor regulation. Thus for equal load sharing all units should have equal governor regulation, or in the case of dissimilar units, their respective governor regulation can be set to assure proper load sharing.

Frictional forces in the governor, in the connected linkage, and in the control valve must be overcome before the weights can move. This means that the governor will not react to small speed changes. This small range of speed in which no governor action occurs is called the governor dead band.

For most applications the direct-acting mechanical governor does not develop enough force to operate the turbine control valve, so that a force amplifier or servomotor is needed. In the governor shown in Fig. 5-15 movement of the governor stem causes the servomotor relay valve to move, directing operating oil to one side of the servomotor power piston and opening the other side of the power piston to drain. The power piston movement is fed back through the servomotor linkage to the relay valve, using the speed governor stem as a fulcrum, returning the pilot valve to neutral.

Another type of servomotor is used in the governor shown in Fig. 5-16. In this governor movement of the governor stem causes changes in the speed-governor oil-line pressure. This is possible because the pilot valve has a larger capacity than the orifice which supplies the speed-governor oil line. The speed-governor oil pressure acts on the relay piston against the relay-valve spring to position the relay valve and cause the power piston to move. As in the previous servomotor the power-piston movement is fed back to the relay valve, returning it to neutral. The pilot valve on the speed-governor stem is subject to loading from the pressure in the speed-governor oil line. This pressure loading makes the pilot valve harder to move and increases the governor regulation.

Another common governor is a pressure governor. Inlet- or exhaust-pressure governors are commonly used on turbines driving generators where the unit speed is held constant by operating in parallel with other generators. In the example of an exhaust-pressure governor shown in Fig. 5-17 the exhaust pressure working on a spring-loaded bellows operates a pilot valve which causes changes in the exhaust-pressure-governor oil-line pressure. The exhaust-pressure-governor oil-line pressure, in turn, controls the inlet-nozzle-valve servomotor. A decrease in the exhaust pressure relaxes the

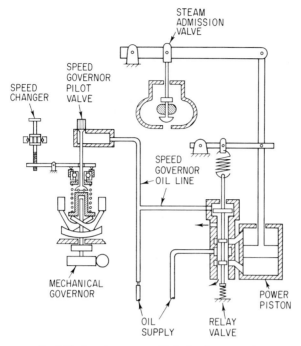

Fig. 5-16 Speed governor with hydraulic servomotor.

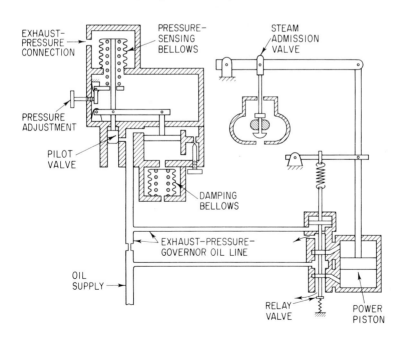

Fig. 5-17 Exhaust-pressure governor.

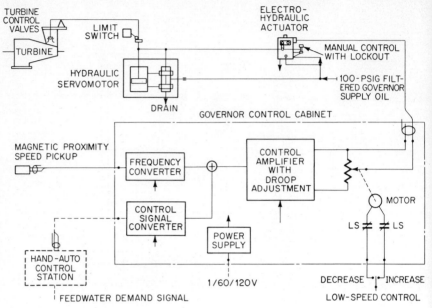

Fig. 5-18 Electrohydraulic governor.

sensing bellows, moves the pilot valve in the opening direction, and causes a drop in the exhaust-pressure-governor oil-line pressure. The decrease in the exhaust-pressure-governor oil-line pressure lowers the servomotor pilot valve. This causes the servomotor power piston to move upward, opening the nozzle valves. As the nozzle valves are opened, more steam passes through the turbine to maintain the desired exhaust pressure within the limits of the governor regulation. The action of the exhaust-pressure governor is damped by a piston with a bypassing needle valve and by a spring-loaded bellows.

The governor now coming into common use is the electric governor. This governor substitutes an electric speed-sensing element whose signal is converted, amplified, and transmitted to the electrohydraulic converter which drives the same primary relay valve as that shown in the other governors. This governor has the advantage of wider speed range and more precise control.

This speed-governor control system, shown in Fig. 5-18, features a typical boiler-feed-pump turbine-electric speed-governor control system which receives a feedwater demand signal (0–5 volts dc or other suitable signal) and uses it to set unit operating speed during normal unit operation, 70–100 percent speed, or to set valve position from 0–70 percent speed during startup.

The system consists of:

A *hand-auto control station* to facilitate manual control of the unit, mounted where desired.

A *governor control cabinet* which provides the electronic circuits necessary for establishing startup valve position and normal speed control.

A *magnetic proximity speed pickup* and gear mounted on the turbine shaft, which produces a frequency signal proportional to the unit speed.

An *electrohydraulic actuator* mounted on the hydraulic servomotor, which positions the servo relay valve in response to a control signal from the electric governor circuits.

A *hydraulic servomotor* for positioning the valve operating the gear-steam-control valves, in response to the electrohydraulic actuator.

Extraction Governors

Another form of pressure governor is the extraction governor. This governor could operate, through a servomotor, a set of nozzle valves (secondary valves) which

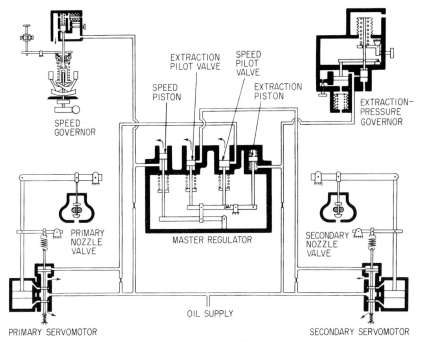

Fig. 5-19 Extraction governor with master regulator.

as they are opened pass more steam through the latter stages of the turbine and less into the extraction line. Normally where an extraction governor is fitted, it must be coordinated with a speed governor to assure complete control of the turbine. This can be done by using a master regulator to connect the speed-governing and the extraction-governing systems as shown in Fig. 5-19. Pistons in the master regulator receive control-pressure signals from the speed governor and from the extraction-pressure governor. The control piston movements are transmitted through the regulator linkage to the pilot valves which control the pressure in the servomotor-control oil lines. These controlled pressures cause the servomotors to make the necessary corrections in the nozzle-valve settings.

Steam and Exhaust Pipes

To determine the size of steam and exhaust pipes for steam turbines, two different methods may be employed. Preliminary estimates are usually made by assuming empirical steam velocities while final calculations are based on permissible pressure drop in the complete pipeline including the loss in valves, fittings, and bends.

Many other factors are involved in the design of steam piping such as type or class of construction as covered by various specification and codes (ANSI code for pressure piping). As a general rule, cast-iron fittings are permissible up to 250 psi and 450°F, and carbon-steel fittings are used for 300 to 600 psi and a maximum temperature of 750°F. For pressures above 600 psi and temperatures over 750°F alloy steels are required. Welded joint construction is usually employed for high-pressure and high-temperature piping.

The chart in Fig. 5-20 may be used to determine approximate pipe sizes when detail information is not available regarding length of pipe and number of valves, bends, and fittings. The chart is based on a steam velocity of 150 fps for steam pipes and noncondensing exhaust pipes and 300 fps for condensing exhaust pipes; if other values are selected, the flow will be in direct proportion to the steam velocities. Dry and saturated steam volumes have been used; therefore, corrections should be made for mois-

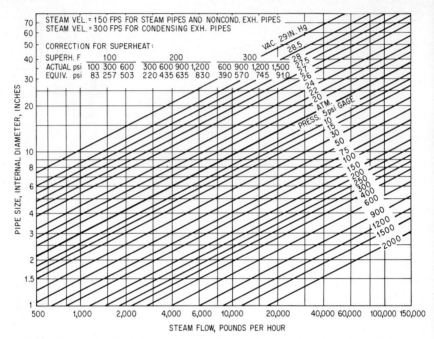

Fig. 5-20 Steam and exhaust pipe sizes (dry and saturated steam; correction to be made for superheat and quality).

ture or superheat. This may be made in the case of superheated steam by using an "equivalent" pressure which can be obtained directly from the steam tables, or approximated from the tabulation on the chart. The pipe size is actual internal diameter; for "nominal" size the appropriate diameter found from tables in Sec. 1 may be used. However, this would be an unnecessary refinement for preliminary estimates. Equivalent areas of exhaust openings may be obtained from a table of areas of circles in Sec. 1.

Example: Find steam and exhaust pipe sizes for the 500-hp multistage turbine referred to under Turbine Performance: steam pressure 300 psi, 100°F superheat, exhaust pressure 10 psi, steam flow 10,000 lb/hr, 1¾ percent moisture in the exhaust.

Starting at the bottom of Fig. 5-20 at 10,000 lb/hr, using the correction for 100°F superheat, the "equivalent" steam pressure is 257 psi and the steam pipe size is found to be 2.4 in. internal dia. Extra strong steel pipe, 2½ in. nominal size, has an internal diameter of 2.32 in. and would also meet the requirements for pressure and temperature.

For the exhaust pipe the moisture, which is 1¾ percent, is deducted, making the corrected flow about 9,825 lb/hr. The required internal diameter of the exhaust pipe at 10 psi is 7.4 in.; thus a standard 8-in. pipe would be selected providing a margin for possible overload or for operation at a lower back pressure.

After layouts have been made, the pressure drop in the steam and exhaust pipes can be estimated with the aid of the alignment chart shown in Fig. 5-21. This chart gives the pressure drop in psi per 100-ft length of pipe. The total loss in the pipe is obtained by measuring the lengths from the drawing and adding the loss in valves and fittings expressed in equivalent length of straight pipe.

To estimate the length of straight pipe, equivalent to the pressure drop in terms of pipe diameters, the following values may be used. The equivalent length is in feet; therefore, the pipe diameter must be also expressed in feet.

Globe valve = 400 × dia   90° pipe bend = 25 × dia
Gate valve = 20 × dia   Standard elbow = 100 × dia

The examples worked out in Fig. 5-21 serve to illustrate its use. Checking the preliminary pipe sizes previously determined for the 500-hp turbine, the pressure drop per 100-ft length would be about 20 psi for a 2.32 in. actual ID or 2½-in. nominal size extra heavy pipe and about 6.5 psi for a 3-in. extra heavy pipe. The 8-in. standard-weight exhaust pipe will have a pressure drop of about 0.40 psi per 100-ft equivalent length. Assuming that a maximum pressure drop of about 10 percent is permissible in the steam pipe, the 2½-in. size would be sufficient up to about 150 ft equivalent length, and if a 5 percent drop is allowed in the exhaust pipe the 8-in. size would be ample for about 300 ft.

Other considerations, such as heat loss from pipes carrying highly superheated steam

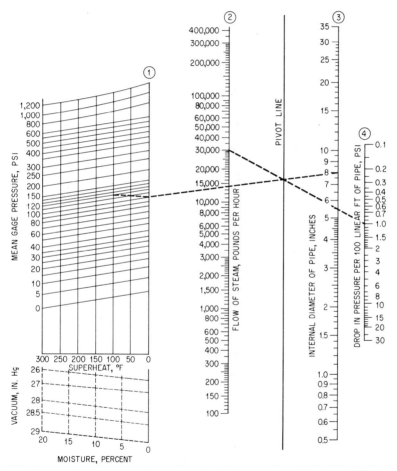

Fig. 5-21 Pressure drop in steam piping. Based on Gutermuth formula: $W = 324\sqrt{Pcd^5}$. $W =$ steam flow, lb/hr; $P =$ pressure drop, psi; $c =$ density, lb/cu ft; $d =$ actual internal pipe diameter, in.

Example: Steam flow, 30,000 lb/hr; initial pressure, 125 psi; superheat, 100°F. Final pressure desired is 115 psi. Equivalent length of pipe, 1,000 ft. Pressure drop per 100 ft, 1 lb; average gage pressure, 120 psi.

Find necessary pipe diameter: Join 30,000 on scale 2 to 1 on scale 4. Locate intersection of 120-lb diagonal and 100° vertical and proceed horizontally to scale 1. Project line from this point on scale 1 through intersection on pivot line to scale 3. Final answer on scale 3: 8-in.-diameter pipe. (*Redrawn from "Power's Data Sheets" by courtesy of Power.*)

or from large-sized pipes conveying process steam for long distances, may present special problems in connection with the final selection and design of steam piping for turbines, but the examples given may serve to illustrate the methods commonly used.

GAS TURBINES, TURBOCHARGERS, AND EXPANDERS

Gas Turbines

Gas turbines have achieved ever-increasing importance during the last decades. Their applications are many. Their design varies from great simplicity to a certain sophisticated complexity.

The gas turbine is found in the following *areas of application:*

Propulsion of the modern aircraft, military, commercial, and civil
Peaking power facilities
Compressor and pump drive
Total energy systems
Vehicle drive for locomotives, ships, trucks, off-road vehicles, cars
Process air and gas generation
Airborne and ground support equipment for aircraft

The gas turbine has found its application because of some or all of the following potential *advantages* over competitive equipment:

Small size and weight per horsepower
Self-contained unit of moderate first cost
Reliability through turbomachinery components
Easy maintenance
Instant power
Ability to burn a variety of fuels
No cooling water required

Some of the simpler gas-turbine arrangements are described below.

The basic cycle may be demonstrated by the simple open-cycle *single-shaft gas turbine* sketched in Fig. 5-22. Ambient air is compressed in the compressor C. Heat is added to the compressed air at essentially constant pressure by burning fuel in the combustion chamber CC. The hot combustion gas is expanded in the turbine T. The power produced by the turbine is larger than the power required to drive the compressor. The difference in power is available to drive the load L.

The turbine T may be split into two turbines in series. Figure 5-23 is a sketch of the simple open-cycle *two-shaft gas turbine*. The turbine T_1 is sized to drive the compressor C. Turbine T_1, compressor C, and the combustion chamber CC constitute a gas generator. The turbine T_2 drives the load L. Turbine T_2 is mechanically independent of the gas generator, may run at different speeds, and is often called a power turbine.

The gas generator produces a combustion gas (essentially air) at moderately elevated pressure and temperature. The energy contained in this gas may be put to other uses than driving a power turbine. The gas may be expanded to a high velocity in a nozzle

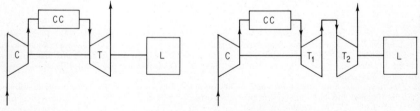

Fig. 5-22 Open-cycle single-shaft gas turbine.   **Fig. 5-23** Two-shaft gas turbine.

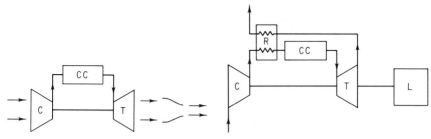

Fig. 5-24 Aircraft gas turbine. **Fig. 5-25** Regenerative single-shaft gas turbine.

for the propulsion of the modern aircraft.   Figure 5-24 is a sketch of a simple *aircraft gas turbine* (turbojet).

On the other hand, the aircraft gas generator, highly developed for aircraft use, has found interesting ground applications.   In combination with an industrial power turbine, a gas-turbine arrangement as shown in Fig. 5-23 results.

The *efficiency* of the gas turbine poses a certain problem.   As the output is the difference of comparatively large powers, the component efficiencies must be very high and the cycle conditions are liable to be stringent.

The efficiency of the gas turbine is also improved by the adoption of a more complex cycle.   As the larger part of the fuel energy leaves with the exhaust gas, waste-heat recovery in one form or another will improve the system efficiency greatly.

Waste heat may be recovered by means of a regenerator which preheats the compressed air with the exhaust gas before it enters the combustion chamber.   The efficiency is improved as less fuel has to be burned to bring the gas up to turbine inlet temperature.   Figure 5-25 is a sketch of a *regenerative* open-cycle single-shaft *gas turbine*.

Waste heat may be recovered by means of a waste-heat boiler in the exhaust stack. The steam generated by the waste-heat boiler may drive a steam turbine for additional power, it may be used in a process, or it may be used for heating and air-conditioning a building.

Utilization of the exhaust heat has led to the adaptation of the total-energy concept to gas turbines.   A *total-energy system* is a system of high overall thermal efficiency designed around a gas turbine which meets (the total) different and varying energy requirements.

The combustion of fuel in the airstream is the simplest and most common way to add heat to the cycle.   As an alternate, heat may be added entirely by heat exchange.   The heat source may be a fired heater burning a cheap fuel such as coal.   In this case the cycle gas does not become contaminated and may be used over and over again in a closed cycle.   In a closed cycle, the pressure level may be raised and varied, leading to a smaller unit with good part-load efficiency.   Gases other than air may be used as a cycle gas, which facilitates the use of an atomic reactor as a heat source for the gas turbine.   Figure 5-26 is a sketch of a regenerative *closed-cycle gas turbine*.

Every component of the gas turbine has a history.   As far as the *turbomachinery* is concerned, the compressor may be a centrifugal or axial type or a combination of both, and the turbine may be a radial or axial type or a combination of both.   Turbomachinery is high-flow machinery on which the small specific size and weight advantage of the gas turbine is based.   For the same reason, the use of radial-flow machinery, centrifugal compressor, and radial turbine has been restricted more and more to smaller units as the gas turbine has grown in size.   The field of high power belongs to the highly efficient axial compressor and axial reaction turbine.

Gas-turbine development is a continuing process.   It could not be otherwise, as aviation progress is depending on it.   Component efficiencies, pressure ratios, and turbine inlet temperatures are higher now than just a few years ago, and there is an intensive search for ever better high-temperature materials.

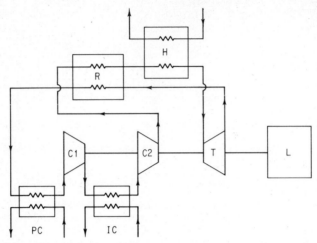

Fig. 5-26 Regenerative closed-cycle gas turbine. C1, C2 = compressors, T = turbine, L = load, H = heater, R = regenerator, PC = precooler, IC = intercooler.

Industrial gas turbines range in size from a few hundred horsepower to about 30,000 kw, although smaller and larger units are being built.

References

"Diesel and Gas Turbine Catalog," vol. 32, Diesel and Gas Turbine Progress, Milwaukee, Wis., 1967.

Gas Turbine International Magazine, a bimonthly publication by Gas Turbine Publications, Inc., Stamford, Conn.

D. G. Shepherd, "Introduction to the Gas Turbine," 2d ed., D. Van Nostrand Company, Inc., Princeton, N.J., 1960.

Turbochargers

Turbochargers are used to increase the operating pressure level of internal-combustion engines, thereby increasing the power output of the engine. The turbocharger serves to uprate the engine or to restore sea-level performance at high altitude. At the same time, a saving in specific fuel consumption is achieved.

Main industrial applications are on two- and four-cycle diesel engines, gas engines, and dual-fuel engines.

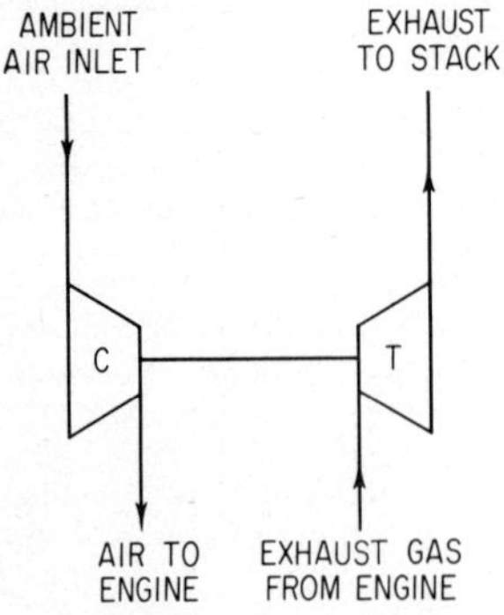

Performance parameters vary, and close cooperation between the turbocharger and engine manufacturers is required in order to adjust the turbocharger to an individual application.

Basically, the turbocharger is a gas turbine consisting of a compressor and a turbine with the engine replacing the combustion chamber as shown in the sketch in Fig. 5-27. The air consumed by the engine is drawn from atmosphere, compressed by compressor C, and discharged through a cooler in some designs into the intake manifold of the engine. The exhaust gas from the engine is expanded in turbine T and is exhausted to atmosphere.

Typically, there is no mechanical connection between the shaft of the turbocharger and the engine. The power produced by the turbine matches the power absorbed by the compressor. This balance adjusts itself by speed variation.

Pressure ratios are typically 1.5 to 3 and higher in some instances. The turbine

AMBIENT AIR INLET   **EXHAUST TO STACK**

C   T

AIR TO ENGINE   **EXHAUST GAS FROM ENGINE**

Fig. 5-27 Turbocharger.

pressure ratio is somewhat smaller than the compressor pressure ratio because of the pressure drop in the engine.

The compressor consists of a single centrifugal stage and the turbine of a single radial or axial stage which may be arranged between or outboard of the turbocharger bearings. If the pressure ratio exceeds the capability of the single stages, two turbochargers of different standardized sizes may be used in series.

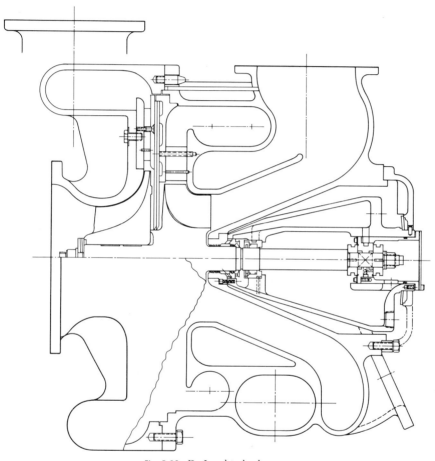

Fig. 5-28 De Laval turbocharger.

A cross section of the De Laval turbocharger is shown in Fig. 5-28. A mixed-flow centrifugal compressor stage and a mixed-flow radial turbine stage are arranged back to back on one side of the bearing case.

Expanders

Expansion of gas in a turbine produces work and lowers the temperature of the gas stream as energy is removed. Turbines which produce work from the expansion of process gases and which serve the recovery of process waste energy are often called expanders. Some of these expanders are of considerable horsepower size. Representative gas conditions are: inlet temperature = 1000°F; inlet pressure = 300 psia; exhaust pressure = atmospheric or above.

A turbine whose primary purpose is to remove energy from the gas stream or to produce refrigeration is called a turbo-expander. The following description pertains to turbo-expanders.

Turbo-expanders are part of low-temperature process equipment and refrigerators and are widely used in the cryogenic industry. Typical applications are air-separation plants for the production of gaseous and liquid oxygen and nitrogen where the turbo-expander operates on an air or nitrogen stream down to the vicinity of −300°F. Applications involving the lowest temperature are helium liquefiers where the turbo-expander may operate at a temperature as low as −450°F.

The single-stage radial turbine has almost become a standard, although some axial turbo-expanders have been built. The turbine is arranged outboard of the bearing case and separated from the bearing case by a seal. Most designs have oil-lubricated sleeve bearings. The use of bearings lubricated by the cycle gas is very attractive, and several experimental units with gas-lubricated bearings have been built. The load horsepower is of secondary importance and is usually absorbed by a single-stage centrifugal compressor arranged outboard of the bearing case at the opposite end. The compressor may compress atmospheric air and dissipate the load by throttling, or some use may be made of the horsepower by compressing seal or process gas. Some larger units have been built with a load-absorbing generator driven through a reduction gear. Small units may dissipate the load by an oil brake.

Low-temperature materials are used for the turbine, materials such as type 304 stainless steel for the case and aluminum for the turbine wheel.

With the pressure ratio limited by the requirement for efficient single-stage expansion and the temperature level of the application decreasing with the molecular weight of the gas, the turbine head is usually not high, resulting in moderate turbine-wheel peripheral speeds and stresses. The hydrogen turbine is somewhat of an exception because of the very small molecular weight of hydrogen.

Flow and horsepower sizes vary over a wide range. Turbo-expanders with 4- to 6-in.-diameter turbine wheels are typical. Turbo-expanders have been built with wheel diameters over 13 in. and as small as 5/16 in. Miniature turbo-expanders with wheel diameters below 1 in. have a rotative speed above 100,000 rpm where only gas-lubricated bearings made a successful design possible.

Reference

"Gas Turbine Engineering Handbook," Gas Turbine Publications, Inc., Stamford, Conn., 1966.

GAS AND OIL ENGINES

Introduction

Gas and oil engines are prime movers of the reciprocating, internal-combustion type. They cover a wide range of output horsepower and speeds, and are in widespread use in applications where their combination of good fuel economy at full and partial load, their compactness, durability, reliability, and reasonable first cost make them the most economical and effective choices.

Oil engines, more commonly referred to as diesel engines, have a dominant position as propulsion plants for heavy-duty transportation and mobile equipment. One notable exception is the demonstrated preference shown for steam turbines in the propulsion of large ships of American registry. Diesel, dual-fuel, and gas engines, however, are widely used as primary power sources for generators, pumps, compressors, and similar equipment. In the industrial field gas and oil engines compete with gasoline engines, electric motors, gas turbines, steam turbines, and hydraulic turbines. The choice depends upon many factors and circumstances, the selected unit normally being that which will give the best economy over its anticipated lifetime while being compatible with the requirements of the purchaser.

This subsection will mainly concern itself with oil and gas engines of the *medium-speed range* for industrial and marine use. The medium-speed range is generally accepted to be the 300- to 1,000-rpm range, with horsepower output ranging from a few hundred to more than 20,000 bhp per unit. The slow-speed range (100 to 500 rpm) covers most direct-drive marine main propulsion units which may have unit outputs higher than 40,000 bhp at approximately 100 rpm. High-speed units (750 to more than 3,000 rpm) are used in the automotive and industrial fields of application, and range from a few horsepower to approximately 4,000 bhp. Engine manufacturers usually concentrate their efforts in one or two of these speed ranges because of the wide differences in production technology and equipment needed for economical production of the various engine types.

Classification of Engines

Reciprocating, internal-combustion engines are classified according to their fuel type and ignition method. There are also many subclassifications which group engines according to cycle arrangements and modifications, mechanical arrangements, and other design features. The more important main classifications of medium-speed engines are:

Diesel Engines Diesel engines are compression-ignition engines which operate on liquid fuel. The compression ratio and the resulting temperature of the compressed-air charge are high enough to ignite suitable fuels when they are injected into the cylinders, beginning at the end of the compression stroke. Diesel engines do not really operate on the diesel cycle which stipulates combustion at constant pressure. High-speed diesel engines approach constant-volume combustion, or the Otto cycle, and engines running at very low speed can approach combustion at constant pressure. In most diesel engines the combustion phase of the actual cycle is a mixture of the Otto and the diesel cycles, and is often referred to as a combination or limited-pressure cycle.

Gas Engines Gas engines use gaseous fuel which is spark-ignited. Combustion takes place at essentially constant volume (Otto cycle). Compression pressures may be as high as those in diesel engines, but more commonly they are lower. Autoignition of the air/gas mixture must not take place, as the resulting detonations will rapidly damage or destroy the engine. The fuel gas is mixed into the combustion air during the induction part of the engine cycle or is injected into the cylinder during the compression stroke. The first arrangement is common on four-stroke-cycle engines, the latter on two-stroke-cycle engines. High-voltage energy, usually from magnetos or solid-state electronic devices and transformers, fires one or more spark plugs per cylinder for ignition of the combustible mixture.

Dual-fuel Engines Dual-fuel engines have two modes of operation. One is operation as a diesel engine; in the other mode a "pilot" injection of liquid diesel fuel ignites as in a diesel engine, and subsequently ignites the main charge of fuel gas and air. The pilot fuel usually constitutes 5 to 7 percent of the total fuel energy input at full load. Dual-fuel engines generally resemble diesel engines but have additional equipment for control of combustion air and fuel gas. Controls are provided for switching from one mode to the other, and on some dual-fuel engines the pilot fuel to fuel gas ratio may be varied to select any fuel proportion from minimum pilot fuel to full diesel operation.

Tri-fuel Engines Tri-fuel engines are usually dual-fuel engines which can be converted to spark-ignited gas engines with minor modifications.

Engine Subclassifications

Some of the more common subclassifications of gas and oil engines are:

Four-stroke-cycle Engines The four-stroke engine cycle is completed in two crankshaft revolutions, and consists of the following piston strokes:

1. Induction (suction/intake) stroke
2. Compression stroke
3. Expansion (power) stroke
4. Exhaust stroke

Ignition and combustion take place at the end of the compression stroke and the beginning of the expansion stroke.

Two-stroke-cycle Engines   The two-stroke cycle is completed in one revolution of the crankshaft and consists of two piston strokes:

1. Compression stroke
2. Expansion (power) stroke

Scavenging and combustion air recharging take place at the end of the expansion and the beginning of the compression strokes.   Ignition and combustion take place at the end of the compression and the beginning of the expansion strokes.

Supercharged Engines   A supercharged engine is one in which the density of the combustion air charge is increased over that of the surrounding atmosphere by precompression of the air before it is inducted into the cylinders.   The purpose of supercharging is to increase the power output from a given cylinder size by increasing the mean effective pressure.   Two general methods of supercharging are used:

1. Mechanically driven blowers which are normally driven by an engine auxiliary output shaft.   They may also be driven by an electric motor or other separate prime mover.
2. Exhaust-turbine-driven blower where the blower is driven by a turbine which derives its power from the engine exhaust gases.   The turbine and the blower are mounted on the same shaft, and this combination is called a turbocharger.

Naturally Aspirated Engines   A naturally aspirated engine is one in which the combustion air inducted into its power cylinders is of a density not greater than that of the surrounding atmosphere.   Two-stroke-cycle engines usually have a blower which forces air through the cylinders for scavenging and recharging, but they are termed naturally aspirated if this does not result in a substantially higher than atmospheric combustion air density (pressure) at the beginning of the compression stroke.

Aftercooled Engines   The term aftercooled is used when referring to an engine equipped with equipment for cooling the combustion air after it is supercharged and before it is inducted into the power cylinders.   The purpose of aftercooling is to improve internal cooling, to increase combustion air density, and to reduce detonation tendencies in gas-burning engines.

Number and Arrangement of Cylinders   Engines may be classified according to the number of power cylinders, and the arrangement of those cylinders.   Two common arrangements are:

1. "V-type" engines where the cylinders are arranged in two banks along the crankshaft, the two banks forming a V when viewed from the end of the engine.   (See Fig. 5-29.)
2. "In-line" engines where the cylinders are in line in a single bank, parallel to the crankshaft.   (See Fig. 5-30.)

There are other less common arrangements such as horizontal and radial, but these are of declining importance in the medium-speed field.

Valve Type and Location   Four-stroke-cycle engines have intake and exhaust valves of a type known as poppet valves.   These valves and their associated parts are normally part of the cylinder head, an arrangement known as "overhead valves."   A simpler arrangement having the valves in the block (side valves) does not permit a sufficiently compact combustion chamber for high-compression engines, and gives poorer performance than overhead valves where the compression ratio is suitable.

Engine Description

No matter what the engine classification, there are certain parts of any engine that are basically the same, and their method of operating essentially alike.   Fuel, in gaseous or liquid form, is introduced into a power cylinder and ignited.   The resulting expansion of the burning fuel mixture transforms the chemical energy of the fuel into mechanical energy by forcing a piston downward, which causes a crankshaft to rotate.

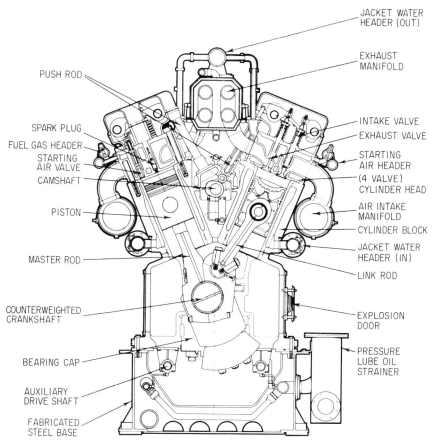

JACKET WATER
HEADER (OUT)

EXHAUST
MANIFOLD

PUSH ROD

INTAKE VALVE
EXHAUST VALVE

SPARK PLUG

FUEL GAS HEADER
STARTING
AIR VALVE
CAMSHAFT

STARTING
AIR HEADER
(4 VALVE)
CYLINDER HEAD

PISTON

AIR INTAKE
MANIFOLD
CYLINDER BLOCK

MASTER ROD

JACKET WATER
HEADER (IN)

LINK ROD

COUNTERWEIGHTED
CRANKSHAFT

EXPLOSION
DOOR

BEARING CAP

PRESSURE
LUBE OIL
STRAINER

AUXILIARY
DRIVE SHAFT

FABRICATED
STEEL BASE

Fig. 5-29 Enterprise model HV spark-ignited gas engine.

This rotation is then utilized to drive some mechanical device, performing work. The basic parts of a gas or oil engine are:

1. Cylinder block
2. Cylinder heads
3. Pistons and connecting rods
4. Crankshaft
5. Valve mechanisms
6. Intake and exhaust manifolds
7. Fuel pumps or metering valves

Crankshafts may be bedded in the frame of the engine, and retained by shell-type bearings which are held in place with bearing caps. In some applications, crankshafts are underslung. The cylinder block provides support for the cylinder liners, pistons, and cylinder heads. The cylinder head usually contains the intake and exhaust valves and rocker assemblies and forms the upper part of the combustion chamber. It is normally water-cooled by jacket water circulating through passages in the head. The cylinder head may also contain fuel injectors (diesel and dual-fuel engines),

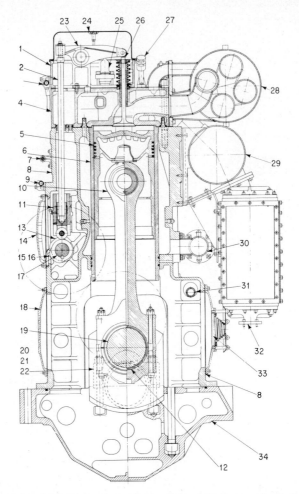

Fig. 5-30 Enterprise model R engine in-line four-stroke-cycle turbocharged and aftercooled diesel engine. (1) Subcover—cylinder head; (2) pushrod—exhaust and intake; (3) fuel-oil header; (4) cylinder head; (5) piston; (6) cylinder liner; (7) fuel-control shaft; (8) cylinder block; (9) fuel-oil drain header; (10) connecting rod; (11) tappet and guide; (12) connecting-rod bearing; (13) cam exhaust; (14) cover camshaft; (15) cam bearing, front; (16) cam bearing, intermediate; (17) camshaft; (18) side cover, block; (19) crankshaft; (20) main bearing, front; (21) main bearing, intermediate; (22) main bearing, rear; (23) rocker arms; (24) cover, cylinder head; (25) air starting valve; (26) valves—exhaust and intake; (27) relief valve; (28) exhaust manifold; (29) intake manifold; (30) water manifold; (31) lube-oil header; (32) intercooler; (33) relief door; (34) engine base.

gas-admission valves (dual-fuel and spark-ignited engines), air-starting valves, and spark plugs (gas engines).

In V-type engines, connecting rods may be in either a side-by-side or a master and articulating-rod arrangement. In the side-by-side design, each piston has a connecting rod, and each cylinder pair is attached to the same crankshaft journal. The master and articulated-rod design uses a master rod which is connected to the crankshaft, and a link rod which is attached to a link box on the master rod.

Terms and Definitions

There are a great number of terms used in connection with engines and their performance. Some of the more important ones are:

Horsepower (hp) A unit of work rate. One horsepower in the United States and British system of units equals 550 ft-lb/sec (33,000 ft-lb/min). The metric horsepower equals 75 kg-m/sec, which is slightly less than the United States unit.

Brake Horsepower (bhp) The brake horsepower of an engine is the horsepower delivered to the driven equipment by the engine output shaft. The relationship between brake horsepower torque and output shaft speed is

$$\text{bhp} = \frac{2\pi \times T \times \text{rpm}}{33,000}$$

where T = output shaft torque, ft-lb

Indicated Horsepower (ihp) Indicated horsepower is a measurement of the net rate of work done on the piston by the gases in the cylinders. Its determination requires the use of an engine-cylinder-pressure indicator capable of producing a plot of cylinder pressure vs. volume for a complete engine cycle. The net working pressure is called mean indicated pressure (mip), or indicated mean effective pressure (imep).

$$\text{ihp} = \frac{(\text{imep}) \times ASN}{33,000}$$

where A = piston area, sq in.
S = piston stroke, ft
N = number of power strokes per minute
imep is given in psi

Friction Horsepower (fhp) Friction horsepower is normally defined as the difference between indicated horsepower and brake horsepower. It is a measure of power lost between engine cylinders and the output shaft. Part of this loss is caused by friction between engine parts; the rest is usually power required by the engine-driven auxiliaries such as oil and water pumps.

Mechanical Efficiency The ratio of brake horsepower to indicated horsepower.

Brake Mean Effective Pressure (bmep) Brake mean effective pressure is calculated from the following formula:

$$\text{bmep} = \frac{\text{bhp} \times 33,000}{SAN} \quad \text{psi}$$

where S = piston stroke, ft
A = piston area, sq in.
N = number of power strokes per min of all pistons

Thermal Efficiency The thermal efficiency of an internal-combustion engine equals the ratio of energy (work) output rate over energy (heat) input rate. Input and output are usually expressed in Btu per time unit. Fuels used in engines have both a low and a high heating value; it is therefore proper to designate which value is being used. Normal custom for oil and gas engines is to use the high heating value for liquid fuels and the low heating value for gaseous fuels. Brake thermal efficiency is based on the brake horsepower output; indicated thermal efficiency is based on the indicated horsepower.

Brake Thermal Efficiency Brake thermal efficiency divided by indicated thermal efficiency equals the mechanical efficiency of the unit.

The theoretical cycle-efficiency relationship to the compression ratio for the Otto cycle (spark-ignition engine) is

$$\text{Cycle efficiency} = 1 - \left(\frac{1}{r}\right)^{k-1}$$

where r = compression ratio
k = isentropic constant for working medium

The actual relationship of compression pressure and brake mean effective pressure to thermal efficiency cannot be expressed by a formula as it varies from engine to engine and condition to condition.

Brake Horsepower Guarantees Brake horsepower capacity and fuel consumption guarantees are usually made by the manufacturer, either based on tests conducted on development and/or original models of an engine or as the result of factory tests conducted on an engine prior to shipment. Guarantees for engines operating below 1,500 ft altitude are generally made contingent on an atmospheric pressure of not less than 28.25 in. Hg and an air intake temperature not exceeding 90°F. The bhp capacity will be reduced on naturally aspirated engines operating above that altitude or temperature.

Limited-speed-range Characteristics of Stationary Units Most stationary engines are used to drive equipment with a limited range of speed requirements, such as generators, pumps, and blowers. Therefore, the need for a wide speed range is not significant, and the engine can be designed to operate near the optimum point for best engine efficiency.

Speed-to-Power Relationships In general, the higher the required power output, the larger the engine and the slower the engine speed. High-speed engines are usually smaller and have lower power outputs.

Engine Performance and Rating Limitations

Engine power ratings are determined by certain practices and usages which provide a yardstick for the measurement of engine performance, forming a common ground of reference for the manufacturer and the purchaser of engines. The type of engine has to be considered when determining how it will be rated. Bmep, engine speed, and piston speed are important factors. A naturally aspirated engine will present certain problems which are not significant when considering a turbocharged engine. The naturally aspirated engine is usually limited by its air supply, and may be rated at that power output where it first shows evidence of smoking. On the other hand, the turbocharged engine may be limited by the air supply that can be retained in the power cylinders (degree of turbocharging). Engine-strength limitations, or that point where an engine will produce the greatest power output without any harmful mechanical or thermal stresses, may determine the power rating. The speed rating is based on mechanical stresses and the piston's and ring's ability to receive adequate lubrication. Excessively high piston speeds will prevent lubricants from reaching vital areas, such as the ring-belt area. Another factor to be considered is the bearing loading limits.

If a gas or dual-fuel engine can be adequately cooled, detonation will become the primary factor in determining engine rating. The gas used, ignition timing, the air-fuel mixture, the combustion-chamber design, engine speed, and inlet-air-manifold temperatures are some of the factors that will affect detonation in a gas-fueled engine.

Effects of Supercharging and Inlet-air Cooling on Rating Supercharging and/or cooling of the inlet air will have the effect of improving engine rating by placing a denser air charge in the power cylinders, which will increase the power output of a given size cylinder. When rating an engine, performance is calculated at an elevation of not more than 1,500 ft, and not exceeding 90°F. Supercharging will improve performance at sea level and will compensate for loss of atmospheric pressure above that level. Additionally, supercharging will provide more air during the scavenging period, after the power stroke, thereby providing improved cooling to the cylinder and the exhaust valves.

Effects of Altitude on Power Ratings Altitude has little effect on a turbocharged engine; however, for naturally aspirated engines an increase in altitude will result in decreased power output. As the altitude increases, air density decreases, resulting in a reduction of intake-air charge density. The same effect is true for increased temperatures.

Load and Fuel Relationship to Supercharging Supercharging allows for a greatly increased bmep rating and usually will result in a slightly improved specific fuel consumption. If the engine is placed in an overloaded condition, however, the specific fuel consumption will increase, and economy of operation will be degraded.

Relationship of Continuous Rating and Overload Operation to Thermal Efficiency When a diesel engine is operating in an overload condition, the thermal efficiency is reduced, and this may also be the case with dual-fuel and spark-ignited engines. Engines are usually designed to operate at their best thermal efficiency at 75 percent or more of their continuous rating.

Effects of Operation above Continuous Rating If an engine is operated for any great length of time above the continuous rating power level, the higher mechanical thermal stresses will cause abnormal wear, and possible damage to the engine, as well as a loss in operational economy.

Economical Relationship of Unit Price to Fuel Consumption As in other situations, the use to which the engine is put will determine the controlling element of the unit price/fuel consumption ratio. If the engine is going to be in continuous or nearly continuous service, the rate of fuel consumption is a large factor in the selection of an engine. On the other hand, if the engine is to be used infrequently, as the prime mover for standby equipment, emergency auxiliary use, or such, then the rate of fuel consumption is of little practical importance as related to the unit price of the engine, and the engine which proved least expensive while still providing the capability to perform its intended use would be the logical selection.

Torsional Vibration and Critical Speeds

Every reciprocating engine has torsional criticals—those speeds at which it is either unsafe or noisy to operate. Criticals are found in every power drive operated by reciprocating engines, whether they be gasoline, steam, or diesel. Sometimes these criticals are below operating speeds and are therefore passed through too quickly to be noticed. In other installations criticals may be above the operating range and, as they are never reached, escape notice. When the critical falls within the operating range, this "rough spot" may break shafting, damage gears, or at least create objectionable vibrations.

Torsional vibration is the repeated twisting of a shaft, back and forth, about its axis. If the shaft of an engine is twisted and then released, it will vibrate back and forth in a number of vibrations per second (natural frequency) which will be determined by the stiffness of the shaft and the type of weights attached to various parts of the shaft. If the shaft is left alone, these vibrations will gradually die out, but if a vibrating force is applied which rises and falls at a time rate close to the natural frequency, torsional vibration will build up and may eventually destroy the shaft. Therefore, since the turning effort of an engine varies during each revolution, it is possible to run the engine at a speed at which the frequency of turning-effort variations coincides with the natural frequency of the shaft system, thus causing torsional vibrations to build up.

Torsional vibration is different from other forms of vibration in that there may be no visible or audible indication that dangerous vibrations are present. Furthermore, an engine-generator set with dangerous torsional vibrations may not show any defects during inspection, yet shaft failure may occur after many hours of operation. It is possible for the engine manufacturer to calculate the torsional criticals accurately, provided he is furnished with complete and accurate data concerning any driven apparatus which is not provided by him.

The problem of overcoming damaging or objectionable criticals involves the choosing of an operating speed so that the number of firing impulses per minute does not coincide with the system's natural frequency, or of changing the natural frequency of the system so that it is different from the number of firing impulses.

In actual practice the range of engine speed is generally determined when the engine is specified, and the shaft dimensions are the only factors that can be changed. Since shafting length is also determined by the type of drive, only the diameters of the main and stub shafts are left for consideration. When unfavorable torsional conditions are encountered, the diameter of the shafting can be changed. Fortunately, a relatively small change of shaft diameter results in a great change in the natural frequency.

The shaft designer considers certain salient points to keep major torsional criticals out of the operating range of the engine.

1. To keep criticals *above* the maximum speed, use as light a flywheel as possible

(one with low WR^2 effect), use the shortest possible shaft, or use a relatively large shaft diameter.

2. To keep excessive torsional vibrations *below* the operating range of the engine, use as heavy a flywheel as possible, the longest shaft possible, and as small a diameter as will safely carry the normal horsepower load.

There is a trend toward the use of hydraulic, magnetic, or spring couplings to eliminate or dampen the transmission of torsional pulsations to the shaft. The installation of torsion dampeners between the engine and the shaft does not solve all the torsional-critical problems. Power hammers, compressors, and other driven reciprocating machines have pulsations that can harmonize with the natural shaft torsional period, and their effects have to be considered and allowed for.

The engine builder, when furnishing all the driven equipment, is responsible for the design of the shafting, bearings, connections, etc., between the engine and the driven equipment with respect to torsional vibrations. When the driven equipment is furnished by anyone other than the engine builder, it is the buyer's responsibility to furnish the engine builder accurate and complete information on the driven equipment so that the engine builder can design and recommend construction details.

The engine manufacturer will normally make a thorough torsional analysis, and furnish the purchaser with the results as a curve of stress vs. rpm, showing the location and magnitude of all significant criticals. The purchaser should not alter the arrangement of the driven apparatus, or add any additional equipment (or remove any) from the unit without consulting the manufacturer as to the effect this will have on the location and magnitude of the critical speeds. It is likewise true that the range of operating speeds should not be changed without consulting the engine manufacturer, as the new range may be close enough to a critical speed to become dangerous.

Engine Design

Piston speed is determined by

$$\text{Piston speed} = \text{stroke in feet} \times \text{rpm} \times 2$$

At piston speeds where the frictional losses are the least, the engine is operating below its point of maximum specific output; therefore, a compromise is made in design to achieve a combination of high output with an acceptable frictional loss. Constant-speed heavy-duty engines are now designed with piston speeds up to approximately 1,600 fpm, and variable-speed high-output engines will operate with even higher piston speeds. Engines running at very high piston speeds will normally have shorter lifetimes than more conservatively rated engines because of higher wear rates.

Valve Arrangements Two configurations are in general use: a two-valve head and a four-valve head, the latter becoming more widely used on high-output engines to overcome frictional effects present with two-valve arrangements. The prevailing design is the overhead valve, actuated by rocker arms and pushrods. In a four-stroke-cycle engine the exhaust valve is held open during the exhaust stroke, following the power stroke, and the inlet valve is opened on the next downward, or intake, stroke. The valves remain open for longer periods than the corresponding piston strokes to provide time for opening and closing, and to utilize the inertia effects of the high velocity at which the gases flow. The opening and closing points of both valves are therefore displaced somewhat from dead center. The exhaust valve is timed to open before the piston reaches bottom dead center of the power stroke. This provides a blowdown period to release the gases from the cylinder and reduce the pressure approximately to exhaust manifold pressure by the end of the power stroke. Some useful work near the end of the power stroke is lost by this early valve opening, but additional negative work during the exhaust stroke is avoided by not requiring the piston to ascend against back pressure. The exhaust valve remains open past top dead center, allowing the kinetic energy of the outflowing gases to reduce the pressure within the combustion chamber below atmospheric pressure and decrease the exhaust gases remaining that would dilute the next charge. The inlet valve is opened before top dead center to take advantage of the pulling effect at the end of the exhaust period. An overlap results between the opening of the intake valve and the closing of the exhaust valve which helps scavenge the combustion chamber of gases.

Supercharging Supercharged intake-air systems are the predominant systems for medium- and large-sized engines, and exist to a great degree in small engines. Supercharging provides the engine with combustion air at a greater density than that of the surrounding air, providing an increased power output for a given size cylinder.

The turbocharger is a self-contained unit, composed of a gas turbine and a centrifugal blower attached to a common shaft. The exhaust gas from the power cylinders of the engine is discharged through manifolds to the turbine, which makes use of some of the energy in the exhaust gas which would otherwise be wasted. This salvaged energy is used to drive the blower, which furnishes all the air required by the engine at a pressure above atmospheric.

There are two general classifications of supercharging systems: the turbine-driven blower and the mechanically drive blower. In the former the supercharger is driven by the exhaust gases from the engine through a turbine which is shafted to a compressor. The mechanically driven blower may be driven from the engine, or separately by an electric motor or other prime mover. Turbine-driven blowers may be of either a constant-pressure or a pulse type. The constant-pressure type receives the entire exhaust output through its turbine, at a constant pressure, whereas the pulse type receives its driven force through multiple pipe manifolds; thereby it receives a series of pulses to drive it.

The pulse-type (Buchi) system of pressure charging and scavenging a four-cycle diesel or gas engine accomplishes two purposes. First, it scavenges the hot residual gases otherwise left in the cylinder at the end of the exhaust stroke, and replaces these with cooler, fresh air. Second, it fills the cylinder with an air charge of higher density at the end of the suction stroke. The provision of a greater amount of fresh air permits the combustion of a greater amount of fuel, and consequently a higher output from a turbocharged engine than one not so equipped.

The valve timing of an engine arranged for the Buchi system of pressure charging differs primarily from that of the same engine normally aspirated in that the exhaust valves of the pressure-charged engine close later, and the inlet valves open earlier. Thus the valve overlap, or period when both valves are open, is considerably greater, permitting nearly perfect scavenging when the piston is near top dead center. Timing of the valves and dimensions of the exhaust manifold are so proportioned that timed pressure fluctuations are induced in the manifold. Both valves are open when the pressure in the exhaust manifold is at a minimum, thus permitting scavenging with a lower blower pressure than would otherwise be possible.

Scavenging the combustion space with cool air effects a considerable degree of cooling of the cylinder head, cylinder walls, valves, and piston. For this reason, a greater amount of fuel can be burned, and greater power developed by an engine turbocharged with the Buchi system without harmful effects on these engine parts due to excessive heat.

No control over the turbocharger is necessary, as the correlated action of the turbine and blower is entirely automatic. The speed and output of the turbocharger vary automatically and instantaneously with variations in load or speed, or both, of the engine. No consideration need be given to direction of rotation of the turbocharger when applied to a direct reversing engine. The turbocharger rotates in one direction only, regardless of the direction of rotation of the engine.

Combustion Chambers The engine builder will design combustion chambers to meet the requirements of the particular engine. In general, diesel and dual-fuel engines have combustion chambers to make maximum use of the air charge, while spark-ignited engines have chambers designed to minimize or suppress detonation tendencies of the fuel.

The shape of the space forming the combustion chamber when the piston is at its closest approach to the cylinder head, and the volume contained therein in relation to the piston displacement volume are very important in their effects on performance. The size of the combustion chamber relative to the volume displaced by the piston establishes the compression ratio of the engine, which is an important factor in the starting characteristics of a diesel engine. High compression ratios also tend to increase thermal efficiency of engines, but this must be weighed against the detrimental effects of high maximum combustion pressures, and the possibility of running into conditions which result in detonation of gaseous fuels.

Firing Order Engine firing order is influenced by the requirements for crankshaft balance. The position of each throw along the crankshaft will determine the firing order, depending on the direction of engine rotation. Firing sequence is chosen to distribute the power impulses along the length of the engine to minimize vibration. Consideration is also given, when selecting firing order, to the fluid-flow pattern in the intake and exhaust manifolds. Balancing of the crankshaft may be further improved by adding counterweights to the shaft to offset the eccentric masses of metal in the crank throws.

The arrangement of the throws of the crankshaft for a multicylinder, four-stroke-cycle engine is chosen with regard to the firing order of the cylinders and the angular interval between firing impulses. The average number of degrees through which the crankshaft must turn between successive firings is found by dividing 720° (the two turns completed by the crankshaft during a complete cycle) by the number of cylinders for an in-line engine, or the number of cylinders in a single bank for a V-type engine. Regardless of the number of pistons in a four-cycle engine (even numbers only being considered), two pistons must arrive at top dead center in unison so that one cylinder is ready to fire 360° after the other cylinder fires. Half the cylinders will fire on each revolution of the crankshaft.

Air/Fuel Mixture Requirements Dual-fuel and spark-ignited gas engines usually operate with air/fuel mixtures on the lean side of the ideal (stoichiometric) ratio. This is done to reduce the cylinder exhaust temperatures and to reduce the tendency toward detonation.

Diesel engines operate with air/fuel ratios much leaner than the stoichiometric ratio. This is necessary because the nonhomogeneous distribution of fuel in the combustion air makes a large surplus of air necessary in order to have complete combustion of the injected fuel.

Ignition Systems Most ignition systems are of the magneto or the solid-state electronic type, the latter coming into more general use as designs are improved. Reliability, spark-plug life, firing accuracy, voltage output, and cost are the primary considerations for an ignition system, and the requirements for a particular installation will help determine the best type to use. A conventional magneto system poses problems due to the erosion and wear on the breaker points, and the difficulties involved in providing ignition wiring that will withstand the stress and wear placed on it with the attendant tendencies for the high-tension circuits to create safety hazards. The breakerless magneto eliminated most of the point problems by using breaker points only for starting, and then using pulse generators to provide the necessary voltage to the spark plugs. The solid-state ignition system eliminates many of the problems found in magneto systems. A typical solid-state system uses an alternator to provide current, which is then rectified to charge a tank, or firing capacitor and a smaller trigger capacitor. A trigger vane rotates around the drive shaft, and as it passes a trigger coil (one for each cylinder) it induces a small current which gates a silicon control switch. This allows the trigger capacitor to discharge, triggering the gate on a silicon control rectifier. The voltage from the tank capacitor then discharges through the primary winding of the transformer, which is mounted on or near the spark plug. This induces the necessary high voltage in the secondary windings of the transformer to fire the spark plug. This system eliminates long, high-tension leads by mounting the transformer on or near the spark plugs.

Starting Systems Many methods are used to bring engines up to the speed necessary for starting. Compressed air is usually employed, and in such cases opening of air starting valves automatically admits compressed air to the power cylinders in predetermined sequence.

Medium- and large-sized high-speed engines may be brought up to starting speed by various methods such as an attached electric motor, air motor, or gasoline engine. Engines driving direct-current generators are sometimes cranked by motorizing the generator from a separate source of direct current.

Air Starting. This system is the one most used in low and medium engines. Most engine builders design their engines for starting air pressures of 250 to 350 psi, although some older engines used pressures ranging up to 1,000 psi. In this system, compressed air from a suitable source is piped to the engine and flows to the cylinders through a distributor. Air is admitted to the cylinder through an air-admission valve, and forces the piston down, turning the crankshaft.

Motor Starting. Electric motors or air motors driven by either compressed air or fuel gas are geared to the engine to rotate the crankshaft until the engine is brought up to starting speed. On large engines, a number of motors may be used.

Automatic Starting. On some installations, particularly where the engine is driving standby or emergency pumps, generators, etc., it may be necessary to have automatic-starting provisions incorporated in the engine.

In systems using a direct air-admission system, only compressed air may be used. The introduction of fuel gas or other flammable gases may well result in an explosion due to gas in the power cylinders and in the exhaust system.

Cooling-water Systems Cooling-water systems are required to maintain the engine at a good operating temperature by cooling the cylinders and cylinder heads, and to provide a cooling method to remove heat from lubricating oil and intake air. The water system used for cooling the engine proper is normally referred to as the *jacket-water system*, and the one used for cooling lubricating oil and combustion air is called raw-water system (or some manufacturers refer to it as *lubricating-oil* and *aftercooler* cooling systems). Many design considerations must be observed when specifying the particular system to be used.

The system should be designed so that all the water flows through the engine at all times. The water flow should never be throttled to raise the outlet temperature. To maintain a uniform heat transfer and a high efficiency of cooling through the engine jackets, only soft water or treated water should be circulated through the engine. The character of the water should be such that there will be no deposit in the water spaces. It should be free of corrosive properties, and a pH value between 8.0 and 9.5 should be maintained for minimum corrosion.

In designing a cooling-water system, and in selecting equipment for it, many factors must be considered, such as the following:

1. Water supply. What are the hardness and corrosive characteristics? Is the supply ample or limited? Is it sea water, river water, lake water, or well water? Is it brackish?

2. Atmospheric conditions. What are maximum and minimum wet- and dry-bulb temperatures? What is the average wind velocity and its direction? Is the locality subject to dust storms?

3. Space available. Can all the equipment be installed indoors? In either case, how much space is available to accommodate the cooling equipment?

4. Heat recovery. Is it desirable to recover heat from the jacket water for space heating or for other uses around or near the plant?

Equipment to dissipate heat from jacket water has become highly specialized. The amount of heat to be removed from the engine jackets and from the lubricating oil and the limiting water temperatures should always be obtained from the engine manufacturer. It is then the cooling-equipment manufacturer's entire responsibility to supply adequate heat-exchange equipment to dissipate the specified amount of heat for actual service conditions during the life of the equipment.

There are two general types of cooling systems: the closed system and the open system.

Open System. The open cooling system is one in which the water under pressure flows through the engine jackets and is wasted or recirculated through a cooling tower. The recooling of water by cooling tower or spray pond is a process dependent upon evaporation. Continued evaporation and addition of makeup water increases the concentration of either hardness or impurities and causes the water to become increasingly objectionable for use in the engine jackets.

The accumulation of scale-forming materials will not remain in solution but will be deposited in the jackets of the engine, retarding the transfer of the heat from the metal walls to the cooling water. This is detrimental to the engine. Therefore, the open cooling system is generally not recommended.

Closed Cooling System. The closed cooling system is recommended. The arrangement may consist of either one or two complete systems of circulating water. If, for example, a radiator is used with air as the cooling medium, a single system is used with water flowing through the engine jackets and then through the radiator.

Other examples are the shell-and-tube heat exchanger, a cooling tower with heat exchanger, and an evaporative cooler. These types have two water-circulating systems: the jacket water and the raw water.

Jacket-water outlet temperature and the rate of flow of water must be specified by the engine builder. Raw-water temperatures, rate of flow, and heat load govern the requirements of the cooling apparatus.

A/C and L/O Cooling-water System. A separate independent system of the closed-loop variety may be used to furnish a cooling medium for aftercooler and lubricating-oil cooling. This system is not directly an engine-cooling system but indirectly provides engine cooling by the removal of heat from the lubricating oil, after the oil has removed the heat from pistons, bearings, etc.

Heat Recovery. Heat may be removed from the cooling water for use in space heating, or other purposes. The outlet water from the engine is passed through radiators, or other heat-exchanging devices, before being cooled further for return to the engine.

Lubrication Systems

In oil and gas engines the primary function of the lubricating oil is to prevent contact between moving parts, to cool critical areas, and to remove contaminants from within the engine. Oil is drawn from a sump, either the engine base itself or an exterior tank, by a motor- or engine-driven pump, then forced through a cooler/filter system and introduced into the engine system at a controlled pressure. (See Figs. 5-31 and 5-32.) It is led through drilled passages or tubing into the crankshaft to lubricate main and connecting-rod bearings. On large units the connecting rods contain an axial passage which conducts oil to the piston pin and the underside of the piston crown where combustion-heat loading in the piston is relieved. Lubrication of cylinder liners and piston rings is of prime importance. If oil is allowed to pass the piston rings in ex-

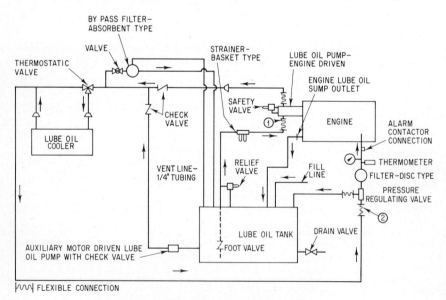

Fig. 5-31 Typical dry-sump oil-piping diagram.

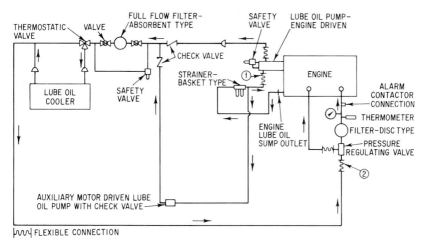

Fig. 5-32 Typical wet-sump oil-piping diagram.

cessive quantities, harmful deposits may result from combustion of some oils; also it
increases oil costs.

Auxiliary tubing leads oil from the main inlet header to the camshaft bearings, cams,
tappets, rocker arms, gears, and various accessory drives. Oil normally returns to the
engine base and/or sump tank by gravity flow; however, marine engines may require a
return or scavenging pump to accomplish this.

Controls

Engine-governing systems for oil and gas engines may be broadly divided into two
categories: those which regulate engine speed only, regardless of external conditions,
and those which control not only speed but load as well to achieve a preplanned program of power output in response to one or more external conditions or demands.

Governors for medium-speed engines, because of the force level required to regulate
fuel input, usually employ a highly responsive speed sensor. Normally, this is a flyball
configuration which has very little force output, but which operates a servosystem,
normally hydraulic, which can deliver sufficient force to operate the fuel control. In
the case of a diesel engine equipped with individual fuel-injection pumps, the governor
servo acts through linkage to rotate the injection-pump plungers. By means of helical
exhaust grooves on the plungers, the length of the pumping portion of the plunger
stroke is controlled, and hence the quantity of fuel delivered. On a gas engine,
whether spark- or pilot-oil-ignited (dual-fuel), the servo acts to control the position of
a fuel-gas metering valve or valves, to control fuel-gas flow only.

A speed-only governing system normally acts to maintain a desired steady-state speed
regardless of external loading. When the unit's load capacity is reached, the fuel input
will remain at maximum and the speed will drop. When transient or sudden loads are
applied, or removed, small temporary speed increases or decreases occur, the magnitude of which depends on engine and governor configuration.

Alternating-current power generation presents a special situation. When two or
more alternators are operated in parallel, that is, connected to the load, only one unit
can control the frequency of the system if stability is to be maintained. Therefore, a
function termed *speed droop* is built into governors for such applications. The effect
of the speed-droop system is to cause the governor-speed set point to decrease as load
is applied; that is, as the servo acts to increase fuel it also, through linkage, acts to reduce speed setting. Since the unit is tied to a constant-frequency load it cannot change
speed; therefore, it tends to operate at a fixed load with the frequency-controlling unit,

which has no speed droop, accepting all system-load changes. If automatic load-change sharing is to be obtained on all plant units using the above system, line-frequency deviation must be accepted since all units must operate with speed droop.

Speed/load governing systems are usually used in applications where engine speed is a variable as well as the load. Controllable-pitch propellers, compressors, pumps, dc generators, and mechanical drives are examples of this type of application. The governor is arranged to provide an output signal, either electric or hydraulic, which bears a predesigned relationship with engine speed and/or load, and which operates to control this load. By careful design of the system, a power output can be automatically obtained which will make best advantage of engine performance characteristics and load requirements. Modifications to the power program can be achieved automatically in response to atmospheric or subsystem performance changes.

A special case is that of the electrohydraulic governing system used for alternator service. It basically consists of an electrical load- and/or frequency-sensing device, a computer which translates these inputs into a single electrical output, and an electrical device which operates the governor servo. With this system, more than one alternator may be operated in parallel, with all units sharing system load changes equally, and with no basic speed change. Automatic start and synchronization may be accomplished, with the oncoming unit automatically assuming its programmed share of the total load. This is an extremely fast and stable method, and may be used where precise control of frequency is mandatory, such as for computer or radar service.

Governor-system Performance The performance of a governing system depends not only on the type of governor used but equally upon the configuration of the engine and the governor match to that engine. The basic system parameters are control of basic steady-state speed, the amount of speed change during a load change, and the rapidity of return to the set speed after such a load change has occurred. The response of the governor/servosystem itself varies with type, the mechanical-hydraulic type generally being the slowest, and the electric governor being fastest. The engine type, and the time required to convert a fuel-input change to a torque-output change, the inertia of the rotating assembly, the basic speed, and the number of cylinders all influence the total response time of the system. For example: A new fuel setting in a diesel engine will result in a new torque output much sooner than in a gas engine because fuel is admitted on inlet stroke in a gas engine, whereas the diesel engine produces torque from the fuel almost as it is injected. Furthermore, the fuel-gas-admission system in a gas engine requires time to fill and drain in response to the governor action. The more cylinders an engine has, and the higher its basic speed setting, the less time required to produce a new total torque output from a fuel-input change, and the faster its response. The inertia of rotating parts is quite important. Larger flywheels will reduce the speed excursion but will increase recovery time. When turbocharged engines accept very large load changes, the inertia of the turbocharger becomes important since it requires time to produce enough air to allow the new fuel input to burn.

Since a diesel engine with an electric governor is able to control speed more precisely than any other prime mover, it is by far the best choice where such control is required. The unit can be designed to achieve control such as absolutely no reduction of basic speed throughout the load range; ± 0.3 percent control of steady-state speed; one-half cycle speed deviation for an instantaneous 50 percent load change; recovery time in the 1-sec range. It may do this in parallel or in isolated operation.

The gas engine, equipped with mechanical-hydraulic governing such as normally used in municipal or industrial power generation, is somewhat wider in control range but still much faster than water, steam, or gas-turbine units.

Although the controls installed on any particular engine will vary according to the type, model, manufacturer, and the requirements of the installation, certain controls are common to nearly all engines.

Overspeed Governor Engines may be equipped with an overspeed trip which automatically shuts off fuel, or otherwise stops the engine in case the engine operates at a speed in excess of some predetermined value. This overspeed governor should be separate from the regular speed governor.

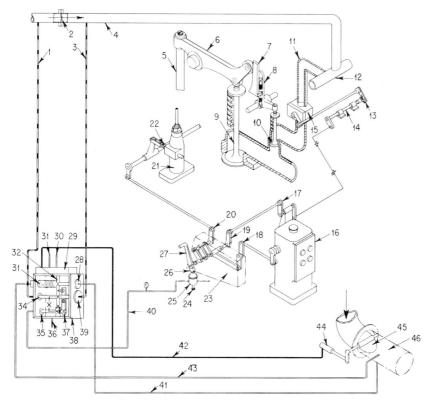

Fig. 5-33 Dual-fuel control system (two-valve head). (1) Upstream gas; (2) gas-flow nozzle; (3) downstream gas; (4) gas-supply pipe; (5) pushrod; (6) intake rocker arm; (7) gas cam; (8) gas rocker arm; (9) intake valve; (10) gas-admission valve; (11) elbow; (12) gas header; (13) adjustable gas lever; (14) gas control shaft; (15) gas plug valve; (16) governor; (17) jack shaft; (18) governor lever; (19) gas lever; (20) diesel lever; (21) fuel pump; (22) fuel-pump rack; (23) Select-O-Matic control; (24) adjustment screw; (25) regulator; (26) cam; (27) S-O-M control handle; (28) air diaphragm; (29) pilot valve; (30) lubricating-oil exhaust; (31) lubricating-oil supply; (32) pivot rod; (33) thermostatic bellows and spring; (34) upstream gas diaphragm; (35) control air diaphragm; (36) lubricating-oil drain; (37) air-control crank; (38) airflow-control regulator; (39) downstream gas diaphragm; (40) control air line; (41) air line; (42) hydraulic line; (43) temperature-compensator line; (44) air butter-fly valve cylinder; (45) air butterfly valve; (46) intake manifold.

Fuel-selector Control (Dual-fuel engines) A control mechanism which permits selection of diesel or dual-fuel mode of operation. Some controls permit selection of any proportion of fuel ranging from dual-fuel with pilot oil to full diesel operation. (See Fig. 5-33.)

Fuel-Air Ratio Control This control is used on dual-fuel and spark-ignited engines to control the volume of intake combustion air to achieve the necessary ratio of air to fuel gas. (See Fig. 5-34.)

Ignition Control (Spark Advance) Regulates ignition advance based upon various factors such as engine speed, intake-manifold air temperature, and pressure. On engines so equipped, automatic control is possible. Ignition advance may be manually set, automatically set, or preset, depending on the particular requirements of the installation.

Alarm and Safety Shutdown Controls These controls provide for visual and/or audio alarm and shutdown of the engine when some malfunction occurs, such as excessive

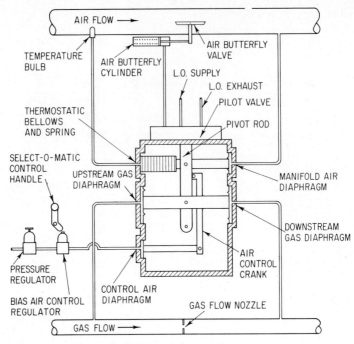

Fig. 5-34 Airflow regulator.

temperatures or insufficient pressures. A wide variety of control features are available, and the extent of an installation will depend on the needs of the plant and the desires of the operator. Most systems utilize pneumatic relays coupled to sensing devices such as pressure switches, vibration switches, and temperature-sensing elements. The sensing elements are set for predetermined values, and if these values are met, they will initiate an automatic shutdown of the engine by cutting off the fuel, or by other means. An audio alarm system may be utilized which will sound at a point before shutdown occurs, which will give the operator an opportunity to correct the condition before the engine is shut down, this to prevent loss of engine operating time. A system of pneumatic relays, connected in a series circuit and pressurized with air, gas, or oil, is installed. Each relay is controlled by a sensing device for a particular function. If a sensing device detects an unsatisfactory condition, at the preset value it will trip, causing its relay to vent. This releases pressure on the system, and fuel will be cut off and the engine will stop. A feature of this system is that the relay involved will indicate itself, informing the operator as to the cause of the stoppage and shutdown. The overspeed governor normally is connected to this system, and if the engine overspeeds, the governor will trip a sensing device, which in turn vents its relay, and the engine is shut down.

Starting Controls Engine-starting controls are provided, the exact installation depending on the requirements and specifications of the engine. Because of the different starting methods available, there is no standard arrangement.

Temperature Controls (Thermostatic Valves) Various arrangements may be designed to achieve temperature control of cooling water and lubricating oil. Thermostatically controlled valves can be used to modulate flow, depending on temperature of the fluid, by directing the flow through heat exchangers, radiators, etc., when the temperature is above a preset value.

Load Controls Various controls may be incorporated on an engine, which will signal the driven equipment (particularly in the case of a compressor) that the engine is approaching an overload. This will activate control circuits or mechanisms in the compressor to cause it to unload before the engine is overloaded.

Lubricants

The high unit and thermal loading of various parts within the modern medium-speed engine imposes stringent requirements on the lubricating oil. To achieve these requirements, oils contain a rather large percentage of special additives. These are compounds which resist oxidation at high temperatures, resist foaming under severe agitation, impart great wear resistance to highly loaded areas such as cam lobes and tappet rollers, neutralize corrosive acid compounds formed by combustion, and dissolve and/or carry in suspension to the filter the dirt and foreign matter that invariably find their way into the system. In addition to those requirements, it must maintain a film between moving parts and in itself be noncorrosive to the wide array of materials used in the engine.

An additional requirement for oils used in gas engines is that the oil, when exposed to the heat of combustion, must not form deposits which build up on the combustion chamber. Such deposits form hot spots which may cause preignition or detonation and thereby lower the load-carrying ability of the engine.

The viscosity of an oil, or its resistance to shearing, primarily affects its ability to maintain a film (load-carrying ability) and its ability to flow into small clearances. Furthermore, the oil must not change its viscosity excessively with temperature changes. It must be free-flowing enough at low temperatures to allow the unit to be started with adequate lubrication, but when the unit is warmed up, it must not thin so much as to reduce its load-carrying ability. This characteristic of oils is called *viscosity index*, and is normally a property of the base oil stock.

Oils are classified by various agencies, generally in categories broadly describing overall oil performance. The American Petroleum Institute (API) has defined three types of service conditions normally encountered, and has developed oil specifications meeting the requirements of each. These are the MS and DG types of classifications so familiar to automotive users. U.S. Military Specifications (MIL Specs) are frequently more important to large-engine owners. These are also rather wide descriptions of oils which have been found by test and experience to function acceptably under various service conditions.

It may be seen from the above that selection of a lubricating oil for a given unit is a complex problem, involving engine design, service conditions, fuels, and the properties of the lubricating oil. Therefore, it is normal for the owner, the lubricating-oil manufacturer, and the engine builder to work closely together in selecting an oil for a particular job.

Fuels

Oil and gas engines, as their names imply, utilize two categories of fuel: liquid and gaseous. Within these two categories, however, is a wide variety of fuel classifications. Since fuel, probably more than any other factor, affects engine performance, economy, and life, the selection of a fuel is of the utmost importance.

Gaseous Fuels *Natural Gas.* Of the gaseous fuels, natural gas is by far the most widely used. It is mainly composed of methane (CH_4) and has an octane rating of approximately 110. This fuel burns extremely clean, thus reducing contamination, corrosion, and abrasion of engine parts. Lubricating-oil life is significantly extended, with a resultant economy of operation. Since the combustion of natural gas produces less infrared than most liquid fuels, thermal loading of combustion-chamber surfaces is less. Performance variations are reduced for engines burning natural gas because of the generally consistent quality of this natural product.

The source of supply is frequently a transmission pipeline, or a commercial distribution system; therefore, installation costs are reduced by the elimination of storage requirements.

Manufactured Gas. The more commonly used fuels of this classification are propane, butane, and sewage gas. Two main factors affect the use of these fuels: octane rating and the inclusion of unstable components in the fuel. As propane has an octane rating of about 100, and butane about 92, the detonation limit and/or load-carrying ability for these fuels is somewhat lowered. This can be offset to a degree by decreasing the compression ratio of the engine, but this is nearly always done at the expense of efficiency. Both fuels burn clean and have the same general advantages as natural gas.

Sewage, or digester, gas is a by-product of the sewage-treatment process and makes an acceptable engine fuel having many of the advantages of natural gas. It is usually produced on the jobsite. It contains little more than half the Btu content of natural gas; however, it requires higher admission pressures, it displaces more combustion oxygen than does natural gas, and an adjustment to the apparent air-fuel ratio is necessary.

In some instances manufactured gas contains unstable compounds which produce sporadic detonation at high loads. Sewage gas contains compounds of sulfur which may be corrosive to engine materials, particularly copper alloys.

Liquid Fuels *Diesel or Distillate Fuels.* Diesel fuel is a term which encompasses a range of fuel oils which are suitable for use in diesel and dual-fuel engines. This type of fuel must be injected into the combustion chamber in an atomized state, vaporized, and then caused to ignite by the heat of compression. The overall ability to ignite promptly is measured by a value called the cetane number, the lower numbers indicating those fuels which are more prone to produce knock in an engine. Distillate diesel fuels are normally in the 40- to 60-cetane range.

The heat values of diesel fuels vary widely, and this has a marked effect on load-carrying ability and/or thermal efficiency. Those fuels having less volumetric heat content produce less load-carrying ability and higher fuel consumption for a given engine. The volumetric heat content is proportional to the American Petroleum Institute (API) gravity index of the fuel, the higher-gravity fuels having less volumetric heat.

Diesel fuels are classified by the American Society for Testing and Materials (ASTM) into groups bearing numerical designations, Number 1 fuel oil, Number 2 fuel oil, etc. In nearly all cases fuels of lower viscosity, higher cetane ratings, and less volumetric heat fall into the lower numerical classes. Number 1 fuel oil is used primarily for high-speed, cold-starting, automatic engines; Number 2 for slower, medium-speed engines, etc. Engine builders design and tune their product for one given fuel oil, and unless specifically modified for a different fuel, less than optimum performance will be the normal result if other than the recommended fuel is used.

If use of ASTM Number 4, 5, or 6 fuel is contemplated, the range of residual, heavy, or bunker fuels is being entered. Such fuels are normally the by-products of a refining process, and their properties may vary widely. If correctly applied to a properly designed engine, these fuels may be used successfully and a saving in fuel costs may be realized.

Residual fuels are normally highly viscous, and when cold will require heating for pumping, filtering, and injection. The cetane number is low, which requires warmer combustion air to avoid knock; however, the volumetric heat content is higher than in distillate fuels. Residual fuels may contain undesirable contaminants, even salt water, and must be centrifuged and filtered to remove these contaminants before they are used. Other nonremovable compounds, notably sulfur, vanadium, and sodium, may be present, whose oxides are corrosive under certain conditions. Care in oil selection can sometimes reduce these undesirable effects.

The compatibility of different residual-fuel stocks is of particular concern to operators of marine installations. Certain fuels, particularly those which have been through a thermal-cracking process, may become unstable in storage. As the marine operator may receive his fuel supply from many different sources, it is very important that he select a fuel that will not react unfavorably with the fuel already on board in bunkers.

Engine Testing

The performance of an engine is expressed in terms of power, speed, and fuel economy. The three quantities are evaluated with a dynamometer which applies a controllable load in the form of resistance to turning of the crankshaft, and also measures the torque exerted on the shaft coupling. The resistance imposed by the dynamometer may be so adjusted that the desired engine speed is established at any throttle position. It is thus possible to run the engine at various speeds throughout its operating range, to maintain these operating conditions continuously, and to measure the precise loads and speeds at which each run is made. Additional test equipment permits measurement of the exact quantity of fuel consumed as well as the duration of the runs. From these data the engine designer and builder can calculate the power-speed-economy relationships, plot the performance curves, and gain much information regarding the suitability of the engine for its intended purpose. Other tests may be conducted to determine the durability of the engine, quietness, and smoothness of operation, accelerating ability, cooling requirements, fuel limitations, etc.

The testing of production engines may be done by the manufacturer at his factory, or in some cases at the installation site, to determine if the engine does in fact perform as specified.

Factory testing of oil and gas engines is performed for three primary purposes:

1. To obtain a correct run-in of the various critical mating parts in the engine
2. To discover and correct deficiencies or malfunctions of the unit before the engine is shipped to the purchaser
3. To prove, as far as practical in a shop test, the capability of the unit to perform as guaranteed

To achieve these objectives, each engine is run on a test stand against either an electric or water dynamometer, or against a generator. By careful design of the test procedure, conditions closely approximating the full range of the jobsite speeds and loads are obtained, and test runs are conducted at each desired condition. There are normally five or more test conditions, and complete operational and engineering data are recorded so that a good evaluation may be obtained. Complete external and internal mechanical inspections are performed before, during, and after the test.

Performance evaluations center mainly upon load-carrying ability and thermal efficiency. Test results are compared not only with guaranteed performance specifications but also with various norms which have been established through experience. Deviations from these norms are investigated and corrected. In this way, the engine builder and the owner are reasonably assured that the machinery will be accepted at the installation site.

A test report, incorporating the test results and evaluations, is furnished to the owner or his engineer. This report contains procedures, instrumentation records and calibrations, calculations, performance curves, control-adjustment records, inspection results, and test log sheets.

Acceptance tests, conducted on the installation site after the complete installation is finished, should be conducted to confirm the ability of the unit and auxiliaries to perform as specified. This test normally involves fuel economy, ability to carry full-rated load and specified overload, and such other tests as may be mutually agreed on by the engine builder and the purchaser.

Applications

The process of selecting engines which will be suitable for an application must take into consideration a number of factors in addition to the engine's ability to produce the required number of horsepower. Other major factors are output shaft rotational speed, fuel requirements, physical size, weight, and service record.

Estimates of first costs must be weighed against fuel and maintenance costs. In some cases it will be found most economical to use a compact, high-speed engine with a reduction gear for driving a certain piece of equipment. In other cases, a medium-speed direct-drive engine may be found the most economical choice. The first cost of the latter choice will usually be higher, but the better fuel consumption and greater durability, normal for the medium-speed engine, may more than compensate for the higher first cost, especially if the number of running hours per year is high.

Consideration must be given to auxiliary systems, switchgear, and other equipment required, and the cost of this installation. Supercharging may or may not be necessary, and the overall cost should be weighed against the increased power output of the engine. The compatibility of the engine selected with existing facilities may require special design features, and must be considered.

For any power application, the following conditions should be satisfied when selecting size and number of engines:

1. Must produce sufficient horsepower to satisfy the maximum demand for power.
2. Should provide the necessary power at the lowest total cost for both operating expenses and fixed charges.
3. Should provide for future growth.

Installation

Building Stationary engines are generally installed in buildings which have been specifically constructed for this purpose. The architectural design of the building will depend upon a great many factors; however, certain features should be incorporated which are in general common to all sites:

1. Sufficient clearance and an overhead crane should be provided for maintenance, taking into account the distances necessary for piston removal and similar disassembly of the engine.
2. Provisions should be made for future installation of additional units (if this is provided for in expansion plans). Also, any one unit should be able to be removed without disturbing the other units.
3. There should be adequate ventilation.
4. There should be protective guards around flywheels and other exposed, moving machinery.

Foundations It is accepted practice for engine builders to provide drawings for engine foundations. Before final details of the foundation design are established, the bearing capacity and suitability of the footings on which the foundations will rest should be determined. In all cases the purchaser should consult an expert in soil mechanics. It may be found advisable to modify the manufacturer's drawings to meet special requirements set up by local conditions. The engine builder should furnish information regarding the values of horizontal and vertical unbalanced inertia forces, and the dead weight of the machinery to be supported.

Piping Systems The engine builder normally furnishes suitable piping diagrams for each engine in which he recommends minimum pipe sizes for all service lines. In addition, the following should be observed:

1. Piping must never cause deflection in the mountings of reciprocating or rotating auxiliary equipment, nor should a heavy piece of auxiliary equipment ever be supported by engine service piping.
2. Whenever there is a possibility of deflection, flexibility must be designed into the piping.
3. Chill rings should not be used in welded pipe joints as they tend to retain scale, welding slag, and beads, which can come loose as the pipe becomes hot during engine operation.

All lubricating-oil and fuel-gas system piping should be pickled after fabrication to remove varnish, mill scale, welding debris, dirt, and grease. Serious engine damage can result from failure to clean these pipes properly. Other piping systems should be thoroughly wire-brushed. Pickling should be done under controlled conditions, using the phosphoric acid process or equal; then the interior should be neutralized and wire-brushed to remove all black iron oxide down to a uniform-gray-color metal. Immediately after pickling, the pickled surfaces should be coated with a rust-preventive compound which is soluble with the lubricating oil that will be used in the engine.

Engine Alignment with Driven Equipment The engine builder will furnish instructions for alignment of the engine on its subbase or foundation and, if he is also furnishing the driven equipment, alignment procedures for aligning the engine with the driven equipment. In other cases, the producer of the driven equipment will provide alignment procedures for his units.   Engine-alignment procedures will include adjusting crank-shaft-web deflections in the engine.   Where flexible couplings are used, the coupling manufacturer will furnish information concerning alignment procedures for the coupling.

Operation and Maintenance

A complete knowledge of the engine and its auxiliary systems is necessary to permit the operator to operate the engine properly and safely.   All valves and cutoffs, strainers, filters, etc., must be properly identified and their operating position ascertained.

Before starting for the first time, all systems should be checked, and after it has been determined that they are ready for operation, the engine should be barred over by hand for a few revolutions to ensure that there are no restrictions.   After other necessary preparations preliminary to starting have been made, and the engine has been started, it should be run at a speed as low as practical while all gages are observed.   The engine speed should be increased gradually while pressures and temperatures are observed to make sure all parts and systems are working properly.

Manufacturers issue specific instructions for each of their engines, and such instructions are the result of wide experience.   To secure the utmost in reliability and efficiency, these instructions should be read, understood, and followed.

Cleanliness is an absolute necessity, particularly in relation to the fuel- and lubricating-oil systems.   A large number of delays and repairs result from neglect of this fundamental truth.

Energy-conversion Machines

CENTRIFUGAL PUMPS

General

The centrifugal pump is one of the most versatile types of machinery for industry. Every plant has operating a multitude of pumps of this type, and modern civilization could not be visualized without this equipment.

Compared with other types of pumps, i.e., reciprocating and rotary, centrifugal pumps operate at relatively high speeds and, consequently, are smaller and lighter when designed for comparable capacity and head. Required floor space, weight, initial cost, and building costs are therefore reduced.

Owing to their relatively high speed, centrifugal pumps are usually direct-connected to the driver, the majority being electric-motor-driven. Having no reciprocating parts, centrifugal pumps are inherently balanced. There are no internal rubbing parts, and as the running clearances are relatively large, wear is minimized. The liquid is delivered in a steady stream so that no receiver is needed to even out pulsations.

In contrast to positive-type displacement pumps, centrifugal pumps develop a limited head at constant speed over the operating range from zero to rated capacity, and excessively high pressures cannot occur. They can therefore be started against a closed discharge valve but should be operated at this condition for a minimum period (see pages 6-20 to 6-25). Generally, the bearings are located outside the casing, so that the liquid does not come in contact with the lubricating oil and is not contaminated by it.

Classification

There are three general classes of pumps, depending on the configuration of the pump impellers.

Centrifugal or radial pump
Mixed-flow pump
Axial-flow pump

Those classes can be subclassified according to

Number of stages—single-stage pump, multistage pump
Arrangement of liquid inlet—single-suction pump, double-suction pump
Position of shaft—horizontal pump, vertical pump (dry-pit type), vertical pump (submerged type)

Specific Speed

Specific speed is a correlation of pump capacity, head, and speed at *optimum* efficiency which classifies the pump *impellers* with respect to their geometric similarity corresponding to the classification mentioned above (see also Fig. 6-1).

VALUES OF SPECIFIC SPEED

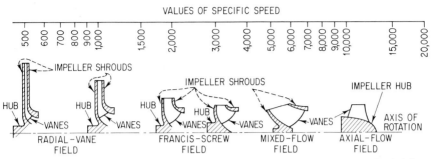

Fig. 6-1 Profile of several pump-impeller designs ranging from the low-specific-speed radial flow on the left to a high-specific-speed impeller design on the right, placed according to where each design fits on the specific-speed scale. (*Courtesy of the Hydraulic Institute.*)

Specific speed is a number usually expressed as[1]

$$\text{Specific speed } N_s = \frac{N\sqrt{Q}}{H^{3/4}} \quad \text{or} \quad N_s = \frac{N\sqrt{Q}H^{1/4}}{H}$$

where N_s = specific speed
N = rotative speed, rpm
Q = flow, gpm, at or near optimum efficiency
H = head, ft per stage

The specific speed of an impeller is defined as the revolutions per minute at which a geometrically similar impeller would run if it were of such a size as to discharge 1 gallon per minute against 1 foot head.

Specific speed is indicative of the shape and characteristics of an impeller, and it has been found that the ratios of major dimensions vary uniformly with specific speed. Specific speed is useful to the designer in predicting proportions required and to the application engineer in checking suction limitations of pumps.

Impeller form and proportions vary with specific speed, as shown in Fig. 6-1.

Pumps are traditionally divided into three classes: the centrifugal or radial flow, the mixed flow, and the axial flow, but it can be seen from the chart in Fig. 6-1 that there is a continuous change from the radial-flow impeller, which develops pressure principally by the action of centrifugal force, to the axial-flow impeller, which develops most of its head by the propelling or lifting action of the vanes on the liquid.

In the specific-speed range of approximately 1,000 to 4,000, double-suction impellers are used as frequently as single-suction impellers.

Table 6-1 gives values of $H^{3/4}$ for the accurate determination of the specific speed N_s.

The chart of Fig. 6-2 may be used to find the specific speed with sufficient accuracy for practical purposes, without calculating the head to the three-fourths power. The point located by plotting the total head and capacity in gpm at the design point is moved parallel to the sloping lines to the correct speed in rpm. The specific speed is read at the top of the chart directly above this final point. The procedure is illustrated by the heavy dashed lines.

For double-suction impellers, the total flow through the pump should be divided by 2 in calculating the specific speed; i.e., they should be considered to be two single-suction impellers operating in parallel.

For multistage pumps, the head per stage is used in the specific-speed equation. Generally, this is the total head of the pump divided by the number of stages.

Impeller performance curves are intimately related to their types or specific speeds. Higher-specific-speed impellers operating at partial loads have higher heads, require

[1] The value of $H^{3/4}$ may be found on page 6-4.

TABLE 6-1   Values of $H^{3/4}$

Head	$H^{3/4}$	Head	$H^{3/4}$	Head	$H^{3/4}$	Head	$H^{3/4}$
0	0	50	18.8	225	58.1	1,050	184.4
1	1.00	52	19.4	230	59.0	1,100	191.0
2	1.68	54	19.9	235	60.0	1,150	197.4
3	2.28	56	20.5	240	61.0	1,200	203.8
4	2.83	58	21.0	245	62.0	1,250	210.2
5	3.34	60	21.6	250	62.9	1,300	216.4
6	3.83	62	22.1	260	64.8	1,350	222.7
7	4.30	64	22.6	270	66.6	1,400	228.8
8	4.75	66	23.2	280	68.4	1,450	234.9
9	5.20	68	23.7	290	70.2	1,500	241.0
10	5.62	70	24.2	300	72.0	1,550	247.0
11	6.03	72	24.7	310	73.9	1,600	252.9
12	6.45	74	25.2	320	75.7	1,650	258.8
13	6.85	76	25.7	330	77.4	1,700	264.7
14	7.24	78	26.2	340	79.2	1,750	270.5
15	7.62	80	26.8	350	80.9	1,800	276.3
16	8.00	82	27.3	360	82.6	1,850	282.0
17	8.38	84	27.7	370	84.4	1,900	287.7
18	8.73	86	28.2	380	86.1	1,950	293.4
19	9.09	88	28.7	390	87.8	2,000	299.0
20	9.45	90	29.2	400	89.4	2,100	310.2
21	9.80	92	29.7	410	91.1	2,200	321.2
22	10.2	94	30.2	420	92.8	2,300	332.1
23	10.5	96	30.7	430	94.4	2,400	342.8
24	10.8	98	31.1	440	96.1	2,500	353.5
25	11.2	100	31.6	450	97.7	2,600	364.1
26	11.5	105	32.8	460	99.3	2,700	374.5
27	11.8	110	33.9	470	101	2,800	384.9
28	12.2	115	35.0	480	103	2,900	395.1
29	12.5	120	36.2	490	104	3,000	405.3
30	12.8	125	37.4	500	106	3,100	415.4
31	13.1	130	38.5	520	109	3,200	425.4
32	13.5	135	39.6	540	112	3,300	435.3
33	13.8	140	40.6	560	115	3,400	445.2
34	14.1	145	41.8	580	118	3,500	455.0
35	14.4	150	42.8	600	121	3,600	464.7
36	14.7	155	43.9	620	124	3,700	474.4
37	15.0	160	45.0	640	127	3,800	483.9
38	15.3	165	46.0	660	130	3,900	493.5
39	15.6	170	47.1	680	133	4,000	502.9
40	15.9	175	48.1	700	136	4,100	512.3
41	16.2	180	49.2	720	139	4,200	521.7
42	16.5	185	50.2	740	141	4,300	531.0
43	16.8	190	51.2	760	145	4,400	540.2
44	17.1	195	52.2	780	148	4,500	549.4
45	17.4	200	53.2	800	150	4,600	558.5
46	17.7	205	54.2	850	157	4,700	567.6
47	18.0	210	55.1	900	164	4,800	576.6
48	18.2	215	56.2	950	171	4,900	585.6
49	18.5	220	57.1	1,000	178	5,000	594.6

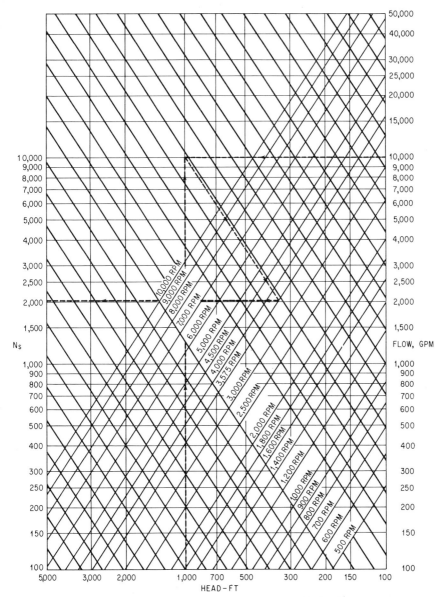

Fig. 6-2 Chart for determination of specific speed. Using chart, plot head-capacity point; move from this point, parallel to heavy lines, to correct speed; from there move horizontally to the left and read specific speed. *Example* (dashed lines): $H = 1,000$ ft, $Q = 10,000$ gpm, $N = 3,575$ rpm, $N_S = 2,015$.

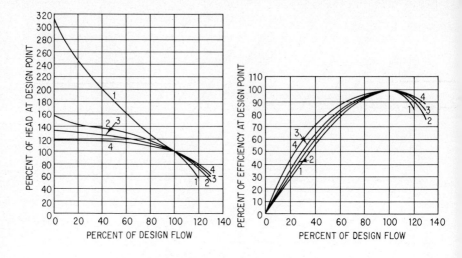

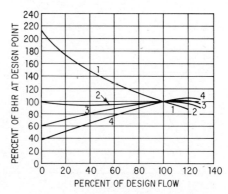

Fig. 6-3 Comparison of performance curves for various types of impellers: (1) propeller; (2) mixed flow; (3) Francis; (4) radial.

more horsepower, and have lower efficiency. This is illustrated in Fig. 6-3 on a percentage basis for the three general types mentioned above.

Hydraulics

Definition of Static, Pressure, and Velocity Heads One of the most useful relationships of hydraulics is the *continuity equation*, which is based upon the principle that after steady conditions in any system have been established, the weight flow of fluid per unit of time passing any point is constant. Since most liquids are practically incompressible, this may be put in equation form as $Q = AV$, where Q = flow, cfs, A = cross-sectional area, sq ft, and V = velocity, fps. This equation may be rewritten in the form $V = 0.321Q/a$,[1] where V = velocity, fps, Q = volume flow, gpm, and a = area of pipe, sq in. This equation is of importance in determining the velocity of the fluid at various points in either the piping or the pump itself.

Another important term is that of *head*, which is the energy contained in a pound of fluid. It is the height to which a column of the same fluid must rise to contain the same

[1] For velocities in pipes from 1 to 72 in. in size, see pages 3-22 to 3-28.

amount of energy as a unit weight of the fluid has under the conditions considered. It may appear in any of three forms which are interchangeable.

The *potential* or *static head* is based upon the elevation of the fluid above some arbitrarily chosen datum plane. Thus, a column of fluid z ft high contains an amount of energy due to its position, and is said to have a head of z ft of water.

The *pressure head* is the energy contained in a unit weight of the fluid due to its pressure and equals P/γ, where P is the pressure, psf, and γ is its specific weight, lb/cu ft. If an open manometer tube is set perpendicular to the flow, the fluid in it will rise to a height equal to P/γ.

The *kinetic* or *velocity head* is the energy contained in a unit weight of the fluid due to its motion, and is given by the familiar expression for kinetic energy $V^2/2g$ where $V =$ velocity, fps, and $g =$ acceleration due to gravity (32.17 ft/sec²). Values of this velocity head for various velocities are given on page 3-6. It may be measured by a pitot tube facing the flow, with the second leg of the manometer connected to the tube at right angles to the flow to equalize the pressure existing at this point.

The total energy of the fluid is equal to the sum of the three heads, or

$$\frac{P}{\gamma} + \frac{V^2}{2g} + z = H$$

Since energy cannot be created or destroyed, H is constant at any point of a closed hydraulic system (neglecting losses). This equation is known as *Bernoulli's theorem*. The various forms of head may vary in magnitude at different sections, but neglecting losses, their sum is always the same.

When liquid flows through a pipe, there will be a drop in pressure or head due to friction losses. The approximate drop in head for water flowing through various size pipes may be found from the table on pages 3-22 to 3-28. For viscous fluids the pressure drop in psi may be estimated from the charts on pages 3-34 to 3-46 for various pipe sizes.

The *total head H* developed by a centrifugal pump is the measure of energy increase of the liquid imparted to it by the pump, and is the difference between the total discharge head and the total suction head. Expressed in equation form,

$$H = h_d - h_s$$

where $H =$ total pump head, ft
$\quad h_d =$ total discharge head, ft, above atmospheric pressure at datum elevation
$\quad h_s =$ total suction head, ft, above atmospheric pressure at datum elevation

NOTE: h_d and h_s are negative if the corresponding pressures at the datum elevation are below the atmospheric pressure.

The common datum is taken through the pump centerline for horizontal pumps and at the entrance eye of the suction impeller for vertical-shaft pumps.

Suction lift h_s exists where the total suction head is below atmospheric pressure. The total suction lift as determined on test is the static pressure (vacuum) as measured by a mercury column expressed in feet of the liquid being pumped less the velocity head at the point of gage connection. This is equivalent to the static lift plus entrance and friction losses in the piping if the water-supply level is below the centerline of the pump. In the case of water-supply level above the pump centerline and at atmospheric pressure, suction lift will exist if the entrance and friction losses in the suction piping are greater than the static head.

Suction head h_s exists when the total suction head is above atmospheric pressure. Total suction head as determined on test is the gage reading expressed in feet of the liquid being pumped plus the velocity head at the point of gage connection.

The total suction head is equivalent to the static head less entrance and friction losses in the suction piping.

The *total discharge head h_d* as determined on test is the pressure gage reading expressed in feet of liquid being pumped plus the velocity head at the point of gage connection. It is thus equivalent to the static discharge head plus all losses in the discharge piping if the discharge water level is at atmospheric pressure.

In the case of a discharge into a closed vessel under pressure, the total discharge head is equivalent to the static head corresponding to the water level in the vessel, plus the gage pressure expressed in feet of liquid corrected to this water level, plus the friction losses in the discharge piping.

If the pump discharges to a level below the pump centerline or into a vessel under vacuum, the static head and pressure are taken as negative.

Determination of Head   Figure 6-4 shows the usual arrangement for determining the total head developed by a pump working with suction pressure below atmospheric. Suction head is measured by means of a mercury U tube which is connected to the suction through an *air*-filled tube.   Discharge head is measured by means of a Bourdon gage connected to the pump discharge through a *water*-filled tube.

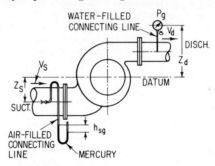

Fig. 6-4   Determination of head.

The total head for the arrangement shown in Fig. 6-4 is derived from the following expressions:

$$h_s = -\frac{\gamma_m}{\gamma} h_{sg} - z_s + \frac{V_s^2}{2g}$$

$$h_d = \frac{144 P_g}{\gamma} + z_d + \frac{V_d^2}{2g}$$

$$H = h_d - h_s$$

$$= \frac{144 P_g}{\gamma} + z_d + \frac{V_d^2}{2g} + \frac{\gamma_m}{\gamma} h_{sg} + z_s - \frac{V_s^2}{2g}$$

$$= \frac{144 P_g}{\gamma} + \frac{\gamma_m}{\gamma} h_{sg} + z_d + z_s + \left(\frac{V_d^2}{2g} - \frac{V_s^2}{2g} \right)$$

where H = total pump head, ft
   P_g = discharge gage reading, psi
   h_{sg} = suction gage reading, ft Hg
   γ = specific weight of liquid being pumped, lb/cu ft
   γ_m = specific weight of mercury, lb/cu ft
   V_d = average velocity in discharge pipe, fps
   V_s = average velocity in suction pipe, fps
z_d and z_s = elevation, ft

NOTE: For water at 68°F, 1 psi = 2.3107 ft, and $(144/\gamma)P_g = 2.3107 P_g$.   The specific gravity of mercury at 68°F is $\gamma_m/\gamma = 13.57$.   Therefore, for water and mercury at 68°F, the formula simplifies to

$$H = 2.3107 P_g + 13.57 h_{sg} + z_d + z_s + \left(\frac{V_d^2}{2g} - \frac{V_s^2}{2g} \right)$$

Example: Determine the head developed, given a pump with a 10-in. suction and 8-in. discharge with a capacity of 2,000 gpm.   The suction U tube reads 11 in. mercury

and the discharge pressure gage 50 psi.   The distance from the pump centerline to the U-tube connection is 7 in. and to the center of the discharge gage + 18 in.
    Therefore,

$$P_g = 50 \qquad\qquad V_d = 12.8 \text{ fps}^\circ$$

$$h_{sg} = \frac{11}{12} \text{ or } 0.916 \text{ ft} \qquad V_s = 8.17 \text{ fps}^\circ$$

$$z_d = 1.5 \text{ ft} \qquad\qquad \frac{V_d^2}{2g} = 2.55\dagger$$

$$z_s = \frac{7}{12} \text{ or } 0.583 \text{ ft} \qquad \frac{V_s^2}{2g} = 1.03\dagger$$

Substituting in the formula,

$$H = 2.3107 \times 50 + 13.57 \times 0.916 + 1.5 + 0.583 + (2.55 - 1.03)$$

$$= 115.5 + 12.4 + 1.5 + 0.6 + 1.5 = 131.5 \text{ ft}$$

Determination of Power Required   The work required for pumping depends on the total head and the weight or volume of the liquid to be pumped in a given time.   This will give a theoretical liquid horsepower (Lhp) as expressed in the following formula:

$$\text{Lhp} = \frac{wH}{33{,}000}$$

where w = lb liquid pumped per min
      H = total head, ft of liquid

    When the liquid is water at 68°F weighing 62.318 lb/cu ft, the formula becomes

$$\text{Lhp} = \frac{\text{gpm} \times H}{3{,}960}$$

    If a liquid other than water is pumped, or water at a temperature other than 68°F, the formula must be corrected for the specific gravity of the liquid so that

$$\text{Lhp} = \frac{\text{gpm} \times H \times sg}{3{,}960}$$

where sg = specific gravity of the liquid referred to water at 68°F

    In case the total head is expressed as pounds per square inch (psi), the specific gravity does not enter into the final equation, which is as follows:

$$\text{Lhp} = \frac{\text{gpm} \times (\text{total head, psi})}{1{,}714}$$

    The theoretical horsepower is less than the actual or brake horsepower because of losses in the pump such as friction and leakage.   The efficiency of the pump is therefore the ratio of the liquid horsepower output to the brake horsepower input, or

$$\text{Efficiency, percent} = \frac{\text{Lhp}}{\text{bhp}} \times 100$$

and the bhp required at the coupling will be

$$\text{bhp} = \frac{\text{Lhp}}{\eta}$$

where η = pump efficiency, percent/100

    If the entire unit is considered, it is necessary to include the efficiency of the driver and any other associated equipment to arrive at the overall efficiency.

° From table, page 3-24.
† From table, page 3-6.

Pump Performance

When studying the flow of liquid through a pump impeller, three types of velocities must be considered. The first is the velocity of a point on the impeller, and is designated by the symbol U. The second is the velocity of the fluid relative to the casing, known as the absolute velocity and designated by the symbol C. The third is the velocity of the liquid relative to the impeller, known as the relative velocity and designated by the symbol W. The relative velocity W is found by taking the vector sums of the absolute velocities U and C. Subscripts are generally used with these symbols, the subscript 1 designating the velocities at the inlet to the vanes, and 2 at the outlet of the vanes. The angle between the vectors U and W is designated as β and is the angle which the vane makes with a tangent to the impeller. The angle α between vectors C and U represents the angle at which the fluid enters or leaves the wheel. This is illustrated in Fig. 6-5 for a typical impeller.

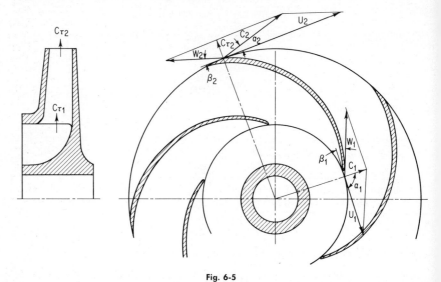

Fig. 6-5

The ideal head developed by the wheel is given by the equation

$$H_i = \frac{U_2^2 - U_1^2}{2g} + \frac{W_1^2 - W_2^2}{2g} + \frac{C_2^2 - C_1^2}{2g}$$

where the first term represents the head due to the centrifugal action, the second that due to the change in the relative velocity, and the third that due to the change in the absolute velocity. The first two terms represent the pressure head which is developed in the impeller, while the last is the velocity head developed in the impeller and converted into pressure in the volute or diffuser. This expression may also be written

$$H_i = \frac{1}{g} \left(U_2 C_2 \cos \alpha_2 - U_1 C_1 \cos \alpha_1 \right)$$

The actual head developed by the pump will be less than the ideal owing to fluid friction and shock losses, and a circulatory flow which takes place between the vanes.

The basic formula can be expressed in a simplified form for the actual head developed by a pump impeller at rated design conditions as follows:

$$H = \mu \frac{U_2^2}{g}$$

where H = actual head, ft
U_2 = impeller-tip velocity, fps
g = acceleration of gravity, ft/sec² (32.17 ft/sec²)
μ = pressure coefficient (varying from 0.45 to 0.52 for radial-type impellers)

From this it follows that the impeller diameter will be

$$D_2 = \frac{1{,}300}{n}\sqrt{\frac{H}{\mu}}$$

where D_2 = impeller diameter, in.
n = pump speed, rpm

The above equations give the basis for estimating the effect of speed and impeller changes on the head. The weight or volume flow is directly proportional to the rpm of the pump. It may be observed from the above equations that the head is proportional to the square of the rpm. The horsepower required to drive the pump is the product of the head and weight flow divided by a constant. The efficiency of a pump is little affected by reasonable changes in either the speed or impeller diameter.

The net effect of changes in the outside diameter of the impeller is similar to that of varying the speed of the unit.

The effect of changes in operating conditions may be summarized by the following equations, where the subscript a refers to the original condition, while b refers to the new.

$$\text{Volume or weight flow } Q_b = Q_a \frac{n_b}{n_a}\frac{D_b}{D_a}$$

$$\text{Head } H_b = H_a \left(\frac{n_b}{n_a}\right)^2\left(\frac{D_b}{D_a}\right)^2$$

$$\text{Horsepower hp}_b = \text{hp}_a \left(\frac{n_b}{n_a}\right)^3\left(\frac{D_b}{D_a}\right)^3$$

$$\text{Efficiency } \eta_b = \eta_a$$

where n = speed, rpm
D = impeller outside diameter, in.

These relations may be applied over the entire range of a pump characteristic curve but should be used only for relatively small changes in speed or impeller diameter.

Example: Assume that a pump is delivering 2,500 gpm of water against a head of 150 ft when running 1,760 rpm with an efficiency of 81 percent. The brake horsepower is then 117. The outside diameter of the impeller is 13½ in. What would be the performance if the impeller diameter is reduced to 13 in. and the pump speeded up to 1,800 rpm?

$$Q_b = Q_a \frac{n_b}{n_a}\frac{D_b}{D_a} = 2{,}500 \frac{1{,}800}{1{,}760}\frac{13}{13.5} = 2{,}460 \text{ gpm}$$

$$H_b = H_a \left(\frac{n_b}{n_a}\right)^2\left(\frac{D_b}{D_a}\right)^2 = 150 \left(\frac{1{,}800}{1{,}760}\right)^2\left(\frac{13}{13.5}\right)^2 = 146.7 \text{ ft}$$

$$\text{hp}_b = \text{hp}_a \left(\frac{n_b}{n_a}\right)^3\left(\frac{D_b}{D_a}\right)^3 = 117 \left(\frac{1{,}800}{1{,}760}\right)^3\left(\frac{13}{13.5}\right)^3 = 112 \text{ hp}$$

$$\eta_b = \eta_a = 81 \text{ percent}$$

Figure 6-6 shows a typical performance curve for a centrifugal pump. It illustrates the variations of head, power, and efficiency as a function of capacity at constant speed. These curves are called *characteristic curves* of pump performance, and they are determined experimentally for each pump type.

Figure 6-7 shows diagrammatically the characteristic curves of a pump at two speeds N_1 and N_2, where points of similar flow conditions are related according to the formulas given above.

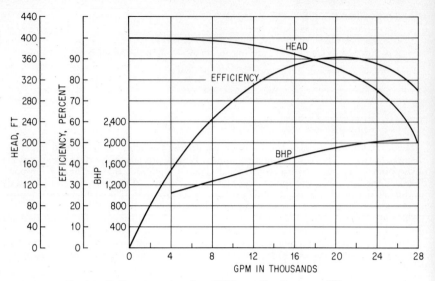

Fig. 6-6 Performance curve for a 24/20 centrifugal pump at 885 rpm.

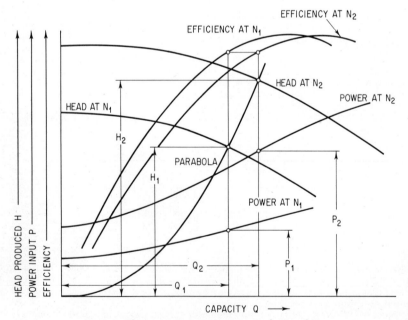

Fig. 6-7 Characteristic curves at two speeds N_1 and N_2

Parallel and Series Operation

When the pumping requirements are variable, it may be more desirable to install several small pumps in parallel rather than use a single large one. When the demand drops, one or more smaller pumps may be shut down, thus allowing the remainder to operate at or near peak efficiency. If a single pump is used with lowered demand, the discharge must be throttled (for constant speed), and it will operate at reduced efficiency. Moreover, when smaller units are used opportunity is provided during slack demand periods for repairing and maintaining each pump in turn, thus avoiding plant shutdowns which would be necessary with single units. Similarly, multiple pumps in series may be used when liquid must be delivered at high heads.

In planning such installations a head-capacity curve for the system must first be drawn. The head required by the system is the sum of the static head (difference in elevation and/or its pressure equivalent) plus the variable head (friction and shock losses in the pipes, heaters, etc.). The former is usually constant for a given system, whereas the latter increases approximately with the square of the flow. The resulting curve is represented as line AB in Figs. 6-8 and 6-9.

Connecting two pumps in parallel to be driven by one motor is not a very common practice, and offhand, such an arrangement may appear more expensive than a single pump. However, it should be remembered that in most cases it is possible to operate such a unit at about 40 percent higher speed, which may reduce the cost of the motor materially. Thus, the cost of two high-speed pumps may not be much greater than that of a single slow-speed pump.

For units to operate satisfactorily in parallel, they must be working on the portion of the characteristic curve which drops off with increased capacity in order to secure an even flow distribution. Consider the action of two pumps operating in parallel. The system head-capacity curve AB shown in Fig. 6-8 starts at H static when the flow is zero and rises parabolically with increased flow. Curve CD represents the characteristic curve of pump A operating alone; the similar curve for pump B is represented by EF. Pump B will not start delivery until the discharge pressure of pump A falls below that of the shutoff head of B (point E). The combined delivery for a given head is equal to the sum of the individual capacities of the two pumps at that head. For a

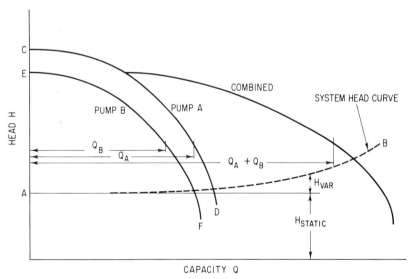

Fig. 6-8   Head-capacity curves of pumps operating in parallel.

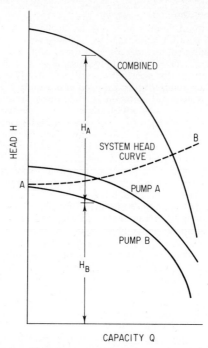

Fig. 6-9 Head-capacity curves of pumps operating in series.

given combined delivery head, the capacity is divided between the pumps and designated as Q_A and Q_B. The combined characteristic curve shown on the figure is found by plotting these summations. The combined brake horsepower curve can be found by adding the brake horsepower of pump A corresponding to Q_A to that of pump B corresponding to Q_B, and plotting this at the combined flow. The efficiency curve of the combination may be determined by dividing the combined power $\gamma(Q_A + Q_B)H/550$ by the corresponding combined brake horsepower (Q taken as cfs).

If two pumps are operated in *series*, the combined head for any flow is equal to the sum of the individual heads as shown in Fig. 6-9. The combined brake horsepower curve may be found by adding the horsepowers given by the curves for the individual pumps. Points on the combined efficiency curve are found by dividing the combined fluid horsepower $(H_A + H_B)Q\gamma/550$ by the combined brake horsepower; Q is again in cfs.

Pump Performance for Viscous Liquids

As the viscosity of the liquid being handled by a centrifugal pump is increased the effect on the performance is a marked increase in the brake horsepower, a reduction in the head, and some reduction in the capacity.

The chart shown as Fig. 6-10 is taken from the Standards of the Hydraulic Institute and may be used to estimate the magnitude of these effects for a particular liquid. The chart should be used only for the conventional radial-type impeller; and should not be extrapolated or used for nonuniform liquids such as gels, slurries, or paper stock, or where the NPSH is inadequate.

The procedure for selecting a pump for a given head-capacity-viscosity requirement when the desired capacity and head of the viscous liquid and the viscosity and specific gravity at the pumping temperature are known is as follows: Enter the chart at the base with the desired viscous capacity Q_{vis} and proceed upward to the desired viscous head H_{vis} in feet of liquid. For multistage pumps use the head per stage. Proceed horizontally (either left or right) to the fluid viscosity, and then go upward to the correction curves. Divide the viscous capacity Q_{vis} by the capacity correction factor C_Q to get the approximate equivalent water capacity $\dot{Q}_w$. Divide the viscous head H_{vis} by the head correction factor C_H from the curve labeled "1.0 × Q_n" to get the approximate equivalent water head H_w. Having this new equivalent water head-capacity point, select a pump in the usual manner. The viscous efficiency and the viscous brake horsepower may then be calculated.

To illustrate, assume it is desired to select a pump to deliver 750 gpm at 100 ft total head of a liquid having a viscosity of 1,000 SSU and a specific gravity of 0.90 at the pumping temperature.

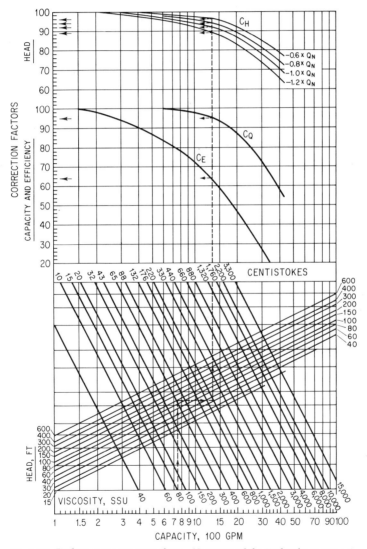

Fig. 6-10 Performance-correction chart. (*Courtesy of the Hydraulic Institute.*)

Enter the chart at 750 gpm, go up to 100 ft head, over to 1,000 SSU, and then up to the correction factors:

$$C_Q = 0.95 \qquad Q_W = \frac{Q_{vis}}{C_Q} = \frac{750}{0.95} = 790 \text{ gpm}$$

$$C_H = 0.92 \text{ for } Q_n = 1.0 \qquad H_W = \frac{H_{vis}}{C_H} = \frac{100}{0.92} = 108.8 \text{ ft head, or roughly 109 ft}$$

Select a pump for a water capacity of 790 gpm at 109 ft head. The selection should be at or close to the maximum efficiency point for water performance. If the pump selected has an efficiency with water of 81 percent at 790 gpm, then the efficiency for the viscous liquid will be

$$E_{vis} = C_E \times E_W = 0.635 \times 81 \text{ percent} = 51.5 \text{ percent}$$

The brake horsepower for pumping the viscous liquid will be

$$\text{bhp}_{vis} = \frac{Q_{vis} \times H_{vis} \times \text{sp gr}}{3{,}960 \times E_{vis}} = \frac{750 \times 100 \times 0.90}{3{,}960 \times 0.515} = 33.1 \text{ hp}$$

The procedure to determine the pump performance on a viscous liquid when its performance with water is known is as follows: From the efficiency curve locate the water capacity ($1.0 \times Q_n$) at which maximum efficiency is obtained. From this capacity determine the capacities $0.6 \times Q_n$, $0.8 \times Q_n$, and $1.2 \times Q_n$. Enter the chart at the bottom with the capacity at best efficiency ($1.0 \times Q_n$), go upward to the head developed (in one stage) H_w at this capacity, then horizontally (either left or right) to the desired viscosity, and then proceed upward to the various correction curves. Read the values of C_E and C_Q, and of C_H for all four capacities. Multiply each capacity by C_Q to obtain the corrected capacities. Multiply each head by its corresponding head correction factor to obtain the corrected heads. Multiply each efficiency value by C_E to obtain the corrected efficiency values, which apply at the corresponding corrected capacities. The head at shutoff can be taken as approximately the same as that for water. Calculate the viscous brake horsepower from the equation

$$\text{bhp}_{vis} = \frac{Q_{vis} \times H_{vis} \times \text{sp gr}}{3{,}960 \times E_{vis}}$$

Suction Head, or NPSH

If the pressure at any point inside a pump drops below the vapor pressure corresponding to the temperature of the liquid, the liquid will vaporize. These bubbles of vapor will be carried along to a point of higher pressure where they will suddenly collapse. This phenomenon is known as cavitation. It is accompanied by removal of metal in the pump, reduced flow, loss in efficiency, and noise and hence should be avoided. It occurs around the pump suction and inlet edge of the vanes when the absolute suction pressure is low.

The net positive suction head of a pump, or NPSH, is the equivalent total head at the pump centerline corrected for vapor pressure. It is found from the equation

$$\text{NPSH} = H_p \pm H_z - H_{vp} - H_f$$

H_p is the head corresponding to the absolute pressure on the surface of the liquid from which the pump draws. This will be the barometric pressure if the tank is open to the atmosphere or the absolute pressure in the closed tank or condenser from which the pump takes liquid. H_z is the height in feet of the fluid surface above or below the pump centerline. If above, it is considered to be plus since the suction head is then increased; if below, it is minus. H_{vp} is the head corresponding to the vapor pressure at the existing temperature of the liquid. H_f is the head lost because of friction and turbulence between the surface of the liquid and the pump suction flange.

In designing a pump installation and purchasing a pump there are two types of NPSH to be considered. One is the *available* NPSH of the system, and the other is the *required* NPSH of the pump to be placed in the system. The former is determined by the plant designer and is based upon the pump location, fluid temperature, etc., while the latter is based upon suppression pump tests of the manufacturer. To secure satisfactory operating conditions, the available NPSH must be equal to or greater than the required suction head.

The calculation of the available NPSH will be illustrated by two examples. The head corresponding to a given pressure is given by the equation $H_p = 2.31p/sg$ where p is the pressure in psi and sg the specific gravity of the liquid. The atmospheric pressures corresponding to various altitudes are given on page 3-56; the vapor pressure and specific gravity of water are given on pages 3-2 and 3-3.

Assume that water at 80°F is to be pumped from a sump. The unit is located at an altitude of 800 ft above sea level, and the suction lift (from water surface to pump centerline) is 7 ft. The pipe losses amount to 1 ft head. What is the available NPSH?

From page 3-56, the atmospheric pressure at an altitude of 800 ft is 14.27 psia. From page 3-2 the specific gravity of the water at 80°F is 0.9984 and the vapor pressure is 0.5069 psia.

$$H_p = \frac{2.31p}{sg} = \frac{2.31 \times 14.27}{0.9984} = 32.97 \text{ ft}$$

$$H_z = -7 \text{ ft (negative since it is a lift)}$$

$$H_{vp} = \frac{2.31p}{sg} = \frac{2.31 \times 0.5069}{0.9984} = 1.17 \text{ ft}$$

$$H_f = 1 \text{ ft}$$

$$\text{NPSH} = H_p - H_z - H_{vp} - H_f = 32.97 - 7 - 1.17 - 1 = 23.80 \text{ ft}$$

Determine the available NPSH of a condensate pump drawing water from a condenser in which a 28-in. vacuum, referred to a 30-in. barometer, is maintained. The friction and turbulence head loss in the piping is estimated to be 2 ft. The minimum height of water in the condenser above the pump centerline is 5 ft. The absolute pressure in the condenser is $30 - 28 = 2$ in. Hg, or 0.982 psi. The corresponding specific gravity from page 3-2 is 0.9945.

$$H_p = H_{vp} = \frac{2.31p}{sg} = \frac{2.31 \times 0.982}{0.9945} = 2.28 \text{ ft}$$

$$H_f = 2 \text{ ft} \qquad H_z = 5 \text{ ft}$$

$$\text{NPSH} = H_p + H_z - H_{vp} - H_f = 2.28 + 5 - 2.28 - 2 = 3 \text{ ft}$$

The required net positive suction head must be determined, in most cases, by means of suppression tests. The Hydraulic Institute has prepared a series of charts to estimate this required head. See Figs. 6-11 to 6-14 inclusive. These charts are not to be considered as the highest values which can be obtained by careful design, but may be used for estimating as they represent average results of good present-day practice.

The use of the charts is simple and may be illustrated by an example. A double-suction pump operating at 3,600 rpm delivers 1,000 gpm against a total head of 200 ft. What should be the minimum NPSH for satisfactory operation? The specific speed as found from Fig. 6-2 is 2,200. Referring to Fig. 6-11, the point corresponding to this specific speed for double-suction pumps and a total dynamic head of 200 ft gives a 12 ft suction lift as the safe maximum. If the same conditions were applied to a single-suction pump with the shaft through the eye of the impeller, the safe minimum suction condition would require at least a 1 ft positive head (i.e., the suction head would have to be at least +1 ft rather than −12 ft; hence the required NPSH would be 35 ft instead of 22 ft).

These curves are based upon handling clear water at 85°F and sea-level barometric pressure. If the water temperature is higher, the difference in head corresponding to the difference in vapor pressures between 85°F and the temperature of the water pumped should be subtracted from the suction lift or added to the suction head. Also if the unit is to be located above sea level, the difference in head corresponding to

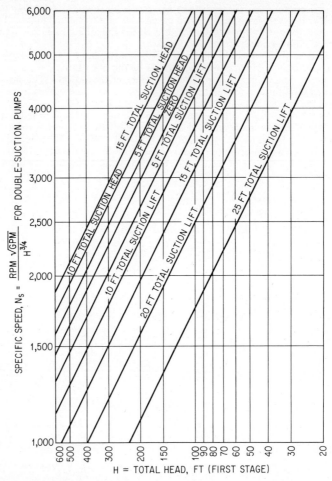

Fig. 6-11 Upper limits of specific speeds. Double-suction pumps handling clear water at 85°F at sea level. (*Courtesy of the Hydraulic Institute.*)

the difference in atmospheric pressures should be subtracted from the suction lift or added to the suction head.

Thus, in the above example, if the water temperature is 140°F and the plant is located at an altitude of 2,000 ft, the correction for vapor pressure (see page 3-2) will be $2.889 - 0.596 = 2.293$ psi, and for altitude (see page 3-56) will be $14.69 - 13.66 = 1.03$ psi. The corresponding head change will be $2.31 (2.293 + 1.03)/0.9850 = 7.8$ ft. For the double-suction pump the maximum suction lift would be $12.0 - 7.8 = 4.2$ ft, and for the single-suction pump the positive suction head would have to be $1.0 + 7.8 = 8.8$ ft.

A series of charts (Figs. 6-15, 6-16 and 6-17) have been prepared by the Hydraulic Institute to determine the NPSH based upon the flow, operating speed, and discharge pressure for hot water and condensate pumps. They may also be used to find the maximum permissible flow for a given available NPSH.

Hot Water Two curves, Figs. 6-15 and 6-16, have been prepared for pumps handling hot water at temperatures of 212°F and above. These curves show the recommended minimum net positive suction heads in feet for different design capacities and speeds.

Figure 6-15 applies to single-suction pumps and Fig. 6-16 to double-suction pumps. These curves serve as guides in determining the net positive suction head for hot-water pumps and do not necessarily represent absolute minimum values.

Net Positive Suction Head (NPSH) for Condensate Pumps   Figure 6-17 indicates net positive suction head (NPSH) for condensate pumps with shaft passing through the eye of the impeller.   It applies to pumps having a maximum of three stages; the lower scale representing single-suction pumps and the upper scale double-suction pumps or pumps with double-suction first-stage impeller.

For single-suction overhung impellers the curve may be used by dividing the specified capacity, if 400 gpm or less, by 1.2, and if greater than 400 gpm, by 1.15.

The curve may be used for capacities and speeds other than shown by the relation that, for a definite NPSH, the product of rpm × √gpm remains constant.

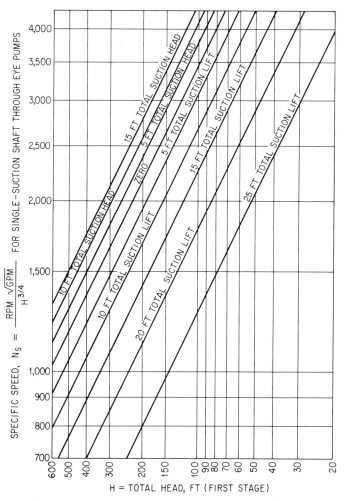

Fig. 6-12   Upper limits of specific speeds.   Single-suction shaft through eye pumps handling clear water at 85°F at sea level.   (*Courtesy of the Hydraulic Institute.*)

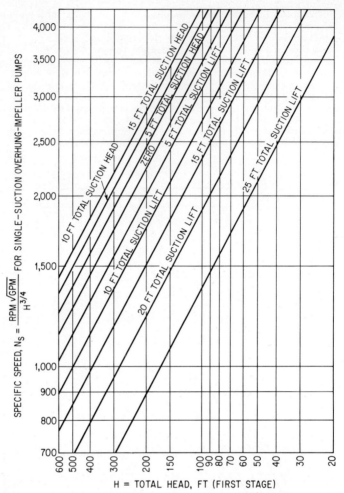

Fig. 6-13 Upper limits of specific speeds. Single-suction overhung impeller pumps handling clear water at 85°F at sea level. (*Reprinted from the Standards of the Hydraulic Institute, 11th ed., courtesy of the Hydraulic Institute.*)

Minimum Flow-through Pump

The difference between the power put into a centrifugal pump and the useful power performed by the pump, or the difference between the brake and water horsepowers, is converted into heat, most of which appears as increased temperature of the water. The brake horsepower curve of a pump rated at 500 gpm against a 2,600-ft head and the corresponding water horsepower curve are shown in Fig. 6-18. Neglecting bearing losses, which are minor, the difference between these curves at any capacity represents the horsepower absorbed by the water in the form of heat. Multiplying these differences by 42.4 gives the Btu generated in the pump per minute. Dividing these values by the flow in pounds per minute gives the temperature rise at each capacity. This curve is plotted in Fig. 6-18.

This temperature rise is generally not important in single-stage pumps, particularly if they are handling cold water; but for pumps handling hot liquids, such as boiler-feed pumps, it may become a serious matter. Then the resulting rapid temperature rise may cause the internal rotating parts to expand more rapidly than the heavier encircling parts so that severe rubbing may occur, or the impeller may even become loose on the shaft. Also the temperature of the water may rise to a point where the water flashes into steam, causing the pump to become vapor-bound.

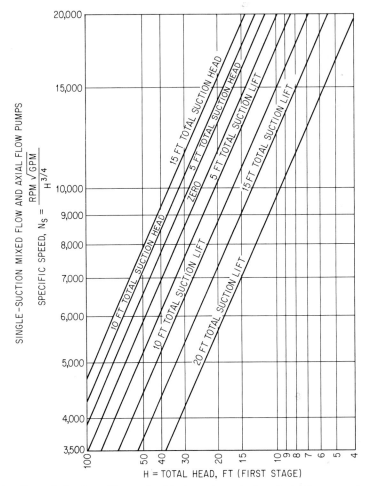

Fig. 6-14 Upper limits of specific speeds. Single-suction, mixed- and axial-flow pumps handling clear water at 85°F at sea level. (*Reprinted from the Standards of the Hydraulic Institute, 11th ed., courtesy of the Hydraulic Institute.*)

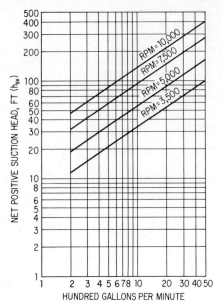

Fig. 6-15 Net positive suction head for centrifugal hot-water pumps, single-suction. (*Courtesy of the Hydraulic Institute.*)

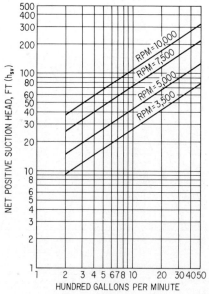

Fig. 6-16 Net positive suction head for centrifugal hot-water pumps, double-suction first-stage. (*Reprinted from the Standards of the Hydraulic Institute, 11th ed.*)

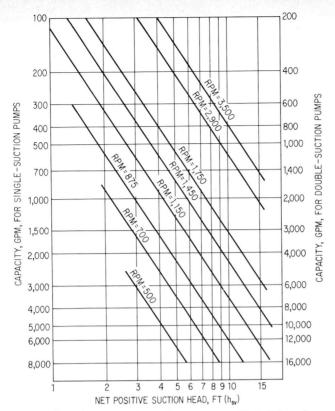

Fig. 6-17 Capacity and speed limitations for condensate pumps with shaft through eye of impeller. *(Reprinted from the Standards of the Hydraulic Institute.)*

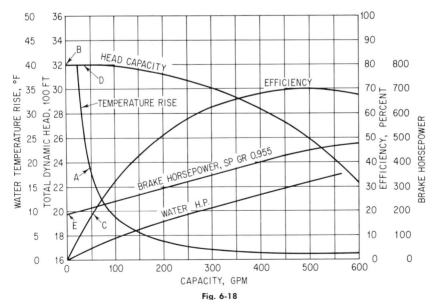

Fig. 6-18

The temperature rise in a pump may be calculated from the formula

$$\Delta t = \frac{(1 - \eta)H}{778c\eta}$$

where Δt = temperature rise, °F
η = overall pump efficiency, expressed as a decimal
c = specific heat of fluid being pumped (equals 1.0 for water)
H = total head of pump, ft

The allowable temperature rise of the water before it flashes into steam depends upon the suction conditions, or NPSH, of the pump. NPSH is the net head above the vapor pressure corresponding to the temperature of the liquid handled. As outlined on page 6-16, every installation has two types of NPSH: that available in the installation and that required by the pump. The maximum allowable vapor pressure at the pump inlet is found by converting the available NPSH into pounds per square inch, and adding this to the vapor pressure corresponding to the temperature of the liquid being handled. This pressure is the vapor pressure corresponding to the temperature to which the liquid may be raised before it will flash into vapor.

After the allowable temperature rise has been established, an approximate minimum safe continuous flow efficiency can be obtained by rewriting the previous equation in the form

$$\eta = \frac{H_{so}}{778(\Delta t)c + H_{so}}$$

where H_{so} = heat at no flow, or shutoff head
c = specific heat of liquid

The flow corresponding to this efficiency is found on the pump-performance curves.

In boiler-feed pumps having single-suction impellers, all facing in the same direction, a leak-off balancing arrangement is used to compensate hydraulic thrust. If the balancing leak-off flow is returned to the suction of the pump, flashing can occur at extremely low rates of delivery. Therefore, it is recommended that the balancing flow be piped to an open heater in the feed system ahead of the pump, where, by flashing, the temperature of the water will be reduced to that corresponding to the pressure and there should be no valve of any kind between the junction of the balancing connection and the heater.

Recirculation Connection

At low flows the temperature rise of the liquid being pumped is enough to cause flashing in the pump, which in turn may result in pump seizure. To prevent this, a recirculation line from a discharge-line connection to the suction source is used. This line has a recirculation orifice designed to pass the required minimum flow.

The recirculation connection is in the pump discharge line between the discharge nozzle and the check valve.

All valves in the recirculation line must be open whenever the pump is operating under any of the following conditions:

1. Low flows
2. Starting pump
3. Stopping pump

The valves may be opened or closed either manually or by automatic controls. If automatic controls are used, they should be checked at initial starting and occasionally thereafter during starting procedures.

Figure 6-19 shows a diagram of the piping arrangement.

Materials for Pumping Various Liquids

The materials used for pumps must be suitable for the liquids handled to prevent excessive corrosion. The Standards of the Hydraulic Institute give the materials to be used for the more common liquids and should be consulted for selecting the applicable material combination.

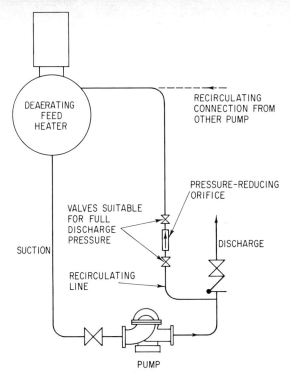

Fig. 6-19 Diagram of recirculating connections for boiler-feed service.

Summary of Material Selections and National Society Standards Designations°

Corresponding national society standards designation†			Remarks
ASTM	ACI	AISI	
A48, Classes 20, 25, 30, 35, 40, and 50	. . . . .	. . .	Gray iron—six grades
A339, A395, and A396	. . . . .	. . .	Nodular cast iron—five grades
B143, 1B and 2A; B144, 3A; B145, 4A	. . . . .	. . .	Tin bronze—six grades (includes two grades not covered by ASTM Specifications)
A216—WCB	. . . . .	1030	Carbon steel
A217—C5	. . . . .	501	5% chromium steel
A296—CA15	CA15	410	13% chromium steel
A296—CB30	CB30	. . .	20% chromium steel
A296—CC50	CC50	446	28% chromium steel
A296—CF-8	CF-8	304	18-8 austenitic steel
A296—CF-8M	CF-8M	316	18-8 molybdenum austenitic steel
A296—60T	CN-7M	. . .	A series of highly alloyed steels normally used where the corrosive conditions are severe
. . . .	. . . . .	. . .	A series of nickel-base alloys
. . . .	. . . . .	. . .	High-silicon cast iron
. . . .	. . . . .	. . .	Austenitic cast iron
A439	. . . . .	. . .	Nodular austenitic cast iron
. . . .	. . . . .	. . .	Nickel-copper alloy
. . . .	. . . . .	. . .	Nickel

° Reprinted from the Standards of the Hydraulic Institute, 11th ed., New York, 1965.
† ASTM = American Society for Testing and Materials, ACI = Alloy Casting Institute, AISI = American Iron and Steel Institute.

There are three basic types of pumps from the standpoint of materials which may be designated as: standard fitted (combination of iron and bronze), all iron, and all bronze.

Other materials, including corrosion-resisting steels, are listed in the subject standards. The table on page 6-25 gives a summary of the various materials used for centrifugal pumps.

If the liquid to be handled is an electrolyte, the use of dissimilar metals in close combination, especially those that are widely separated in the galvanic series, should be avoided as much as possible. The use of bronze and iron in the same pump handling seawater will greatly accelerate the corrosion of the cast-iron parts.

A table of the galvanic series is given below.

Galvanic Series of Metals and Alloys°

Corroded End (Anodic, or Least Noble)

Magnesium
Magnesium alloys

Zinc

Aluminum 2S

Cadmium

Aluminum 17ST

Steel or iron
Cast iron

Chromium stainless steel, 400 series (active)

Austenitic nickel or nickel-copper cast-iron alloy

18-8 chromium-nickel stainless steel, type 304 (active)
18-8-3 chromium-nickel-molybdenum stainless steel, type 316 (active)

Lead-tin solders
Lead
Tin

Nickel (active)
Nickel-base alloy (active)
Nickel-molybdenum-chromium-iron alloy (active)

Brasses
Copper
Bronzes
Copper-nickel alloy
Nickel-copper alloy

Silver solder

Nickel (passive)
Nickel-base alloy (passive)

Chromium stainless steel, 400 series (passive)
18-8 chromium-nickel stainless steel, type 304 (passive)
18-8-3 chromium-nickel-molybdenum stainless steel, type 316 (passive)
Nickel-molybdenum-chromium-iron alloy (passive)

Silver

Graphite
Gold
Platinum

Protected End (Cathodic, or Most Noble)

° Reprinted from the Standards of the Hydraulic Institute, 11th ed., New York, 1965.

Pump Application

General As outlined under Classification, there are on the market a multitude of centrifugal-pump types. Some of the most basic types will be mentioned here.

Single-stage Double-suction Pump See Fig. 6-20. This type of centrifugal pump is the most common one and is used for general service in industrial and municipal plants. In the larger sizes, their use is almost universal for municipal water distribution, and pumps of this type are in service in practically every major city of the United States. For heads up to 300 ft or higher, single-stage pumps are used, while for higher heads two or more units are arranged in series. Figure 6-21 shows an installation of two motor-driven units arranged in series.

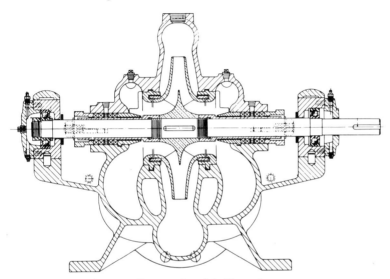

Fig. 6-20 Cross section of double-suction pump.

Fig. 6-21 Installation of two double-suction pumps arranged in series, motor-driven.

Boiler-feed Pumps For industrial use, multistage split-case pumps having two to six or more stages are used for this service; see Figs. 6-22 and 6-23.

For utility service the pressures are now generally in the range of 2,000 to 5,000 psi and barrel-type multistage units are used; see Fig. 6-24.

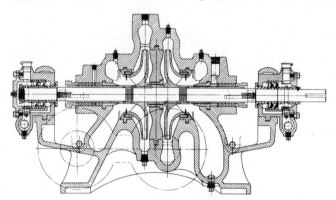

Fig. 6-22 Cutaway view of two-stage pump.

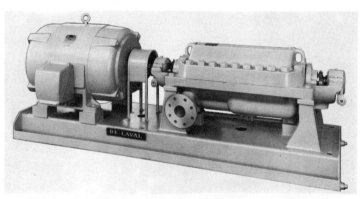

Fig. 6-23 Motor-driven multistage pump.

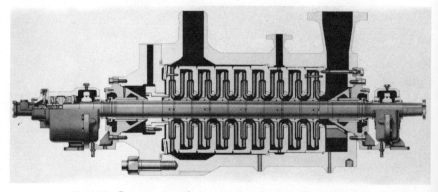

Fig. 6-24 Cutaway view of nine-stage barrel-type boiler-feed pump.

Hydraulic-pressure Pumps Pumps similar to those used in boiler-feed service are used for this application.

Condensate Pumps Special pumps, usually of the single-suction type, are used for this service, designed to operate at low submergence. Figure 6-25 shows a three-stage vertical unit of this type.

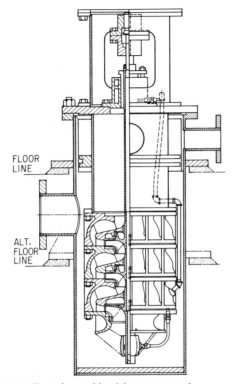

Fig. 6-25 Typical assembly of three-stage condensate pump.

Nonclogging Pumps Pumps for this service are designed to assure maximum freedom from clogging. They are usually of the single-suction type. For the larger sizes, mixed-flow pumps are used as shown in Fig. 6-26.

Design Details The general arrangement of several basic centrifugal-pump types has been covered under Pump Application; see Figs. 6-20 to 6-26. Some special design features are discussed below.

Axial Balance

The impeller of a single-suction centrifugal pump has an unbalanced hydraulic thrust directed axially toward the suction. This is due to the difference in pressure of the fluid which has passed through the impeller and of the fluid on the suction side. Several methods have been devised to counteract this force and avoid the use of large thrust bearings.

If a double-suction impeller (Fig. 6-20) is used, the pressures are symmetrical about the centerline and no unbalanced thrust should exist.

On multistage units single-suction impellers placed back to back, as illustrated in Fig. 6-22, may be employed. The axial thrust created in one impeller is thus balanced

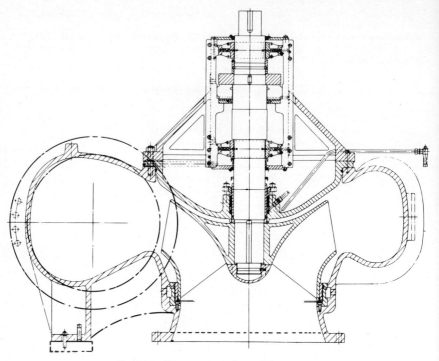

Fig. 6-26 Cutaway view of mixed-flow pump.

by the corresponding thrust in the other, any remaining thrust being taken by a small thrust bearing.

An alternate method of automatically providing a balance thrust arrangement in boiler-feed pumps is shown in Figs. 6-24 and 6-27. Referring to Fig. 6-27, water at essentially discharge pressure enters the clearance between the rotating and stationary drums at A. The water follows a path through the first fixed orifice (A to B), through the variable orifice (B to C), and then through the second fixed orifice (C to D). Chamber D is connected by a pipe to the suction source.

Should a condition of increased impeller thrust toward suction occur, the rotor tends to move toward suction, closing the variable orifice between the drum faces (B to C). By thus reducing the balance flow, the pressure drop between A and B decreases. The resulting greater pressure at B creates an increased thrust in the outboard direction, thereby providing self-compensation for the increased impeller thrust.

A similar type of self-compensating balance occurs should the impeller thrust toward suction decrease. The rotor is free to move axially and hence permits the variable gap at the drum faces to match the requirements for hydraulic balance.

Double-volute Pumps

The pressure within the casing of any pump develops radial forces when operating at capacities other than normal. The result of these radial forces in single-volute casings is shaft deflection. This is especially true if the pump operates for extended periods at other than design capacity, since imbalance from the radial forces becomes greater. For such applications, double-volute pumps are used (Fig. 6-28).

In the double-volute casing, the water leaving the impeller is collected in two similar volutes, the tongues of which are set 180° apart. The two volutes merge into a common

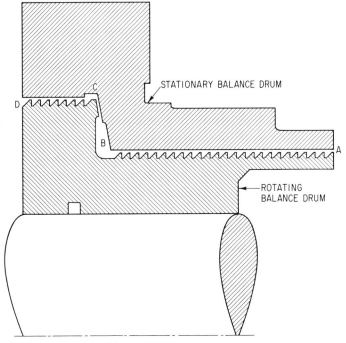

Fig. 6-27 Axial balance drums.

outlet to form the discharge of the pump. Hydraulic forces (indicated by arrows) produced by the pressure in one volute are balanced by equal forces produced by the pressure in the other volute. Thus, radial thrust is counterbalanced and for all practical purposes is eliminated.

The double-volute pumps provide insurance against shaft deflection and savings in repairs and shutdown time.

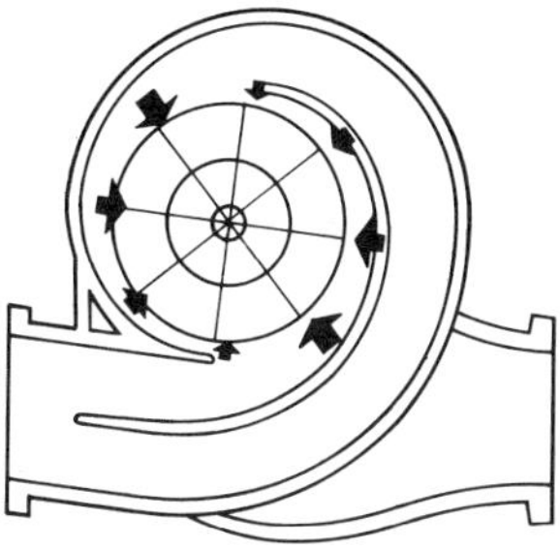

Centrifugal-pump Stuffing Boxes

Stuffing boxes are located on pumps where the rotating shaft enters the pump case. They contain

Fig. 6-28 Double-volute pump.

packing or mechanical seals which control the leakage of fluid from within or of the air from without.

Stuffing Boxes A typical stuffing box using packing, as shown in Fig. 6-29, has a plain throat bushing, seal ring, and packing gland.   Figure 6-30 shows a water-cooled stuffing box with quench glands and breakdown bushing. Stuffing boxes may have various combinations of the features shown in Figs. 6-29 and 6-30, depending upon operating conditions.

The innermost packing ring is usually placed against a solid removable throat bushing. The plain bushing of Fig. 6-29 is used for suction lifts and moderate pressures. Higher pressures require the breakdown bushing of Fig. 6-30. This relieves the pressure on the packing, reduces mechanical losses, and lessens wear on the shaft sleeve.

Seal rings are placed between rows of packing (see Fig. 6-29). They provide a space

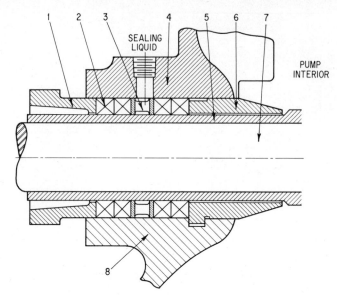

Fig. 6-29 (1) Packing gland; (2) packing; (3) seal ring; (4) pump cover; (5) shaft sleeve; (6) throat bushing; (7) shaft; (8) pump case.

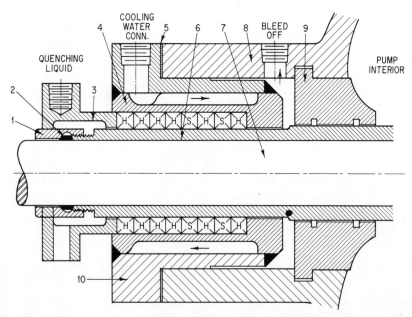

Fig. 6-30 (1) Packing nut; (2) packing ring; (3) quench gland; (4) packing box; (5) gasket; (6) shaft sleeve; (7) shaft; (8) pump cover; (9) breakdown bushing; (10) pump case; H = metallic packing; S = plastic packing.

surrounding the shaft for the sealing liquid. This forms a seal which, when a vacuum exists in the suction chamber of the pump, prevents air from entering. In addition, it assures lubrication for the packing. The liquid comes from either an outside source or a high-pressure portion of the pump.

Packing is held in the stuffing box by packing glands. These are usually split, making it possible to remove them without taking the pump apart. Quench glands are used when the liquid being pumped exceeds a safe margin on its vapor pressure. Glands are pulled into place by gland bolts. Frequently these are swing bolts, making disassembly easier.

Renewable-shaft sleeves usually protect the shaft where it passes through the stuffing boxes. Bronze is most commonly used for cold-water applications. High suction pressures, elevated temperatures, dirty water, and many liquids call for special materials.

The packing-ring cross section is square. A good grade of braided asbestos impregnated with graphite is most commonly used, especially for water service. This often comes in a continuous coil which is cut into proper lengths for making rings. The cut should preferably be on a diagonal, with a slight gap to allow for expansion when put in place. Gaps for adjacent rings should be staggered. Metallic packing rings are required for some service, and one of the recommended combinations for high-pressure boiler-feed service is shown in Fig. 6-30. These packings are usually purchased in molded sets from the packing manufacturer. Also note the special water-jacketed stuffing box in Fig. 6-30.

Packing does its sealing along the shaft. It is pliable in order to form itself around the shaft. Cutting down the leakage by tightening up on the packing increases friction, resulting in more power required and increased wear on the shaft or shaft sleeve.

Packing requires a certain amount of leakage to keep it lubricated. Certain applications cannot allow leakage, such as corrosive acids and inflammable, gritty, or contaminated liquids. Mechanical seals are now being used for these applications, as well as for high-pressure water seals.

Mechanical Seals Mechanical seals consist of a stationary and rotating member with some manner of auxiliary seal. The liquid in the stuffing box is prevented from passing along the shaft by means of the auxiliary seal (an O ring, bellows, wedge ring, or other device). The rotating member is forced against the stationary member by a spring(s) and pressure in the stuffing box. The liquid tries to leak through the contacting surfaces and forms a liquid-pressure wedge which prevents the seal faces from actually making contact during operation.

Three general types of mechanical seals are used: single seal, double seal, or balanced seal.

A typical single-seal mechanical seal used for most applications is shown in Fig. 6-31. Hydraulic forces on the sealing washer are unbalanced, as shown in Fig. 6-32, limiting the use of single-seal mechanical seals to moderate pressures.

A typical *balanced* mechanical seal used for high pressures (see Figs. 6-33 and 6-34) shows how areas on each side of the sealing washer are adjusted to reduce unbalanced forces by stepping down the shaft. This keeps the pressure between sealing surfaces within allowable limits.

A typical double mechanical seal is shown in Fig. 6-35. Simply stated, this is two single seals mounted back to back having a space for an isolating liquid between. Such seals are used for liquids which have high temperatures or are gritty, corrosive, volatile, contaminating, etc.

Seals for Boiler-feed Pumps In the boiler-feed-pump applications that exceed the limitations of packing or mechanical seals, serrated bushing seals and multifloating ring seals are generally used. Examples of these latter two are shown in Figs. 6-36 and 6-37, respectively. In both cases, a cool, external water supply—generally condensate—is injected into the seals. The cold injection water prevents flashing in the seals that would otherwise occur if the high-temperature water in the pump were permitted to flow through the seals to atmospheric pressure.

In differential-pressure control systems, a constant differential between seal injection-water pressure and seal chamber pressure permits some water to enter the seal

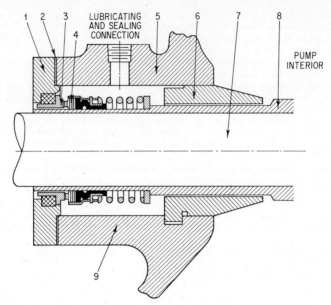

Fig. 6-31 Mechanical seal: (1) packing gland; (2) gasket; (3) stationary seal; (4) rotating seal; (5) pump cover; (6) throat bushing; (7) shaft; (8) shaft sleeve; (9) pump case.

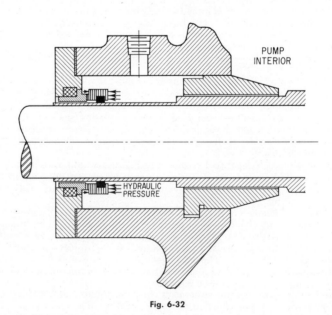

Fig. 6-32

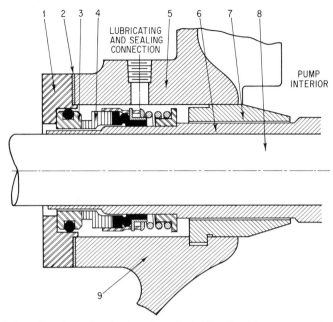

Fig. 6-33 Balanced mechanical seal: (1) packing gland; (2) gasket; (3) stationary seal; (4) rotating seal; (5) pump cover; (6) shaft sleeve; (7) throat bushing; (8) shaft; (9) pump case.

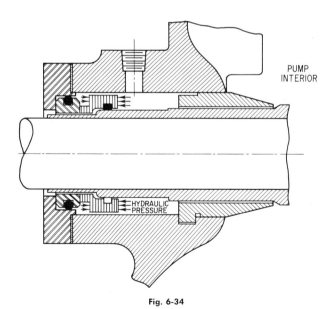

Fig. 6-34

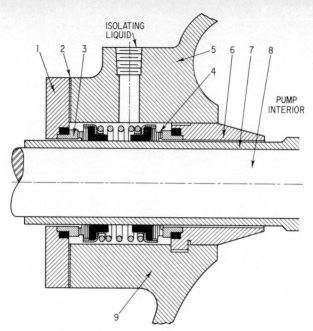

Fig. 6-35 Double mechanical seal: (1) packing gland; (2) gasket; (3) stationary seal; (4) rotating seal; (5) pump cover; (6) throat bushing; (7) shaft sleeve; (8) shaft; (9) pump case.

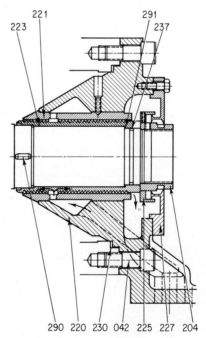

Fig. 6-36 Injection-type serrated bushing seal: (042) capscrew; (204) checknut; (220) housing; (221) bushing; (223) sleeve; (225) guard; (227) cover; (230) gasket; (237) O ring; (290) key; (291) O ring (metallic).

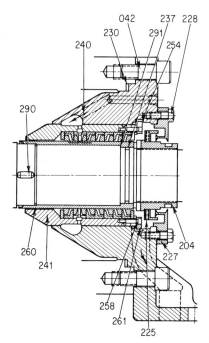

Fig. 6-37 Injection-type multifloating ring seal: (042) capscrew; (204) checknut; (225) guard; (227) cover; (228) bolt; (230) gasket; (237) O ring; (240) housing; (241) seal subassembly; (254) key; (258) capscrew; (260) sleeve; (261) ring; (290) key; (291) O ring (metallic).

chamber and the larger portion of the injection water to pass outboard to an atmospheric drain. This has the advantage of having no out-leakage from the pump and that only highly filtered water flows through the seals.

In temperature-controlled systems, the amount of seal injection water is regulated by the temperature of the drain water from the seals. One advantage of this system is that no cold water enters the pump since all the seal injection water flows outward.

Warm-up Procedure

In starting boiler-feed pumps, the warm-up procedure plays a vital role. It is important to eliminate temperature gradients within the pump to reduce rotor distortion prior to start-up. These temperature gradients are usually measured by monitoring case temperatures at locations as determined by the manufacturer. The highest temperature differential should not exceed 50°F, and the difference between the inlet temperature and the warmest part of the case should normally be not more than 25°F.

To obtain minimum temperature gradients, the warm-up water should enter the case through a warm-up connection at the bottom of the case and discharge through the suction nozzle. A recommended schematic is shown in the sketch in Fig. 6-38, with water supplied from the bleed-off connection of the operating pump.

Effect of Operating Temperature on Pump Efficiency at Constant Speed[1]

Variations in temperature of the fluid pumped cause changes in the specific weight and viscosity, with resultant changes in the performance of the pump.

Any reduction in specific weight, as caused by an increase in temperature, results in a directly proportional reduction in Lhp (as covered on page 6-9) and in input power; so the efficiency is not changed.

[1] Courtesy of the Hydraulic Institute.

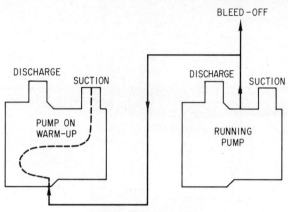

Fig. 6-38   Warm-up piping.

Reduced viscosity will have an influence on efficiency, and for pumps in the lower range of specific speed, such as high-pressure, multistage boiler-feed pumps and large, single-stage hot-water-circulating pumps, reduced viscosity will

1. Increase the internal leakage losses
2. Reduce disk friction losses
3. Reduce hydraulic skin friction or flow losses

The net effect of a reduction in viscosity due to higher temperature will depend on specific speed and on the design details of the pump. Where substantiating data are available and where a high degree of understanding exists between the manufacturer and the user, consideration may be given to adjusting the performance data from a cold-water test to hot-water operating conditions on the basis of the following formula:

$$\eta_0 = 1 - (1 - \eta_t) \left(\frac{v_0}{v_t}\right)^n$$

where η_t = efficiency at test temperature, decimal value
      η_0 = efficiency at operating temperature, decimal value
      v_0 = kinematic viscosity at operating temperature
      v_t = kinematic viscosity at test temperature
      n = exponent to be established by manufacturers' data (probably in the range of 0.05 to 0.1)

Typical Example of Adjustment of Efficiency for Increased Temperature   A test on water at 100°F resulted in an efficiency of 80 percent. What will be the probable efficiency at 350°F?

$$\eta_0 = 1 - (1 - \eta_t) \left(\frac{v_0}{v_t}\right)^n$$

$$\eta_0 = 1 - (1 - 0.80) \left(\frac{0.0000076}{0.00000185}\right)^{0.1}$$

$$\eta_0 = 1 - (0.2)0.915$$

$$\eta_0 = 0.817 = 81.7 \text{ percent}$$

Vibration Limits of Centrifugal Pumps

General   Recommendations for upper limits of vibration of centrifugal-pump units under field operating conditions are shown in the curves in Figs. 6-39 and 6-40.

Figure 6-39 is for centrifugal pumps handling clean liquids.

Figure 6-40 is for vertical or horizontal centrifugal, nonclog, dry-pit pumps.

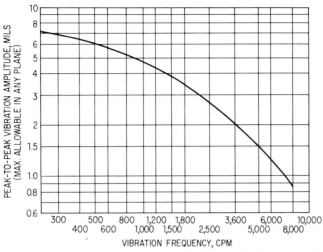

Fig. 6-39 Acceptable field vibration limits for centrifugal pumps handling clean liquids. Frequency corresponds to rpm when dynamic unbalance is cause of vibration. Vertical pumps: measure vibration at top motor bearing. Horizontal pumps: measure vibration on bearing housing. (*Courtesy of the Hydraulic Institute.*)

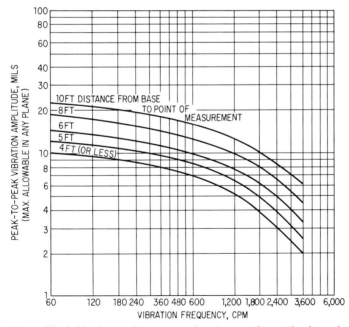

Fig. 6-40 Acceptable field vibration limits—vertical or horizontal centrifugal nonclog pumps. Frequency corresponds to rpm when dynamic unbalance is the cause of vibration. Vertical pumps: measure vibration at top motor bearing. Horizontal pumps: measure vibration on bearing housing. (*Courtesy of the Hydraulic Institute.*)

In using these curves, the following conditions apply:

1. Curves are applicable when the pump is operating at rated speed within plus or minus 10 percent of rated capacity.
2. Measurements should be made as indicated on the appropriate curve sheet.
3. Piping should be connected so as to avoid strains on the pump.

The curves should be used as a general guide, with recommendations that vibrations in excess of the curve may require investigation and correction. Often more important than the actual vibration itself is the change of vibration over a period of time. Vibrations in excess of the curves may often be tolerated if they show no increase over considerable periods of time, and if there is no other indication of damage, such as increase in bearing clearance.

Factors Affecting Vibration   There are a number of factors besides physical unbalance of the rotating parts which may cause vibration. Among these are:

1. Resonance between the unit and its foundation or piping, or resonance within the unit due to natural frequency of the pump, the motor frame, the motor-supporting pedestal, or the foundation. Resonant vibrations may also be caused by other equipment in operation in the area.
2. Operation at or near a critical speed. The amount of vibration observed will depend on the degree of unbalance and damping present. Normal design practice is to avoid a critical speed by approximately 25 percent.
3. Vibrations due to hydraulic disturbances caused by improper design of the suction piping or sump. Disturbances may also be caused by improperly designed valves, piping supports, piping, and other components exterior to the pump. Such vibrations are usually at random frequencies.
4. For the nonclog pumps, sudden increases in the vibration levels may be due to the passage of large solids through the pump. If the vibration condition persists, solids may be lodged in the impeller, and remedial measures should be taken to clear it.

Pump Installation and Operation

In addition to consideration of the correct suction head on the pump (pages 6-16 to 6-18) there are other precautions which must be followed to ensure satisfactory operation. A few of these factors are:

1. *Accessibility.* The unit should be located where it may be easily inspected and repaired.
2. *Foundation.* The foundation should be heavy and rigid to avoid misalignment and vibration.
3. *Alignment.* The pump and driver should be correctly aligned to avoid excessive wear of the coupling, packing, and bearings. Pumps handling hot liquids should be aligned at their operating temperature.
4. *Piping.* Both suction and discharge lines should be independently supported near the pump to avoid strains on the casing. It should have as few bends as possible and be larger than the pump nozzles to reduce head losses.

If an expansion joint is installed in the piping between the pump and the nearest point of anchor in the piping, it should be noted that a force equal to the area of the expansion joint (which may be considerably larger than the normal pipe size) times the pressure in the pipe will be transmitted to the pump proper. Some slip-type couplings have the same effect. This force may exceed the allowable pump loading. If an expansion joint or slip-type coupling must be used, it is recommended that either an anchor be installed between it and the pump or that the joint be restrained or otherwise designed so as to prevent this force from being transmitted to the pump. If properly installed, this will eliminate the objectionable forces mentioned above.

The suction pipe should slope upward to the pump nozzle to avoid pockets in which dissolved air may be liberated (see Fig. 6-41). The reducer at the pump suction nozzle should be eccentric rather than a straight taper for the same reason. Any bends should have a long radius, and on the suction side should be as far from the pump as possible.

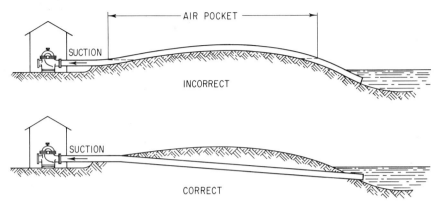

Fig. 6-41   Slope of suction pipe.   (*Courtesy of the Hydraulic Institute.*)

5. *Valves.*   A check valve and gate valve should be placed in the discharge line. The former is placed next to the pump to prevent water from running back through the pump if the driver should fail and to protect the pump from excessive line pressure. The latter is used to regulate the flow and in priming.

Priming   Before a centrifugal pump can deliver fluid it is necessary that the suction side of the impeller be submerged and the suction line filled.   The pump should never be run unless the impeller is filled with liquid since the wearing rings may rub and seize; also the packing must be lubricated by the liquid leaking past it.   If air should leak into the suction line or casing, the unit may become air-bound and lose its prime, i.e., cease delivery.   It is then necessary to stop the pump and prime it before starting up again.

If the impeller is submerged below the water level, it is only necessary to open a petcock leading from the volute to release any entrapped air and ensure that the pump is primed.   If the pump is above the water level, it may be primed by using either a water or steam jet exhauster, or a small priming pump, to remove the air from the pump casing.   In such cases there must be a shutoff valve in the discharge line.   Water from an outside source (such as a reservoir, or from a filled discharge line) may be used to fill the suction line and pump.   A foot valve or check valve must then be placed below the water level in the suction line.

The foot valve is installed in the suction line for priming with low- or medium-suction lifts.   Foot valves should not be used for high lifts, as failure of the driver would cause the water to rush back suddenly and cause water hammer.   A screen is placed before the foot valve to prevent foreign matter from lodging in it.

For large units, or those located in remote localities, automatic priming devices are employed which maintain the water level in the pump at a safe level continuously.

Operating Difficulties

The following table is taken from the Standards of the Hydraulic Institute and gives the causes of common operating difficulties:

1. *No water delivered*
    a. Pump not primed
    b. Speed too low°
    c. Discharge head too high
    d. Suction lift higher than for which pump is designed
    e. Impeller completely plugged up
    f. Wrong direction of rotation
2. *Not enough water delivered*
    a. Air leaks in suction or stuffing boxes
    b. Speed too low°

    c. Discharge head higher than anticipated
    d. Suction lift too high. Check with gages. Check for clogged suction line or screen
    e. Impeller partially plugged up
    f. Not enough suction head for hot water
    g. Mechanical defects:
        Wearing rings worn
        Impeller damaged
        Casing packing defective
    h. Foot valve too small
    i. Foot valve or suction opening not submerged deep enough
3. *Not enough pressure*
    a. Speed too low°
    b. Air in water
    c. Mechanical defects
        Wearing rings worn
        Impeller damaged
        Casing packing defective
    d. Impeller diameter too small
4. *Pump works for a while and then loses suction*
    a. Leaky suction line
    b. Water seal plugged
    c. Suction lift too high
    d. Air or gases in liquid
5. *Pump takes too much power*
    a. Speed too high
    b. Head lower than rating, pumps too much water
    c. Specific gravity or viscosity too high
    d. Mechanical defects:
        Shaft bent
        Rotating element binds
        Stuffing boxes too tight
        Wearing rings worn
        Casing packing defective

° When direct-connected to electric motors, check up whether motor is across the line and receives full voltage. When direct-connected to steam turbines, make sure that turbine receives full steam pressure.

ROTARY PUMPS (IMO Pumps)

General

    The rotary pump is one of the most versatile and widely used types of pump serving industry today. It is the vital "heart" of the fluid-power systems providing the "muscle" for most of the equipment involved in this aerospace age. It is the "workhorse" of the rapidly expanding fluid-power industry, which is providing much of the energy-transfer systems for today's advanced and highly sophisticated machines and tools. It is finding ever-widening use in diversified fields of application such as navy and marine fuel-oil service, marine cargo, oil burners, crude oil, chemical processing, and lube service. Its broadest field of application is in the handling of fluids having some lubricating value and with sufficient viscosity to prevent excessive leakage at required pressure.
    The rotary pump is built in capacities from a fraction of a gallon to more than 5,000 gpm, with pressures ranging up through 10,000 psi and handling viscosities from less than 1 centistoke to more than 1,000,000 SSU.
    The rotary pump is quite often defined as a positive-displacement type by most authoritative engineering references because of the characteristic close-running clearances generally employed which substantially limit internal leakage. It might be more logical and technically correct to drop the "positive" term and refer to this type as simply "displacement pumps." In the rotary pump, mechanical displacement of the fluid from inlet to outlet is produced by trapping a slug of fluid between one or more moving elements such as gears, cams, screws, vanes, lobes, plungers, or other similar devices within a stationary housing or casing. The rotary motion of the centrifugal pump is combined with the positive-pressure characteristic of the reciprocating pump,

resulting in a displacement device which delivers a given quantity of fluid with each revolution of the input shaft.

Unlike the centrifugal, it is generally self-priming and produces a delivery not severely affected by pressure variations. Speeds of operation are much higher than normally found in reciprocating pumps, with the result that in many instances direct-connected drivers can be used.

Rotaries are available for pumping practically any fluid that will flow, although their greatest specialty is the handling of very viscous fluids. Rotaries are generally simple, compact and light in weight.

Classification

There are many different types of pumps which fall under the general category of "rotaries." It is recommended that the reader refer to the Standards of the Hydraulic Institute, Rotary Pumps, for a detailed description of the various types. A number of the major types are listed and described briefly here.

1. *Vane (sliding)* (Fig. 6-42). Vanes, blades, or rollers located in the periphery of a rotor surrounded by a stator to form cavities between two successive vanes which carry fluid from inlet to outlet.

2. *Piston (axial)* (Fig. 6-43). A number of pistons reciprocating within cylinders arranged axially around the periphery of a rotor moving past inlet and outlet ports.

3. *Gear (external)* (Fig. 6-44). Fluid is carried between teeth of two external gears and displaced as they mesh.

4. *Gear (internal)* (Fig. 6-45). Fluid is carried between teeth of one internal and one external gear and displaced as they mesh.

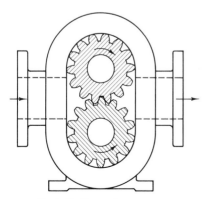

Fig. 6-42 Sliding-vane pump.

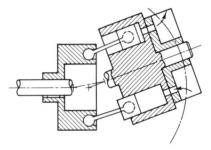

Fig. 6-43 Axial piston pump.

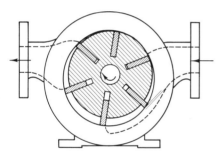

Fig. 6-44 External-gear pump.

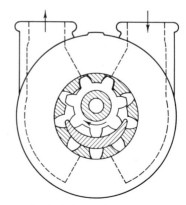

Fig. 6-45 Internal-gear pump.

5. *Lobe* (Fig. 6-46). Fluid is carried between one or more lobes on each of two rotors which are timed by separate means.

6. *Screw.* Fluid is carried between screw threads on two or more engaged rotors and is displaced axially as they mesh.

a. Timed (Fig. 6-47). Separate timing gears, located either internally or externally, are required to maintain proper meshed relationship of the screw threads, and rotors are also generally supported by separate sets of bearings.

b. Untimed (Fig. 6-48). Rotors incorporate the use of generated thread forms which provide a synchronized gearing action making separate timing unnecessary.

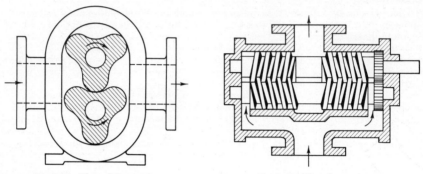

Fig. 6-46   Three-lobe pump.   **Fig. 6-47**   Timed screw pump.

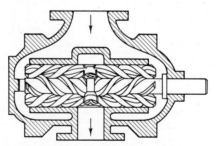

Fig. 6-48   Untimed screw pump.

The De Laval IMO pump (see Fig. 6-49) falls into the untimed screw category, and it will serve as a base for all further discussions of rotary pumps in general. As the fundamental characteristics of all rotaries are similar, many of the IMO pump features can be related to other types of rotaries without comment; however, when characteristics unique to the IMO pump are mentioned, it will be so stated.

Characteristics

The De Laval IMO pump normally is offered as a three-screw type having no need for timing gears or conventional support bearings. It is simple and rugged and has no valves or reciprocating parts to foul. It can run at high speeds, is quiet-operating, and produces a steady pulsation-free flow of fluid.

Properly applied, the IMO pump can handle a wide range of fluids from molasses to gasoline, including the modern-day fire-resistant types, even to 5 percent soluble oil in water. It can be made with hardened wear-resistant rotors to handle some types of contamination and abrasives. Wide ranges of flow and pressure are available.

In the IMO pump, as in most screw pumps, it is the intermeshing of the threads on the rotors and the close fit of the surrounding housing which create one or more sets

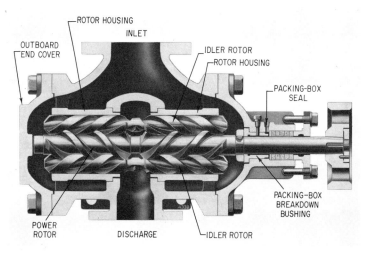

Fig. 6-49 Cutaway view of double-end IMO pump.

of moving seals between pump inlet and outlet. These sets of seals act as a labyrinth and provide the screw pump with its positive-pressure capability. Between successive sets of moving seals or threads are voids which move continuously from inlet to outlet. These moving voids, when filled with fluid, carry the fluid along and provide a smooth flow to the outlet which is essentially pulsationless. Increasing the number of threads or seals between inlet and outlet increases the pressure capability of the pump, again similar to classic labyrinth seals.

The flow of fluid through the screw pump is parallel to the axis of the screws as opposed to travel around the periphery of centrifugal, vane, and gear-type pumps. This axial flow gives the screw pump the ability to handle fluids at low relative velocities for a given input speed, and it is therefore suitable for running at higher speeds, with 1,750 and 3,500 rpm common for IMO pumps.

The fundamental difference between the IMO pump and other types of screw pumps lies in the method of engaging or meshing the rotors and maintaining the running clearances between them. Timed screw pumps require the use of separate timing gears between the rotors to provide the proper phasing or meshing of the threads. Some sort of support bearing also is required at the ends of each rotor to maintain proper clearances and proper positioning of the timing gears themselves.

The IMO pump rotors are precision-made gearing in themselves, having mating generated thread forms such that any necessary driving force can be transmitted smoothly and continuously between the rotors without need for the use of additional timing gears. The center or driven rotor, called the power rotor, is in mesh with two or three close-fitting unsupported sealing or idler rotors symmetrically positioned about the central axis by the close-fitting rotor housing. This close-fitting housing and the idlers provide the only transverse bearing support for the power rotor. Conversely, the idlers are transversely supported only by the housing and the power rotor.

The real key to all IMO pump operation is the means employed for absorbing the transverse idler rotor-bearing loads which are developed as a result of the hydraulic forces built up within the pump to move the fluid against pressure. These rotors and the related housing bores are, in effect, partial journal bearings with a hydrodynamic fluid film being generated to prevent metal-to-metal contact. This phenomenon is most often referred to as the *journal-bearing theory*, and IMO pump behavior is closely related to the applied principles of this theory. The three key parameters of speed, fluid viscosity, and bearing pressure are related exactly as in a journal bearing. If viscosity is reduced, speed must be increased or bearing pressure reduced in order not to exceed acceptable operating limits.   For a constant viscosity, however, the bearing-pressure capability can be increased by increasing the speed.   It is this phenomenon that gives the IMO its high-speed capability; in fact, with proper inlet conditions, the higher the IMO pump speed the better the performance and the better the life. This is directly opposite to most rotary-pump behavior.

Since the IMO pump is a displacement device, like all rotaries, it will deliver a definite quantity of fluid with every revolution of the power rotor.   If no internal clearances exist, this quantity, called *theoretical capacity Qt*, would be dependent only upon the physical dimensions of the rotor set and the speed.   Clearances, however, do exist, with the result that whenever a pressure differential occurs, there always will be internal leakage from outlet to inlet.   This leakage, commonly called slip *S*, varies depending upon the pump type or model, amount of clearance, fluid viscosity at pumping conditions, and the differential pressure.   For any given set of conditions, it is usually unaffected by speed.   The delivered capacity or net capacity *Q*, therefore, is the theoretical capacity less slip.

The theoretical capacity of any pump can readily be calculated with all essential dimensions known.   Basically, IMO pump theoretical capacity varies directly as the cube of the power rotor OD, which is generally used as the pump-size designator. Thus a relatively small increase in pump size can give a large increase in capacity. Slip can also be calculated but usually is based upon empirical values developed by extensive testing.

Performance

Inlet Conditions   The key to obtaining good performance from an IMO pump, as with all other rotaries, lies in a complete understanding and control of inlet conditions and the closely related parameters of speed and viscosity.   To ensure quiet, efficient operation, it is necessary to completely fill with fluid the moving voids between the rotor threads as they open to the inlet, and this becomes more difficult as viscosity, speed, or suction lift increases.   Basically, it can be said that if the fluid can properly enter into the rotor elements, the pump will perform satisfactorily.

Remember that a pump does not pull or lift fluid into itself.   Some external force must be present to push the fluid into the voids.   Normally, atmospheric pressure is the only force present, but there are some applications where a positive inlet pressure is available.

Naturally the more viscous the fluid, the greater is the resistance to flow and, therefore, the lower the rate of filling the moving voids of the threads in the inlet.   Conversely, light-viscosity fluids will flow quite rapidly and will quickly fill the moving voids.   It is obvious that if the rotor elements are moving too fast, the fill will be incomplete and a reduction in output will result.   The rate of fluid flow must always be greater than the rate of void travel or closing to obtain complete filling.   Safe rates of flow through the pump for complete filling have been found from experience when atmospheric pressure is relied upon to force the fluid into the rotors.   The following table gives these safe axial velocity limits for various fluids and pumping viscosities.

Fluid*	Viscosity, SSU	Velocity, fps
Diesel oil.	32	30
Lube oil	1,000	12
No. C fuel oil . . .	7,000	7
Castor oil.	20,000	2
Cellulose.	60,000	½

* For characteristics of fuel oils see Table 6-2 on page 6-60.

It is thus quite apparent that pump speed must be selected to satisfy the viscosity of the fluid to be pumped.   The pump manufacturer generally must supply the determination of the axial velocity through a screw pump, although the calculation is quite simple when the driving-rotor speed and screw-thread lead are known. The lead is the advancement made along the thread during a complete revolution of the rotor as measured along the axis. In other words, it is the travel of the fluid slug in one complete revolution.

In this text, the more general term "fluid" is used to describe the fluids handled by rotaries which may contain, or be mixed with, matter in other than the liquid phase. The word "liquid" is used only to describe true liquids that are free of vapors and solids. Most of the fluids handled by rotary pumps, especially petroleum oils, because of their complex nature, contain certain amounts of entrained and dissolved air or gas which is released as vapor when the fluid is subjected to pressures below atmospheric. If the pressure drop required to overcome entrance losses to push such a fluid into the rotor voids is sufficient to reduce the pressure so that vapors are released in the rotor voids, cavitation results. This leads to noisy operation and an attendant reduction in output. It is therefore very important to be aware of the entrained air and gas characteristics of the fluids to be handled. In fact, it is so important that a more detailed study of this relatively complex subject is included on pages 6-56 to 6-59.

Speed The speed N of a rotary pump is the number of revolutions per minute of the driving rotor. In most instances this is the input shaft speed; however, in some geared-head units the driving-rotor speed can differ from the input shaft speed.

Capacity The actual delivered capacity of any rotary pump, as stated earlier, is theoretical capacity less internal leakage or slip when handling vapor-free fluids. For a particular speed, this may be written $Q = Q_t - S$ where the standard unit of Q and S is the U.S. gallon per minute. Again, if the differential pressure is assumed to be zero, the slip may be neglected and $Q = Q_t$.

The term displacement D is of some general interest, although it is no longer used in rotary-pump calculations. It is the theoretical volume displaced per revolution of the driving rotor and is related to theoretical capacity by speed. The standard unit of displacement is cubic inches per revolution; thus $Q_t = DN \div 231$. The terms "actual displacement" and "liquid displacement" are also less frequently used for rotary-pump calculations but continue to be used for some theoretical studies. Actual displacement is related to delivered capacity by speed.

The actual delivered capacity of any specific rotary pump is reduced by

1. Decreasing speed
2. Decreased viscosities
3. Increased differential pressure

The actual speed must always be known and most often differs somewhat from the rated or nameplate specification. This is the first item to be checked and verified in analyzing any pump operating performance. It is surprising how often the speed is incorrectly assumed and later found to be in error.

Because of the internal clearances between rotors and the housing of a rotary pump, lower viscosities and higher pressure increase slip, which results in a reduced delivered capacity for a given speed. The impact of these characteristics can vary widely for the various types of rotary pumps encountered. The slip, however, is not measurably affected by changes in speed and thus becomes a smaller percentage of the total flow with the use of higher speeds. This is a very significant factor in dealing with the handling of light viscosities at higher pressures, particularly in the case of devices, such as the IMO pump, which favor high speed. Always run at the highest speed possible for best results and best volumetric efficiency with the IMO pump. This will not generally be the case with types of rotaries having support-bearing speed limits.

Pump volumetric efficiency Vy is calculated $Vy = Q/Q_t = (Q_t - S)/Q_t$, with Q_t varying directly with speed.

As stated previously, theoretical capacity of an IMO pump is a function which varies directly as the cube of the power rotor OD size for a standard three-rotor pump configuration. For a constant speed, a 2-in. rotor will have a theoretical capacity eight times that of a 1-in. rotor size. However, for a given model, slip varies directly as the square of the rotor size; therefore, the slip of the 2-in. rotor is four times that of a 1-in. rotor with all fluid variables held constant.

On the other hand, viscosity change affects the slip inversely to some power which has been determined empirically. An acceptable approximation for 100 to 10,000 SSU is obtained by using the one-half power. Slip varies directly with approximately the square root of differential pressure, and a change from 400 to 100 SSU will double the slip the same as will a differential-pressure change of 100 to 400 psi.

Pressure   The pressure capability of the different types of rotary pumps varies widely. Some of the gear and lobe types are fairly well limited to 100 psi, normally considered low pressure. Other gear and vane types perform very well in the moderate-pressure range (100 to 500 psi) and beyond. Some types can operate well in the high-pressure range, while others such as axial piston pumps can work at 5,000 psi and above. The slip characteristic of a particular pump is one of the key factors which determines the acceptable operating range, which generally is well defined by the pump manufacturer; however, all applications for high pressure should be approached with some caution, and the manufacturer or his representative should be consulted.

The IMO pump is suitable for a wide range of pressures from 50 to 5,000 psi, dependent upon the selection of the right model. Internal leakage can be restricted for high-pressure applications by introducing increased numbers of moving seals or threads between inlet and outlet (see Figs. 6-50 to 6-52). The number of seals between inlet and outlet normally is specified for a particular model in terms of number of closures. The number of closures is increased to obtain higher-pressure capability, which also results in increased pump length for a given rotor size.

IMO pumps generally are available with predetermined numbers of closures vs. maximum pressure rating when rated at 150 SSU and 3,500 rpm in the 10- to 100-gpm range:

No. of closures	Max pressure, psi
1	100
2	500
3	1,500
5	3,000
11	5,000

Horsepower   The brake horsepower (bhp) required to drive a rotary pump is the sum of the theoretical liquid horsepower and the internal power losses. The theoretical liquid horsepower is the actual work done in moving the fluid from its inlet-pressure condition to the outlet at discharge pressure.

NOTE: This work is done on all the fluid of theoretical capacity, not just delivered capacity, as slip does not exist until a pressure differential occurs. Rotary-pump power ratings are expressed in terms of horsepower (550 ft-lb/sec), and theoretical liquid horsepower can be calculated: tLhp $= Q_t \, \Delta P \div 1{,}714$. It should be noted that the theoretical liquid horsepower is independent of viscosity and is concerned only with the physical dimensions of the pumping elements, the rotative speed, and the differential pressure.

The internal power losses are made up of two types: mechanical and viscous. The mechanical losses include all the power necessary to overcome the mechanical friction drag of all the moving parts within the pump, including rotors, bearings, gears, mechanical seals, etc. The viscous losses include all the power lost from the fluid viscous-drag effects against all the parts within the pump as well as from the shearing action of the fluid itself. It is probable that the mechanical loss is the major component when operating at low viscosities and high speeds while the viscous loss is the larger at high viscosity and slow-speed conditions.

No direct comparison can be easily made between various types of rotary pumps for internal power loss, as this falls into the category of closely guarded "trade secrets." Most manufacturers have established their own data on a basis of tests made under closely controlled operating conditions, and they are very reluctant to divulge their findings. In general, the losses for a given type and size of pump vary with viscosity and rotative speed and may or may not be affected by pressure, depending upon the type and model of pump under consideration. These losses, however, must always be based upon the maximum viscosity to be handled since they will be highest at this point.

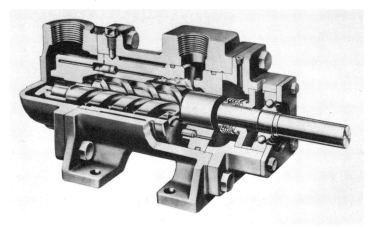

Fig. 6-50 Cutaway view of single-end IMO pump, A3D series, two closures.

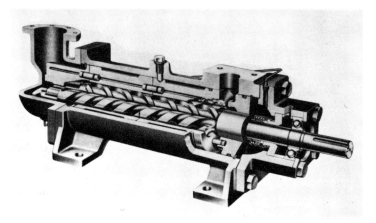

Fig. 6-51 Cutaway view of single-end IMO pump, A6D series, five closures.

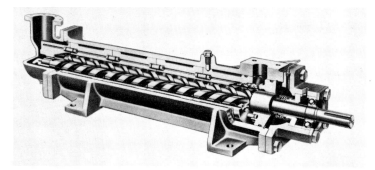

Fig. 6-52 Cutaway view of single-end IMO pump, A12D series, eleven closures.

The actual pump power output (whp) or delivered liquid horsepower is the power imparted to the fluid by the pump at the outlet. It is computed like theoretical liquid horsepower using Q in place of Q_t; hence the value will always be less.

The pump efficiency (Ep) is the ratio of the pump power output (whp) to the brake horsepower (bhp).

Application and Selection

In the application of rotary pumps there are certain basic factors which must be considered in order to ensure a successful installation. These are fundamentally the same regardless of the fluids to be handled or the pumping conditions.

The pump selection for a specific application is not difficult if all the operating conditions are known. It is often quite difficult, however, to obtain accurate information as to these conditions. This is particularly true with reference to inlet conditions and viscosity, since it is a common feeling that inasmuch as the rotary pump is a positive-displacement device, these items are unimportant.

In any rotary-pump application regardless of the design, suction lift, viscosity, and speed are inseparable. Speed of operation, therefore, is dependent upon viscosity and suction lift. If a true picture of these two items can be obtained, the problem of making a proper pump selection becomes simpler, and it is probable that the selection will result in a more efficient unit.

Viscosity It is not very often that a rotary pump is called upon to handle fluids having a constant viscosity. Normally, because of temperature variations, it is expected that a range of viscosity will be encountered and this can be quite wide; for instance, it is not unusual that a pump is required to handle a viscosity range of 150 to 20,000 SSU, the higher viscosity usually being due to cold-starting conditions. This is a perfectly satisfactory range insofar as a rotary pump is concerned; but if information can be obtained concerning such things as the amount of time the pump is required to operate at the higher viscosity, whether the motor can be overloaded temporarily, a multispeed motor can be used, or the discharge pressure can be reduced during this period, a better selection can often be made.

Quite often no viscosity is given but only the type of fluid. In such cases assumptions can sometimes be made if sufficient information is available concerning the fluid in question. For instance, "Bunker C or No. 6 fuel oil" is known to have a wide latitude as to viscosity and usually must be handled over a considerable temperature range. The normal procedure in a case of this type is to assume an operating viscosity range of 20 to 700 SSF. The maximum viscosity, however, might very easily exceed the higher value if extra heavy oil is used or exceptionally low temperatures are encountered. If either should occur, the result may be improper filling of the pumping elements, noisy operation, vibration, and overloading of the motor.

Although it is the maximum viscosity and the expected suction lift that determine the size of the pump and set the speed, it is the minimum viscosity that determines the capacity. Rotary pumps must always be selected to give the specified capacity when handling the expected minimum viscosity, since this is the point at which maximum slip, hence minimum capacity, occurs. If this rule is not followed, the pump will not meet the requirements of the system unless a considerable margin has been allowed initially in specifying capacity, or there is overcapacity available in the pump. The latter is often the case, since practically all rotary pumps are made in certain stock sizes and it is standard practice to apply the next larger pump when a capacity is specified that falls between sizes.

It should also be noted that the minimum viscosity often sets the model of the pump selected since it is more or less standard policy on the part of most manufacturers to downrate their pumps, insofar as allowable pressure is concerned, when handling liquids having a viscosity of less than 100 SSU. This is done for two reasons: first, to avoid the poorer volumetric efficiency as a result of increased slip under these conditions; and second, because a film of the liquid must be maintained between the closely fitted parts which is likely to break down if a combination of low viscosity and high pressure should occur. Although viscosity is not necessarily a definite criterion of film strength, it is generally so used by pump manufacturers.

Entrained Air As mentioned previously, a factor which must also be given careful consideration is the possibility of entrained air or gas in the fluid to be pumped.   This is particularly true of installations where recirculation occurs and the fluid is exposed to air through either mechanical agitation, leaks, or improperly located drain lines.

Likewise, most fluids will also dissolve air or gas, retaining it in solution, the amount being dependent upon the liquid itself and the pressure to which it is subjected.   It is known, for instance, that lubricating oils under conditions of atmospheric temperature and pressure will dissolve up to 10 percent air by volume and gasoline up to 20 percent.

When pressures below atmospheric exist at the pump inlet, dissolved air will come out of solution, and both this and entrained air will expand in proportion to the existent absolute pressure.   This expanded air will accordingly take up a proportionate part of the available volume of the moving voids with a consequent reduction in delivered capacity.   See below under Effect of Entrained or Dissolved Gas on Performance.

One of the apparent effects of handling fluids containing entrained or dissolved air or gas is noisy pump operation.   When such a condition occurs, it is usually dismissed as "cavitation" and let go at that; then too, many operators never expect anything but noisy operation from rotary pumps.   This should not be the case.   With properly designed systems of pumps, quiet, vibration-free operation can be produced and should be expected.   Noisy operation is inefficient, and steps should be taken to make corrections until the objectionable conditions are overcome.   It is true, of course, that some types of pumps are more critical to the handling of air than others; this is usually due to the high inlet losses inherent in these types, but proper design and speed selection can go a great way toward overcoming the problem.

It should be pointed out that if a pump will be called on to handle fluids containing entrained air, this fact should be included in any specifications which may be written and the percentage specified.

Non-Newtonian Fluids   The viscosity of most liquids, as, for example, water and mineral oil, is unaffected by any agitation to which they may be subjected as long as the temperature remains constant; these liquids are accordingly known as *true* or *Newtonian* fluids.   There is another class of liquids, however, such as cellulose compounds, glues, greases, paints, starches, slurries, and candy compounds, which changes in viscosity as agitation is varied at constant temperature.   The viscosity of these fluids will depend upon the shear rate at which it is measured, and these fluids are termed *non-Newtonian*.

If a fluid is known to be non-Newtonian, the expected viscosity under actual pumping conditions should be determined, since it can vary quite widely from the viscosity under static conditions.   One instance comes to mind concerning the handling of a cellulose product where the viscosity was given as 20,000 SSU, which was its actual static, or apparent, viscosity.   It later developed that under actual pumping conditions the viscosity was approximately 500 SSU.   No serious harm was done, but a large low-speed pump was installed where a smaller, cheaper, higher-speed unit could have been used.

Since a non-Newtonian fluid can have an unlimited number of viscosity values (as the shear rate is varied) the term *apparent viscosity* is used to describe its viscous properties.   Apparent viscosity is expressed in absolute units and is a measure of the resistance to flow at a given rate of shear.   It has meaning only if the shear rate used in the measurement is also given.

The grease-manufacturing industry is very familiar with the non-Newtonian properties of its products, as evidenced by the numerous curves which have been published wherein *apparent viscosity* is plotted against *rate of shear*.   The occasion is rare, however, when one is able to obtain accurate information as to viscosity when it is necessary to select a pump for handling this fluid.

It is understood that it is practically impossible, in most instances, to give the viscosity of grease in the terms most familiar to the pump manufacturer, i.e., Saybolt Seconds Universal or Saybolt Seconds Furol; but if only a rough approximation could be given, it would be of great help.

For applications of this type, data taken from similar installations are most valuable.   Such information should consist of type, size, capacity, and speed of already installed pumps, suction pressure, and temperature at the pump-inlet flange, total working suction head, and above all the pressure drop in a specified length of piping. From the latter, an excellent approximation of viscosity under actual operating conditions can be obtained.

Suction Conditions Suction lift occurs where the total suction head at the pump inlet is below atmospheric pressure. It is normally the result of a static lift and pipe friction. Although rotary pumps are capable of producing a high vacuum, it is not this vacuum that forces the fluid to flow. As previously explained, it is atmospheric pressure that forces the fluid into the pump. Since atmospheric pressure at sea level corresponds to 14.7 psia, or 30 in. Hg, this is the maximum amount of pressure available for moving the fluid, and suction lift cannot exceed these figures. Actually, it must be somewhat less since there are always pump inlet losses which must be taken into account. It is considered the best practice to keep suction lifts just as low as possible.

The majority of rotary pumps operate with suction lifts of approximately 5 to 15 in. Hg. Lifts corresponding to 24 to 25 in. Hg are not uncommon, and there are numerous installations operating continuously and satisfactorily where the absolute suction pressure is within 1/2 in. of the barometer. In the latter cases, however, the pumps are usually taking the fluid from tanks under vacuum and no entrained or dissolved air or gases are present. Great care must be taken in selecting pumps for these applications, since the inlet losses can very easily exceed the net suction head available for moving the fluid into the pumping elements.

There are many known instances of successful installations where pumps were properly selected for high suction conditions. There are also, unfortunately, many other installations with equally high suction lifts which are not so satisfactory. This is because proper consideration was not given, at the time the installations were made, to the actual suction conditions at the pump inlet. Frequently, suction conditions are given as "flooded" simply because the source feeding the pump is above the inlet flange. Absolutely no consideration is given to outlet losses from the tank or pipe friction, and these can be exceptionally high when dealing with extremely viscous fluids.

Where it is desired to pump extremely viscous fluids such as grease, chilled shortening, and cellulose preparations, care should be taken to use the largest possible size of suction piping, eliminate all unnecessary fittings and valves, and place the pump just as closely as possible to the source of supply. In addition, it may be found necessary to supply the fluid to the pump under some pressure which may be supplied by elevation, air pressure, or mechanical means.

Speed It was previously stated that viscosity and speed are closely tied together and it is impossible to consider one without the other. Although rotative speed is the ultimate outcome, the basic speed which the manufacturer must consider is the velocity of the fluid going through the pump; this is a function of pump type and design. Certain types, such as gear and vane pumps, carry the fluid around the periphery of the pumping elements, and as a result, the velocity of the fluid through the pump can become quite high unless relatively low rotative speeds are used. On the other hand, in screw-type pumps the flow is axial and fluid speeds are relatively lower, with the result that higher rotative speeds can be used. Based on handling light fluids, say 100 to 500 SSU, gear- or vane-type pumps rarely exceed a rotative speed of 1,200 rpm except in the case of a very small unit or special designs for a particular use such as for aircraft purposes. Screw pumps, however, where timing gears are not required, commonly operate without difficulty at speeds up to 5,000 rpm, and IMO pumps have been run in the field to 24,000 rpm.

Although rotative speeds are relative and dependent upon the pump type, they usually should be reduced when handling fluids of high viscosity. This is due not only to the difficulty of filling the pumping elements but also the mechanical losses which result from the shearing action of these parts on the fluid handled. The reduction of these losses is frequently of more importance than relatively high speeds, even though the latter might be possible because of positive inlet conditions.

Rotary pumps do not in themselves create pressure; they simply transfer a quantity of fluid from the inlet to the outlet side. The pressure developed on the outlet side is solely the result of resistance to flow in the discharge line. If, for example, a pump were to be set up and run without a discharge line, a gage placed at the pump outlet flange would register zero, no matter how fast or how long it was run.

Pipe Size Resistance usually consists of differences of elevation, fixed resistances such as orifices, and pipe friction. Nothing much can be done about the first two, since these are the basic reasons for using a pump. Something, however, can be done about pipe friction. Literally millions of dollars are thrown away annually because of the use of piping that is too small for the job. To be sure, all pipe friction cannot be eliminated as long as fluids must be handled in this manner, but every effort should be made to use the largest pipe that is economically feasible. Numerous tables are available from which friction losses in any combination of piping may be calculated, among the most recent of which are those published by the Hydraulic Institute, also available in this handbook in condensed form.

Before any new installation is made, the cost of larger-size piping which will result in lower pump pressures should be carefully balanced against the cost of a less expensive pump, smaller motor, and a saving in horsepower over the expected life of the system. The larger piping may cost a little more in the beginning, but the ultimate savings in power will often offset the original cost many times. These facts are particularly true of the handling of extremely viscous fluids, and although most engineers dealing with fluids of this type are conscious of what can be done, it is surprising how many installations are encountered where considerable savings could have been made if a little more study had been made initially.

Abrasives There is one other point that we have not as yet touched, and that is the handling of fluids containing abrasives. Because rotary pumps depend upon close clearances for proper pumping action, the handling of abrasive fluids will usually cause rapid wear. Much progress has been made in the use of harder and more abrasive-resistant materials for the pumping elements, so that a good job can be done in some instances. It cannot be said, however, that performance is always satisfactory when handling fluid laden excessively with abrasive materials. On the whole, rotary pumps should not be used for handling fluids of this character unless shortened pump life and an increased frequency of replacement are acceptable.

Design Details

It is virtually impossible to include a discussion of the design details for the many varieties of rotary pumps within the framework of this text; therefore, this section will be limited to only a brief discussion of IMO pump design with some reference to other types where applicable.

Basic Construction The IMO pump, as well as other types and makes of rotary screw pumps, is available in two basic configurations: single- and double-end construction. The double-end construction (see Fig. 6-49) is probably the most well known version, as it was by far the most widely used, for many years, because of the relative simplicity and compactness of design. As pressure requirements were raised, however, the single-end version developed increased usage, until today it is by far the largest portion of the total IMO pump annual production. (See Fig. 6-56.)

The general double-end screw-pump construction usually is limited to low- and medium-pressure applications, with 400 psi a good practical limit to be used for planning purposes. However, with special design features incorporated, applications to 800 psi can be handled. Double-end pumps generally are employed where large flows are required or very viscous fluids are handled.

There is one other principal IMO pump construction variation in use which must be mentioned briefly, that is, the four-rotor design having three idlers which is sometimes used for low-pressure lube service. The introduction of the third idler, in effect, makes the pump nonpositive, which gives it some additional capability for handling heavily air-laden lube oil without cavitation or the related heavy vibration. This design, however, is restricted only to very low pressure use because of the resulting increased slip characteristic.

The single-end screw-pump construction (see Fig. 6-50) is most often employed for handling low-viscosity fluids at high pressure or hydraulic-type fluids at very high pressure. It is most practical to provide the additional number of moving seals or closures between inlet and outlet necessary to handle high pressure in the single-end construction.

This is accomplished in IMO pumps by literally stacking a number of medium-pressure single-end pumping elements in series within one pump casing. The single-end construction also offers the best design arrangement for high-production manufacture even though the design itself is more complex than the relatively simple double-end construction.

The double-end (see Fig. 6-49) is basically two opposed single-end pumps or pump elements of the same size with a common power rotor of double-helix design within one casing. As can be seen from the illustration, the fluid normally enters a common inlet, with a split flow going to the outboard ends of the two pumping elements, and is discharged from the middle or center of the pump elements. The two pump elements are, in effect, pumps connected in parallel. The design can also be provided with a reversed flow for low-pressure applications.

Axial Balance Whichever design is employed, means must always be provided to absorb the mechanical and hydraulic axial thrust on the rotors of a screw pump. The double-end design provides the simplest arrangement for accomplishing this, as both the power and idler types of rotor (see again Fig. 6-49) are constructed with opposed-thread helices on the same shaft, which provides true axial balancing, both mechanically and hydraulically, as all thrust forces between the opposed pump elements are canceled out.

In the case of single-end designs, special axial balancing arrangements must be employed for both the power and idler rotors, and in this respect, they are thus more complicated than the double-end construction. Mechanical thrust-bearing arrangements (see Fig. 6-56) are used for the idlers for 150 psi differential pressures and below while a hydraulic-balance arrangement (see Fig. 6-50) is used for pressures above 150 psi. Here hydraulic balance is accomplished by directing discharge pressure to a bearing area on the inlet end of the idler, which is equal and opposite to the area exposed to discharge pressure on the outlet end of the same idler.

Hydraulic balance is provided for the power rotor through the balance piston (see Fig. 6-50) mounted on the power rotor between the outlet and seal chambers. This piston is exposed to discharge pressure on the outlet side and is equal and opposite in area to the exposed area of the power rotor thread; thus the discharge-pressure hydraulic forces on the rotor threads are canceled out.

Seals The IMO pump, like most other modern-day equipment, makes extensive use of mechanical-face seals for shaft sealing. Packing is now used only where absolutely necessary as dictated by the fluid handled. Seal technology has advanced rapidly in the last two decades, with many new materials introduced such as Buna-N, Neoprene, Viton, and Teflon for elastomers. Ni-resist, carbon, carbide, and ceramics are now available in addition to the original standby pearlitic cast iron for use in the sealing faces. All this has made the use of packing virtually obsolete.

In all but some of the small low-pressure series, the IMO pump always has the seal located in a chamber connected to the suction side. In order to accomplish this in the single-end design where the outlet is at the shaft end, the aforementioned power-rotor balance piston also serves as a breakdown bushing or flow restrictor between outlet and seal chambers to limit the pressure in the seal chamber. This seal chamber, in turn, is connected to the suction side of the pump through a small internal drilled conduit or through external tubing (see Fig. 6-50).

In most cases where a mechanical seal is used in an IMO pump, an external grease-sealed ball bearing is employed on the power-rotor drive shaft to maintain precise shaft positioning. This assures long mechanical seal life. This bearing also serves to minimize flexible-coupling-misalignment conditions which can adversely affect the performance of high-speed equipment such as the IMO pump. The use of the ball bearing also provides a means for taking overhung loads, such as from belt drives, on certain models.

Inlet Pressures Standard IMO pumps are normally designed to handle positive inlet pressures up to 40 psig. This limitation of pressure concerns the resulting thrust on the rotors, and design modifications can be made for much higher inlet pressures as required. The double-end design is ideal for adapting to high-inlet-pressure applications because the idlers are in thrust balance at all times and the power rotor can be thrust-balanced by making it double-ended so that both ends are exposed to the inlet pressure identically. The drawback is the need for two seals, but this is not too significant if the high inlet pressure really is important to obtain.

The above double-shaft arrangement also is used when two or more pumps are to be driven in tandem, which is quite advantageous in some applications. Shaft tapers are always used on larger IMO pumps for locating the coupling. The use of this taper helps to protect the mechanical seals and bearings from shock damage that can arise when installing a large coupling on a straight shaft.

Casings Standard IMO pumps normally are provided with high-grade cast iron for the casing of low- and medium-pressure models. Standard high-pressure pumps employ ductile iron or cast steel for the casings with fabricated steel used for special orders when necessary. Casings also are made suitable for steam jacketing when absolutely necessary for high-viscosity applications; however, the use of heat tracing with either steam coils or electric tape covered with a good insulation blanket is the recommended preference.

IMO pumps can normally be mounted in virtually any position including vertical as well as all horizontal rotations. Double-end designs usually are arranged with opposed side inlet and outlet positions parallel to the foot mounting. Side inlet and top discharge can also be furnished if necessary

Rotor Materials The rotors and housings of the IMO pump can be made of various types and grades of hardened materials for use in handling corrosive-type fluids as well as those containing some abrasives. One of the popular material combinations in use in many of the medium- and high-pressure models is nitrided-steel power rotors and induction-hardened ductile-iron idlers with pearlitic gray-iron housings.

Most of the rotors of IMO pumps are finish-machined after hardening by thread grinding in order to obtain a high degree of accuracy. Very small and very large rotor sets at the extremes of the size range are finish-thread-milled. Thread forms are controlled very accurately to obtain the proper mating action of all rotor sets as well as to maintain the running clearances between rotors to a minimum for limited internal leakage.

Installation and Operation

Rotary-pump performance can be improved by following the recommendations on installation and operation given below.

The pump should be placed on a smooth solid foundation readily accessible for inspection and repair. It is essential that the power shaft and drive shafts be in perfect alignment. De Laval practice normally requires a concentricity and parallelism of 0.003 FIR.

The suction pipe should be as short and straight as possible with all joints airtight. There should be no points at which air or entrapped gases may collect. If it is not possible to have the fluid flow to the pump, a foot or check valve should be installed at the end of the suction line or as far from the pump as possible. All piping should be independently supported to avoid strains on the pump casing.

A priming connection should be provided on the suction side and a relief valve set from 5 to 10 percent above the maximum working pressure on the discharge side.

Starting the unit may involve simply opening the pump suction and discharge valves and starting the motor, but it is always better to prime the unit on initial starting. On new installations, the system is full of air which must be removed. If not removed, the performance of the unit will be erratic, and in some cases air in the system can prevent the unit from pumping. Priming the pump should preferably consist of filling not only the pump with fluid but as much of the suction line as possible.

The discharge side of the pump should be vented on the initial starting. Venting is especially essential where the suction line is long or the pump is discharging against system pressure upon starting.

If the pump does not discharge after being started, the unit should be shut down immediately. The pump should then be primed and tried again. If it still does not pick up fluid promptly, there may be a leak in the suction pipe or the trouble may be traceable to excessive suction lift from an obstruction, throttled valve, or other causes. Attaching a gage to the suction pipe at the pump will help find the trouble.

Once the pump is in service, it should continue to operate satisfactorily with practically no attention other than an occasional inspection of the mechanical seal or packing for excessive leakage and a periodic check to be certain alignment is maintained within reasonable limits for prolonged periods.

NOTE: Although mechanical seals are becoming more widely used, there are some applications where packing will continue to be preferred, and it is therefore necessary to make some brief comment concerning the proper installation and care of packing. The packing gland should never be set up too tight. Packing properly used will require some leakage in order to maintain correct lubrication. The recommended leakage rate is somewhat dependent upon the type of fluid being handled but should never be less than several drops per minute.

Excessive gland pressure on the packing causes scoring of shaft and rapid deterioration of the packing itself. The best practice is to keep the gland stud nuts about finger-tight.

Should the pump develop a noise after satisfactory operation, this is usually indicative of either excessive suction lift due to cold fluid, air in the fluid, misalignment of the coupling, or in the case of an old pump, excessive wear.

Whenever the unit is shut down, if the operation of the system permits, both suction and discharge valves should be closed. This is particularly important if the shutdown is to be for an extended period, as leakage in the foot valve, if the main supply is below the pump elevation, could drain the fluid from the unit and necessitate repriming as in the initial starting of the system.

Effect of Entrained or Dissolved Gas on Performance

A very important factor in rotary-pump applications is the amount of entrained and dissolved air or gas in the fluid handled. This is especially true if the suction pressure is below atmospheric. It is generally neglected since rotary pumps are of the displacement type and hence are self-priming. If the entrained or dissolved air and gases are a large percentage of the volume handled and if their effect is neglected, there may be noise and vibration, loss of liquid capacity, and pressure pulsations.

The amount of entrained air or gas is extremely variable depending upon the viscosity, type of liquid, and the time and manner of agitation it may have received.

There is little information available covering the solubility of air and other gases in liquids, especially all those handled by rotary pumps. Dr. C. S. Cargoe of the National Bureau of Standards developed the following formula about 1930 based on literature data available at the time to show the solubility of air at atmospheric pressure in oils, both crude and refined, and other organic liquids:

$$\log_{10} A = \frac{792}{t + 460} - 4 \log_{10} sg - 0.4$$

where A = dissolved air, cu in./gal
t = temperature, °F
sg = specific gravity of the liquid

This equation is plotted as Fig. 6-53 as taken from a paper on Rotary Pumps by Sweeney in the February, 1943, issue of the *Journal of the Society of Naval Engineers.* The equation and curve should be considered as approximate only, since some liquids have a higher affinity for air and gases. For example, gasoline at atmospheric pressure will dissolve as much as 20 percent of air by volume.

This actual displacement is measured in terms of volume of fluid pumped, and will be the same whether it is liquid, gas, or a mixture of both as long as the fluid can get to and fill the pump moving voids.

If the fluid contains 5 percent entrained gas by volume and no dissolved gas, and the suction pressure is atmospheric, the mixture is then 95 percent liquid and 5 percent gas. This mixture fills up the moving voids on the inlet side, but 5 percent of the space is filled with gas, the remainder with liquid. Therefore, in terms of amount of liquid handled, the output is reduced directly by the amount of gas present, or 5 percent. The liquid displacement as a function of the theoretical displacement when the suction pressure is atmospheric then becomes

$$D' = D(1 - E)$$

where D = theoretical displacement
D' = liquid displacement
E = percent entrained gas by volume at atmospheric pressure, divided by 100

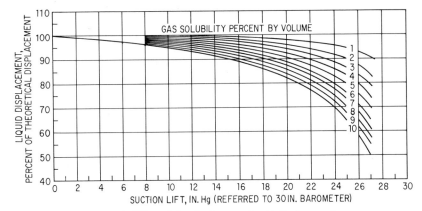

Fig. 6-53 Effect of dissolved gas on liquid displacement.

Assume the fluid handled is a liquid mixture containing 5 percent entrained gas by volume at atmospheric pressure, no dissolved gas, but with the inlet pressure at the pump p_i in psia which is below atmospheric. The entrained gas will increase in volume as it reaches the pump in direct ratio to the absolute pressures. The new mixture will have a greater percentage of gas present, and the portion of theoretical displacement available to handle liquid becomes

$$D' = \frac{D(1-E)}{(1-E)+Ep/p_i}$$

where p = atmospheric pressure, psia
p_i = inlet pressure, psia

Note that p_i depends upon the vapor pressure of the liquid, the static lift, and the friction and entrance losses to the pump.

In the above equation, if the atmospheric pressure is 14.7 psia, the pump inlet pressure 5 psia, and the vapor pressure is very low; the liquid displacement is 86.6 percent of the theoretical.

If dissolved gases in liquids are considered, the effect on the liquid displacement reduction is the same as that due to entrained gases, since in the latter case the dissolved gases come out of solution when the pressure is lowered. For example, assume a liquid free of entrained gas, but containing gas in solution at atmospheric pressure and the pumping temperature. So long as the inlet pressure at the pump does not go below atmospheric pressure and the temperature does not rise, gas will not come out of solution. If pressure below atmospheric does exist at the pump inlet, gas will evolve and expand to the pressure existing. This will have the same effect as entrained gas taking up available displacement capacity, and reduce the liquid displacement accordingly. The liquid displacement then will be

$$D' = \frac{D}{1 + y(p - p_i)/p_i}$$

where the symbols have the meanings given above and y is the percent of dissolved gas by volume at pressure p divided by 100. If the operating conditions are 9 percent of dissolved gas at 14.7 psia with a pump inlet pressure of 5 psia, the liquid displacement will be 85.2 percent of the theoretical displacement.

If both entrained and dissolved gases are considered as existing in the material to be pumped, the liquid displacement becomes

$$D' = \frac{Dp_i(1-E)}{(1-E)[p_i + y(p - p_i)] + Ep}$$

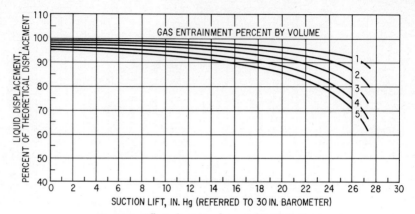

Fig. 6-54 Effect of entrained gas on liquid displacement.

where the symbols have the meanings given above. For the operating conditions 5 percent entrained gas, 9 percent dissolved gas at 14.7 psia, and a pump inlet pressure of 5 psia, the liquid displacement is 75.2 percent of the theoretical. Figure 6-54 shows graphically the reduction in liquid displacement as a function of pump inlet pressure, expressed in terms of suction lift, for different amounts of dissolved gas, neglecting slip.

Figure 6-55 shows the reduction in liquid displacement as a function of pump inlet pressure, expressed as suction lift, for different amounts of entrained air only, neglecting slip. From this figure it may be noted that a very small air leak can cause a large reduction in liquid displacement, especially if the suction lift is high.

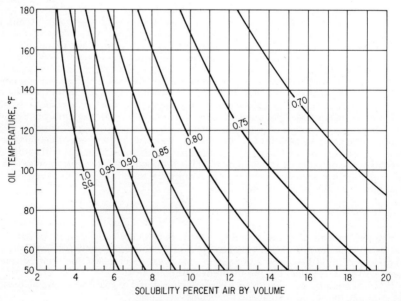

Fig. 6-55 Solubility of air in oil.

From these few examples and curves it would appear that the question of entrained and dissolved gases could be cared for by providing ample margins in pump capacity. Unfortunately, capacity reductions from the causes mentioned are attended by other and usually more serious difficulties.

The operation of a rotary pump is such that as rotation progresses, closures are formed which fill and discharge in succession. If the fluid pumped is compressible, such as a mixture of oil and air, the volume within each closure is reduced as it comes in contact with the discharge pressure. This produces pressure pulsations, the intensity and frequency of which depend upon the discharge pressure, the number of closures formed per revolution, and the speed of rotation. Under some conditions the pressure pulsations are of high magnitude and can cause damage to piping and fittings or even the pump, and will almost certainly be accompanied by undesirable noise.

The amount of dissolved air or gas may be reduced by lowering the suction lift. This may often be controlled by pump location, suction pipe diameter, and piping arrangement.

Many factors are associated with the amount of entrained air that can exist in a given installation. It is prevalent in systems where the liquid is handled repeatedly and during each cycle is exposed to, or mechanically agitated in, air. Unfortunately in many cases the system is such that air entrainment cannot be entirely eliminated, as in the case of the lubrication system of a reduction gear. Considerable work has been done by the various oil companies on foam dispersion, and while it has been recommended that special oils be used which are inhibited against oxidation and corrosion, all agree that the best cure is to remove or reduce the cause of foaming, namely, air entrainment.

Even though air entrainment cannot be entirely eliminated, in many cases it is possible, by adhering to the following rules, to reduce it and its ill effects on rotary-pump performance.

1. Keep liquid velocity low in the suction pipe to reduce turbulence and pressure loss. Use large and well-rounded suction bell to reduce entrance loss.

2. Keep suction lift low. If possible locate the pump to provide positive head on the inlet.

3. Locate the suction piping within a reservoir to obtain the maximum submergence.

4. Submerge all return lines particularly from bypass and relief valves, and locate them away from the suction.

5. Keep the circulation rate low and avoid all unnecessary circulation of the fluid.

6. Do not exceed rated manifold pressures on machinery lubricating systems, as the increased flow through sprays and bearings increases the circulation rate.

7. Heat the fluid where practical to reduce viscosity and as an expedient to drive off entrained air. Fluids of high viscosity will entrain and retrain more air than fluids of low viscosity.

8. Avoid all air leaks no matter how small.

9. Provide ample vents; exhauster fans to draw off air and vapors have been used with good results.

10. Centrifuging will break a foam and remove foreign matter suspended in the oil, which promotes foaming.

11. Use a variable-speed drive for the pump to permit an adjustment of pump capacity to suit the flow requirements of the machinery.

TABLE 6-2 Detailed Requirements for Fuel Oils[a]

| Grade of fuel oil | | Flash point, °F | Pour point, °F | Water and sediment, % | Carbon residue on 10% residuum, % | Ash, % | Distillation temp, °F | | | Viscosity | | | | | | | | Gravity, °API |
No.	Description	min	max	max	max	max	10% point max	90% point max	End point max	Saybolt Universal at 100°F max	Saybolt Universal at 100°F min	Saybolt Furol at 122°F max	Saybolt Furol at 122°F min	Kinematic centistokes at 100°F max	Kinematic centistokes at 100°F min	Kinematic centistokes at 122°F max	Kinematic centistokes at 122°F min	min
1	Distillate oil intended for vaporizing pot-type burners and other burners requiring this grade[c]	100 or legal	0	Trace	0.15	...	420	...	625	...	...	...	...	2.2	1.4	...	...	35
2	Distillate oil for general-purpose domestic heating for use in burners not requiring No. 1	100 or legal	20[d]	0.10	0.35	...	[e]	675	...	...	...	...	...	(4.3)	...	...	...	26
4	Oil for burner installations not equipped with preheating facilities	130 or legal	20	0.50	...	0.10	...	...	...	125	45	...	...	(26.4)	(5.8)	...	...	...
5	Residual-type oil for burner installations equipped with preheating facilities	130 or legal	...	1.00	...	0.10	...	...	...	...	150	40	...	...	(32.1)	(81)	...	...
6	Oil for use in burners equipped with preheaters permitting a high-viscosity fuel	150 or legal	...	2.00[f]	...	...	...	...	...	...	...	300	45	...	...	(638)	(92)	...

Reprinted by permission from Commercial Standard CS 12-48 on Fuel Oils of U.S. Department of Commerce.

[a] Recognizing the necessity for low-sulfur fuel oils used in connection with heat treatment, nonferrous metal, glass and ceramic furnaces, and other special uses, a sulfur requirement may be specified in accordance with the following table:

Grade of fuel oil	Sulfur, max, %
No. 1	0.5
No. 2	1.0
Nos. 4, 5, and 6	No limit

Other sulfur limits may be specified only by mutual agreement between the buyer and seller.

[b] It is the intent of these classifications that failure to meet any requirement of a given grade does not automatically place an oil in the next lower grade unless in fact it meets all requirements of the lower grade.

[c] No. 1 oil shall be tested for corrosion for 3 hr at 122°F. The exposed copper strip shall show no gray or black deposit.

[d] Lower or higher pour points may be specified whenever required by conditions of storage or use. However, these specifications shall not require a pour point lower than 0°F under any conditions.

[e] The 10 percent point may be specified at 440°F. Maximum for use in other than atomizing burners.

[f] The amount of water by distillation plus the sediment by extraction shall not exceed 2.00 percent. The amount of sediment by extraction shall not exceed 0.50 percent. A deduction in quantity shall be made for all water and sediment in excess of 1.0 percent.

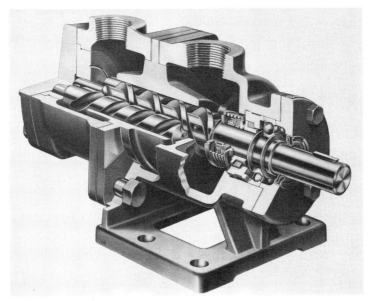

Fig. 6-56   Cutaway view of IMO pump.

CENTRIFUGAL AND AXIAL COMPRESSORS (DYNAMIC COMPRESSORS)

General

Dynamic compressors develop pressure by the action of rotating blading imparting velocity and pressure to the flowing medium.   Both centrifugal and axial machines are of this type.

Dynamic compressors are relatively large volume machines, which find their primary application in chemical process industries, steel plants, oil refineries, sewage-treatment works, aircraft test facilities, gas transmission, etc., where significant flows are encountered.

The range of application of centrifugals, at present, is for *inlet volumes* of 500 to 200,000 cfm.   For axials the range is from approximately 50,000 to 300,000 cfm and larger.

Dynamic compressors operate at relatively high speeds and can be direct-connected to steam or gas turbines.   With electric motor or reciprocating-engine drivers, they are usually driven through a speed-increasing gear.   Because they are smaller and lighter than positive-displacement compressors, for an equivalent gas volume, they require less floor space, the foundations are reduced, and they can be serviced by lighter cranes.   They also operate without flow pulsations and therefore do not need receivers to even out the flow.   They have the additional advantages of not adding oil to the gas stream, and can pass moisture or dirt particles with less damage.

Figure 6-57 shows an axial section through a multistage compressor.   The gas, in the inlet pipe, is picked up by the curved vanes and "thrown" outward from the wheel into the diffuser, leaving a lower gas pressure at the wheel inlet and thus permitting more gas to be forced in by the external pressure in the suction line.   The diffuser may be a single vaneless passage formed by the diaphragms surrounding the impeller, as shown in Fig. 6-57, or it may be subdivided by vanes into a number of parallel passages. Its purpose is to lower the gas velocity, thereby converting the kinetic energy into pressure.   After leaving the first-stage diffuser in a multistage compressor, the gas passes through the return guide vanes into the second-stage impeller where the process

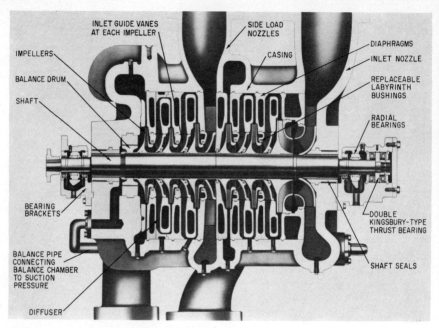

Fig. 6-57 Cross section of compressor with nozzles for intercooling.

is repeated.   As the gas passes through each stage, its pressure is further increased until it finally leaves at the discharge pressure of the unit.

Machines of the type in Fig. 6-57 are horizontally split at the centerline, to facilitate maintenance.   For higher pressures, the casings may be built as complete cylinders as shown in Fig. 6-58, and the internals are removed axially.   Other variations include reentry connections for external cooling and side-stream connections for adding or subtracting flow at intermediate points in the compression cycle.

For pressure ratios within the range of one impeller, single-stage designs are available.   A typical unit of this type, as provided for high-pressure gas-transmission pipelines, is shown in Fig. 6-59.

The flow in axial compressors is parallel to the machine axis and the compression cycle involves passing the gas through alternating rows of rotating and stationary blading.   In De Laval axials, the function of the stationary blades is only to give proper direction to the gas approaching each rotating stage.   This design, which is referred to as 100 percent reaction, has an exceptionally high efficiency and a broader stability range than generally found in other axials.   An axial compressor may also incorporate a final centrifugal stage to reduce the bearing span, and Fig. 6-60 illustrates such a machine.

Compression of Gases

The relationship between the volume, absolute pressure, and absolute temperature of a perfect gas, based upon Boyle's and Charles' laws, is

$$PV = WRT$$

where P = absolute pressure of gas, psf
V = volume of gas, cu ft
W = weight of gas, lb
T = absolute temperature, °F = 460° + temperature Fahrenheit
R = gas constant, ft-lb

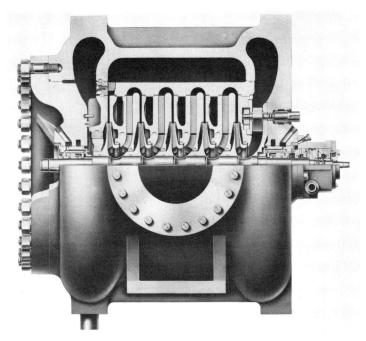

Fig. 6-58   Cross section of barrel compressor.

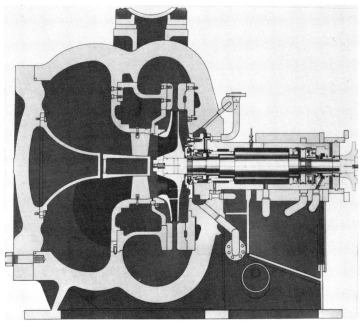

Fig. 6-59   Cross section of single-stage pipeline compressor.

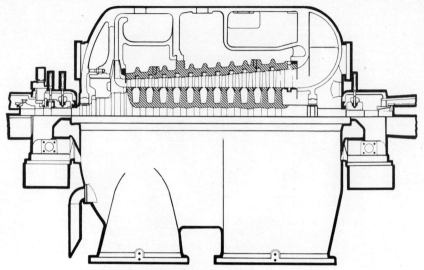

Fig. 6-60 Axial compressor.

The *specific heat* of a gas is the amount of heat in Btu required to raise the temperature of one pound of gas one degree Fahrenheit. If the volume of the gas is kept constant while the heat is added, all of the heat is used in increasing the internal energy, i.e., in raising the temperature. This specific heat at constant volume is denoted as c_v. If the pressure is kept constant and the volume is allowed to vary while the heat is added, more heat will be required. In addition to raising the temperature, the gas expands and external work equal to $1/778 \int P \, dV$ is done. This specific heat at constant pressure is called c_p.

The external work done when a pound of gas is heated at constant pressure $\int p \, dV$ is equal to the gas constant R, or

$$c_p - c_v = \frac{R}{778}$$

The ratio of the specific heat at constant pressure to the specific heat at constant volume is known as k. Hence, $k = c_p/c_v$. For air or perfect diatomic gases the commonly accepted value of k is 1.3947.

In the following discussion the subscripts i and f indicate the initial and final conditions of the gas, respectively.

If heat is neither added to nor removed from the gas during the compression, the process is said to be *isentropic*. The relationship between the pressure and volume follows the law $PV^k = $ a constant. The total work (Wk) in ft-lb done on one pound of gas is

$$Wk = 778c_p(T_f - T) = \frac{v_i P_i}{(k-1)/k} X = \frac{RT_i X}{(k-1)/k}$$

where $v_i = $ initial specific volume, cu ft/lb
$X = (P_f/P_i)^{k-1/k} - 1$

For air or perfect diatomic gases the value of $(k-1)/k$ is 0.283 and $R = 53.34$ so that the equations become

$$Wk = \frac{v_i P_i}{0.283} X = 188.5 T_i X$$

Values of $X = (P_f/P_i)^{0.283} - 1$ for air or perfect diatomic gases are given on pages 6-70 to 6-72 for various ratios of P_f/P_i.

It has been found that for all gases, the gas constant R in ft-lb/(lb)(°F) is equal to 1.544/M, where M is the molecular weight of the gas. The specific gravity of air by definition is unity, and its molecular weight is 28.95. Hence, the specific gravity of any gas or mixture having a molecular weight M is $M/28.95$. R for any gas is then 53.34/sg, where sg = specific gravity.

Work in a compressor is commonly called *head*, and the equation for head becomes

$$\text{Head} = \frac{53.34 T_i X}{(k-1)/k \times sg} \quad \text{ft-lb/lb}$$

The foregoing equation, however, is true for perfect gases only. Because many gases do not obey the theoretical gas law exactly, their deviation must be accounted for. This deviation is termed *compressibility* Z and is defined as the ratio of actual gas volume at a given temperature and pressure to the volume calculated by the theoretical law. Adding this correction, the general equation for work becomes

$$H(\text{head}) = \frac{53.34 Z T_i X}{(k-1)/k \times sg} \quad \text{ft-lb/lb}$$

The final temperature after compression may be found from the equation

$$T_f = T_i + \frac{T_i X}{\eta}$$

where η = isentropic efficiency

Multiplying the work done on one pound of gas, or head, by the number of pounds of gas compressed per minute w and dividing by 33,000 gives the horsepower.

$$\text{hp}_{\text{isen}} = \frac{wH}{33,000\eta}$$

If the inlet volume flow in cfm is Q_i and the absolute inlet pressure in psi is P_i, the equation for isentropic air horsepower becomes

$$\text{hp}_{\text{isen}} = 0.01542 Q_i P_i X$$

By abstracting heat from the gas during the compression, the temperature may be held constant, and the process is called *isothermal*. The relationship between the pressure and volume is PV = a constant. The work done per pound of gas or head in feet is

$$Wk = P_i v_i \log_e \frac{P_f}{P_i} = RT_i \log_e \frac{P_f}{P_i}°$$

The isothermal air horsepower for an inlet volume flow of Q_i cfm and an absolute inlet pressure of P_i psi is

$$\text{hp} = 0.004363 P_i Q_i \log_e \frac{P_f}{P_i} = 0.01005 P_i Q_i \log_{10} \frac{P_f}{P_i}$$

The ratio of the isentropic work to the actual work is known as the *isentropic efficiency*, while the ratio of the isothermal work to the actual work is the *isothermal efficiency*.

Uncooled compressors are figured on an isentropic basis. Occasionally on compressors with cooling the isothermal process may be used, so that the ratio between the two efficiencies or amounts of work to be done on the two bases may be desired. This is

$$\frac{\eta_{\text{isen}}}{\eta_{\text{iso}}} = \frac{Wk_{\text{isen}}}{Wk_{\text{iso}}} = \frac{X}{[(k-1)/k] \log_e (P_f/P_i)}$$

° $\log_e = 2.3026 \log_{10}$. Values of $\log_{10}$ are given on pages 1-18 and 1-19.

This relationship is plotted in curve form in Fig. 6-61 for various pressure ratios of air. It also illustrates the increased work required to compress air isentropically rather than isothermally.

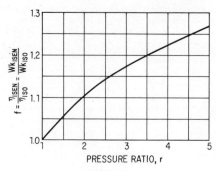

Fig. 6-61

Polytropic Process   The actual compression curve seldom follows either the isentropic or isothermal process but is generally of the form $PV^n = $ a constant.   In such cases the work in ft-lb/lb required for compression is given by

$$Wk = v_i P_i \frac{n}{n-1} X_n = RT_i \frac{n}{n-1} X_n$$

where n is the exponent of polytropic compression.   The factor $(n-1)/n$ may be found from the relation

$$\frac{n-1}{n} = \frac{k-1}{k} \frac{1}{\eta_p}$$

where η_p is the polytropic efficiency.
    Therefore,

$$X_n = r^{n-1/n} - 1$$

where $r = P_f/P_i$

    For the same actual performance, the value of the polytropic efficiency will be somewhat higher than the isentropic (adiabatic) efficiency.   Both efficiency values are used by the industry as a basis for evaluating compressor performance.   A comparison of the values is shown in Fig. 6-62.

Compressibility

    The relationship of specific volume to pressure and temperature for a perfect gas is defined by the equation $Pv = RT$ for one pound of the gas.   Therefore,

$$\text{Specific volume } v = \frac{RT}{P} = \frac{RT}{P_1 \times 144} \qquad \text{cu ft/lb}$$

where p_i is the pressure in psia.   Many gases do not obey the theoretical law exactly. The deviation is referred to as compressibility and is stated as a ratio of actual gas volume at a given temperature and pressure to the volume calculated by the theoretical law, in which case

$$v = \frac{ZRT}{P_1 \times 144}$$

where $Z = $ compressibility factor

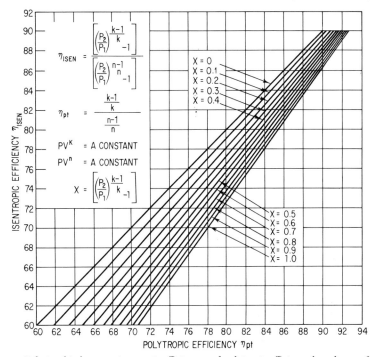

Fig. 6-62 Relationship between isentropic efficiency and polytropic efficiency based on perfect gas.

The deviation, or compressibility factor, is calculated by using ratios of actual temperature and pressure to critical temperature and pressure, which are defined respectively as

$$\text{Reduced temperature } T_R = \frac{T}{T_c}$$

$$\text{Reduced pressure } P_R = \frac{P_1}{P_c}$$

Values of the critical constants T_c and P_c for individual gases are given in Table 6-3, Physical Constants of Gases, page 6-75. As an example, T_R and P_R for a gas mixture with a volumetric composition of 14 percent ethane, 85 percent methane, and 1 percent nitrogen are calculated as follows:

Gas	V vol. %	T_c	VT_c	P_c	VP_c
C_2H_6	14	550.09	77.01	708.3	99.16
CH_4	85	343.5	292.00	673.1	572.19
N_2	1	227.2	002.27	492.0	4.92
		For mixture $T_c = 371.28$		$P_c = 676.27$	

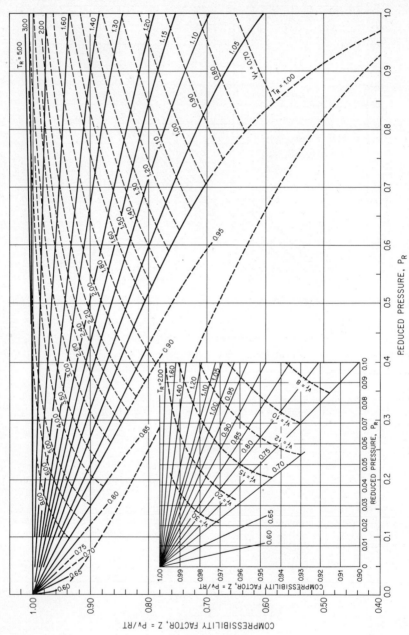

Fig. 6-63 Gas-compressibility factor in function of reduced pressure P_R.

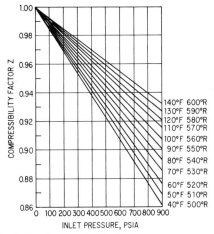

Fig. 6-64 Compressibility factor of natural gas.

Using the above values of T_c and P_c and assuming the gas at conditions of 100°F and 350 psia,

$$T_R = \frac{100 + 460}{371.27} = 1.507$$

$$P_R = \frac{350}{675.02} = 0.517$$

When the reduced temperature and reduced pressure have been found, the compressibility may be taken from the curves in Fig. 6-63. For the foregoing example it will be found that $Z = 0.95$.

Figure 6-64 gives the values of the supercompressibility factor Z as a function of the temperature and pressure for a typical natural gas.

Properties of Gas Mixtures

Before a compression cycle can be calculated, it is first necessary to know the specific-heat ratio k, molecular weight M, and compressibility Z of the gas to be compressed. For a pure gas or air, these can be taken directly from Table 6-3, page 6-75. For a gas mixture these properties must be calculated.

The chemical composition of the mixture is customarily given on a volumetric (rather than weight) basis and may be so considered unless otherwise specified. The properties of the mixture are determined by the composite properties of the constituent gases. Each constituent exerts a partial pressure which is determined by the amount of the constituent, the volume occupied, and the temperature, just as if the constituent alone were present. The total pressure is the sum of the partial pressures exerted separately by the constituents. The partial pressures are the same fractions of the total pressure as the volumes of the constituents, as given by a volumetric analysis, are of the whole volume.

The specific heats are the same for each constituent as if it alone were present. The values of the specific heats of the mixture are equal to the summation of the products of the proportional weight of each constituent and its specific heat; i.e.,

$$CG = c_1 g_1 + c_2 g_2 + \text{etc.}$$

where G = weight of mixture
C = specific heat of mixture
c_1, c_2, etc. = specific heats of constituents
g_1, g_2, etc. = percentage weights of constituents

VALUES OF X FOR NORMAL AIR AND PERFECT DIATOMIC GASES

$$X = \left(\frac{P_f}{P_i}\right)^{0.283} - 1 \qquad \text{Let } r = \frac{P_f}{P_i}$$

r	0	1	2	3	4	5	6	7	8	9
1.00	.00 000	028	057	085	113	141	169	198	226	254
1.01	282	310	338	366	394	422	450	478	506	534
1.02	562	590	618	646	673	701	729	757	785	812
1.03	840	868	895	923	951	978	006	034	061	089
1.04	.01 116	144	171	199	226	253	281	308	336	363
1.05	390	418	445	472	500	527	554	581	608	636
1.06	663	690	717	744	771	798	825	852	879	906
1.07	933	960	987	014	041	068	095	122	148	175
1.08	.02 202	229	255	282	309	336	362	389	416	442
1.09	469	495	522	549	575	602	628	655	681	708
1.10	734	760	787	813	840	866	892	919	945	971
1.11	997	024	050	076	102	129	155	181	207	233
1.12	.03 259	285	311	337	363	389	415	441	467	493
1.13	519	545	571	597	623	649	675	700	726	752
1.14	778	804	829	855	881	906	932	958	983	009
1.15	.04 035	060	086	111	137	162	188	213	239	264
1.16	290	315	341	366	391	417	442	467	493	518
1.17	543	569	594	619	644	670	695	720	745	770
1.18	796	821	846	871	896	921	946	971	996	021
1.19	.05 046	071	096	121	146	171	196	221	245	270
1.20	295	320	345	370	394	419	444	469	493	518
1.21	543	567	592	617	641	666	691	715	740	764
1.22	789	813	838	862	887	911	936	960	985	009
1.23	.06 034	058	082	107	131	155	180	204	228	253
1.24	277	301	325	350	374	398	422	446	470	495
1.25	519	543	567	591	615	639	663	687	711	735
1.26	759	783	807	831	855	879	903	927	951	974
1.27	998	022	046	070	094	117	141	165	189	212
1.28	.07 236	260	283	307	331	354	378	402	425	449
1.29	472	496	520	543	567	590	614	637	661	684
1.30	708	731	754	778	801	825	848	871	895	918
1.31	941	965	988	011	035	058	081	104	128	151
1.32	.08 174	197	220	243	267	290	313	336	359	382
1.33	405	428	451	474	497	520	543	566	589	612
1.34	635	658	681	704	727	750	773	795	818	841
1.35	864	887	910	932	955	978	001	023	046	069
1.36	.09 092	114	137	160	182	205	228	250	273	295
1.37	318	341	363	386	408	431	453	476	498	521
1.38	543	566	588	611	633	655	678	700	723	745
1.39	767	790	812	834	857	879	901	923	946	968
1.40	990	012	035	057	079	101	123	145	168	190
1.41	.10 212	234	256	278	300	322	344	366	389	411
1.42	433	455	477	499	521	542	564	586	608	630
1.43	652	674	696	718	740	761	783	805	827	849
1.44	871	892	914	936	958	979	001	023	045	066
1.45	.11 088	110	131	153	175	196	218	239	261	283
1.46	304	326	347	369	412	433	455	476	498	
1.47	520	541	562	584	605	627	648	669	691	712
1.48	734	755	776	798	819	840	862	883	904	925
1.49	947	968	989	010	032	053	074	095	116	138

r	0	1	2	3	4	5	6	7	8	9
1.50	.12 159	180	201	222	243	264	286	307	328	349
1.51	370	391	412	433	454	475	496	517	538	559
1.52	580	601	622	643	664	685	706	726	747	768
1.53	789	810	831	852	872	893	914	935	956	977
1.54	997	018	039	060	080	101	122	142	163	184
1.55	.13 205	225	246	266	287	308	328	349	370	390
1.56	411	431	452	472	493	513	534	554	575	595
1.57	616	636	657	677	698	718	739	759	780	800
1.58	820	841	861	881	902	922	942	963	983	003
1.59	.14 024	044	064	085	105	125	145	165	186	206
1.60	226	246	267	287	307	327	347	367	387	408
1.61	428	448	468	488	508	528	548	568	588	608
1.62	628	648	668	688	708	728	748	768	788	808
1.63	828	848	868	888	908	928	948	968	988	007
1.64	.15 027	047	067	087	107	126	146	166	186	206
1.65	225	245	265	284	304	324	344	363	383	403
1.66	423	442	462	481	501	521	540	560	580	599
1.67	619	638	658	678	697	717	736	756	775	795
1.68	814	834	853	873	892	912	931	951	970	990
1.69	.16 009	028	048	067	087	106	125	145	164	184
1.70	203	222	242	261	280	299	319	338	357	377
1.71	396	415	434	454	473	492	511	531	550	569
1.72	588	607	626	646	665	684	703	722	741	760
1.73	780	799	818	837	856	875	894	913	932	951
1.74	970	989	008	027	046	065	084	103	122	141
1.75	.17 160	179	198	217	236	255	274	292	311	330
1.76	349	368	387	406	425	443	462	481	500	519
1.77	538	556	575	594	613	631	650	669	688	706
1.78	725	744	762	781	800	818	837	856	874	893
1.79	912	930	949	968	986	005	023	042	061	079
1.80	.18 098	116	135	153	172	191	209	228	246	265
1.81	283	302	320	339	357	376	394	412	431	449
1.82	468	486	505	523	541	560	578	596	615	633
1.83	652	670	688	707	725	743	762	780	798	816
1.84	835	853	871	890	908	926	944	962	981	999
1.85	.19 017	035	054	072	090	108	126	144	163	181
1.86	199	217	235	253	271	289	308	326	344	362
1.87	380	398	416	434	452	470	488	506	524	542
1.88	560	578	596	614	632	650	668	686	704	722
1.89	740	758	776	794	811	829	847	865	883	901
1.90	919	937	954	972	990	008	026	044	061	079
1.91	.20 097	115	133	150	168	186	204	221	239	257
1.92	275	292	310	328	345	363	381	399	416	434
1.93	452	469	487	504	522	540	557	575	593	610
1.94	628	645	663	681	698	716	733	751	768	786
1.95	804	821	839	856	874	891	909	926	944	961
1.96	979	996	013	031	048	066	083	101	118	135
1.97	.21 153	170	188	205	222	240	257	275	292	309
1.98	327	344	361	379	396	413	431	448	465	482
1.99	500	517	534	552	569	586	603	620	638	655

Reprinted from Moss and Smith, Engineering Computations for Air and Gases, *Transactions of the American Society of Mechanical Engineers*, APM-52-8, 1930.

VALUES OF X FOR NORMAL AIR AND PERFECT DIATOMIC GASES (Continued)

$$X = \left(\frac{P_f}{P_i}\right)^{0.283} - 1 \qquad \text{Let } r = \frac{P_f}{P_i}$$

r	0	1	2	3	4	5	6	7	8	9
2.00	.21 672	689	707	724	741	758	775	792	810	827
2.01	844	861	878	895	913	930	947	964	981	998
2.02	.22 015	032	049	066	084	101	118	135	152	169
2.03	186	203	220	237	254	271	288	305	322	339
2.04	356	373	390	407	424	441	458	474	491	508
2.05	525	542	559	576	593	610	627	644	660	677
2.06	694	711	728	745	762	778	795	812	829	846
2.07	863	879	896	913	930	946	963	980	997	013
2.08	.23 030	047	064	080	097	114	130	147	164	181
2.09	197	214	231	247	264	281	297	314	331	347
2.10	364	380	397	414	430	447	463	480	497	513
2.11	530	546	563	579	596	613	629	646	662	679
2.12	695	712	728	745	761	778	794	811	827	844
2.13	860	877	893	909	926	942	959	975	992	008
2.14	.24 024	041	057	074	090	106	123	139	155	172
2.15	188	204	221	237	253	270	286	302	319	335
2.16	351	368	384	400	416	433	449	465	481	498
2.17	514	530	546	563	579	595	611	627	644	660
2.18	676	692	708	724	741	757	773	789	805	821
2.19	838	854	870	886	902	918	934	950	966	983
2.20	999	015	031	047	063	079	095	111	127	143
2.21	.25 159	175	191	207	223	239	255	271	287	303
2.22	319	335	351	367	383	399	415	431	447	463
2.23	479	495	511	526	542	558	574	590	606	622
2.24	638	654	669	685	701	717	733	749	765	780
2.25	796	812	828	844	859	875	891	907	923	938
2.26	954	970	986	001	017	033	049	064	080	096
2.27	.26 112	127	143	159	175	190	206	222	237	253
2.28	269	284	300	316	331	347	363	378	394	409
2.29	425	441	456	472	488	503	519	534	550	566
2.30	581	597	612	628	643	659	675	690	706	721
2.31	737	752	768	783	799	814	830	845	861	876
2.32	892	907	923	938	954	969	984	000	015	031
2.33	.27 046	062	077	092	108	123	139	154	169	185
2.34	200	216	231	246	262	277	292	308	323	338
2.35	354	369	384	400	415	430	446	461	476	492
2.36	507	522	538	553	568	583	599	614	629	644
2.37	660	675	690	705	721	736	751	766	781	797
2.38	812	827	842	857	873	888	903	918	933	948
2.39	964	979	994	009	024	039	054	070	085	100
2.40	.28 115	130	145	160	175	190	205	220	236	251
2.41	266	281	296	311	326	341	356	371	386	401
2.42	416	431	446	461	476	491	506	521	536	551
2.43	566	581	596	611	626	641	656	671	686	701
2.44	716	730	745	760	775	790	805	820	835	850
2.45	865	879	894	909	924	939	954	969	984	998
2.46	.29 013	028	043	058	073	087	102	117	132	147
2.47	162	176	191	206	221	235	250	265	280	295
2.48	309	324	339	353	368	383	398	412	427	442
2.49	457	471	486	501	515	530	545	559	574	589

r	0	1	2	3	4	5	6	7	8	9
2.50	.29 604	618	633	647	662	677	691	706	721	735
2.51	750	765	779	794	808	823	838	852	867	881
2.52	896	911	925	940	954	969	984	998	013	027
2.53	.30 042	056	071	085	100	114	129	144	158	173
2.54	187	202	216	231	245	260	274	289	303	318
2.55	332	346	361	375	390	404	419	433	448	462
2.56	476	491	505	520	534	548	563	577	592	606
2.57	620	635	649	663	678	692	707	721	735	750
2.58	764	778	793	807	821	836	850	864	879	893
2.59	907	921	936	950	964	979	993	007	021	036
2.60	.31 050	064	079	093	107	121	136	150	164	178
2.61	193	207	221	235	249	264	278	292	306	320
2.62	335	349	363	377	391	405	420	434	448	462
2.63	476	490	505	519	533	547	561	575	589	603
2.64	618	632	646	660	674	688	702	716	730	744
2.65	759	773	787	801	815	829	843	857	871	885
2.66	899	913	927	941	955	969	983	997	011	025
2.67	.32 039	053	067	081	095	109	123	137	151	165
2.68	179	193	207	221	235	249	262	276	290	304
2.69	318	332	346	360	374	388	402	416	429	443
2.70	457	471	485	499	513	527	540	554	568	582
2.71	596	610	624	637	651	665	679	693	707	720
2.72	734	748	762	776	789	803	817	831	845	858
2.73	872	886	900	913	927	941	955	968	982	996
2.74	.33 010	023	037	051	065	078	092	106	119	133
2.75	147	161	174	188	202	215	229	243	256	270
2.76	284	297	311	325	338	352	366	379	393	407
2.77	420	434	448	461	475	488	502	516	529	543
2.78	556	570	584	597	611	624	638	651	665	679
2.79	692	706	719	733	746	760	773	787	801	814
2.80	828	841	855	868	882	895	909	922	936	949
2.81	963	976	990	003	017	030	044	057	070	084
2.82	.34 097	111	124	138	151	165	178	191	205	218
2.83	232	245	259	272	285	299	312	326	339	352
2.84	366	379	393	406	419	433	446	459	473	486
2.85	500	513	526	540	553	566	580	593	606	620
2.86	633	646	660	673	686	700	713	726	739	753
2.87	766	779	793	806	819	832	846	859	872	886
2.88	899	912	925	939	952	965	978	991	005	018
2.89	.35 031	044	058	071	084	097	110	124	137	150
2.90	163	176	190	203	216	229	242	255	269	282
2.91	295	308	321	334	347	361	374	387	400	413
2.92	426	439	452	466	479	492	505	518	531	544
2.93	557	570	584	597	610	623	636	649	662	675
2.94	688	701	714	727	740	753	767	780	793	806
2.95	819	832	845	858	871	884	897	910	923	936
2.96	949	962	975	988	001	014	027	040	053	066
2.97	.36 079	092	105	118	131	144	157	169	182	195
2.98	208	221	234	247	260	273	286	299	312	324
2.99	337	350	363	376	389	402	415	428	440	453

VALUES OF X FOR NORMAL AIR AND PERFECT DIATOMIC GASES (Continued)

$$X = \left(\frac{P_f}{P_i}\right)^{0.283} - 1 \qquad \text{Let } r = \frac{P_f}{P_i}$$

r	0	1	2	3	4	5	6	7	8	9
3.0	0.3647	0.3659	0.3672	0.3685	0.3698	0.3711	0.3723	0.3736	0.3749	0.3761
3.1	0.3774	0.3786	0.3799	0.3811	0.3824	0.3836	0.3849	0.3861	0.3874	0.3886
3.2	0.3898	0.3911	0.3923	0.3935	0.3947	0.3959	0.3971	0.3984	0.3996	0.4008
3.3	0.4020	0.4032	0.4044	0.4056	0.4068	0.4080	0.4091	0.4103	0.4115	0.4127
3.4	0.4139	0.4150	0.4162	0.4174	0.4186	0.4197	0.4209	0.4220	0.4232	0.4244
3.5	0.4255	0.4267	0.4278	0.4290	0.4301	0.4313	0.4324	0.4335	0.4347	0.4358
3.6	0.4369	0.4380	0.4392	0.4403	0.4414	0.4425	0.4437	0.4448	0.4459	0.4470
3.7	0.4481	0.4492	0.4503	0.4514	0.4525	0.4536	0.4547	0.4558	0.4569	0.4580
3.8	0.4591	0.4602	0.4612	0.4623	0.4634	0.4645	0.4656	0.4666	0.4677	0.4688
3.9	0.4698	0.4709	0.4720	0.4730	0.4741	0.4752	0.4762	0.4773	0.4783	0.4794
4.0	0.4804	0.4815	0.4825	0.4835	0.4846	0.4856	0.4867	0.4877	0.4887	0.4898
4.1	0.4908	0.4918	0.4928	0.4939	0.4949	0.4959	0.4970	0.4980	0.4990	0.5000
4.2	0.5010	0.5020	0.5030	0.5040	0.5050	0.5060	0.5070	0.5080	0.5090	0.5100
4.3	0.5110	0.5120	0.5130	0.5140	0.5150	0.5160	0.5170	0.5179	0.5189	0.5199
4.4	0.5209	0.5219	0.5228	0.5238	0.5248	0.5258	0.5267	0.5277	0.5287	0.5296
4.5	0.5306	0.5316	0.5325	0.5335	0.5344	0.5354	0.5363	0.5373	0.5382	0.5392
4.6	0.5401	0.5411	0.5420	0.5430	0.5439	0.5449	0.5458	0.5467	0.5477	0.5486
4.7	0.5495	0.5505	0.5514	0.5523	0.5533	0.5542	0.5551	0.5560	0.5570	0.5579
4.8	0.5588	0.5597	0.5606	0.5616	0.5625	0.5634	0.5643	0.5652	0.5661	0.5670
4.9	0.5679	0.5688	0.5697	0.5706	0.5715	0.5724	0.5733	0.5742	0.5751	0.5760
5.0	0.5769	0.5778	0.5787	0.5796	0.5805	0.5814	0.5822	0.5831	0.5840	0.5849
5.1	0.5858	0.5867	0.5875	0.5884	0.5893	0.5902	0.5910	0.5919	0.5928	0.5936
5.2	0.5945	0.5954	0.5962	0.5971	0.5980	0.5988	0.5997	0.6006	0.6014	0.6023
5.3	0.6031	0.6040	0.6048	0.6057	0.6065	0.6074	0.6082	0.6091	0.6099	0.6108
5.4	0.6116	0.6125	0.6133	0.6142	0.6150	0.6159	0.6167	0.6175	0.6184	0.6192
5.5	0.6200	0.6209	0.6217	0.6225	0.6234	0.6242	0.6250	0.6258	0.6267	0.6275
5.6	0.6283	0.6291	0.6300	0.6308	0.6316	0.6324	0.6332	0.6340	0.6349	0.6357
5.7	0.6365	0.6373	0.6381	0.6389	0.6397	0.6405	0.6413	0.6421	0.6430	0.6438
5.8	0.6446	0.6454	0.6462	0.6470	0.6478	0.6486	0.6494	0.6502	0.6509	0.6517
5.9	0.6525	0.6533	0.6541	0.6549	0.6557	0.6565	0.6573	0.6581	0.6588	0.6596
6.0	0.6604	0.6612	0.6620	0.6628	0.6635	0.6643	0.6651	0.6659	0.6666	0.6674
6.1	0.6682	0.6690	0.6697	0.6705	0.6713	0.6721	0.6729	0.6736	0.6744	0.6752
6.2	0.6759	0.6767	0.6774	0.6782	0.6789	0.6797	0.6805	0.6812	0.6820	0.6827
6.3	0.6835	0.6843	0.6850	0.6858	0.6865	0.6873	0.6880	0.6888	0.6895	0.6903
6.4	0.6910	0.6918	0.6925	0.6933	0.6940	0.6948	0.6955	0.6963	0.6970	0.6978
6.5	0.6985	0.6992	0.7000	0.7007	0.7014	0.7021	0.7028	0.7036	0.7043	0.7050
6.6	0.7058	0.7065	0.7073	0.7080	0.7087	0.7095	0.7102	0.7110	0.7117	0.7124
6.7	0.7131	0.7138	0.7145	0.7153	0.7160	0.7167	0.7174	0.7181	0.7189	0.7196
6.8	0.7203	0.7210	0.7217	0.7224	0.7232	0.7239	0.7246	0.7253	0.7260	0.7267
6.9	0.7274	0.7281	0.7288	0.7295	0.7302	0.7309	0.7316	0.7323	0.7330	0.7338
7.0	0.7345	0.7352	0.7359	0.7366	0.7373	0.7380	0.7386	0.7393	0.7400	0.7407
7.1	0.7414	0.7421	0.7428	0.7435	0.7442	0.7449	0.7456	0.7463	0.7470	0.7477
7.2	0.7483	0.7490	0.7497	0.7504	0.7511	0.7518	0.7524	0.7531	0.7538	0.7545
7.3	0.7552	0.7559	0.7565	0.7572	0.7579	0.7586	0.7592	0.7599	0.7606	0.7613
7.4	0.7620	0.7626	0.7633	0.7640	0.7646	0.7653	0.7660	0.7666	0.7673	0.7680
7.5	0.7687	0.7693	0.7700	0.7706	0.7713	0.7720	0.7726	0.7733	0.7740	0.7746
7.6	0.7753	0.7760	0.7766	0.7773	0.7779	0.7786	0.7792	0.7799	0.7806	0.7812
7.7	0.7819	0.7825	0.7832	0.7838	0.7845	0.7851	0.7858	0.7864	0.7871	0.7877
7.8	0.7884	0.7890	0.7897	0.7903	0.7910	0.7916	0.7923	0.7929	0.7936	0.7942
7.9	0.7949	0.7955	0.7961	0.7968	0.7974	0.7981	0.7987	0.7993	0.8000	0.8006

In a similar manner, the molecular weight of the mixture is equal to the summation of the products of the proportional volume of each constituent and its molecular weight; i.e.,

$$MV = m_1v_1 + m_2v_2 + \text{etc.}$$

where M = molecular weight of mixture
        V = total volume
m_1, m_2, etc. = molecular weights of constituents
v_1, v_2, etc. = volumes of constituents

The molecular weight of a gaseous substance is the weight in pounds that will occupy 379 cu ft at 14.7 psia and 60°F.

The calculation of the properties of a mixture can best be done in tabular form.   To illustrate, determine the properties of natural gas having the following volumetric percentage composition: 14 percent ethane, 85 percent methane, and 1 percent nitrogen.

Gas	v vol. %	m mol. wt.	vm	$\% G = \dfrac{vm}{M}$	C_p	$\% GC_p$	C_v	$\% GC_v$
C_2H_6.	0.14	30.07	4.21	0.233	0.397	0.0926	0.325	0.0758
CH_4	0.85	16.04	13.63	0.752	0.593	0.4459	0.451	0.3392
N_2	0.01	28.02	0.28	0.015	0.244	0.0037	0.173	0.0026
Total . . .	1.00		$M = 18.12$	1.000		$C_p = 0.5422$		$C_v = 0.4176$

Molecular weight = 18.12   Specific gravity $= \dfrac{M}{28.95} = \dfrac{18.12}{28.95} = 0.626$

Mixture specific heat at constant pressure = 0.5422
Mixture specific heat at constant volume = 0.4176

$$R = \frac{1{,}544}{M} = \frac{1{,}544}{18.12} = 85.2$$

$$k = \frac{C_p}{C_v} = \frac{0.5422}{0.4176} = 1.298$$

$$\frac{k-1}{k} = \frac{1.298-1}{1.298} = 0.231$$

A simplified method for finding k makes use of the molal specific heat Mc_p, as expressed in the following relationship:

$$k = \frac{Mc_p}{Mc_p - 1.99}$$

With this formula it is necessary to know only the value of Mc_p for a gas or a gas mixture in order to calculate its k value, and c_v can be disregarded.   The specific heat of a gas varies somewhat with temperature.   Table 6-3 of gas properties gives the value of Mc_p for various gases at 60°F, 100°F, and 200°F.   Since the calculated head varies only slightly with changes in k value, it is sufficient for most applications to use Mc_p at 60°F. On applications where an accurate value of discharge temperature is required, however, such as a process where polymerization may occur, the Mc_p values should be estimated based on the average temperature of the compression cycle.   A straight-line interpolation of Mc_p values can be made for temperatures not given in Table 6-3. The k value of the same gas mixture used in the previous example may be calculated in tabular form as illustrated below:

Gas	V vol. %	Mc_p at 60°F	$V \times Mc_p$
C_2H_6	14	12.32	1.725
CH_4	85	8.46	7.191
N_2	1	6.95	0.069
	100		8.985

$$k = \frac{8.985}{8.985 - 1.99} = \frac{8.985}{6.995} = 1.284$$

Compressor Performance

The relationships between inlet volume, head, speed, and horsepower of a dynamic compressor are referred to as its characteristic. These relationships are illustrated on a percentage basis for a typical centrifugal compressor by Fig. 6-65 and for a De Laval axial by Fig. 6-66.

The characteristic curve shows that as the resistance on the discharge increases

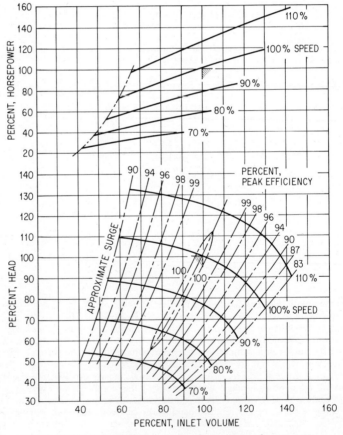

Fig. 6-65 Typical multistage centrifugal compressor characteristic.

TABLE 6-3   Physical Constants of Gases

Compound	Formula	Mol. wt. M	c_p and c_p/c_v at 14.7 psia and 60°F		Critical constants		Mc_p at 60°F	Mc_p at 100°F	Mc_p at 200°F
			c_p	c_p/c_v	Pressure, psia P_c	Temp, °R T_c			
Acetylene	C_2H_2	26.036	0.3966	1.238	905.0	557.4	10.33	10.69	11.53
Air	N^+O_2	28.966	0.2470	1.395	547	238.7	6.96	6.96	6.99
Ammonia	NH_3	17.032	0.5232	1.310	1,657	731.4	8.91	8.57	9.02
Benzene	C_6H_6	78.108	0.2404	1.118	714	1,013.0	18.78	20.47	24.46
1,2-Butadiene . . .	C_4H_6	54.088	(0.3458)	(1.12)	653	799.0	18.70		
1,3-Butadiene . . .	C_4H_6	54.088	(0.3412)	1.12	628	766.0	18.45		
N-Butane	C_4H_{10}	58.120	0.3970	1.094	550.7	765.6	23.07	24.51	26.16
Isobutane	C_4H_{10}	58.120	0.3872	1.097	529.1	734.9	22.50	23.96	27.62
N-Butene	C_4H_8	56.104	0.3703	1.105	583	755.6	20.77	22.09	25.18
Isobutene	C_4H_8	56.104	0.3701	1.106	579.8	752.5	20.76		
Butylene	C_4H_8	56.104	0.3703	1.105	583	755.6	20.78	21.94	24.86
Carbon dioxide . .	CO_2	44.010	0.1991	1.300	1,073	548.0	8.76	9.00	9.35
Carbon monoxide .	CO	28.010	0.2484	1.403	510	242.0	6.96	6.96	6.98
Chlorine	Cl_2	70.914	0.1149	1.366	1,120	751	8.15		
Ethane	C_2H_6	30.068	0.4097	1.193	708.3	550.1	12.32	12.96	14.68
Ethyl alcohol	C_2H_5OH	46.069	0.3070	1.130	927.0	929.6	14.14		
Ethylene	C_2H_4	28.052	0.3622	1.243	742.1	509.8	10.16	10.68	12.08
N-Hexane	C_6H_{14}	86.172	0.3984	(1.062)	439.7	914.5	34.33	36.23	41.08
Helium	He	4.003	1.2480	1.6598	480	510	5.00		
Hydrogen	H_2	2.016	3.408	1.408	188.0	60.2	6.87	6.90	6.95
Hydrogen sulfide .	H_2S	34.076	0.254	1.323	1,306	672.7	8.66	8.18	8.36
Methane	CH_4	16.042	0.5271	1.311	673.1	343.5	8.46	8.65	9.30
Methyl alcohol . . .	CH_3OH	32.042	0.2700	1.203	1,157.0	924.0	8.65		
Nitrogen	N_2	28.016	0.2482	1.402	492.0	227.2	6.95	6.96	6.963
N-Octane	C_8H_{18}	114.224	0.3998	(1.046)	362.1	1,025.2	45.67		
Oxygen	O_2	32.00	0.2188	1.401	730	278.2	7.00	7.03	7.120
N-Pentane	C_5H_{12}	72.146	0.3972	1.074	489.5	845.9	28.66	30.30	34.41
Isopentane	C_5H_{12}	72.146	0.3880	1.075	483.0	830.0	27.99	29.90	34.44
Propane	C_3H_8	44.094	0.3885	1.136	617.4	666.2	17.13	18.21	20.90
Propylene	C_3H_6	42.078	0.3541	1.154	667	657.4	14.90	15.77	17.88
Sulfur dioxide . .	SO_2	64.060	0.1470	1.246	1,142	775.0	9.42		
Toluene	C_7H_8	92.134	0.2599	1.091	611	1,069.5	23.95		
Water	H_2O	18.016	0.4446	1.335	3,206	1,165.4	8.01	8.03	8.12
Hydrogen chloride	HCl	36.465	0.1939	1.410	1,199.2	584.5	7.07		

(speed remaining constant), the volume decreases until a peak head is reached.   This is the *surge* or *pumping point*.   At this point, a flow reversal takes place and the flow from the machine pulsates.   Operation of a dynamic compressor is, thereby, limited to flows greater than the surge volume.

NOTE: The stability range for the sample performance curves in Fig. 6-65 would be that expected from a compressor with five or fewer stages.   For a greater number of stages, the following stable ranges would be typical:

No. of stages	"Surge" point, % flow
2–5	60
6	65
7	70
8	75
9	80

The effect of speed changes on centrifugal compressor performance is similar to that of pumps (page 6-11); i.e., the flow is directly proportional to the speed in rpm, the

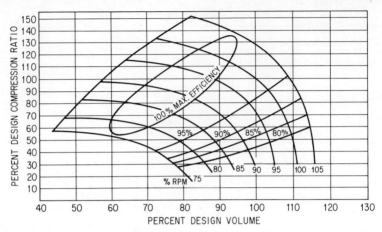

Fig. 6-66 Typical De Laval axial compressor characteristic.

head is proportional to the speed squared, and the horsepower to the speed cubed, while the efficiency remains practically constant.

Reducing the outside diameter of the impeller will have the approximate effect of reducing the flow directly, reducing the head in the ratio of the square of the diameters, and the horsepower in the ratio of the cubes, while the efficiency remains approximately constant.

It should be realized that the foregoing relationships will not be precise where the change in speed or diameter being considered is more than a small percentage of the known quantities, particularly in multistage centrifugal compressors. For example, it would be quite inaccurate to correct test data taken at half-speed to full-speed condition.

Effect of Varying Inlet Conditions   As has already been mentioned, the pressure delivered by any given dynamic unit depends on the density of the gas being compressed. This is demonstrated by Fig. 6-67 in which centrifugal characteristic curves for constant speed have been drawn for varying inlet conditions. Curve *FG* represents the characteristic for a centrifugal compressor designed to handle air at an inlet pressure of 14.4 psia, inlet temperature of 60°F, molecular weight of 28.95 (dry air), and k value of 1.398. This unit develops 15 psig at an inlet capacity of 20,000 cfm. If the inlet temperature increases to 100°F, all other conditions remaining the same, the discharge pressure developed at 20,000 cfm is 13.7 psig. Likewise, if the inlet pressure drops to 12.4 psia, but the inlet temperature and other conditions remain as first specified, the discharge pressure at 20,000 cfm is 12.9 psig. Further, if the molecular weight is the only variable, then with a 17.35-molecular-weight gas and 20,000 cfm, the discharge pressure developed will be 8.2 psig. A decrease in the k value to 1.15, all other conditions unchanged, will result in a discharge pressure of 16.4 psig.

Specific Speed

Specific speed is a term used to classify compressor impellers on the basis of their performance and proportions, regardless of their actual size or the speed at which they operate. Since specific speed is a function of impeller proportions, it is constant for any series of impellers having the same proportions and angles or for one particular impeller operating at any speed.

Specific speed can be defined as the speed in revolutions per minute at which an impeller would rotate if reduced proportionately in size so as to deliver one cubic foot of gas per minute against total head of one foot. It may be found from the equation

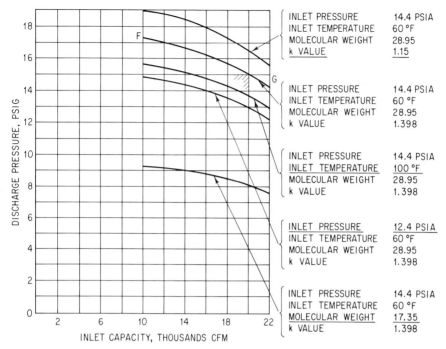

Fig. 6-67 Characteristic curves for a given centrifugal compressor.

$$\text{Specific speed } N_s = \frac{N \sqrt{Q}}{H^{3/4}}$$

where N = operating speed, rpm
Q = rated inlet capacity corresponding to maximum efficiency, cfm
H = total head per stage, ft, at capacity Q

It is not necessary to grasp the physical significance of the definition of specific speed to make use of it. It should be considered to be a type characteristic of the impeller which specifies its general proportions and characteristics rather than as an rpm for special conditions.

For double-suction impellers, the total flow through the compressor should be divided by 2 in calculating the specific speed; i.e., they should be considered to be two single-suction impellers operating in parallel.

Typical impeller proportions at various specific speeds may be visualized as shown in Fig. 6-69.

In general, the radial impeller will be used for specific speeds between 400 and 950 rpm. Below 400 rpm efficiency will suffer badly, deteriorating to less than 50 percent at 200 rpm.

From specific speeds of 800 to 1,500 rpm the mixed-flow impeller is used, and axial compressors operate in the 1,300 rpm and higher ranges.

Obviously, these ranges are overlapping, since specific speed is only a generalized guide to design. Its usefulness lies in providing an estimating evaluation of compatibility of compressor operating requirements and driver speed.

The chart in Fig. 6-68 may be used to find the specific speed of an impeller.

Figures 6-70, 6-71, and 6-72 show compressor rotors having different specific speeds.

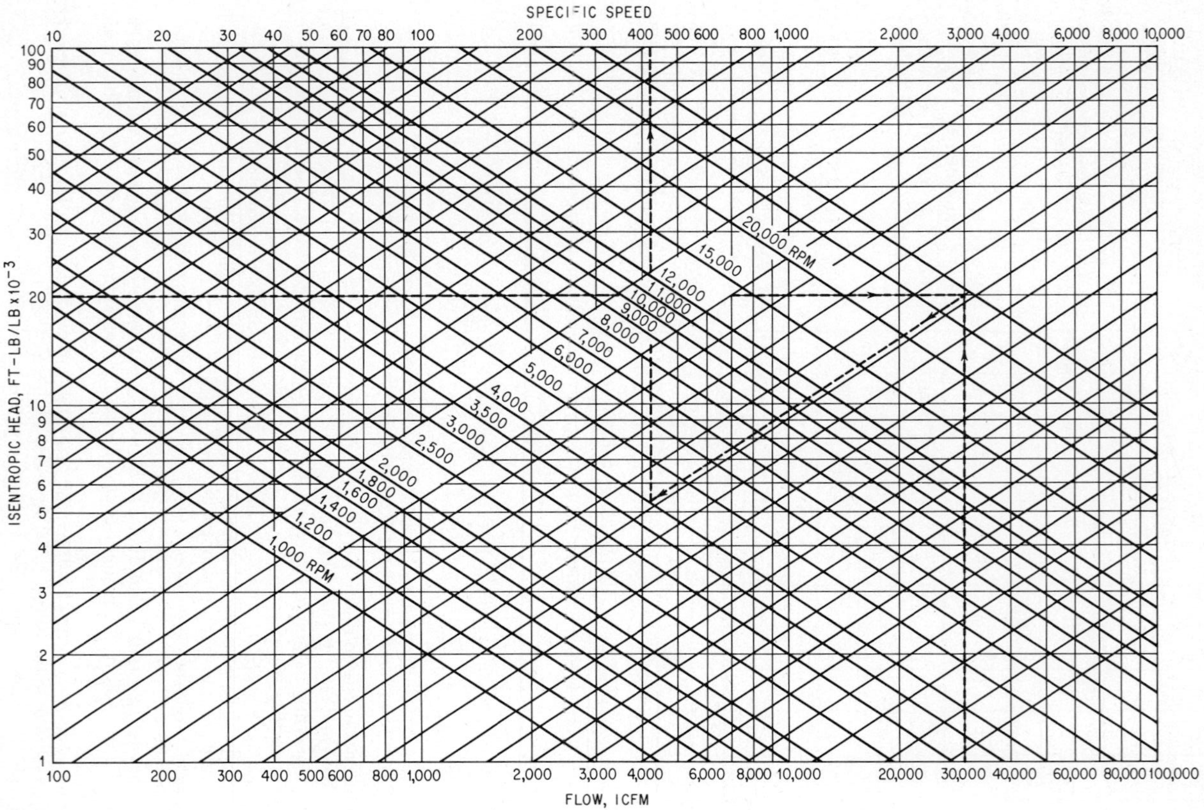

Fig. 6-68 Chart for determination of specific speed.

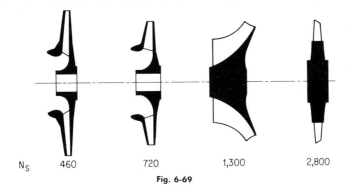

N_S 460   720   1,300   2,800

Fig. 6-69

Fig. 6-70   Typical small-capacity low-specific-speed multistage rotor.

Fig. 6-71   Combined mixed-flow and medium-specific-speed centrifugal-compressor rotor.

Fig. 6-72   Typical axial-compressor rotor.

Seals for Compressors

The many applications of rotary equipment handling air or gases require various methods for shaft sealing. Dynamic compressors and exhausters employ labyrinths, carbon rings, bushings, or contact seals either separately or in combination to effect the desired sealing.

Labyrinth Seals The labyrinth seal is the simplest, cheapest, and most reliable sealing device used. It consists of a series of annular orifices through which pressure breakdown is accomplished by dissipation of velocity head.

Three types are illustrated in Fig. 6-73: an axial straight-pass labyrinth (Fig. 6-73*a*); an axial staggered labyrinth (Fig. 6-73*b*); and a running-knife labyrinth (Fig. 6-73*c*). The straight-pass is used where pressures are relatively low, while the more efficient staggered labyrinth is preferred for higher pressures and/or where space limitations are important. The running-knife labyrinth is a straight-pass labyrinth which can be installed with small original clearance, and its performance approaches that of the staggered type.

Clearances selected for fixed labyrinth seals are governed by manufacturing tolerances, journal-bearing clearances, vibration of the rotor during operation, and relative thermal expansion of rotor and labyrinth through the operating temperature range. Minimum practicable radial clearances vary from a few thousandths of an inch for small seals to $^1/_{32}$ in. or more for very large seals. Where a large range of temperatures is encountered, a segmental labyrinth mounted on springs is used to maintain more nearly constant clearance as the temperature changes.

Carbon Rings Shown in Fig. 6-74 is a typical carbon ring seal in which each ring is characterized by a radial sealing surface, positive suspension within gland housing, and low operating clearance over the shaft. This design allows radial motion of the carbon ring when contacted by the shaft but maintains pressure between the ring and the radial sealing surface at all times.

The thermal coefficient of expansion of carbon is approximately one-fourth that of steel. Therefore, the hot clearance is in most cases less than the cold clearance. When determining the minimum practical clearance, consideration is given to the shaft deflection, transverse journal motion, and thermal deformation of shaft. Operating clearances of 0.003 to 0.004 in. on the diameter are usually feasible.

Leakage through well-made and properly mounted carbon rings will be 15 to 25 percent of the leakage from a well-designed knife-edge labyrinth utilizing the same shaft length. The ordinary laws of gas flow apply to carbon ring seals. Carbon rings, sealing clean gases having no highly oxidizing component, can be expected to give approximately 20,000 hr of satisfactory service. Dirt-laden atmosphere drastically reduces seal life.

Bushing Seals A bushing seal is, basically, simply a close-clearance sleeve surrounding the shaft. Sealing is effected by the sealing face between the end of the bushing and its housing, and by the restriction of the small clearance area between the sleeve and the shaft.

A typical bushing seal is illustrated in Fig. 6-75. Freedom of radial movement is inherent in the design, and motion in this plane occurs during start-up as the shaft journals rise in their bearings as well as in response to equalizing pressures from within the flow-path annulus.

Hydraulic pressure acting on exposed surfaces of the floating bushing exerts sufficient closing force to prevent leakage past the sealing face. Springs are provided to keep the bushing in place against the seal face until sufficient hydraulic pressure is applied.

The rate of liquid leakage through a bushing seal is a function of viscosity, temperature, differential pressure across the seal, seal geometry, and concentricity of shaft and seal. The rate of leakage will vary directly with the differential pressure and wetted perimeter, with the cube of the clearance and with the square of the eccentricity; and will vary inversely with viscosity and length. Shear work done on the sealing fluid during its passage through the bushing raises its temperature.

Clearance between the bushing and the shaft and the length of the bushing must be selected to obtain minimum leakage without exceeding temperature limitations for the fluid. Flatness, parallelism, and surface finish of the mating seal faces must also be carefully controlled to obtain maximum seal effectiveness.

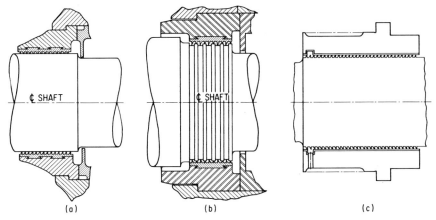

Fig. 6-73 Labyrinth types. (*a*) Axial straight-through labyrinth. (*b*) Axial staggered labyrinth. (*c*) Running-knife labyrinth.

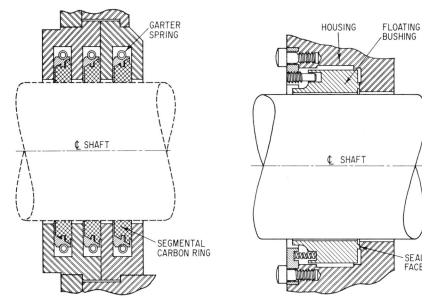

Fig. 6-74 Segmental carbon ring.

Fig. 6-75 Bushing seal.

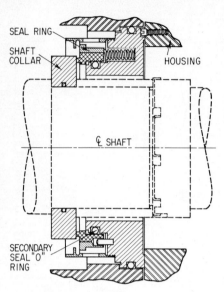

SEAL RING

SHAFT
COLLAR

HOUSING

℄ SHAFT

SECONDARY
SEAL "O"
RING

Fig. 6-76 Carbon face-contact seal.

Contact Seals A contact seal (Fig. 6-76) is a mechanical seal consisting of a rotating collar and a nonrotating seal ring. Contact between the collar and seal ring is maintained by calibrated springs and a small, designed closing force resulting from unbalanced hydraulic pressure acting on the exposed surfaces of the seal ring.

The seal ring is suspended so that it may float in both the radial and axial directions. This feature enables it to compensate for displacement of the collar due to rotor vibration, thermal expansion, or minute out-of-true location on the shaft.

An elastic O ring usually comprises the secondary sealing element between the seal ring and the stationary mounting piece. This element is carefully proportioned and mounted so as to offer minimum resistance to motion of the seal ring. In some cases, particularly for dry seals, an accurately fitted piston ring is used instead of the O ring.

The effectiveness of this type of seal depends upon the maintenance of parallelism and flatness of the mating faces on the collar and seal ring. The collar is made of stable, abrasion-resistant die steel. It is specially heat-treated and lapped to a surface flatness of 15×10^{-6} in. The seal ring is made of a refined grade of carbon, shrunk within a steel shroud. The ring is geometrically so contoured that dimensional stability is ensured and surface flatness preserved for long life.

Figure 6-77 shows a combination of an oil-contact seal and a bushing seal adapted for high-pressure sealing service.

Leakage Comparison The relative effectiveness of the several types of seal described for dry sealing may be seen from the following table:

Seal	Leakage index
Straight-pass labyrinth	100
Staggered labyrinth.	56
Segmental carbon rings	20
Dry contact	2

A typical contact oil seal, with a mean face diameter of 6¾ in. and a 30 psi differential pressure, operating at 5,000 rpm, will leak approximately 0.024 gal/hr. Under similar operating conditions, a ⅝-in.-long, 5½-in.-diameter bushing seal with 0.007-in. diametral clearance and an oil temperature rise of 60°F, will leak approximately 1¾ gal/hr. The diametral clearance in a bushing seal may be reduced to the point where the leakage approaches that of a contact seal, but the oil-temperature rise becomes so great that the leakage oil is unfit for further use and must be discarded.

Sealing Systems

Single Seals The simplest sealing system is one in which a single dry seal is used at the point where the compressor shaft emerges from the casing, or where the shaft passes between two internal chambers at different pressures. A certain amount of leakage is allowed, and the type of seal selected depends on the permissible leakage.

Evacuation Systems In an evacuation system two dry seals are employed at each sealing point and the chamber between these two seals is connected to an ejector which creates a low pressure in the chamber. Leakage through both seals is withdrawn and discarded or returned to the system at a lower-pressure location.

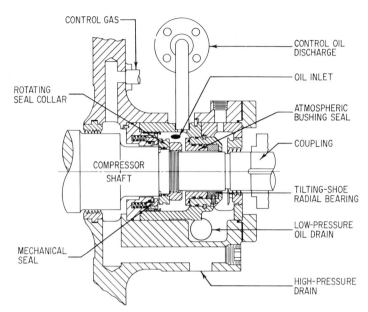

Fig. 6-77 Combination contact seal and bushing seal.

Figure 6-78 illustrates a typical gas-compressor evacuation system where the inner seals are labyrinths and the outer seals are carbon rings. The ejector is powered by gas from the discharge of the compressor and the evacuated gas and air mixtures from the seal chambers are returned to the compressor suction. The gas required to power the ejector and the evacuated leakage, all recirculated through the compressor, repre-

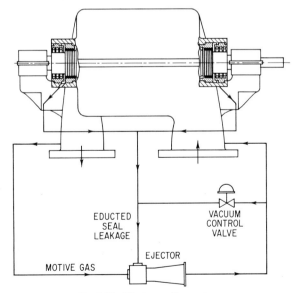

Fig. 6-78 Ejector sealing system.

sent a power loss which must be considered in selecting this type of system. The advantages of such a system are relatively low cost and a simple, self-contained system with few moving parts.

Injection Systems In an injection system two seals are again used at each sealing point, but in this case a sealing fluid is injected into the chamber between the seals at a pressure above that to be sealed. With dry seals the leakage from the seal chamber through the inner seal goes into the compressor, while the leakage from the seal chamber through the outer seal escapes to atmosphere. With wet seals the leakage in both directions is collected as it leaves the seals and returned to the system.

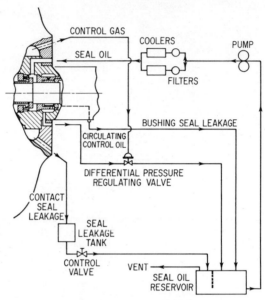

Fig. 6-79 Typical sealing system using injected medium between compressor gas and atmospheric seal.

Figure 6-79 illustrates a typical oil-injection seal for a high-pressure gas compressor. The inner seal, between the seal chamber and the compressor, is a wet-contact seal. The outer seal is a floating-bushing seal. Cooled and filtered oil is pumped into the seal chamber at a pressure slightly higher than the gas pressure in the compressor. A very small quantity of this oil leaks past the contact seal and is collected and returned to the reservoir through a high-pressure drain system. A larger quantity of oil leaks through the bushing seal to atmospheric pressure and is also drained back to the reservoir. Enough oil to maintain proper temperatures is circulated through the seal chamber at all times. This circulating oil is led out of the chamber, through a differential-pressure controller, and back to the reservoir.

In Fig. 6-79 the inward oil leakage through the contact seal is exposed to the compressed gas and may absorb appreciable amounts of this gas. In some applications this oil becomes contaminated and must be discarded rather than returned to the system. In such cases the extremely low leakage rates obtainable with the contact seal minimize the cost of replacing the discarded seal leakage. The outward leakage through the bushing seal is not exposed to the gas and is therefore not subject to contamination.

Governing of Compressors

In any compressor application it is generally necessary to install some type of regulating device in order to secure the desired performance. Governors may be designed to secure (1) constant inlet pressure, (2) constant discharge pressure, (3) constant inlet volume or weight flow, or (4) to control pulsation.

There are two general ways in which these control devices act, namely, by a change in speed of the unit or by throttling the flow at some point in the compressor.

If the driver can operate at a variable speed as is the case with a steam turbine, the most economical control will result since no power is lost in the throttling process.

If throttling is used with a constant-speed machine, it is possible to place the valve either at the inlet to the blower or in the discharge line. It is somewhat more economical to throttle the suction, since the density of the gas in the compressor will then be reduced slightly, resulting in lower power consumption.

Another method used on constant-speed units, which acts similarly to throttling, is to place movable guide vanes before the wheels. By changing the direction at which the air enters the wheel, the head, flow, and power consumption may be varied. This is known as *prerotation*.

When the flow of gas through a compressor is small, unstable operation, known as *pulsation*, occurs. The compressor delivers alternately large and small quantities of gas with varying pressure. Since this action puts a heavy strain on the compressor and the piping system, it should be avoided. This may be done by either manual or automatic governing. Pulsation will occur when the compressor is operated at flows less than those corresponding to the highest point on the head-capacity curve (known as the pulsation point).

For constant-speed machines, the use of a relief or blowoff valve in the discharge line provides a simple method of preventing pulsation. When the system demand falls below the critical flow, the valve is opened and sufficient air or gas is discharged to the atmosphere (or suction line) to bring the total flow through the compressor above the critical flow. Suction throttling, speed reduction, and prerotation may be used to reduce the pulsation point to a lower value.

References

Recommended additional references for centrifugal and axial compressors are as follows:

"Compressed Air and Gas Handbook," Compressed Air and Gas Institute, Griswold-Eshelman, Cleveland, Ohio.
ASME Power Test Code, PTC 10-1965, American Society of Mechanical Engineers, New York.
A. H. Church, "Centrifugal Pumps and Blowers," John Wiley & Sons, Inc., New York.
Compressed Air and Gas Institute Standards, Standards for Centrifugal Air Compressors, Standards for Basic Pressure Lube Systems for Centrifugal Air Compressors, Vibration Standard for Centrifugal and Axial Compressors, Compressed Air and Gas Institute, New York.
API Standard 617, Centrifugal Compressors for General Refinery Services, 2d ed., American Petroleum Institute, Division of Refining, New York.

RECIPROCATING COMPRESSORS

General

Reciprocating gas compressors are required for a great many widely varied industrial services. Their basic function is to raise the pressure level of the gas being compressed. Raising the pressure level is desirable for any of the following reasons:

Storage—natural-gas storage in natural underground reservoirs, bottled gases for industrial uses, shop air compression and storage.

Transmission—natural-gas-transmission pipelines.

Process—some chemical reactions take place at elevated pressures (example: ammonia synthesis at 5,000 psi).

Energy conversion—mechanical to thermal energy conversion (refrigeration systems).

Reciprocating compressors have inherent advantages over other compressors in their ability to adapt to a wide range of load, speed, pressure conditions, and pressure ratios ($P_{discharge}/P_{suction}$). The load may be varied from 0 to 100 percent; the speed may have a wide range, depending on the driver.

Pressures may vary from a few inches of mercury absolute suction pressure in the case of a vacuum pump to 30,000 psi or more discharge pressure for process-gas compressors.

Pressure ratios may vary from slightly over 1, in the case of natural-gas-transmission pipeline service, to 8 or more in the case of shop air compressors. Several stages of compression are often used when the overall pressure ratio is high.

There are many available prime movers suitable for driving reciprocating compressors. These include electric motors, turbines, natural-gas engines, diesel engines, and dual-fuel engines. Many electric motors and reciprocating engines have rotative speeds similar to the reciprocating compressors and can be direct-connected, eliminating speed reduction (or multiplication) between the prime mover and the compressor.

Description of an Ideal Compressor Cycle Positive-displacement compressors are machines in which successive volumes of gas are confined within a closed space and elevated to a higher pressure. The reciprocating compressor is a special type of positive-displacement compressor that elevates the pressure of the trapped gas by decreasing the volume that the trapped gas occupies. A piston moving in a cylinder is used to reduce the volume of the trapped gas (see Fig. 6-80).

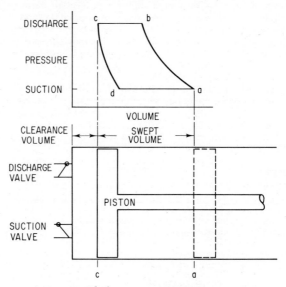

Fig. 6-80 Ideal compression cycle.

Compression $(a–b)$. The cylinder has filled with gas at the suction pressure with the piston at position a. The piston moves from a toward b, compressing the gas isentropically (no heat transfer and with no turbulent or frictional losses) until the pressure within the cylinder reaches the discharge-line pressure.

Discharge $(b–c)$. At this point the discharge valve opens and permits gas to flow from the cylinder into the discharge line until the piston has reached the end of its stroke at point c.

Expansion $(c–d)$. Since it is impossible to build a compressor with zero clearance volume, there is gas remaining in the cylinder's clearance volume at the end of the discharge stroke. The gas remaining expands isentropically to suction pressure as the piston moves from c to d.

Suction $(d–a)$. When the pressure within the cylinder reaches the suction pressure, the suction valve opens and permits gas at suction pressure to enter as the piston moves from d to a.

Since points b and d are determined by the pressures during the cycle, the cycle is described as having a suction stroke (piston moves from c to a) and a discharge stroke (piston moves from a to c).

Compressor Arrangements and Their Application

Small air compressors are usually single-acting while most of the higher-horsepower units are double-acting. Double-acting compressors have pistons that compress gas on both ends, so that one end is on its suction stroke while the other end is on its discharge stroke (see Figs. 6-81 and 6-82). The force resulting from the pressure and area differential across the piston is referred to as the piston-rod load. Reciprocating compressors are rated in terms of their rod-load capability rather than by horsepower. Rod-load ratings range up to 175,000 lb. Higher-horsepower compressors are built with a basic frame, with a wide range of cylinders that are interchangeable on the frame. The cylinders range from small-diameter high-pressure cylinders to large-diameter low-pressure cylinders. A line of cylinders is usually designed so that each cylinder matches the rod-load

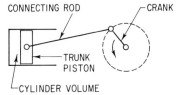

Fig. 6-81 Single-acting design.

capability of the compressor frame at the maximum working pressure of the cylinder and the expected pressure ratio of the applications for which the cylinder is intended.

Double-acting compressor cylinders of the type described above are mounted on several types of frames. The two basic classifications of compressor frames are the balanced-opposed type and the integral type (Figs. 6-83 and 6-84).

The balanced-opposed frame is characterized by an adjacent pair of crank throws 180° out of phase separated by a crank web only. With this configuration the inertia forces are balanced if the reciprocating weights of opposing throws are balanced. The balanced-opposed design is a separable frame so that the basic compressor may be driven by any number of prime movers, including diesel, natural gas, and dual-fuel engines, gas and steam turbines, and electric motors.

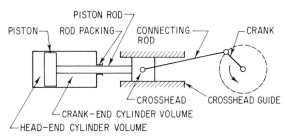

Fig. 6-82 Double-acting design.

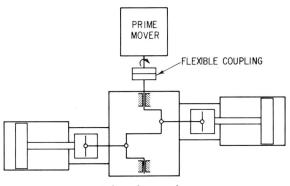

Fig. 6-83 Balanced-opposed compressor.

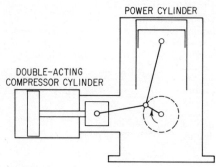

Fig. 6-84   Integral-type gas-engine compressor.

The integral compressor has compressor cylinders and power cylinders mounted on the same frame and driven by the same crankshaft.   Some integrals have in-line power cylinders mounted vertically and compressor cylinders out one or both sides in the horizontal plane.   Others are V engines with compressor cylinders out one or both sides.

Figure 6-85 shows a balanced-opposed four-throw reciprocating compressor with many of the parts identified.

Type of Service   Reciprocating compressors are presently used for a large variety of services.   The following is a description of some of the more common applications.

Pipeline Service.   Characterized by large flow rates, very low pressure ratios (1.1 to 1.5), and moderately high pressures (1,000 psig).

Process-gas Compression.   A wide range of cylinders can be applied to process-gas work.   The process itself dictates the requirement of compression.   Gasoline plants may use low pressure (400 psig), and ammonia synthesis plants may require 5,000 psig.

Gas gathering is collecting the output of many gas wells and compressing the gas so that it will flow to a plant for further refinement or to a pipeline.

Gas injection is used for natural-gas storage in large natural underground storage volumes.   Gas is injected at pressures up to 4,000 psig during periods of small demand and withdrawn during periods of high demand (cold winter days).

Industrial air compressors supply air for industrial purposes such as spray painting, drilling, grinding, and riveting.   Air is taken at atmospheric pressure, filtered, and compressed to 100 to 150 psig for most industrial uses.

Compressor cylinder selection is based on the requirements of the application, including operating pressures, type of gas, range of pressure, etc.   Cylinders for pipeline service are designed with large clearance volumes and gas passages, large valve areas, and no water cooling.   The large clearance volumes are desirable from the standpoint of keeping horsepower absorption reasonably constant over a wide range of operating pressures.   Large gas passage and large valve areas are necessary to keep the frictional losses low.   Water cooling is not required in view of the low temperature rise that results from the very low pressure ratios involved in pipeline gas compression.   Most of the other compression services require low clearance volumes and water cooling because of the higher temperatures which accompany higher pressure ratios.

Valve velocities are generally higher in general-purpose cylinders because of the low-clearance-volume requirements for higher-pressure-ratio applications.

Compressor cylinders and packings are normally lubricated by a high-pressure force-feed lubrication system supplying lubricant to individual points in each cylinder bore and packing.   In cases where contamination of the compressed gas is detrimental, the lubrication can be eliminated from the cylinder bore or the cylinder bore and packing.   The nonlubricated compressors must be designed with materials and surface finishes that will operate without lubrication.

Performance Characteristics

Performance calculations are made to determine the throughput of a reciprocating compressor and the horsepower absorbed by the process.   The capacity throughput is determined by the displacement rate of the compressor, the specific volume at suction conditions, and the suction volumetric efficiency.   The piston-displacement rate is determined by the piston area and piston speed.

The specific volume is a function of the pressure, temperature, and gas composition.   The suction volumetric efficiency VE can be determined by thermodynamic calculation as VE percent $= 100 - R - $ (percent clearance) $(R^{1/k} - 1)$, where R is the ratio of abso-

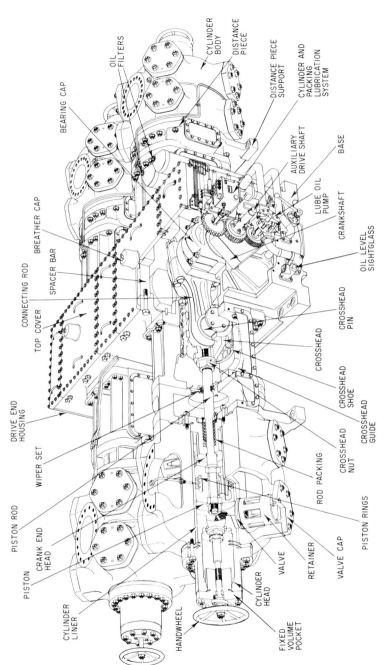

Fig. 6-85 HVC engine—compressor.

OIL FILTERS

CYLINDER BODY

DISTANCE PIECE

DISTANCE PIECE SUPPORT

CYLINDER AND PACKING LUBRICATION SYSTEM

BEARING CAP

AUXILIARY DRIVE SHAFT

BASE

LUBE OIL PUMP

CRANKSHAFT

OIL LEVEL SIGHTGLASS

BREATHER CAP

SPACER BAR

TOP COVER

CONNECTING ROD

CROSSHEAD

CROSSHEAD PIN

CROSSHEAD SHOE

CROSSHEAD GUIDE

CROSSHEAD NUT

ROD PACKING

PISTON RINGS

DRIVE END HOUSING

WIPER SET

PISTON ROD

CRANK END HEAD

PISTON

CYLINDER LINER

HANDWHEEL

FIXED VOLUME POCKET

CYLINDER HEAD

VALVE

RETAINER

VALVE CAP

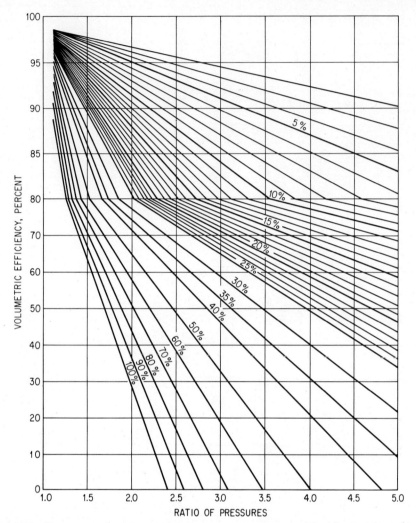

Fig. 6-86 Volumetric efficiency *VE* vs. pressure ratio *R* for varying percent clearance volume ($k = 1.30$).

lute discharge to absolute suction pressure P_d/P_s and the percent clearance is (clearance volume/swept volume) × 100 percent.   Figure 6-86 shows volumetric efficiency vs. pressure ratio for varying clearance.

Horsepower absorbed by the compressor is the product of capacity throughput times horsepower per unit capacity, usually hp/lb, or horsepower per million cubic feet per day (hp/MMCFD).

Figures 6-87 and 6-88 show horsepower vs. pressure ratio for varying clearance with constant discharge pressure and constant suction pressure, respectively.   These two curves are used not quantitatively but to indicate trends in horsepower due to changes in suction or discharge pressures.   The adiabatic efficiency used in the curves was obtained from Fig. 6-89.

Compressor Valves and Losses   In Fig. 6-80 is shown an *ideal* compression cycle.   The cycle includes (1) an isentropic-compression process from a to b, (2) a constant-pressure discharge process from b to c, (3) an isentropic expansion of the gas trapped in the cylinder-clearance volume from c to d, and (4) a constant-pressure suction process. Figures 6-90 and 6-91 show a typical *actual* compression process complete with valve losses.

The suction and discharge valves are actually spring-loaded check valves that permit flow in one direction only. The springs require a small differential pressure to open. For this reason, the pressure within the cylinder at the end of the suction stroke is lower than the line suction pressure by the amount of the differential pressure required to hold the valve off its seat. Likewise, the pressure at the end of the discharge stroke is higher than the line discharge pressure (see Fig. 6-90). The suction and discharge processes are not constant-pressure processes because of the pressure losses associated

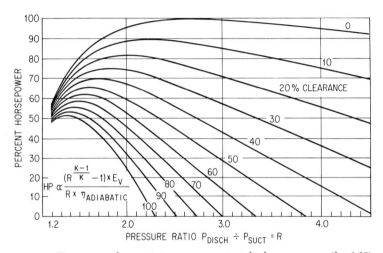

Fig. 6-87 Horsepower characteristic curves—constant discharge pressure ($k = 1.26$).

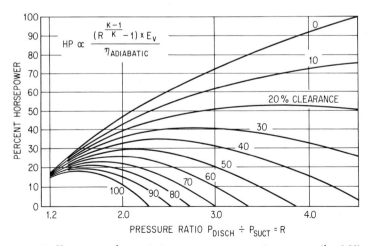

Fig. 6-88 Horsepower characteristic curves—constant suction pressure ($k = 1.26$).

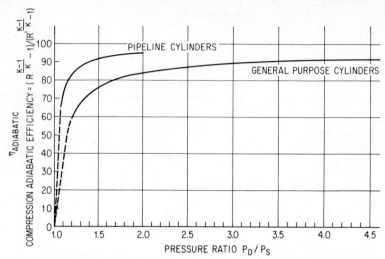

Fig. 6-89   Adiabatic efficiency vs. pressure ratio.

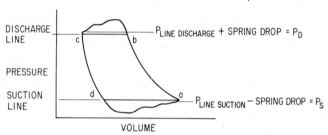

Fig. 6-90   Compressor PV diagram.

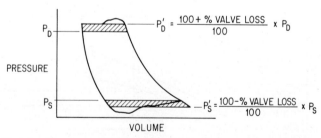

Fig. 6-91   Compressor PV diagram showing valve-loss pressures P_d' and P_s'.

with forcing the gas through the discharge and suction valves at high velocities (see Fig. 6-91). Since the area of the PV diagram is directly related to the work required, the adiabatic efficiency is determined by dividing the ideal work (area $abcd$) by the area of the actual PV diagram.

For ease of calculation, valve losses are determined either analytically or experimentally and are used to determine fictitious pressures P_d' and P_s' and a fictitious pressure ratio R'.

$$P'_d = P_d \frac{(100 + \text{percent discharge-valve loss})}{100}$$

$$P'_s = P_s \frac{(100 - \text{percent suction-valve loss})}{100}$$

$$R' = \frac{P'_d}{P'_s}$$

The fictitious pressure ratio R' is then used to determine the horsepower required for compression by applying it in place of R in the isentropic-compression horsepower formula

$$\frac{\text{ichp}}{\text{MMCFD}} = 43.67 \frac{k}{k-1} (R^{(k-1)/k} - 1)$$

where ichp/MMCFD = isentropic horsepower per million cubic feet (14.4 psia and suction temperature) per day
k = ratio of specific heats c_p/c_v

$$R' = \frac{P'_d}{P'_s} = \frac{P_d}{P_s} \frac{100 + \text{percent discharge-valve loss}/100}{100 - \text{percent suction-valve loss}/100}$$

$$= R \frac{100 + \text{percent discharge-valve loss}}{100 - \text{percent suction-valve loss}}$$

Capacity and Horsepower Control For a given set of temperature and pressure conditions, the horsepower input of a reciprocating compressor is proportional to the capacity throughput. For this reason, it is desirable to be able to control the capacity. The capacity equation is

$$Q \text{ (capacity in MMCFD at 14.4 psia and 60°F)} = \frac{PD \times VE \times P_s}{10^4 \times Z_s}$$

where PD is the piston-displacement rate, cfm, and Z_s is the deviation of the gas from the ideal-gas laws. This shows that for fixed conditions the capacity can be altered by changing the piston displacement rate or the volumetric efficiency. Piston displacement can be varied by changing the compressor rpm. Volumetric efficiency can be varied by changing the clearance volume within the compressor cylinder. Clearance volume can be added in fixed steps by opening fixed-volume pockets such as those shown in Fig. 6-85. The handwheel in the figure is turned to open the fixed-volume-pocket valve, which adds a fixed volume to the existing head end-clearance volume. Variable-volume pockets are also used to control capacity. They provide infinitely variable control over a wide range. With variable-volume pockets, the head end clearance can be varied from about 15 to over 100 percent. Suction-valve lifters can also be used to hold the suction valves open on one end of a cylinder, so that the gas is moved back and forth through the suction valve rather than compressed and pushed out the discharge valve. In this way, the capacity of that end of the compressor cylinder is reduced to zero. These three methods of unloading add greatly to the versatility of the reciprocating compressor.

Power Transmission

HELICAL REDUCTION GEARS

General

The development during the early part of this century of high-speed drivers such as the steam turbine, electric motor, and internal-combustion engine necessitated a comparable development in the design of high-speed gears.

Modern reduction (or increasing) gears are generally of the double-helix type, and are made single- or double-reduction depending upon the speed ratio desired. For transmission ratios less than 10 or 12 to 1, a single-reduction train is used; while for larger ratios a double-reduction train is employed.

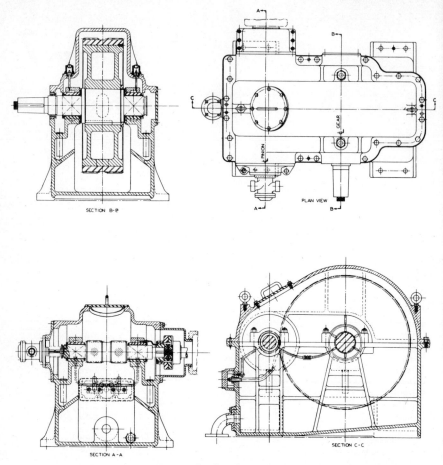

Fig. 7-1   Single-reduction gear.

Figure 7-1 is a section through a typical single-reduction industrial unit, while Fig. 7-2 shows a section through a typical double-reduction marine unit.

The three general methods of arranging marine double-reduction gear trains are illustrated in Fig. 7-3. The arrangement shown in Fig. 7-3A is the "articulated" type, which is the most common form in present-day practice. The first reduction gears and second reduction pinions are connected by means of quill shafts and flexible couplings. Figure 7-3B shows a "nested" type gear train. It has fewer bearings than the articulated type and has no quill shaft or flexible coupling connecting the first and second reduction. The "locked-train" arrangement is illustrated in Fig. 7-3C. This may be considered as a development of the articulated type in which the first reduction pinion has been rolled down on the side of the gear and an additional gear with its second reduction pinion has been added. The purpose of this design is to divide the flow of power in two, thus doubling the capacity of the gear reduction with very little additional weight. It should be noted that this design does not permit a large first reduction and is therefore not suited for reductions in which low propeller speeds are specified. It does lend itself admirably when high propeller speeds are required.

Gear Nomenclature

When two gears mesh with each other, the larger is referred to as the *gear*, and the smaller as the *pinion*.

If a plane is passed perpendicular to the axes of a pair of meshing helical gears with parallel axes, it will cut a profile from each gear entirely similar to that of a pair of meshing spur gears. Helical gears are used in preference to spur gears since the action is quieter and the teeth are stronger.

Figure 7-4 illustrates the profiles of the teeth as cut by such a plane and illustrates most of the terms which follow.

The *pitch circle* is an imaginary circle in a gear that rolls without slipping on a corresponding circle of the meshing gear. The *pitch point* is the point of tangency of the two pitch circles, and is on the line joining the centers of the two gears.

The *addendum* is the height that a tooth projects beyond the pitch circle, or the radial distance between the pitch circle and the addendum circle.

The *dedendum* is the depth of a tooth inside the pitch circle, or the radial distance between the pitch circle and the root circle.

The *clearance* is the amount by which the dedendum of a given gear exceeds the addendum of its mating gear.

The *whole depth* is the sum of the addendum and the dedendum, or it is equal to the sum of the working depth plus the clearance.

The *working depth* is the depth of engagement of two gears, that is, the sum of their addendums.

The *backlash* is the amount by which the width of a tooth space exceeds the thickness of the engaging tooth on the pitch circles.

The *face of the tooth* is the surface of the tooth between the pitch and addendum circles.

The *flank of the tooth* is the surface of the tooth between the pitch and root circles.

The *top land* is the surface of the top of the tooth between the faces of the same tooth.

The *bottom land* is the surface at the bottom of a tooth space between the fillet curves.

The *fillet curve* is the concave portion of the tooth profile where it joins the bottom of the tooth space.

The *circular pitch* is the distance measured along the pitch circle between corresponding profiles of adjacent teeth.

The *diametral pitch* is the ratio of the number of teeth to the number of inches in the pitch diameter. The product of the circular pitch and the diametral pitch equals π (3.1416).

Practically all gear teeth today have an involute profile, which is formed by rolling a straight line on an imaginary circle, known as the *base circle*. The path of contact of mating teeth is known as the *line of action*, and it is a straight line passing through the pitch point and tangent to the base circles.

The *pressure angle* is the angle formed by a tooth profile and a radial line at the pitch point. In involute teeth, pressure angle is often described as the angle between the line of action and the line tangent to both pitch circles.

On a helical gear, the teeth form a helix, where the *helix angle* is a constant, and is the angle between the helix and an element of the cylinder at the pitch diameter unless otherwise specified.

The circular pitches of a mating pair of helical gears must be equal when measured normal to the helix, and are called the *normal circular pitch*. If Ψ is the helix angle, p the circular pitch, and p_n the normal circular pitch, then $p_n = p \cos \Psi$ (see Fig. 7-5).

The helix may be right- or left-handed. A *right-hand helical gear* is one in which the teeth twist clockwise as they recede from an observer looking along the axis. A *left-hand helical gear* is one in which the teeth twist counterclockwise as they recede from an observer looking along the axis. Two external meshing helical gears operating on parallel axes must be of opposite hand.

The *face width* of a gear is the length of the teeth in an axial plane.   The *effective face width* is the portion that may actually come in contact with a mating gear, as occasionally one gear of a pair may have a greater face width than the other.   The *total face width* is the actual dimension of a gear blank that exceeds the effective face width; or as in double helical gears, where the total face width includes any distance separating right- and left-hand helices.

Tooth Loads and Stresses

For slow-speed gearing applications, Lewis' equation to determine the strength of the teeth modified by a factor to account for the pitch-line speed is generally satisfactory.   For high-speed applications, the ability of the teeth to withstand wear is of greater importance.   Hence, the teeth are overly strong and the Lewis equation can no longer be the criterion.

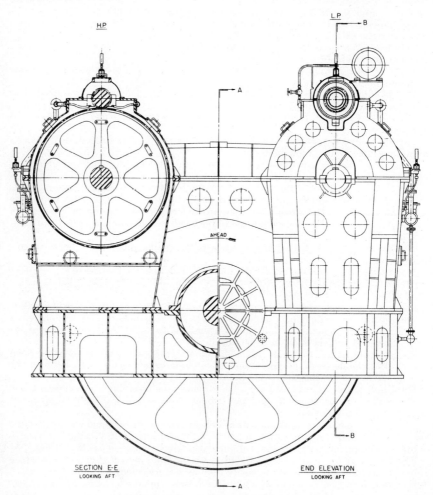

Fig. 7-2   Marine double-reduction gear.

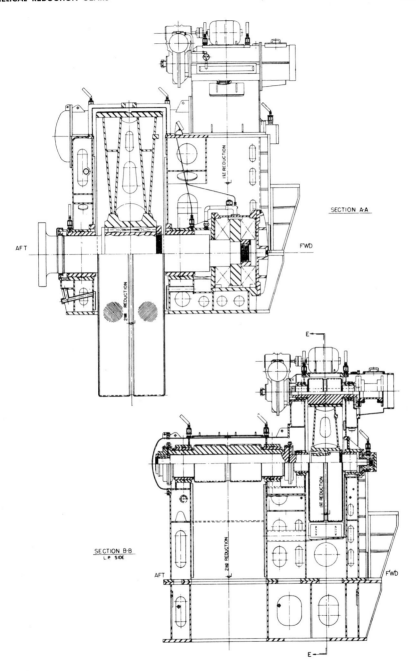

Fig. 7-2 (Continued)

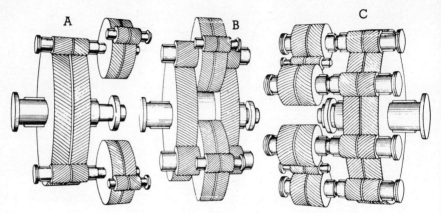

Fig. 7-3 Arrangements of double-reduction gears. (*Reprinted by permission from* Marine Engineering, *published by the Society of Naval Architects and Marine Engineers.*)

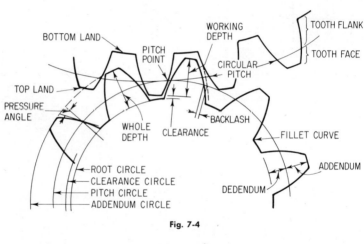

Fig. 7-4

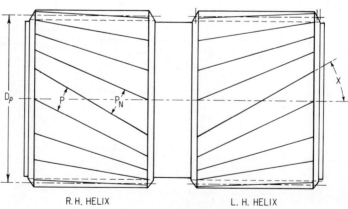

Fig. 7-5

The tangential tooth load P_t in pounds is given by the equation

$$P_t = \frac{33,000 \text{ hp}}{V}$$

where hp = shaft horsepower
V = pitch-line speed, fpm

The load-carrying capacity of the teeth must be based upon the stress developed there because of the load. Hence, it is a function of the curvatures of the tooth surfaces which in turn vary with the pitch diameters of the gears or the transmission ratio.

A formula based upon the maximum compressive stress between two parallel cylinders, as developed by Hertz, may be applied to a pair of contacting spur-gear teeth. This is

$$S_{max} = 4,582 \sqrt{\frac{P_t(1+R)}{LDp \sin 2\alpha R}}$$

where R = transmission ratio (greater than 1)
L = width of working face, in.
Dp = pitch diameter of pinion, in.
α = pressure angle, degrees

While this formula is applied to spur gears, the form will be similar for helical gears, and it may be used in analyzing them by selecting a suitable value of S_{max}.

The value of S_{max} may not be the actual contact pressure in psi but should be considered to be an experience factor. The equation may be reduced to the simpler form

$$\frac{P_t}{LD_p} = K\frac{R}{R+1}$$

where K becomes the experience factor, which depends upon the application of the gear reduction, and the other symbols have the meanings given above. For a given degree of reliability, K factor is a function of service factor and gear- and pinion-material properties. The tabulation below shows the relationship, for unity service factor, between allowable K factor and Brinell hardness number. This is the relationship recommended by the AGMA for high-speed gearing.

Pinion BHN	Gear BHN	K factor
245	210	130
265	225	140
285	245	157
300	255	166
315	270	182
335	285	198
350	300	216

The allowable K factor for a given application may be determined by selecting the appropriate service factor from Table 7-1. The allowable K factor, for unity service factor, should then be divided by the service factor for the specific application.

Materials and Design

The pinions are made of alloy-steel forgings, heat-treated to a Brinell hardness number between 250 and 350. For special applications materials may be used that give a Brinell number as high as 440.

The teeth of the gears are cut in a seamless steel band, having a Brinell number of 200 to 300. These tires are either welded to a built-up spider or shrunk on a cast-iron or steel rotor.

Correct alignment between pinion and gear is essential for perfect operation of gears, and this can be maintained only with a gear casing stiff enough to prevent deflection of

TABLE 7-1   Gear Service Factors

Application	Service factor
Generator (normal application)	1.0
Pumps:	
Centrifugal (general service)	1.1
Gear	1.5
Waterworks	1.5
Centrifugal—hot oil	1.5
Pipeline	1.5
Rotary—lobe type	1.7
Reciprocating	1.7
Descaling (with surge tank)	2.0
Dredge	2.2
Fans and compressors:	
Sliding-vane compressor	1.2
Forced-draft fan	1.3
Centrifugal compressor	1.3
Induced-draft fan	1.5
Industrial blower (repeated starting and stopping cycle such as in steel mill)	1.5
Nash compressor	1.7
Reciprocating compressor	1.7
Lobe-type compressor	1.7
Miscellaneous:	
Paper machine	1.1
Line shaft	1.1
Belt or rope drive for other than reciprocating apparatus	1.1
Belt or rope drive for reciprocating apparatus	1.3
Jordans	1.5
Pulp beaters	1.5
Cane cutters	1.7
Pulverizers	1.7
Reciprocating apparatus	1.7
Sugar mill	1.7
Chipper	2.2

the bearing seats.   It is of utmost importance that these bearing supports have sufficient structural stiffness to prevent any measurable deflection under varying load conditions. The foundation to which the gear case is bolted must also be extremely rigid to prevent misalignment with the driver or driven machine.   The gear cases may be made of cast iron, cast steel, or welded construction.   The last type is built up of steel plates with cast-steel bearing supports.   This permits considerable saving in space and weight, which is important in some applications, such as the marine field.   The weight of double-reduction gears for general marine application varies between 15 to 20 lb/hp.

Many units, particularly in marine applications, are equipped with turning gears attached to a high-speed pinion (see Fig. 7-2).   This device is motor-driven through a worm or reduction gear to cause the low-speed shaft to make one revolution every 5 or 10 minutes.   It provides a means of rotating the turbine rotors during heating and cooling periods to ensure uniform temperature distribution.   If the turbine rotor temperature is allowed to change while remaining stationary, uneven expansion will take place, resulting in a distortion that will not permit bringing the turbine to speed without serious vibration.   The turning gear may also be used for inspection purposes; to facilitate this there is also a provision for turning the gears by hand.   In designing turning gears for marine installations, the reduction is normally proportioned to transmit 60 percent of full-load torque to the propeller shaft at a speed of one revolution in 8 min.

Pinion Deflection

The deflection between the gear and pinion while transmitting load must not be excessive if an even load distribution across the face is to be secured.   The deflection may be due to the lateral bending f plus the torsional twist y of the pinion.   It is usually assumed that the gear does not deflect since it is much heavier and stiffer than the pinion.

The lateral deflection may be limited by empirical rules such as that the working face of the helices plus the gap between them, or the total span, divided by the pitch diameter of the pinion should not exceed 2.5 for a two-bearing pinion or that the active face of each helix divided by the pinion pitch diameter should not exceed 2 for three-bearing units.   However, proportions and tooth loadings somewhat different from those generally used may be required under certain conditions; hence it is desirable to establish methods of calculating the lateral and torsional deflection of a pinion.   Experience has indicated that the total deflection at any point should not exceed 0.001 in.

To simplify the equations, the following assumptions will be made:

1. The torque is uniformly removed from the coupling end to the free end.
2. The pinion is free to move axially; hence each helix transmits its share of the load.
3. The effective diameter in both bending and torsion is taken as the pitch diameter.
4. The pinion is simply supported at the inner ends of the bearings.
5. The face width of the helix is equal to the bearing span, and the distributed load acts over this full span.

With these assumptions the following equations result for the total deflection of a two-bearing pinion (see Fig. 7-6).

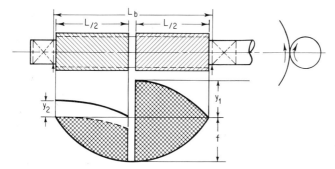

y_1, y_2 = OPENING OF TOOTH CONTACT DUE TO TORSION
f = OPENING OF TOOTH CONTACT DUE TO DEFLECTION
SHADED AREAS = TOTAL TOOTH CONTACT OPENING

Fig. 7-6 Two-bearing pinion.

For the helix nearest the coupling,

$$y_1 + f = \frac{hp}{NDp^3 10^3}\left(10L + \frac{1.115L_b^4}{Dp^2L}\right)$$

For the helix farthest from the coupling,

$$y_2 = \frac{hp}{10^3 NDp^3}\left(\frac{1.115L_b^4}{Dp^2L} - \frac{10L}{3}\right)$$

For a three-bearing pinion the total deflection is given by

$$y_1 = 0.01\frac{hp\,L}{NDp^3} \quad\text{or}\quad y_3 + f = \frac{hp}{10^6 NDp^3}\left(4{,}170L + 29\frac{L_b^4}{Dp^2L}\right)$$

whichever is greatest (see Fig. 7-7).   Usually the former equation will control.

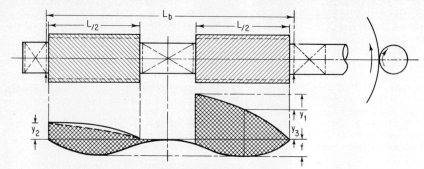

y_1, y_2, y_3 = OPENING OF TOOTH CONTACT DUE TO TORSION

f = OPENING OF TOOTH CONTACT DUE TO DEFLECTION

SHADED AREAS = TOTAL TOOTH CONTACT OPENING

Fig. 7-7 Three-bearing pinion.

Bearings

The bearings are generally of the sleeve type with forced-feed lubrication, although on smaller sets roller or ball bearings are sometimes used. The sleeve bearings are split perpendicular to the action of the load and are made of a cast-iron or steel shell with a babbitt lining.

The transmitted force P_t acts tangentially to the pitch circles at the pitch point and equals 33,000 hp/V, where V is the pitch-line speed in fpm, and hp is the transmitted horsepower. The resultant tooth load acting along the pressure line equals $R/\cos \alpha$, where α is the pressure angle in the plane of rotation in degrees.

The magnitude and direction of the bearing loads are determined graphically by adding the resultant tooth loads to the gear weights vectorially. The resultant of these forces gives the load acting on the bearing.

The procedure is illustrated in Fig. 7-8 for a single-reduction gear being driven by a high- and low-pressure turbine. Vectors H and L are the resultant tooth loads of the high- and low-pressure pinions on the gear, W is the weight of the gear, and R is the resultant load on the gear bearing.

Since the gears and pinions have double helices, there is no end thrust except that which may be introduced by the driving or driven machines.

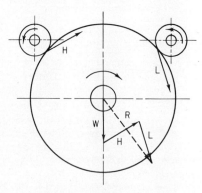

Fig. 7-8

Lubrication of Helical Gears

The general subject of lubrication is discussed on pages 4-53 to 4-58. Of necessity all high-speed gear reductions are designed for forced-feed lubrication.

Bearing lubrication is perhaps more critical in gearing than in other machinery because high journal velocities and high journal loads are often encountered. The direction and magnitude of the load in the gear bearing are governed by the torque transmitted by the gear. To provide adequate lubrication of the load-carrying bearing surface, the bearing is often rotated to a position where the bearing split is located approximately 90° from the direction of the load at full power.

The gear mesh is lubricated by spraying oil into either the ingoing or outgoing side of the mesh. The oil here serves the dual purpose of lubricating the gear mesh and cooling the gear teeth. It is recognized, however, that it is advantageous to locate the sprays on the outgoing side of the mesh. This arrangement permits a more efficient cooling of the gear teeth because the heat of friction produced in the gear mesh is washed away immediately and provides sufficient but not excessive oil for lubrication when the teeth next mesh and causes foreign particles to be thrown off the teeth by centrifugal force instead of passing through the mesh.

As shown in the Oil-selection Chart on page 4-56, heavier oils are recommended for gear drives than for direct drives. The reason for this is that the heavier the oil the larger will be the load-carrying capacity of the oil film between the gear teeth before it breaks down and permits metal-to-metal contact.

Efficiency and Testing

The efficiency of large single-reduction gears is generally between 98 and 99 percent or even higher; while for large double-reduction units it ranges between 97 and 98 percent. The losses are due to friction in the bearings and rubbing of the tooth surfaces. Smaller units will show proportionately greater losses, and hence lower efficiency.

Since the losses are small, it is extremely difficult to measure them by input-output tests. A more accurate method is to join two duplicate units together by coupling corresponding gears and pinions to common quill shafts as shown in Fig. 7-9. The gears may be loaded by introducing a known twist in the quill shafts; and the two sets rotated by an external driver such as a motor dynamometer, or a steam turbine connected to one of the pinions with a torsion meter. The power required to drive the two sets represents the losses involved, and these may be measured over the entire speed range of the units. The loading of the gears may be changed by varying the initial twist in the quill shafts.

A set of typical efficiency curves for a pair of helical gears transmitting 4,200 hp at 4,000 rpm of the pinion, a reduction ratio of 4, and a K factor of 75 is shown in Fig. 7-10. The curves show the performance of a constant-speed unit with load variation; and also the effect of reducing the speed according to the dashed line with percent load. The

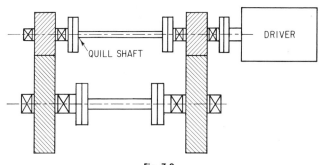

Fig. 7-9

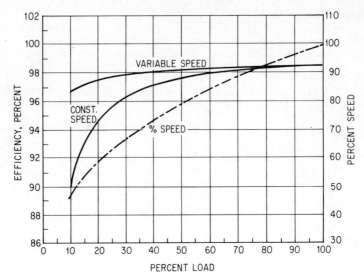

Fig. 7-10 Typical efficiency curves of helical gears.

efficiencies shown hold only for the conditions stated, and should not be considered as those which may be obtained for other applications.

Installation and Operation

Alignment is a factor of vital importance in the operation of reduction gears. It is essential not only that the pinion and gear shaft be in line with the shafts of the driving and driven elements under operating conditions, but also that the gear rotors be parallel.

The parallelism of the gears can be checked by coating the gear teeth with prussian blue or its equivalent and rotating the unit to make simulated running marks. There should be uniform contact across the face of the teeth.

Burrs or dirt in the bearings or unequal wear of the bearings are the most frequent causes of nonparallelism. If a check of the bearings does not satisfy the tooth-contact requirements, the gear case should be checked for distortion. Distortion can only be caused by some change in the supporting structure, assuming that the gears have not been seriously damaged in some way. The nature and extent of the change in the supporting structure must be determined before corrective measures can be applied.

The following checks should be made periodically during the operation of the unit.

1. If vibration, rubbing, unusual noise, or any other abnormal condition should develop, shut down immediately and investigate the cause. Operators should become thoroughly acquainted with the normal operating sounds of the unit to facilitate the detection of abnormal sounds. No unusual noise is too trivial to be neglected.

2. Check the oil pressure as specified for the gear.

3. Oil should be flowing freely in all sight flow indicators.

4. The bearing-oil temperature rise should not exceed 50°F.

5. The oil level should be maintained at the point indicated by the *full* mark on the gage or as specified for the installation.

The unit should be kept clean at all times. When the gears are not in service, every precaution should be taken to prevent the accumulation of moisture in the casing.

The oil should be examined periodically, and if there is any evidence of contamination, the oil system should be drained and recharged with fresh oil.

Epicyclic Gears

Epicyclic gears are a variation of helical gears suitable for installations requiring an increase or decrease in speed of the driven component. They are designed for use in high-torque power-transmission applications requiring in-line arrangement of input and output shafts, reduction in weight, or saving of space. Epicyclic gears have low pitch-line velocities and low WR^2 and are readily adaptable for vertical operation of the input and output shafts. They also allow a choice of same or opposite rotations of the input and output shafts, depending on whether a planetary or star arrangement is selected.

Described here are two basic arrangements: planetary and star gears. The planetary-gear arrangement, as shown in Figs. 7-11 and 7-12, is of the single-speed (reducing or increasing) double-helical type. The centrally located sun pinion, driven by the high-speed (input) shaft, drives three or more planet gears which transmit the power to the planet carrier because of the fixed-orbit gear arrangement. The planet carrier is connected to the low-speed (output) shaft. The input and output shafts rotate in the same direction.

The star-gear arrangement, as shown in Figs. 7-13 and 7-14, is also of the single-speed (reducing or increasing) double-helical type. The centrally located sun pinion, driven by the high-speed (input) shaft, drives three or more star gears. The star gears rotate the orbit gear, which is fixed to the low-speed (output) shaft. The input and output shafts rotate in opposite directions.

Installation   The unit must be secured to a firm support to provide stability of alignment. Alignment is a factor of vital importance in the operation of the unit. It is essential that the high- and low-speed shafts be in line with the shafts of the driving and driven elements under operating conditions.

Operation   The periodic checks, as outlined on page 7-12 for helical reduction gears, apply also to epicyclic gears.

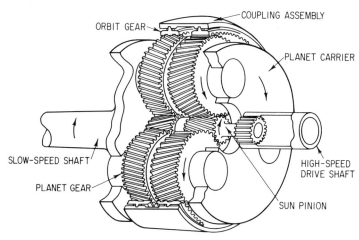

Fig. 7-11   Planetary gears—for high-torque applications at gear ratios of from 3:1 to 12:1. The centrally located sun pinion is driven by the high-speed shaft for reducing service. This pinion drives three or more planet gears which transmit the power to the carrier because of the fixed-orbit gear arrangement. The carrier in turn is connected to the slow-speed shaft.

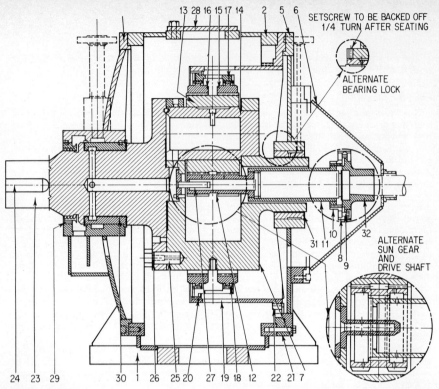

Fig. 7-12 Typical planetary-gear assembly. (1) Case; (2) cover; (3) end cover; (5) end cover; (6) coupling guard; (7) carrier, planet; (8) coupling sleeve; (9) coupling bolt; (10) snap ring; (11) drive shaft; (12) pinion, sun; (13) gear, planet; (14) spindle, planet; (15) orbit gear, left-hand; (16) orbit gear, right-hand; (17) coupling sleeve, inner; (18) snap ring; (19) coupling sleeve, outer; (20) snap ring; (21) coupling sleeve retainer; (22) snap ring; (23) shaft; (24) key; (25) dowel pin; (26) dowel cover; (27) oil spray; (28) cover; (29) oil guard; (30) planet carrier, bearing; (31) planet carrier, bearing; (32) coupling flange.

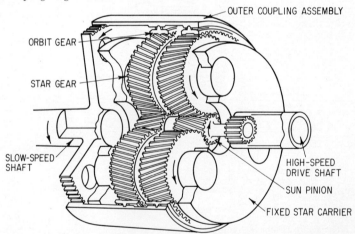

Fig. 7-13 Star gears—for high-speed applications at gear ratios of from 2:1 to 11:1. The centrally located sun pinion is driven by the high-speed shaft for reducing service. This pinion drives

(*Continued at foot of next page*)

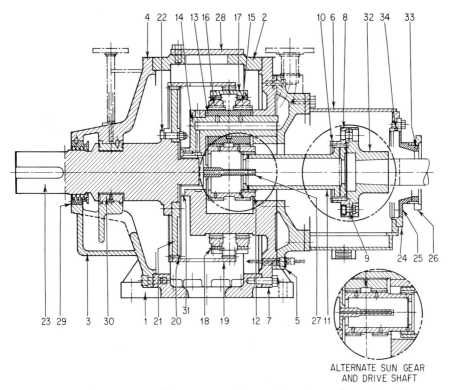

Fig. 7-14 Typical star-gear assembly. (1) Case; (2) cover; (3) end cover, lower; (4) end cover, upper; (5) oil manifold; (6) coupling guard; (7) star carrier; (8) coupling sleeve; (9) coupling bolt; (10) snap ring; (11) drive shaft; (12) sun; (13) star; (14) spindle, star; (15) orbit gear, left-hand; (16) orbit gear, right-hand; (17) coupling sleeve, inner; (18) snap ring; (19) coupling sleeve, outer; (20) snap ring; (21) coupling hub; (22) coupling bolt; (23) shaft; (24) gland; (25) gland; (26) gland; (27) oil spray; (28) cover; (29) oil guard; (30) bearing; (31) bearing; (32) coupling flange; (33) O-ring packing; (34) O-ring packing.

WORM GEARS

General

The use of high-speed drivers for efficient operation makes a speed reduction necessary for many applications.

Worm-gear reducers are very compact, requiring less space than belts, chains, or trains of open gearing. The right-angle drive often permits compact placement of the driving and driven machines. Since three or more teeth are always in contact, there is an even flow of torque which reduces vibration, prolongs the life of the driven machinery, and provides quiet power transmission. There are few moving parts (hence few bearings), and these are enclosed in a dustproof housing which contributes to long life and avoids danger of injury to workmen.

Worm gearing consists of an element known as the worm, which is threaded like a screw, mating with a gear whose axis is at a 90° angle to that of the worm. The gear is throated and partially envelops the worm. The worm may have one or more independent threads, or "starts."

three or more star gears, which, by analogy with our solar system, are so called because they do not revolve about the sun. These star gears in turn rotate the orbit gear which is fixed to the slow-speed shaft.

The ratio of speeds is determined by dividing the number of teeth in the gear by the number of threads in the worm. Since a single-threaded worm acts like a gear with one tooth, and a double-threaded worm as a gear with two teeth, very large ratios can be designed into one set of gearing. Ratios between 3:1 and 100:1 are common for power-transmission purposes, and even higher ratios are employed for index devices.

Mechanical Elements

Dimensions of the worm and worm gear are defined as follows (see Fig. 7-15):

Outer diameter of worm is the diameter of a cylinder touching the tops of the threads.

Pitch diameter of worm is the diameter of a circle which is tangent to the pitch circle of the mating gear in its mid-plane.

Outer diameter of gear is the diameter over the tips of the teeth at their highest points.

Throat diameter of gear is the diameter over the tips of the teeth at the middle plane which is perpendicular to the axis of the gear shaft and passes through the axis of the worm.

Pitch diameter of gear is the diameter of the pitch circle at the mid-plane of the gear which would roll upon the pitch line of the worm if the latter were used as a rack.

Circular pitch is the distance from a point on one gear tooth to the same point of the succeeding tooth measured circumferentially on the mid-plane pitch circle. It is equal to the axial pitch of the worm, that is, the distance from any point on a thread of the worm to the corresponding point on the next thread, measured parallel to the axis.

Lead of worm is the distance parallel to the axis of the worm from a point on a given thread to the corresponding point on the same thread after it has made one turn around the worm. If the worm has only one thread, this distance is equal to the circular pitch, but if the worm has multiple threads it is equal to the circular pitch multiplied by the number of threads. It is the distance that a point on the pitch circle of the gear is advanced by one revolution of the worm.

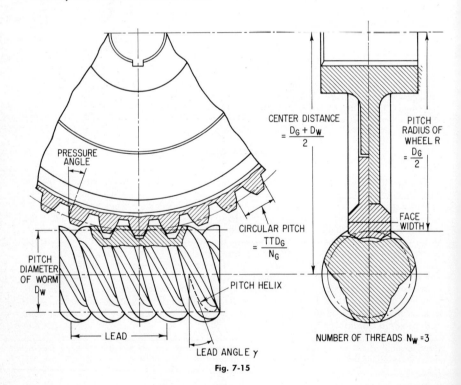

Fig. 7-15

One revolution of the worm advances the gear by as many teeth as there are threads on the worm. Therefore, the *ratio of transmission* is equal to the number of teeth on the gear, divided by the number of threads on the worm, without regard to the pitch.

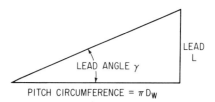

Fig. 7-16   Lead angle.

Lead angle of the worm threads is the angle between a line tangent to the thread helix at the pitch line and a plane perpendicular to the axis of the worm. The pitch lines of the worm threads lie on the surface of a cylinder concentric with the worm and of the pitch diameter. If this cylinder is thought of as unrolled or developed on a plane, the pitch line of the thread will appear as the hypotenuse of a right-angled triangle, the base of which will be the circumference of the pitch circle of the worm and the altitude of which will be the lead of the worm. In Fig. 7-16, the lead angle is γ and the tangent of this angle is equal to the lead L divided by π times the pitch-line diameter D_w of the worm, $\tan \gamma = L/\pi D_w$.

Pressure angle is defined as the angle between a line tangent to the tooth surface at the pitch line and a radial line to that point.

Classification

A large number of arrangements are available and permit flexibility in application to a wide variety of driven machinery. Some of the typical arrangements manufactured by De Laval-Holroyd, Inc. are shown below in Figs. 7-17 to 7-23.

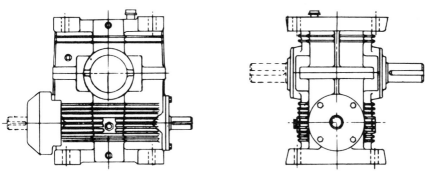

Fig. 7-17   Single worm reduction.

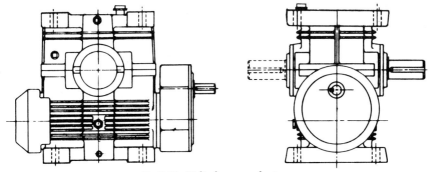

Fig. 7-18   Helical worm reduction.

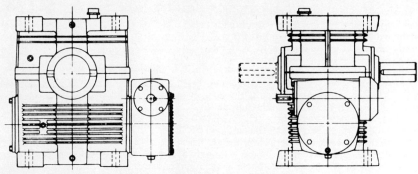

Fig. 7-19 Double worm reduction.

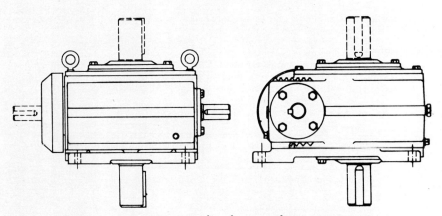

Fig. 7-20 Vertical single worm reduction.

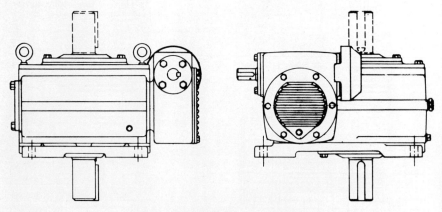

Fig. 7-21 Vertical double worm reduction.

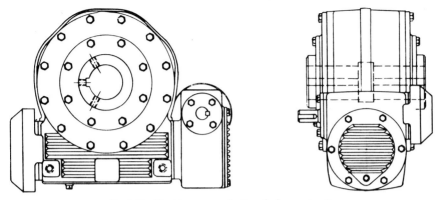

Fig. 7-22   Double-worm-reduction shaft-mount unit.

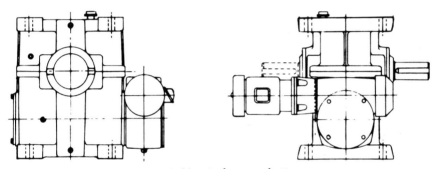

Fig. 7-23   Motorized worm reduction.

Motorized units may be furnished for:

Horizontal-shaft units
   Single worm reduction
   Helical worm reduction
   Double worm reduction
Vertical-output-shaft units
   Single worm reduction
   Helical worm reduction
   Double worm reduction
Shaft-mount units
   Single worm reduction
   Helical worm reduction
   Double worm reduction

Special Reducers   Special reducers in various combinations are also available.   An example is shown in Fig. 7-24 which shows a large vertical-output-shaft unit with a single worm reduction, having 38-in. gear centers, which is used in pulverized-coal service.

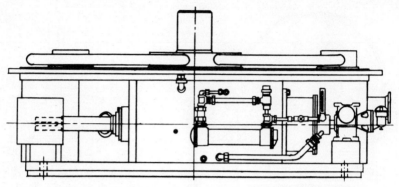

Fig. 7-24 Large vertical-shaft single worm reduction.

Efficiency of Worm Gearset

To determine the approximate efficiency of a worm gearset, where the worm threads are of hardened and ground steel, the gear teeth of nickel bronze, or phosphor bronze, lubricated with a steam cylinder oil, the charts in Figs. 7-25 and 7-26 may be used. To use the coefficient of friction curve, calculate the rubbing speed of the worm from the following formula:

$$\text{Rubbing speed, fpm} = \frac{\text{pitch dia of worm} \times 0.262 \times \text{rpm}}{\cos \text{lead angle}}$$

(See page 7-17 for definition of lead angle.)   With this rubbing speed noted at the bottom of the chart, read vertically upward till you intersect the coefficient of friction curve. Read the value of the coefficient of friction from the left-hand side of the chart.

When the worm is the driver, enter the efficiency chart with the lead angle of the worm at the bottom of the chart.   Read upward to the intersection of the curve with the correct coefficient of friction.   The efficiency of the gearset may be read from the right-hand side of the chart or the efficiency loss on the left-hand side of the chart.

When the gear is the driver, enter the efficiency chart with the lead angle of the worm at the top of the chart, reading down to the curve with the correct coefficient of friction.   Find the efficiency as before.

These efficiencies, while approximate, are very close to the operating efficiency of the gearset alone.   When the gearset is enclosed in a housing, with bearings, seals, and oil reservoir, some allowance must be made for bearing loss, seal drag on shaft, and churning of oil.

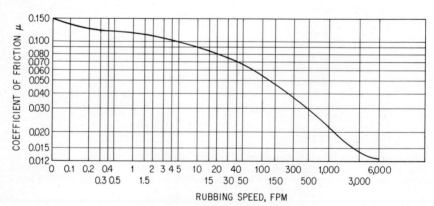

Fig. 7-25 Coefficient of friction curve.

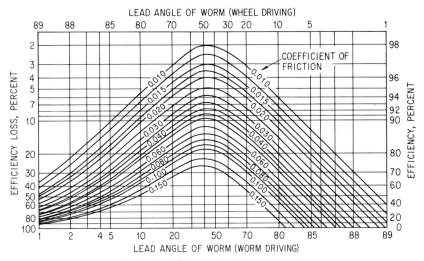

Fig. 7-26 Efficiency chart for worm gearing.

Self-locking

A self-locking gearset is one which cannot be started in motion by applying power at the gear. Theoretically, this can be obtained when the lead angle of the worm is less than the friction angle. For normal static conditions the friction angle would be approximately 8°30', and therefore it might be deduced that gearsets having a worm lead angle less than this value would be self-locking.

However, it is impossible to determine the point of positive self-locking for several reasons. The value of static coefficient of friction varies considerably because of the effect of a number of variables. Furthermore, if a source of vibration is located near a self-locked set, a very slight motion might occur at the gear contact. Since the coefficient of friction decreases rapidly with an increase in rubbing velocity from the static condition, the friction angle may become smaller than the lead angle. Once this occurs, motion will continue and the gearing will accelerate under the action of the power applied to the gear.

Figure 7-27 indicates the rapid increase in efficiency with increase in rubbing speed from the static condition for both the worm driving and the gear driving. For this

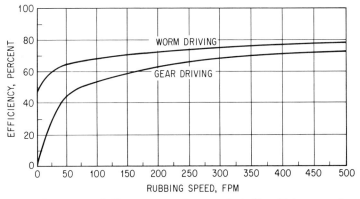

Fig. 7-27 Comparison of efficiencies at tooth contact (ratio 50 on 20-in. center distance).

particular example at a rubbing velocity of 500 fpm, there are only a few points of efficiency difference between the two curves.

The best way to obtain locking is to use a brake, released electrically when the motor is started. With worm gears of high ratios, the braking effect need only be a fraction of full-load motor torque. A solenoid brake is usually best suited for this operation since the braking effect may be adjusted by weights which can be proportioned to stop the load gradually and avoid damage. Dashpots can be employed to ensure gradual setting of the brake.

Tooth Form

The tooth form used by De Laval is the involute helicoid. Figures 7-28 and 7-29 show the straight generating line tangent to the base circle and the convex axial section of thread.

Worm-gear performance is judged in terms of load capacity, smooth silent running, and high efficiency. The attainment of these goals requires accurate methods of producing and inspecting the worm and gear.

Since the involute helicoid worm is based on generation of a straight line tangent to the base circle, the accuracy of this line is very simple to check (Fig. 7-30). This thread form lends itself to accurate manufacture, inspection, and interchangeability, as all worms can be checked to calculated measurable dimensions.

All wheels are checked with a master worm to ensure interchangeability and correctness of form (Fig. 7-31).

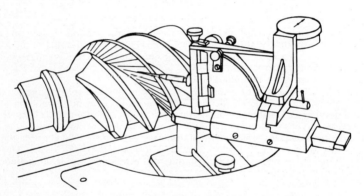

Fig. 7-28 Generation of tooth form.

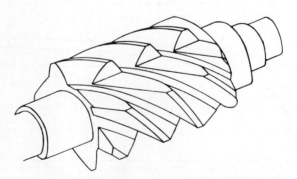

Fig. 7-29 Convex axial section of thread.

Fig. 7-30 Inspection of tooth form.

Fig. 7-31 Checking with master worm.

Tooth Contact

The involute helicoid thread form is a calculated form, and the theoretical contact is maintained more accurately and is more easily determined than any other worm thread, particularly a concave thread flank.

Figure 7-32 shows theoretical "lines" of contact that exist between two worm threads and two gear teeth at a given angular position of the worm. As rotation of the worm occurs in the direction shown, these contact "lines" move progressively across the flanks of the worm and gear teeth, and are inclined at an angle to the direction of sliding. This inclined effect is known to give a highly efficient form of surface lubrication and a low coefficient of friction as compared with a gear form in which the lines of contact are in the approximate direction of sliding. The contacting surfaces are always freshly lubricated, and not subject to the undesirable effects of "double contact."

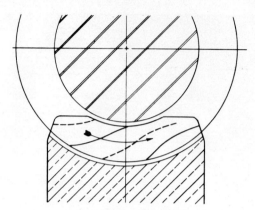

Fig. 7-32 Tooth contact.

Depending on the relative radii of curvature between the two contacting surfaces and the load applied, these "lines" of contact actually have some width, thereby providing area contact. In spite of claims to full area contact, "line" contact occurs on all other thread forms including the double-enveloping thread form. Only the involute helicoid thread form provides the necessary control of the geometry of thread form in design and manufacture to obtain optimum contact conditions.

All gears, bearings, and housings deflect and distort to some extent when operating under load, as compared with conditions under no load. A correction in the tooth-contact pattern is provided to assure proper contact under loaded conditions. This correction is accomplished by producing gears with "leaving-side" contact as shown in Fig. 7-33. This is the ideal contact pattern which should be aimed for, when assembling a worm gearset under no-load condition. This contact pattern allows a lubricant-entry gap in tooth contact. When the gear deflects under load, the contact tends to move to a more central position on the bronze gear face, still allowing a lubricant-entry gap.

A contact pattern such as that shown in Fig. 7-34 is the worst possible contact pattern under no-load condition. This contact does not allow a lubricant-entry gap, and deflection under load will aggravate this condition. A gearset mounted in this manner may cause a temperature rise in oil 20 percent higher than the same gearset mounted as shown in Fig. 7-33. The remedy is to move the gear axially to the left (adjusting by shims or other adjustments provided), until a contact similar to Fig. 7-33 is obtained.

When assembling worm gears which will run in both directions of rotation, it is necessary to consider both driving faces of the gear, and to aim for contact as shown in Fig. 7-35. When the worm is rotating in direction A in Figure 7-35, contact should be at D on the leaving side. When the worm is rotating in direction B in Fig. 7-35, contact should be at C on the leaving side. For gears that will run in one direction only, it is necessary to obtain a contact pattern that is correct for the driving-side flank of gear teeth only.

Assembly Adjustment The gear should be mounted approximately on the centerline of the worm. The worm threads should be coated with prussian blue dye. A section

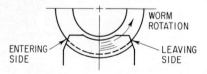

Fig. 7-33 Tooth contact—good.

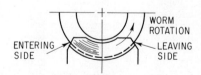

Fig. 7-34 Tooth contact—poor.

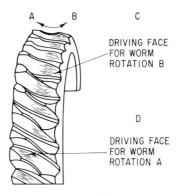

Fig. 7-35

of the gear teeth should be coated with an orange-colored lead paste. The worm and gear should be rotated in both directions of rotation by hand. The blue markings from the worm threads will show the contact against the orange coating on the gear teeth. If the contact pattern is not as desired, the gear should be adjusted axially until a correct pattern is obtained.

Design Considerations for Worm and Gearset

It is assumed that in the start of this design sequence the center distance for this gearset is known.

Minimum Recommended Number of Gear Teeth for General Design

Center distance, in.	Min No. of teeth
2	20
3	25
5	27
10	29
14	35
20	40
24	45

The maximum number of teeth selected will be governed by high ratios of reduction and consideration of strength and load-carrying capacity.

Number of Threads in Worm. The minimum number of teeth in the gear and the reduction ratio will determine the number of threads for the worm. Generally 1 to 10 threads are used.

Gear Ratio

$$\text{Gear ratio} = \frac{\text{No. of teeth in gear}}{\text{No. of threads of worm}}$$

Pitch. Axial pitch of worm = circular pitch of gear. Keep the fraction simple so that accurate factoring can be used to determine change gears.

Worm Pitch Diameter. The pitch diameter of the worm is assumed to be at the mean working depth of the worm thread. The following factors should be considered when selecting worm pitch diameter:

1. Smaller pitch diameters provide higher efficiency and reduce the magnitude of the tooth loading.

2. The root diameter that results from pitch-diameter selection must be sufficiently large to prevent undue deflection and stress under load.

3. For low ratios the minimum pitch diameter is governed by the desirability of avoiding too high a lead angle. Lead angles up to 50° are practical.

Gear Pitch Diameter

Gear pitch dia = 2 × center − pitch dia of worm

Recommended Pressure Angle.   For general usage, pressure angles of from 20 to 25° are common.   Smaller values of pressure angle decrease the separating force, extend the line of action, making the amount of backlash less sensitive to change in center distance, and are used in index gearing.

Larger values of pressure angle provide stronger gear teeth and assist in preventing undercutting of teeth with large lead angle.   They are used in extremely heavily loaded applications.

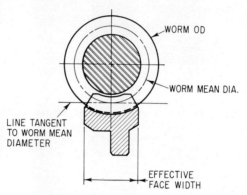

Fig. 7-36   Gear face width.

Gear Face Width (Fig. 7-36).   Maximum effective face width is the length of a line tangent to the mean worm diameter, to a point where the OD of the worm intersects the gear face.   Any face width larger than this effective face width is of very little value and is wasteful of material.

Gear throat dia = gear pitch dia + 2 × gear addendums.   Gear outside dia = gear throat dia + 1 addendum of worm rounded off to the nearest fraction of an inch.

Gear Blank under Rim Diameter (Fig. 7-37)

h_t = tooth depth of gear

Under-rim dimension for bronze gear block = gear-root dia

− 2 to 2½ × gear-tooth depth

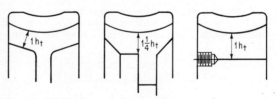

Fig. 7-37   Gear-blank shapes.

Worm Face

Min worm face = 2 $\sqrt{(\text{gear throat dia}/2)^2 - (\text{gear pitch dia}/2 - \text{gear addendum})^2}$

Allowable Shaft Stresses.   All shafting in accord with AGMA Practice 260.01, March, 1953.

Allowable Bolt Stresses.   All bolts in accord with AGMA Practice 255.02, November, 1964.

Bearing Loading.   All bearings selected in accord with AGMA Practice 265.01, March, 1953.   (See Fig. 7-38.)

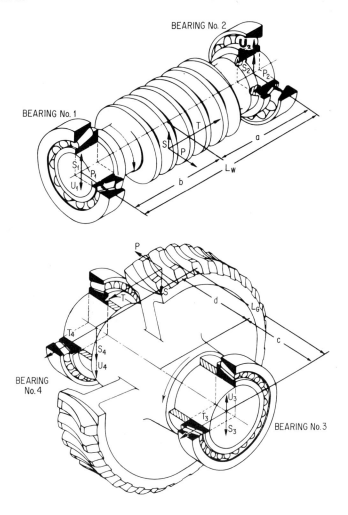

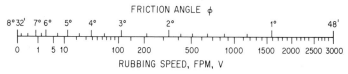

Fig. 7-38 Principal forces and bearing loads in a worm and gearset. D_W = pitch diameter of worm, in.; r_W = pitch radius of worm, in.; r_G = pitch radius of gear, in.; γ = lead angle of worm, deg; P = tangential force on worm, lb; Q = torque input to worm, in.-lb; S = separating force, lb; T = axial thrust of worm, lb; N.P.A. = normal pressure angle; ϕ = friction angle for worm driving; rpm = worm speed; V = rubbing speed, fpm.

$P = Q/r_W$; $S = P \tan$ N.P.A./$\sin (\gamma + \phi)$; $T = P/\tan (\gamma + \phi)$; $V = 0.262 D_W$ rpm/$\cos \gamma$.

(Courtesy of the Timken Roller Bearing Company.)

Ball and roller bearings are selected based on supporting loads equal to the maximum basic rating of the gear reducer and allow a minimum bearing life of 5,000 hr or an average life of 25,000 hr.

Bearing Loads

Resulting from	Bearing No. 1	Bearing No. 2	Bearing No. 3	Bearing No. 4
P	$Pa/L_W = P_1$	$Pb/L_W = P_2$	$Pr_d/L_G = U_3$	$Pr_G/L_G = U_4$
S	$Sa/L_W = S_1$	$Sb/L_W = S_2$	$Sd/L_G = S_3$	$Sc/L_G = S_4$
T	$Tr_W/L_W = U_1$	$Tr_W/L_W = U_2$	$Td/L_G = T_3$	$Tc/L_G = T_4$
Radial load	$\sqrt{P_1^2 + (S_1 - U_1)^2} = R_1$	$\sqrt{P_2^2 + (S_2 + U_2)^2} = R_2$	$\sqrt{T_3^2 + (U_3 - S_3)^2} = R_3$	$\sqrt{T_4^2 + (S_4 + U_4)^2} = R_4$
Thrust load	. . . .	T	. . . .	P

Performance

Mechanical Ratings of Cylindrical Worm Gears The practice for this rating is per AGMA Practice 440.03, September, 1959.

The ratings which are cataloged per this practice are *wear* ratings which the gearset will satisfactorily permit, at the load shown, provided the driven machine has a uniform load requirement free of shock loading, 10 hr/day. This is the basic rating by which worm-gear drives are selected subject to thermal limitations.

Service factors are applied to this basic rating to factor the wear rating for shock loading or intermittent service.

Thermal Ratings of Cylindrical Worm Gears Delroyd reducer thermal ratings above 100 to 200 rpm worm speed represent the input horsepower and output torque which will provide a stabilized 100°F oil-temperature rise over ambient air temperature when operated continuously. For example, if the ambient air temperature is 70°F, a reducer carrying rated thermal horsepower will operate with an average oil temperature of 170°F. Since normal worm-gear lubricants will deteriorate rapidly, require frequent replacement, and may not support the gear-mesh loads when operating continuously at 210 to 220°F, the practical maximum ambient air temperature for worm-gear reducers carrying full thermal rating horsepower is 100°F.

For operation at higher ambient air temperatures, a larger unit with a higher thermal rating must be selected for continuous operation or a cooling system must be employed. For example, if a unit is to operate in an ambient air temperature of 150°F, the increase in oil temperature must be limited to 50°F in order to keep the oil temperature from rising above 200°F. This means that the heat generated in the reducer must be one-half of the heat generated when operating at the catalog thermal rating; or, since bearing and oil losses remain constant for a given speed, applied horsepower must be less than one-half the catalog thermal rating.

For operation at ambients of less than a maximum of 100°F or where artificial or natural air drafts are present, catalog thermal ratings can be exceeded. For a proper evaluation, all data on ambient conditions should be determined.

Allowable Starting Load Worm-gear reducers have a momentary overload strength rating + 300 percent of mechanical "wear" rating. Peak starting load of the driven machine should not exceed 300 percent of the mechanical wear rating.

Lubrication

General Because of the nature of worm-gear sliding and rolling action, lubricants used for other types of gearing are not satisfactory. All units are shipped without oil, but reducer instructions and lubrication nameplates refer to the use of AGMA lubricants. Generally speaking, suppliers of *industrial lubricants, not* service stations, should be contacted and should be able to supply suitable lubricants from stock to meet these AGMA specifications. The units should be filled with the proper lubricant before operating.

These lubricants are basically a steam-cylinder oil. A list of trade names of the various manufacturers of oils which meet the AGMA 7 Comp. and AGMA 8 Comp. specifications is maintained by De Laval. These lubricants are basically petroleum-

BASIC LUBRICANT RECOMMENDATIONS (AGMA)

Worm speed, rpm	Size 60 units and smaller, ambient temp, °F		Size 70 units and larger, ambient temp, °F	
	15–60	50–125	30–60	50–125
Up to 400	7 Comp.	8 Comp.	7 Comp.	8 Comp.
Above 400	. . . . . .	. . . . . .	7 Comp.	7 Comp.

base oils but with 4 to 5 percent acidless tallow additives which provide additional film strength. These are heavy oils, much heavier than normal motor oils. The viscosity of AGMA 7 Comp. is approximately 135 SSU at 210°F, and AGMA 8 Comp. is approximately 150 SSU at 210°F. This heavy viscosity plus the plating action of the additives on the worm and gear contact surfaces is required to provide the long trouble-free life that the gearing is designed to provide.

Lubricants Not Recommended   The following lubricants should never be used for worm gearing:

1. Ordinary motor oils, no matter what viscosity.
2. Automotive rear-end oils.
3. EP lubricants containing compounds of sulfur or phosphorus. These lubricants may claim to be noncorrosive to steel, but they are extremely corrosive to bronze and will not provide the necessary plating action required.
4. Greases of any kind. These do not flow sufficiently to provide the necessary cooling.

Cold-weather Lubricants   If ambient temperatures below 15°F are expected, a winter or cold-weather lubricant must be selected, since the AGMA 7 Comp. or 8 Comp. will solidify and the motion of the gears will channel the solidified oil until no lubricant is present at the gear mesh. For this condition, a minimum ambient temperature to be expected must be estimated and a reputable supplier consulted to recommend an oil with a channel point well below the expected minimum ambient temperature. This will require a lighter-viscosity oil, but the oil should still contain additives. The best selection is usually the mild EP oils containing lead naphthanate with the following viscosities:

For min ambient temp, °F	Use a mild EP oil containing lead naphthanate and having a viscosity of
0	120 SSU at 210°F
−10	100 SSU at 210°F
−20	75 SSU at 210°F
−30	53 SSU at 210°F

The lubricant should be changed to the heavier-viscosity oils when the ambient temperature again goes above 15°F.

Frequency of Oil Changes   The frequency of oil changes varies with the type of service. After the initial 50 to 100 hr of running, a change should normally be made to remove the particles of bronze burnished off the gear during the run-in period. Thereafter, a general rule is that the oil should be changed every 6 months of normal service and every 3 months of severe service. However, if the unit is in a dusty or moist atmosphere, dirt or water accumulation in the oil reservoir may require more frequent changes. Many oil suppliers will test a lubricant after a period of use free of charge and determine its useful life for a specific application.

Procedure for Long Shutdown Periods   If the unit is to be idle for any length of time, particularly outdoors, something must be done to prevent rusting of the bearings, gears, and other internal parts. The easiest solution is usually to fill the unit completely with clean oil. Of course, before the unit is started again, the oil should be drained and refilled to its proper level.

Installation and Operation

Installation Normal good practice must be followed when handling the unit, choosing a foundation, checking alignment, and mounting couplings, pulleys, gears, sprockets, etc. Couplings should be pressed or shrunk on the reducer shafts. Do not drive couplings on shafts, as this may damage the bearings and also cause the shafts to spring. This, in turn, may result in failure of the bearings, vibration, and oil leakage. Sprockets, pulleys, and pinions should be mounted as close to the case as possible in order to avoid undue bearing load and shaft deflection.

Operation The unit is shipped from the factory *without oil* but is slushed internally with a rust-preventive compound, which need not be removed since it is oil-soluble. *Make certain that the reducer is filled to the correct level before start of operation in accordance with lubrication specifications.* The unit must be filled to, but not above, the oil-level gage. The oil level will, of course, change with the mounting arrangement. The oil level should be checked periodically and only at a time when the unit is not operating. A dip stick is provided in the oil-level gage.

All units have been subjected to test before shipment, but it takes additional hours of running under full gear load to attain highest efficiency. The gear may, if necessary, be put to work immediately on full load, but if circumstances permit, it is better for the ultimate life of the gear to run it under gradually increasing load. Immediate application of full load concentrates high unit pressures on tooth surfaces. When new driven equipment requires operation to achieve freedom and minimum friction loss, use precaution in the early stages of operation to prevent the reducer from taking an overload. Where overload tests are specified on a machine before it is shipped, it is better to make preliminary runs under part load before building up to full load and overload. A reasonable running-in procedure is half load for a few hours, building up to full load, in two stages if possible.

Temperature rise on the initial run will be higher than that eventually attained after the gear is fully run in.

Some slight wear and/or pitting of the bronze gear teeth may be observed after a short period of initial operation. This condition is normal, as some initial wear is necessary for the hardened-steel worm to seat itself properly with the bronze gear.

Steam Condensers

STEAM CONDENSERS

General

Steam condensers are used:

1. In the exhaust system of steam-turbine power plants, to augment the cycle temperature range by condensing the steam coming from the turbine in a vacuum.

2. In process plants, for better heat balance, recovery of condensate, low-temperature evaporation, etc. Condensers similar to steam condensers are used in chemical, refrigeration, and other fields to liquefy vapors other than steam.

Steam condensers are classified as:

1. *Direct-contact condensers* in which the steam and cooling water are intermingled (often designated as "barometric" condensers).

2. *Surface condensers* equipped with a shell-and-tube structure in which the steam

is segregated from the cooling water by metal walls through which heat exchange occurs.   The latter type of condenser permits recovery of the condensate as distilled water for boiler-feed purposes.

The Steam Surface Condenser   In the following paragraphs only steam *surface condensers* are discussed in more detail.

Basic Elements   In simple terms a steam surface condenser is a gastight chamber fitted with heat-conductive tubes through which cooling water is circulated—and means provided for continuously removing the condensed steam and the noncondensable gases which enter the steam passages of the turbine through leakage, so as to maintain the partial vacuum in the chamber.

Purpose   The purpose of the surface condenser as used in steam power generation is to reduce the back pressure on the turbine to the lowest practical absolute pressure. This is accomplished by circulating cooling water through the tubes, thus condensing the steam, and shrinking its volume at a high vacuum to that of the liquid (to about $1/_{21,000}$ at 2 in. Hg absolute pressure).   The condensate is almost universally removed from the condenser hot well by a special type of centrifugal pump, and the noncondensable gases (mostly air) are removed by a steam-jet air ejector or a mechanical air pump.

In a well-designed power plant the noncondensable gases are a very low percentage in the steam and have little effect on its condensing temperature (partial-pressure effect is nil up to 0.1 percent).   However, if allowed to accumulate, these gases would detrimentally affect the heat-transfer rate with a resultant decrease in vacuum; so their removal is very important.

Heat-transfer Principles

Before attempting to work out a preliminary condenser calculation, it is necessary to have a clear understanding of simple basic heat-transfer principles and definitions. In order to condense steam, L, the latent heat of condensation, must be removed.   This is the amount of heat involved in the change from vapor state to liquid state at constant temperature and varies slightly according to the absolute pressure or vacuum.   For convenience, in standardizing condenser practice, the value of L is taken as a constant—950 Btu/lb for turbine exhaust steam and 1000 Btu/lb for engine exhaust steam. Since the heat removed from the steam must be absorbed 100 percent in the cooling water (neglecting radiation losses), each pound of engine steam condensed will heat 1,000 lb of cooling water 1°F or 100 lb of water through a range of 10°F.

To conduct this heat through a metal wall requires a definite area or heat flow as well as a positive potential—or temperature gradient in the direction of flow.   If the water were not colder than the steam, the heat would not flow and the steam could not be condensed.   The rate of heat flow depends not only upon the area and temperature gradients but also upon the effectiveness of the conducting area—or heat-transfer coefficient.   This is expressed by the simple expression

$$Q = S \, \Delta T \, U = WL \qquad (1)$$

where W = lb steam condensed/hr
   L = latent-heat content of steam, Btu/lb
   Q = rate of heat flow, Btu/hr
   S = outer-surface area of heat-flow circuit, sq ft
   ΔT = effective mean heat potential or mean temperature difference, °F, between steam and cooling water
   U = overall heat-flow coefficient, Btu/(sq ft)(°F)(hr)

Since the water becomes heated as the steam condenses, it is necessary to consider ΔT as the average or mean temperature difference throughout the condenser.

For the purpose of rough approximation, mean ΔT is often taken as the arithmetic average of the temperature differences between steam and inlet cooling water and steam and outlet cooling water, where arithmetic average equals

$$\frac{(t_s - t_1) + (t_s - t_2)}{2}$$

where t_s is the steam temperature, °F.

This relationship is approximately correct for high-temperature differences; for the low heat potentials in high-vacuum surface condensers, it has been found necessary to use the natural logarithmic average or log mean temperature difference (LMTD).

Cooling-water Requirements

Since all the heat of the steam goes into the cooling water, the cooling-water requirement is as follows:

$$Q = \text{gpm} \times 500 \times (t_2 - t_1)$$
$$\text{gpm} = \frac{Q}{500 \times (t_2 - t_1)} \tag{2}$$

where Q = Btu/hr
  gpm = gallons per minute of cooling water required
  500 = 8.33×60, which converts gpm to lb/hr
  t_1 = inlet water temperature, °F
  t_2 = outlet water temperature, °F

Influencing Factors   From Eq. (1) it follows that

$$S = \frac{WL}{U \times \text{LMTD}} = \frac{Q}{U \times \text{LMTD}} \tag{3}$$

Equation (3) expresses mathematically that the size of the condenser (tube surface) is directly proportional to the steam flow times its latent heat content and inversely proportional to the (log) mean temperature difference (or heat potential) as well as inversely proportional to the U value or overall heat-conductivity constant.   It is obvious that for a given heat load and vacuum, the size of the condenser is then determined by the amount of water, its inlet temperature, and the U value.

As a rule, the water inlet temperature is beyond the control of the condenser designer, and to a lesser degree, the water flow and temperature rise are also likely to be established—at least within limits.   Therefore, most of the ingenuity of condenser designers is focused on obtaining the highest possible U values in their condensers.

There are a great many factors affecting U, the most important of which are as follows:

1. Cooling-water velocity through tubes
2. Viscosity of cooling water (temperature)
3. Thermal conductivity of water
4. Viscosity of condensate
5. Thermal conductivity of condensate
6. Extent of loading (both quantity and distribution) of condensing surface with condensate
7. Quantity of noncondensable gases present
8. Extent of blanketing of surface by noncondensable gases
9. Characteristics of vapor condenser-cooler and air-removal equipment
10. Arrangement of condensing surface
11. Pressure loss through main tube bank
12. Diameter of tubes
13. Thickness of tubes
14. Thermal conductivity of tube material
15. Condition of tube surface (wettable, polished)
16. Cleanliness of tube surfaces

The flow of heat through the tubes of a surface condenser may be likened to the flow of electricity through a number of parallel resistances, each of which is made up of several conductive sections of different metals in series.   The flow of heat through any individual tube is illustrated in Fig. 8-1.

We combine these resistances to heat flow (reciprocals of heat conductance) to determine the overall resistance R, which is generally expressed in terms of its reciprocal U, the overall heat-transfer coefficient in Btu/(sq ft)(°F)(hr).

It has been found that the most influential factor affecting U is the square root of water velocity through the tubes.   As a result, U is generally determined from the

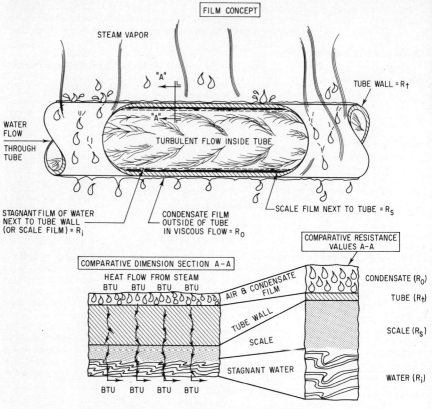

Fig. 8-1   Heat absorbed in cooling water.

HEI curves (see Fig. 8-3) or an equation involving $\sqrt{v}$, with suitable correction for the other influences such as scale, condensate loading, and tube-wall and water temperature.

Air content of the steam has also been found to be a very important factor in commercial condenser operation and is responsible for much of the poor performance of improperly designed condensers—especially at partial load.   Air also must be entirely removed from the condensate to avoid damage to the power-plant boiler and piping system, in which complete removal equipment is a feature of proper design; therefore, entirely adequate air-cooling and air-removal equipment is a "must" for power-plant surface condensers.

The amount of required tube surface, or S, is determined from Q, or Btu heat input, the U value, and the LMTD, or °F logarithmic mean temperature difference between condensing steam and cooling water, by using Eq. (3):

$$S = \frac{Q}{U \times \text{LMTD}}$$

Proper arrangement of the tube surface, however, is vital to such performance, as is predicted by the HEI-U values used in the above equation.   It is only by observance of all the rules of correct steam distribution and penetration that the large multitube power-plant condensers can be made to approximate the performance of the single-tube (ideal) condenser.

Engineering Design

Introduction Having reviewed the basic theories of heat transfer as applied to steam vacuum condensation and devaporization, we are now ready to consider the engineering design and economics of surface condensers.

1. The first and primary function of the condenser is to maintain the lowest economically justified absolute pressure at the turbine-exhaust connection.

2. Its next most important function is to produce pure oxygen-free condensate of substantially saturated exhaust-steam temperature.

3. Secondary functions, such as to heat and deaerate boiler feedwater makeup, supply warm water for process uses, and act as a low-pressure drain catchall, must also be met as specified and within allowable space limitations.

Importance of Good Design The factors which determine the excellence of a surface-condenser design are numerous, and their relative importance varies according to the size of the installation and the underlying economic considerations.

In large, base-load, steam electric generating stations, the entire overall heat balance is very carefully and fully developed to promote the maximum overall efficiency. Because of the size of the equipment and the tremendous output, it is economically justified to add refinement after refinement to reduce the Btu input per kilowatthour output.

Such features are economizers, air preheaters, waterwalls, superheaters, and stage heating of the feedwater are added to the steam generator, and it is built for very high steam pressures and temperatures. The relative steam flow through the turbogenerator is greatly reduced by high-energy-content steam at the throttle, reheating between stages, dividing the flow, cooling of generator windings, and other features. The condenser is designed for the highest practical vacuum even at partial loads, and all the auxiliaries are large enough to add their proportional improvement to overall economy. The net result is that such highly perfected, large-scale power generators regularly produce a kilowatthour of electrical energy with less than half the fuel consumption of the relatively small condensing plant. But with all this efficiency, the surface condenser still must dissipate to the cooling water more than twice as many heat units as are converted to useful electrical energy (see heat-balance chart in Fig. 8-2) so that under these conditions, anything short of a theoretically ideal condenser is hardly acceptable.

The low thermal efficiency of the Rankine cycle is well known, but often not fully appreciated.

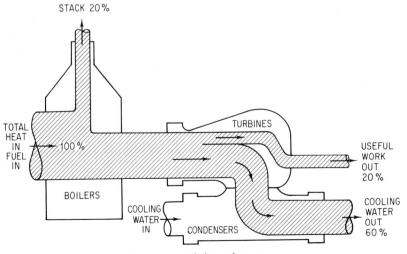

Fig. 8-2 Heat-balance diagram.

The heat-balance diagram in Fig. 8-2 gives the actual distribution of heat units in percent of the heat released for a medium-pressure marine-type power plant.

The simplified diagram summarizes the distribution figures to show the three principal outlets for heat, namely, (1) stack, (2) useful work, and (3) cooling water.

A modern large-scale central station might show perhaps a 30 percent overall thermal efficiency, instead of 20 percent as illustrated. In any event, the surface condenser still must be depended upon to remove the bulk of the heat units from the system.

Yardstick for Good Condenser Design From a practical viewpoint, the following combination of results usually characterizes the product of a good, normal-balanced design for an important installation.

1. Relatively high water velocity through the tubes = high heat-transfer coefficient
2. Economical consideration of cooling-water-tube surface
3. Balance between pumping costs, water quantity, and tube surface
4. Maintains designed vacuum at full load with normal tube cleanliness
5. Low-pressure drop through tube bank at full load
6. High vacuum at light load and with cold water
7. Simple and economical air-removal system
8. Adequate air-removal capacity at high vacuum
9. Condensate at temperature equal to steam temperature
10. Practically zero oxygen in condensate
11. Maintains vacuum when steam is cut off inlet and outlet
12. Devaporizer outlet approaches inlet water temperature at light loads
13. Low maintenance—on tubes and ejector nozzles especially
14. Initial cost well balanced economically with turbine characteristics and station operating costs
15. Reliable—easy to operate and keep clean
16. Meets space, weight, and cost limitations

Not all the foregoing factors have equal or relative importance in all cases. It is wise, therefore, to know the value of the influencing factors before attempting to design a condenser. Certain factors are incompatible with others, and engineering compromises are often necessary, but this should be done with considered judgment based on pure facts. The success of the final design—and ultimately the condenser itself—often depends upon how completely and accurately this information is transmitted to the designer.

Certain intangible considerations do not permit a definite quantitative measure, but they may be assigned a weighting in order to evaluate the final design.

On other occasions, missing factors may be arbitrarily assigned reasonable typical values and a series of selections offered.

Although it is not possible to assign exact values to all the various factors—except in the light of individual applications—certain values may be suggested as typical of good practice:

1. Water velocity from 6 to 8 fps, U from 650 to 800 Btu/(sq ft)(°F)(hr), with clean tubes.
2. Water flow—widely variable—from 20 to 100 times steam flow—with an average of 60 to 80 times steam flow.
3. Water-power-surface ratio: dependent upon relative values.
4. Tubes normally assumed 85 percent clean.
5. Pressure drop of over $1/10$ in. Hg normally considered excessive across tube bank at full load.
6. Minimum absolute pressure not over $1/2$ in. Hg at light loads.
7. Single system of twin ejectors with isolating valves and inter-after condensers.
8. Single element should maintain $1/2$ in. Hg absolute with full air load.
9. 0°F condensate temperature depression during normal operating conditions.
10. Not over 0.02 cu cm/liter oxygen content in condensate.
11. Vacuum should not drop 1 in. in 15 min even with steam flow into condenser and ejectors off.

12. 22°F is the average initial terminal difference between inlet water and condensing steam.

13. 1 in. Hg absolute is a popular condensing pressure in temperate climates. Somewhat higher pressures are encountered in the South.

14. Divided water boxes are used on most of the larger installations.

15. 7/8-in. and 1-in. OD tubes are used in the larger condensers.

16. Two half-capacity circulating pumps and two full-capacity condensate pumps are used with almost all large condensers.

Standard of the Industry Overall Heat-transfer Coefficient U

The most important standard adoption by the industry was to set forth definitely the relationship between water velocity and overall heat-transfer coefficient U. This was the result of coordinating theory with the observed results from the best commercial installations. It took the form of a family of curves with water velocity through various standard diameters of condenser tubes as the independent variable determining directly the overall heat-transfer coefficient or U value for new, clean tubes. A "temperature curve" was added to correct variations observed in U with changes in temperature of inlet cooling water.

Although obviously an approximation, the HEI graph for determining U value (Fig. 8-3) has proved satisfactory in practice and is now quite generally accepted by manufacturers and users of surface condensers.

In view of its wide acceptance and generally conservative results for new, clean tubes, manufacturers currently use the HEI standard graph for U-value determination for performance guarantees in proposals; see Figs. 8-3 and 8-4. It is carefully checked, however, by far more accurate data for actual design purposes, and suitable allowances are made for fouling.

The values shown in Fig. 8-3 are based on use of the formula

$$U = C \sqrt{V}$$

where C = factor for tube size (see Fig. 8-3)

For condenser-performance evaluation, the formula is modified to include tube material, tube thickness, water temperature, and fouling factor. The applicable formula now takes the form of

$$U = C \sqrt{V} \, C_t C_w C_f$$

where C_t = material and gage factor; see Table 8-1
  C_w = inlet water temperature correction factor; see Fig. 8-4
  C_f = fouling or scaling factor

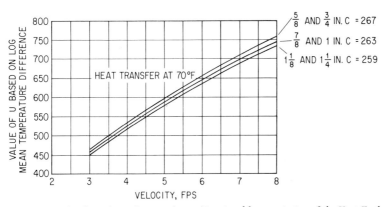

Fig. 8-3 Heat transfer through condenser tubes. (*Reprinted by permission of the Heat Exchange Institute.*)

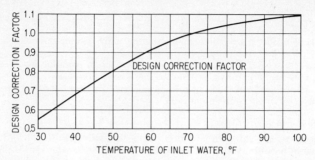

Fig. 8-4 Inlet water temperature correction factor C_w. (*Reprinted by permission of the Heat Exchange Institute.*)

Typical Condenser Construction Typical condensers are shown in Figs. 8-5 to 8-9. Figures 8-5 to 8-7 indicate reverse-flow units.

Figures 8-8 and 8-9 are typical condenser constructions.

De Laval Reverse-flow, On-the-line, Self-cleaning Condensers De Laval reverse-flow condensers were developed, patented, and originally produced by C. H. Wheeler. Now

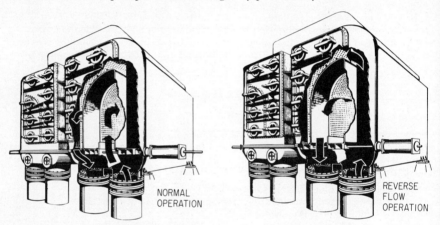

Fig. 8-5 Two-pass reverse-flow condenser.

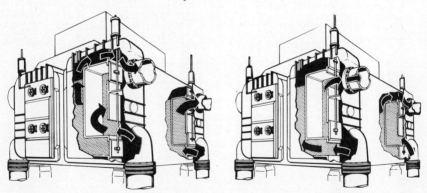

Fig. 8-6 Single-pass reverse-flow condenser.

TABLE 8-1   Material and Gage Factor C_t

Tube materials	Tube-wall gage, BWG						
	24	22	20	18	16	14	12
Admiralty metal	1.06	1.04	1.02	1.00	0.96	0.92	0.87
Arsenical copper	1.06	1.04	1.02	1.00	0.96	0.92	0.87
Aluminum	1.06	1.04	1.02	1.00	0.96	0.92	0.87
Aluminum brass	1.03	1.02	1.00	0.97	0.94	0.90	0.84
Aluminum bronze	1.03	1.02	1.00	0.97	0.94	0.90	0.84
Muntz metal	1.03	1.02	1.00	0.97	0.94	0.90	0.84
90-10 Cu-Ni.	0.99	0.97	0.94	0.90	0.85	0.80	0.74
70-30 Cu-Ni.	0.93	0.90	0.87	0.82	0.77	0.71	0.64
Cold-rolled low-carbon steel.	1.00	0.98	0.95	0.91	0.86	0.80	0.74
Stainless steels:							
Type 410/430.	0.88	0.85	0.82	0.76	0.70	0.65	0.59
Type 304/316.	0.83	0.79	0.75	0.69	0.63	0.56	0.49
Type 329	0.78	0.76	0.74	0.69	0.65	0.60	0.54
Titanium (tentative). . .	0.85	0.81	0.77	0.71			

Reprinted by permission of the Heat Exchange Institute.

manufactured by De Laval, reverse-flow condensers list among their advantages the following:

1. Reverse flow flushes out grass, sticks, leaves, and other foreign matter which clog the inlet ends of condenser tubes.

2. Reverse flow aids in the removal of sand, silt, etc., from the tubes' inner walls before this residue can harden into a damaging coating.

3. Reverse flow causes a sudden change in water temperature.   Although this vari-

Fig. 8-7   Shop view of two-pass reverse-flow condenser.

Fig. 8-8 Shop view of condenser construction.

Fig. 8-9 Shop view of small condenser.

ation amounts to only several degrees, it is enough to destroy many types of marine organisms which might otherwise grow into troublesome blocks in the system.
4. Reverse flow minimizes fouling and maintains higher heat-transfer rates.
5. Reverse flow permits reconsideration of sites with debris-laden cooling water.

CONDENSER AUXILIARIES

Atmospheric Relief Valves

Each surface condenser should be equipped with an atmospheric relief valve to protect the condenser against overpressure in case of failure of the cooling-water supply. They are usually set to open at 10 psig.

The size of atmospheric relief valves is somewhat dependent upon the local operating conditions. It is always understood that they must be of a size to pass all the steam which can be admitted to a turbine or engine through any openings, except from lines which are already protected by relief valves set to open at pressure not exceeding 10 lb gage. As an example, an extraction or bleeder turbine would normally require an atmospheric relief valve of a size to take care of the full throttle flow to the turbine. It should not be based on the steam flow to the condenser under normal operation only.

In Table 8-2, the column "For protection" will give the size of atmospheric relief valves used for normal operation of condensing turbines or engines. For temporary full-load noncondensing operation, the sizes listed under "For Maximum Noncondensing Operation" should be used.

TABLE 8-2   Atmospheric-relief-valve Sizes

Max steam flow, lb/hr	Sizes of atmospheric relief valves, in.	
	For protection°	For max non-condensing operation°
Up to 7,500	6	8
7,501– 11,800	8	10
11,801– 17,000	8	12
17,001– 20,000	8	14
20,001– 23,100	10	14
23,101– 30,200	10	16
30,201– 38,200	12	18
38,201– 45,000	12	20
45,001– 47,200	14	20
47,201– 62,000	14	24
62,001– 68,000	16	24
68,001– 82,000	16	30
82,001–106,000	18	30
106,001–120,000	18	
120,001–170,000	20	
170,001–250,000	24	
250,001–380,000	30	
380,001–550,000	36	

Reprinted by permission of the Heat Exchange Institute.
° The sizes listed "For protection" are normally used under ordinary condensing operation. However, if it is desired to operate the turbine temporarily noncondensing at its maximum noncondensing capacity, the sizes listed under "For maximum noncondensing operation" should be used.

Air-pump Equipment

Steam Ejectors Effective operation of a surface condenser requires that air leakage be held to a minimum. Air leakage into a system under vacuum is subject to considerable variation, as leakage occurs principally through the turbine gland seals, valve stem glands, and pipe joints and connections. Modern construction with welded piping tends to keep the leakage to a minimum.

Required Capacity. The total capacity required in an injector is dependent upon the type of system and may consist only of air leakage into the system, or it may consist of air leakage plus one or more of the following:

1. Noncondensable gases or vapors liberated during the process, which must be removed by the ejector in addition to the air leakage.

2. Water or other condensable vapors associated with the air or noncondensable gases where the ejector is handling a saturated mixture, as in the case of an ejector serving a surface or barometric jet condenser.

3. Air and gases liberated from the injection water when the ejector is serving a barometric or low-level jet condenser. In small industrial applications, this value is sometimes very small compared with the air leakage, and in such cases it can be considered negligible.

Calculation of Total Capacity of Ejectors Serving Surface Condensers. The air withdrawn from a surface condenser is saturated with water vapor, and the amount of water vapor is dependent upon the temperature and absolute pressure at the air outlet of the condenser.

In most condensers, the pressure drop through the condenser can be considered negligible and the absolute pressure at the air outlet assumed to be the same as that at the entrance of the condenser. To provide for sufficient total capacity, the temperature at the air outlet of a well-designed surface condenser is generally assumed to be about $7\frac{1}{2}°F$ below the temperature of saturated steam at the absolute pressure in the condenser.

Calculation of the amount of water vapor associated with the air is best illustrated by the following example:

An ejector is required to remove 20 lb dry air leakage/hr plus the associated water vapor of saturation from a surface condenser at an absolute pressure of 1 in. Hg, temperature of the mixture at the air outlet of the condenser being 71.5°F. What is the total amount of air and vapor mixture to be removed?

Total pressure of mixture is 1.000 in. Hg.

It is found from the chart in Fig. 8-10 that 2.18 lb of water vapor is required to saturate 1 lb dry air under the specified conditions, and the total air and vapor mixture to be handled by the ejector is accordingly

$$20 + (2.18 \times 20) = 63.6 \text{ lb/hr}$$

Recommended Ejector Capacity. Table 8-3 shows accepted values of air leakage for condensers serving turbines and engines. Leakage values for various industrial-process applications can be determined only by careful consideration of all details and previous experience with similar installations.

Determination of Air Leakage in Existing Vacuum Systems. The rate of air leakage into a vacuum system can readily be determined by pulling a vacuum on the system and then noting the time required for the vacuum to drop a certain amount after closing the valve in the suction line to the vacuum pump. Any convenient vacuum can be selected as long as the final vacuum at the end of the test is not less than 15 in. Hg. The rate of leakage can be determined from the following formula:

$$W = \frac{0.15 \times VD}{t}$$

where W = rate of air leakage, lb/hr
$\quad\quad V$ = net volume of system under vacuum, cu ft
$\quad\quad D$ = drop in vacuum during observation, in. Hg (vacuum at start minus vacuum at end)
$\quad\quad t$ = time, min, for vacuum to drop amount D

Example: A 500-cu-ft vacuum system dropped from 25 to 23 in. vacuum in 10 min. From the foregoing formula, the leakage rate is found to be 15 lb air/hr.

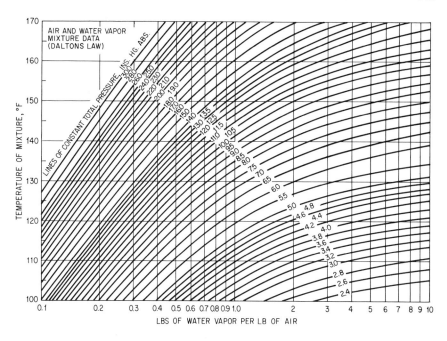

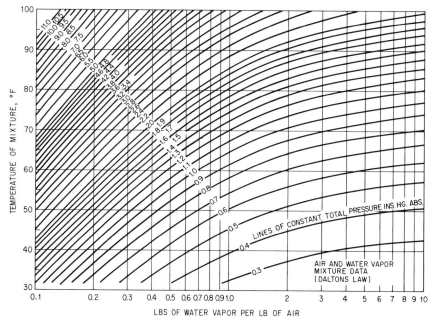

Fig. 8-10 Saturated air and water-vapor mixture. Curves show amount of water vapor required to saturate 1 lb of dry air at various temperatures and absolute pressures.

TABLE 8-3   Ejector Capacity Recommended for Surface Condensers

Max steam condensed, lb/hr	Free dry 70° atmosphere air, cfm	Equiv. saturated air-vapor mixture, lb/hr	Tube-jet air ejector (steam-operated), pressures 3.5 in. Hg abs and lower,° lb/hr steam required at pressures above 300 psi for one 2-stage element†
Up to 25,000	3.0	43.2	196
25,000– 50,000	4.0	57.6	245
50,000– 100,000	5.0	72.0	305
100,000– 250,000	7.5	108.2	465
250,000– 500,000	10.0	144.0	610
500,000–1,000,000	12.5	179.8	770
1,000,000–2,000,000	15.0	216.0	930
2,000,000–3,000,000	17.5	251.8	1,075
3,000,000–4,000,000	20.0	288.0	1,220

Reprinted by permission of the Heat Exchange Institute.

° For installations where back pressures are 3.5 in. Hg abs or lower, two-stage ejectors designed to operate at 1.0 in. Hg abs are usually furnished with surface-type inter- and aftercondensers. For installations where back pressures are 3.5 in. Hg abs or higher, single-stage ejectors designed to operate at 3.5 in. Hg abs may be used.   Units are furnished with aftercondenser.

† Ejectors designed for steam pressures lower than 300 psi are available.   In such cases steam-flow requirements will vary from those tabulated above.

Single-stage Ejectors.   A basic ejector assembly, illustrated in Fig. 8-11, consists of a steam chest, steam nozzle, suction chamber, and diffuser.   High-pressure steam, in passing through the divergent nozzle, emerges at a high velocity, thereby continuously entraining the gases or vapors surrounding the jet of steam in the suction chamber.   Kinetic energy transferred to the gases or vapors thus produces the required suction effect, the mixture then being discharged into a convergent-divergent diffuser.   The divergent portion of the diffuser converts the velocity effect into pressure, thereby elevating the pressure at the diffuser discharge a predetermined amount above the suction inlet pressure.

The degree of compression that can be accomplished satisfactorily in a single stage of compression is dependent upon such factors as steam pressure available for operating the ejector, absolute pressure to be produced, and importance of efficiency.

An ejector is a fixed-capacity machine by reason of its construction; that is, an increase or decrease in the quantity of gas or vapor being handled under constant suction and discharge conditions cannot be accomplished in the basic assembly.

Single-stage ejectors are used for a wide variety of services where moderate vacua are required and are normally designed for maintaining absolute pressures down to 3.5 in. Hg.   However, where conditions of required capacity and available operating steam pressure are favorable, they can be

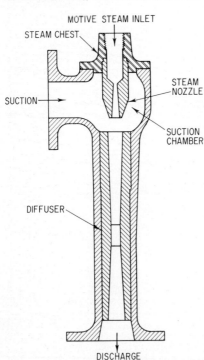

Fig. 8-11   Section through single-stage ejector.

designed for a somewhat lower absolute pressure. They are furnished in any required size from 1½ in. up to extremely large sizes for unusual process applications.

Single-stage tube jets are normally designed for any available operating steam pressure above 50 lb gage, but where the required vacuum is very low, they can be designed for pressures down to 10 lb gage. These ejectors are used in many applications, such as maintaining vacuum in condensers, stills, and evaporators, etc., and are also used extensively as priming or exhausting ejectors for rapid initial evacuation of equipment.

Two-stage Ejectors. Commercial ejectors are arranged in a variety of forms to meet limitations with respect to required degree of compression and flexibility. Where the required degree of compression is beyond the capabilities of a basic single-stage assembly, two are arranged to operate in series, each stage effecting part of the total compression. Where need for flexibility in capacity exists, two or more ejectors, either single- or multistage, as required by the degree of compression, can be arranged to operate in parallel so that each set effects full compression of a portion of the total capacity.

It is evident that ejectors can readily be arranged in any desired combination to suit specific requirements.

Intercondenser. In a two-stage ejector, a condenser may be placed at the discharge of the stage that exhausts to intermediate vacuum, thereby condensing the motive steam and vapors and leaving only air and noncondensable gases to be handled by the subsequent stage. This arrangement has the effect of greatly reducing the amount of live steam required for total compression from suction to final-stage discharge and accordingly permits obtaining large capacities at high vacuum without excessive steam consumption. When condensers are used in this manner, they are called intercondensers.

Since intercondensers operate under a vacuum, it is necessary to provide means for draining the condensed ejector steam from surface-type intercondensers.

Aftercondenser. The use of an aftercondenser for condensing the steam discharged by a single-stage ejector or the final stage of a multistage assembly has no direct bearing on the performance of the ejector itself as to capacity and steam consumption. It is an optional feature determined by the requirements of the installation. For example, surface aftercondensers are used exclusively where ejectors are serving power-plant condensers, for the reason that complete heat recovery of the ejector steam is essential and further, the heat must be recovered in a closed system to prevent absorption of oxygen by the condensate, which is returned to the feed system.

The type most often used in power-plant application will be discussed here.

Two-stage Ejectors with Surface Inter-after Condenser. These units are used principally in connection with surface condensers serving prime movers in power plants and are capable of maintaining the very high vacuum produced in modern well-designed surface condensers (Fig. 8-12).

Modern power-plant turbines are designed to utilize effectively the highest vacuum that can be produced economically in the surface condenser commensurate with the temperature of the cooling water, and it is not uncommon to find condensers operating at absolute pressures considerably less than 1 in. Hg under cold-water conditions.

Main condenser condensate is used for cooling the inter-after condensers of these units, thus recovering practically all the heat in the ejector steam and thereby improving the overall efficiency of the plant. The small amount of condensate from the inter- and aftercondensers (condensed ejector steam) is returned to the condenser hot well and is thus returned to the boilers with deaerated feedwater. When the amount of condensate from the main condenser is inadequate for properly cooling the inter-after condenser, such as might occur during light loads or starting, a portion of the condensate is recirculated back to the main condenser, thus limiting the temperature rise to the required amount.

Figure 8-13 shows in diagrammatic form the installation and piping for a surface condenser equipped with two-stage ejectors and inter-after condenser for a typical power-plant application.

Vacuum Pumps In place of steam ejectors, mechanically driven vacuum pumps can be employed for air removal in surface condensers. The calculation of the required capacity is the same as previously described under Steam Ejectors.

Figure 8-14 shows a view of a typical mechanical vacuum pump used for this service.

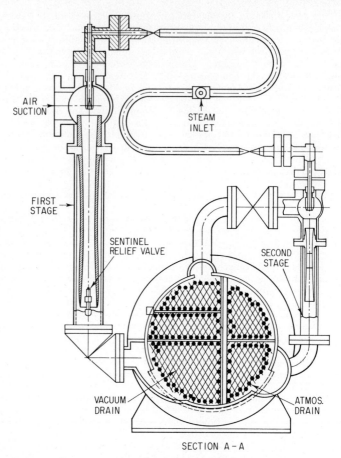

AIR
SUCTION

STEAM
INLET

FIRST
STAGE

SENTINEL
RELIEF VALVE

SECOND
STAGE

VACUUM
DRAIN

ATMOS.
DRAIN

SECTION A – A

Fig. 8-12   Cross section through a typical De Laval two-stage ejector.

Condensate Pumps

Condensate pumps are used to remove the water from the condenser hot well and to pump it to the deaerating heater in the feed system.   They should be sized to handle approximately 125 percent of the condensed steam flow; i.e., a condenser handling 100,000 lb/hr of steam would require a condensate pump rated at 250 gpm.   Condensate pumps usually operate with a small submergence and for this reason are a special design.

Single-stage horizontal pumps are used for the smaller power plant with heads up to 125 ft, while multistage pumps, suitable for heads of 200 ft or more, are used for the larger installations (see Fig. 8-15).   Where the available submergence is extremely low, vertical "pit-type" condensate pumps are frequently used in modern installations (see Fig. 8-16).

Condensate pumps are usually motor-driven and the pump discharge throttled to control condenser hot-well level.   A diagram of this control setup is shown in Fig. 8-17.

Condenser Circulating Pumps

Condenser circulating pumps are used to circulate cooling water through the condenser.   Their required capacity has already been established at the beginning of this

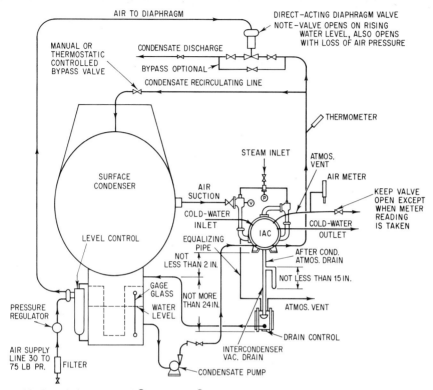

AIR TO DIAPHRAGM

DIRECT—ACTING DIAPHRAGM VALVE
NOTE—VALVE OPENS ON RISING WATER LEVEL, ALSO OPENS WITH LOSS OF AIR PRESSURE

MANUAL OR THERMOSTATIC CONTROLLED BYPASS VALVE

CONDENSATE DISCHARGE

BYPASS OPTIONAL

CONDENSATE RECIRCULATING LINE

THERMOMETER

SURFACE CONDENSER

STEAM INLET

ATMOS. VENT

AIR METER

KEEP VALVE OPEN EXCEPT WHEN METER READING IS TAKEN

AIR SUCTION

COLD-WATER INLET

COLD-WATER OUTLET

IAC

LEVEL CONTROL

EQUALIZING PIPE

NOT LESS THAN 2 IN.

AFTER COND. ATMOS. DRAIN

NOT LESS THAN 15 IN.

GAGE GLASS

WATER LEVEL

NOT MORE THAN 24 IN.

ATMOS. VENT

PRESSURE REGULATOR

DRAIN CONTROL

AIR SUPPLY LINE 30 TO 75 LB PR.

FILTER

INTERCONDENSER VAC. DRAIN

CONDENSATE PUMP

◁ GATE VALVE   ⋈ CHECK VALVE ⓥ VACUUM GAGE ⓟ PRESSURE GAGE

Fig. 8-13 Typical condensate and airflow piping diagram.

Fig. 8-14 Nash CL-1005 main condenser exhauster. (*Courtesy of Nash Engineering Company.*)

Fig. 8-15 Two-stage single-suction horizontally split case condensate pump.

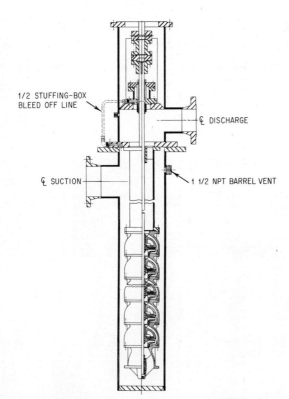

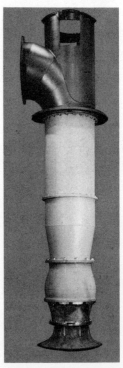

Fig. 8-16 Vertical five-stage condensate pump.
(*Courtesy of Byron Jackson Pump Division.*)

Fig. 8-18 Vertical mixed-flow
circulating-water pump.
(*Courtesy of Baldwin-Lima-
Hamilton Corporation*)

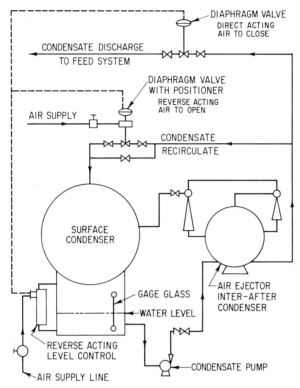

Fig. 8-17 Typical condenser level-control arrangement.

section.   Depending on the temperature of the available water, a rough rule for modern condensers calls for 0.1 to 0.25 gpm of circulating water per pound of steam condensed per hour.

The head required for these pumps is low, consisting mainly of the friction loss through the condenser tubes and the water boxes.   The static head, in many installations, must be overcome only during starting because of siphon action of the piping, and in this case the pump must overcome only the friction head of the system when operating at rated capacity.

The head required is in the neighborhood of 25 to 50 ft.

Vertical submerged units of the propeller or mixed-flow type are used in modern large installations (see Fig. 8-18).

Filtration Systems

Introduction

Filtration is the process of separating suspended solids from liquid by means of a porous media.

Solid materials can be grouped as follows:

1. A soluble phase where the material is soluble in the liquid as a true solution
2. A soluble or insoluble colloidal phase having a diameter of 0.001 to 1.0 micron
3. A supracolloidal phase of particles 1.0 to 100 microns in diameter
4. A coarse-particle phase which settles or floats

Filtration is concerned with groups 2 and 3, for group 1 requires chemical separation and group 4 is usually treated by settling or flotation.

The mechanism of separation within all filter media is not wholly understood but is generally accepted to be any combination of the following: straining, sedimentation, agglomeration, adsorption, molecular cohesion, streaming potential, zeta potential, and ionization.

When the filter media loses porosity because of retention of solids to the point that further filtration is ineffective or uneconomical, it must be cleaned or replaced.

Classification of Filters

Filters may be classified by combinations of:

1. Method of liquid movement through the filter, e.g.,
   a. Pressure
   b. Gravity
   c. Vacuum
2. Method of media handling, e.g.,
   a. Permanent
   b. Periodic replacement
   c. Terminal (end-of-cycle) replacement
3. Type of media, e.g.,
   a. Screen
   b. Cartridge
   c. Cloth or paper
   d. Coarse granular
   e. Filter aid

Simple Screen Filters

Screen filters have fixed pore sizes generally equal in size and not of great depth. Therefore, all solids above that pore size are prevented from passing through. The screen may be made of wire mesh, perforated metal screens, porous membranes, or the edges of a series of disks or spiral-wound wire. Screens are generally cleaned and reused.

Cartridge Filters

Cartridges are removable filter elements, preassembled or molded into the proper shape. They depend on depth filtration, removing solids within the labyrinth path of flow. They are made of fibrous material, metal wool, porous stone or sintered metal, filter aids, or combinations of these items. Cartridges are generally thrown away but may be cleaned or occasionally washed in place.

Cloth Filters

Filter cloths are made of paper, textiles, plastics, rubber, and various other materials or combinations thereof. Although filter cloths are used in cartridge filters, they are more generally used in filter presses or flat-bed indexing filters. Filter presses are a series of chambers formed by recessed filter plates or alternate frames and plates, forced together by a closing device. Filter cloths are placed over the filter plates and removed to be discarded or cleaned at the end of each cycle.

Flat-bed indexing filters use a roll of cloth which is indexed or pulled across the filtering area at the end of the cycle, or on a continuous basis.

Coarse Granular Filters

Granular filters (see Fig. 9-1) all depend to a varying degree on depth filtration. The granules should be of uniform size and density to get the most effective filtration. Some filters use more than one filter media, successively reducing in size so as to give series filtration. In this case, different densities must be used to allow restratification after backwashing. Flow is normally downward but may be upward. Some filters have a moving bed, which is externally cleaned and returned continuously.

Good filtration depends on even distribution of flow across the filter area. This can be a function of the underdrain system which supports and retains the filter media while allowing the liquid to flow through. The underdrain system and the overflow or backwash troughs must evenly distribute the backwash for complete cleaning.

Slow sand filters operate at very low flow rates of about 0.5 gal/(sq ft)(min)[gsfm] and are not backwashed but scraped on the surface. Rapid sand filters produce high clarity up to about 8 gsfm using multiple media. High-rate filters operate up to 20 gsfm or higher and normally produce a lesser degree of clarity.

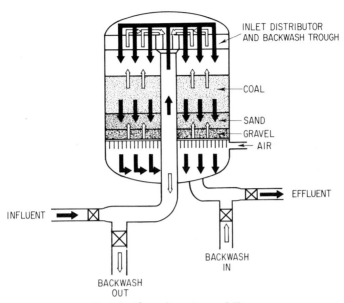

Fig. 9-1 Flow schematic—sand filter.

Precoat Filters

A very fine, porous material such as diatomaceous earth, cellulose fibers, or perlite is used as a filter aid or media in precoat filters (see Figs. 9-2 and 9-3). The filter aid is distributed on and held by a septum or filter element. A very thin coating (about

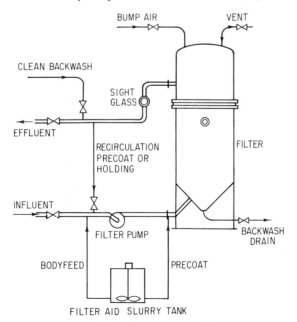

Fig. 9-2 Flow schematic—precoat filter.

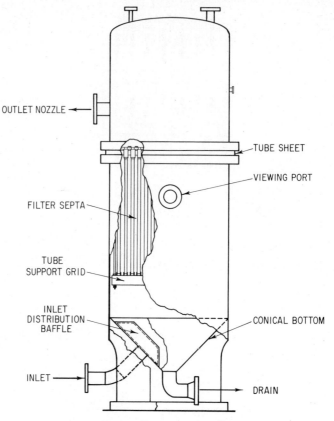

Fig. 9-3 Pressure precoat filter.

$\frac{1}{16}$ in.) is used initially and forms a "precoat." The septa may be tubular or flat but generally are vertical and present a large amount of surface area within a small volume. The filter aids have the property of bridging across openings much larger than their own particle size. The cake is distributed and held on by the velocity of the liquid through it. Therefore, flow must never be stopped, and when filtration ceases temporarily, a recirculating or holding flow is established.

The filter aid itself forms the filter media, and use of varying sizes or grades of particles will change the effluent clarity. Most removal is accomplished on the surface but some is due to the depth filtration of the many labyrinth passages. Most filter aids are also added continuously to the incoming stream as "body feed." This allows the cake to grow, entrapping the removed contaminants and maintaining porosity to increase the cycle length.

Figure 9-4 shows the installation of a precoat filter for municipal water treatment, and Fig. 9-5 shows the control panel for such a system.

Filtration with Otherwise Active Media

Sometimes filtration is accomplished as an adjunct to another type of removal such as ion exchange in high-rate demineralizers or powdered-resin filters. Because of the expense of the other process, filtration is usually treated as secondary and should not be the controlling design factor.

Fig. 9-4 3,500 gpm automatic precoat filter for municipal water treatment.

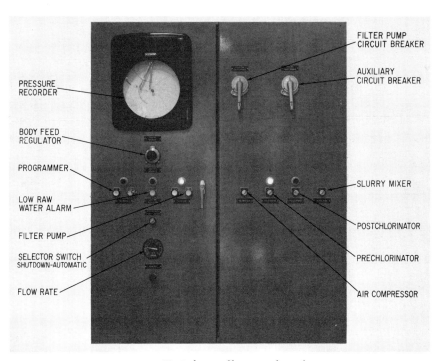

FILTER PUMP
CIRCUIT BREAKER

AUXILIARY
CIRCUIT BREAKER

PRESSURE
RECORDER

BODY FEED
REGULATOR

PROGRAMMER

SLURRY MIXER

LOW RAW
WATER ALARM

FILTER PUMP

POSTCHLORINATOR

SELECTOR SWITCH
SHUTDOWN-AUTOMATIC

PRECHLORINATOR

FLOW RATE

AIR COMPRESSOR

Fig. 9-5 Typical water-filter control panel.

Backwashing

Backwashing is the term applied to cleaning or renewing the filter media using liquid and/or air. For permanent media, backwashing dislodges the entrapped contaminants and transports them to waste. With replaceable media, the media and the contaminants are both removed.

Liquid is used both as a washing and a transporting medium. Generally a substantial velocity is required to perform these functions, although care must be exercised to prevent the loss of any permanent media.

Air is used either for agitation and scouring or to create a pressure release and impart high initial velocity to break free the contaminants.

Backwashing is one of the most important aspects of filtration. The ability to renew the full filtration capability after each cycle contributes to sustained effluent quality, reduced maintenance, and economical operation.

Pretreatment

Pretreatment is used with filtration either to condition the particulate matter by agglomeration so as to simplify or improve filtration, or to precipitate soluble compound into filterable particulate material.

One of the most common pretreatments is with coagulants, such as alum or ferric sulfate, which form a charged floc to attract small particles electrostatically.

Filter Selection

The selection of a filter to suit a specific process requires evaluation of many factors generally interrelated.

1. Required clarity of effluent
2. Maximum size of particle in effluent
3. Variation of inlet flow and/or solids concentration
4. Requirements for media replacement or backwashing
5. Disposal of removed solids and backwash liquid
6. Use of pretreatment
7. Operating economics

Since a greater degree of filtration requires higher operating costs, it is most important that care be exercised in determining this requirement. If a cutoff particle size is absolutely necessary, a screen or fixed-pore-size filter will be needed since depth filtration can give only a nominal rating based on average percentage removal for various sizes.

Filters work best under constant conditions. Variations affect effluent, equipment sizing, and economics.

Also of major importance is tying in the filter application with the backwashing of the equipment. The external requirements for backwashing and the disposal of the materials all affect the selection.

The effect of any pretreatment on the operation of a filter must be considered. Finally, when filters are capable of performing the requirements, a full evaluation of economics must be undertaken.

Economics

The costs of filtration are interrelated. They cover:

1. Power to overcome friction and filter pressure drop and to perform backwash
2. Backwash liquid
3. Media replacement
4. Pretreatment costs, if used
5. Amortization of investment
6. Maintenance
7. Labor

Power is utilized by pumps, compressors, agitators, controls, etc. An increase in maximum pressure drop will increase power consumption but is offset by less backwash cost and media replacement because of longer runs and by a reduction of first cost.

Backwash liquid is an expense if it costs to produce or handle it. Sometimes it is expressed in net output. Backwash air reflects in power and investment cost.

Media replacement is reduced by increasing the length of run with higher terminal pressure drop or lower filtration rates. However, these involve other offsetting costs.

With filter aid, precoat usage is a function of surface area and therefore filtration rate as well as length of run. An increase in body-feed usage will increase length of run and can result in reduced power usage or increased filtration rate with an associated reduction in first cost.

When pretreatment is for precipitation or treatment as an adjunct to filtration, this is an independent cost. Where presettling or conditioning of particles is involved, costs must be weighed against the resultant reduction in other filtration costs.

For true evaluation, first cost should be amortized as a cost of the final product. This should reflect interest rate on money, required time of depreciation, and equipment usage rate.

Maintenance includes not only equipment upkeep but also replacement of permanent filter media.

Most filtration systems can be automated, which may sizably reduce labor costs.

Testing and Instrumentation

TEST CODES

Nationally recognized test codes, standards, and test specifications all serve as a means of guiding the manufacturer and his customer in the evaluation of a piece of machinery either at the manufacturer's test facility or under actual service conditions at the customer's site.

These codes provide a common ground for communication by clearly establishing the goals of a test program, the procedure under which the test will be conducted, and the presentation of final results.

The purpose of the test covered by a code may be simply to verify the mechanical integrity of a machine, or it may include exhaustive testing to verify that performance guarantees have, in fact, been met. Test codes seldom specify absolute levels of performance but often do limit the tolerances, fluctuations, and deviations of both measurements and test conditions.

Most test codes were prepared as a cooperative effort by representatives of the manufacturer, the user of the machine, and the educator. The codes are generally thorough, well-written texts, which are periodically revised and updated by the issuing authorities. As is the case with any document, these test codes require judicial interpretation at times. This is generally accomplished formally or informally through consultations between the parties concerned with the test. Several of the codes even provide detailed lists of items to be discussed prior to the actual test.

By specifying that a machine is to be tested in accordance with a nationally recognized test code, purchasing contract language is simplified and the chance of ambiguity is reduced.

Test codes, therefore, are a convenient authoritative means of conveying a test program to those responsible for the test by those specifying the test.

Copies of the most common codes pertaining to De Laval products can be obtained from the following issuing authorities:

1. American Society of Mechanical Engineers. Power test codes dealing with pumps, compressors, turbines, and heat exchangers. United Engineering Center, 345 East 47th St., New York, N.Y. 10017.

2. American Petroleum Institute Guide for Inspection of Refinery Equipment. Presents requirements for pumps, compressors, turbines, gears, and heat exchangers. 1271 Avenue of the Americas, New York, N.Y. 10020.

3. Institute of Electrical and Electronic Engineers. Codes pertain to generators and generator drives. 345 East 47th St., New York, N.Y. 10017.

4. Hydraulic Institute Standards. Codes deal with centrifugal and positive-displacement pumps. 122 East 42nd St., New York, N.Y. 10017.

5. National Electrical Manufacturers Association. Presents codes dealing with generators and their drives. 155 East 44th St., New York, N.Y. 10017.

6. American Gear Manufacturers Association, 1330 Massachusetts Ave., N.W., Washington, D.C. 20005.

7. American National Standards Institute. Codes pertain to measurement of airborne noise. 10 East 40th St., New York, N.Y. 10016.

8. Heat Exchange Institute. Codes cover heat exchangers and steam-jet ejectors. 122 East 42nd St., New York, N.Y. 10017.

9. American Bureau of Shipping. Rules cover shipboard propulsion machinery, turbogenerators, and auxiliary marine machinery. 45 Broad St., New York, N.Y. 10004.

TEMPERATURE MEASUREMENT

Introduction

Measurement of temperature is generally considered to be one of the simplest and most accurate measurements performed in engineering. The desired accuracy in the measurement can be obtained, however, only by observance of suitable precautions in the selection, installation, and use of temperature-measuring instruments, and in proper interpretation of the results obtained with them.

There are four basic phenomena which form the basis for most temperature-measuring instruments. These are:

Change in physical dimensions or characteristics of liquids, metals, or gases
Changes in electrical resistance

Thermoelectric effect
Radiant energy

The following types of instruments are available for use under appropriate conditions:

Liquid-in-glass thermometer
Filled-system thermometer
Bimetallic thermometer
Resistance thermometer
Thermocouple thermometer
Radiation thermometer
Optical pyrometer

Liquid-in-glass Thermometer

A liquid-in-glass thermometer is one consisting of a thin-walled glass bulb attached to a glass capillary stem closed at the opposite end, with the bulb and a portion of the stem filled with an expansive liquid, the remaining part of the stem being filled with the vapor of the liquid or a mixture of this vapor and an inert gas. Etched on the stem is a scale in temperature degrees so arranged that, when calibrated, the reading corresponding to the end of the liquid column indicates the temperature of the bulb. The three types of liquid-in-glass thermometers (Fig. 10-1) are (1) partial immersion, (2) total immersion, and (3) complete immersion.

1. A partial-immersion thermometer is one which is designed to indicate temperature correctly when used with the bulb and a specified part of the liquid column in the stem exposed to the temperature being measured; the remainder of the liquid column and the gas above the liquid are exposed to a temperature which may or may not be different.

2. A total-immersion thermometer is one which is designed to indicate the temperature correctly when used with the bulb and the entire liquid column in the stem exposed to the temperature being measured, and the gas above the liquid exposed to a temperature which may or may not be different.

3. A complete-immersion thermometer is one which is designed to indicate the

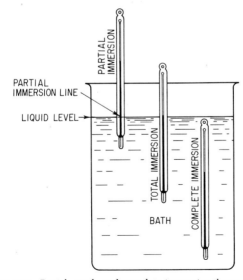

Fig. 10-1 Partial-, total-, and complete-immersion thermometer.

temperature correctly when used with the bulb, the entire liquid column in the stem, and the gas above the liquid exposed to the temperature being measured.

The operation of a liquid-in-glass thermometer depends on having the coefficient of expansion of the liquid greater than that of the bulb glass. As a consequence, an increase in temperature of the bulb causes the liquid to be expelled from the bulb, resulting in a rise in position of the end of the liquid column. The capillary stem attached to the bulb serves to magnify this change in volume on a scale.

The most frequently encountered source of error when using liquid-in-glass thermometers is the misuse or complete neglect of the emergent-stem correction. This correction derives from the use of the thermometer with a portion of the stem exposed to a different temperature from that of calibration. A common example is the use of partial immersion of a thermometer calibrated for total immersion. For detailed information on this correction, see the ASME Power Test Code on Temperature Measurement.

Filled-system Thermometer

A filled-system thermometer (Fig. 10-2) is an all-metal assembly consisting of a bulb, a capillary tube, and a bourdon tube, containing a temperature-responsive fill. Associated with the bourdon is a mechanical device which is designed to provide an indication or record of temperature.

The sensing element (bulb) contains a fluid which changes in physical characteristics with temperature. This change is communicated to the bourdon through a capillary tube. The bourdon provides an essentially linear motion in response to an internally impressed pressure or volume change.

Filled-system thermometers may be separated into two types: those in which the bourdon responds to volume changes and those which respond to pressure changes. The systems that respond to volume changes are completely filled with a liquid and

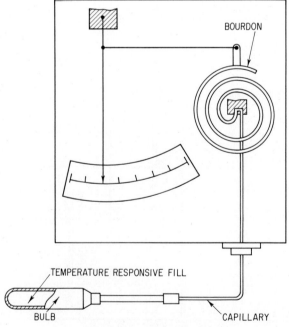

Fig. 10-2 Filled-system thermometer.

the system that responds to pressure changes is either filled with a gas or partially filled with a volatile liquid.   Filled-system thermometers have been classified[1] according to their principle of operation as follows:

Volumetric principle:
  Class I.   liquid-filled system
  Class V.   mercury-filled system
Pressure principle:
  Class II.   vapor-filled system
  Class III.   gas-filled system

Bimetallic Thermometer

A bimetallic thermometer (Fig. 10-3) is one consisting of an indicating or recording device, a sensing element called a bimetallic thermometer bulb, and a means for operatively connecting the two.

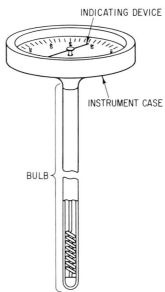

Fig. 10-3   Bimetallic thermometer.

The operation of a bimetallic thermometer depends upon the difference in thermal expansion of two metals.   The most common type of bimetallic thermometer used in industrial applications is one in which a strip of composite material is wound in the form of a helix or helices.   The composite material consists of dissimilar metals which have been fused together to form a laminate.   The difference in thermal expansion of the two metals produces a change in curvature of the strip with changes in temperature.   The helical construction is used to translate this change in curvature to rotary motion of a shaft connected to the indicating or recording device.

Resistance Thermometer

A resistance thermometer is a temperature-measuring instrument in which electrical resistance is used as a means of temperature measurement.   The instrument consists of a resistor, a resistance-measuring instrument, and electrical conductors connecting the two.   The resistor may be metallic (usually in wire form) or a thermistor (a thermally sensitive variable resistor made of ceramic-like semiconducting material).

[1] Scientific Apparatus Makers of America (SAMA).

The basis for resistance thermometry is the fact that most metals and some semi-conductors change in resistivity with temperature in a known, reproducible manner. Several materials are commonly employed for resistance thermometers, the choice depending on the compromises that may be accepted. Although the actual resistance-temperature relation must be determined experimentally, for most metals the following empirical equation holds very closely:

$$R_t = R_0(1 + At + Bt^2) \tag{1}$$

where R_t = resistance at temperature t
  R_0 = resistance at 0°F
  t = temperature, °F
A and B = constants depending on material

The temperature-resistance function for a thermistor is given by the following relationships:

$$R = R_0 e^k \tag{2}$$

$$k = \beta \left(\frac{1}{T} - \frac{1}{T_0}\right) \tag{3}$$

where R = resistance at any temperature T, °K
  R_0 = resistance at reference temperature T_0, °K
  e = base of napierian logarithms
  β = a constant (which usually has a value between 3,400 and 3,900, depending on the thermistor formulation or grade)

Thermocouple Thermometer

A thermocouple thermometer is a temperature-measuring instrument in which the electromotive force developed in a circuit comprised of two dissimilar metals is used as a means of temperature measurement. It consists of a device for measuring electromotive force, a sensing element (thermocouple), and electrical conductors operatively connecting the two.

The thermocouple thermometer operates on the principle that an electric current will flow in a closed circuit of two dissimilar metals when the junctions of the metals are at two different temperatures. Thermocouple materials are available for use within the approximate limits of −300 to 3200°F. Platinum is the generally accepted standard material to which the thermoelectric characteristics of other materials are referred. The emf-temperature relations of the conventional thermoelements vs. platinum are shown in Fig. 10-4.

For commercial application the most commonly used thermocouple material combination is iron-constantan.

The corresponding values of temperature and emf for the various types of thermocouples are given in Table 10-1.

The electrical conductors connecting the thermocouple and the measuring instrument may be the actual thermocouple wires, leads, or extension wires. Thermocouple leads are generally copper when the reference junctions of the thermocouple are maintained at some fixed temperature such as the ice point (32°F). Thermocouple extension wires have such temperature-emf characteristics relative to the thermocouple with which the wires are intended to be used that the thermocouple reference junction is in effect extended to the other end of the wires, as shown in Fig. 10-5.

Thermocouples may be joined in series. The series connection, in which the output is the arithmetic sum of the emfs of the individual thermocouples, may be used to obtain greater measurement sensitivity and accuracy. A series-connected thermocouple assembly is generally referred to as a thermopile and is used primarily in measuring small temperature differences. A schematic diagram of a series-connected thermocouple is shown in Fig. 10-6.

Thermocouples may also be joined in parallel. In the parallel-connected thermocouple circuit, a mean value of the individual thermocouples is indicated, and it will be the true arithmetic mean if all thermocouple circuits are of equal resistance. Should

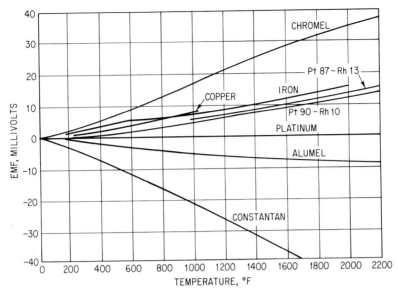

Fig. 10-4 Emfs of various materials vs. platinum.

TABLE 10-1   Temperature-Emf Relationships for Thermocouples

Temp, °F	Emf, mv					
	Pt vs. Pt 10Rh°	Pt vs. Pt 13Rh	Cr vs. alumel	Iron vs. constantan	Cr vs. constantan	Cu vs. constantan
32	0.000	0.000	0.00	0.00	0.00	0.000
200	0.595	0.596	3.82	4.91	5.87	3.967
400	1.474	1.504	8.31	11.03	13.75	9.525
600	2.458	2.547	12.86	17.18	22.25	15.773
						(700) 19.100
800	3.506	3.677	17.53	23.32	31.09	
1000	4.596	4.868	22.26	29.52	40.06	
1200	5.726	6.125	26.98	36.01	49.04	
1400	6.897	7.436	31.65	42.96	57.92	
1600	8.110	8.809	36.19			
1800	9.365	10.237	40.62			
2000	10.662	11.726	44.91			
2200	11.989	13.255	49.05			
2400	13.325	14.798	53.01			
2600	14.656	16.340				
2800	15.979	17.875				
3000	17.292	19.394				

° Pt 10Rh—90 percent platinum, 10 percent rhodium.   Pt 13Rh—87 percent platinum, 13 percent rhodium.   Alumel—94 percent nickel, 3 percent manganese, traces of aluminum and silicon. Constantan—57 percent copper, 43 percent nickel with small amounts of manganese and iron. Chromel—90 percent nickel, 10 percent chromium.

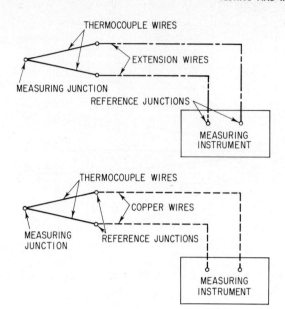

Fig. 10-5   Thermocouple thermometer systems.

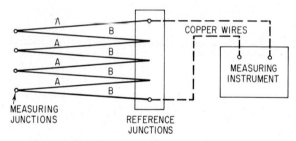

Fig. 10-6   Thermocouples connected in series.

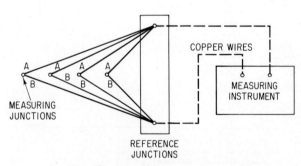

Fig. 10-7   Thermocouples connected in parallel.

one or more of the thermocouples become open-circuited, the indicated reading will be the mean of the remaining thermocouples. A schematic diagram of a parallel-connected thermocouple circuit is shown in Fig. 10-7.

The installation of extensive thermocouple equipment requires the services of qualified instrument technicians, and special attention should be given to extension wires, reference junctions, switches, and terminal assemblies.

Pyrometry

There are two distinct instruments referred to as pyrometers. They are the total-radiation pyrometer and the optical pyrometer. The total-radiation pyrometer accepts a controlled sample of total radiation and, through determination of the heating effect of the sample (thermocouple or thermopile), obtains a measure of temperature. The optical pyrometer employs optical means for estimating the change in average wavelength of visual radiation with temperature.

All bodies above absolute zero temperature radiate energy. This energy is transmitted as electromagnetic waves. Waves striking the surface of a substance are partially absorbed, partially reflected, and partially transmitted. These portions are measured in terms of absorptivity α, reflectivity ρ, and transmissivity τ, where

$$\alpha + \rho + \tau = 1$$

For an ideal reflector, a condition approached by a highly polished surface, $\rho \to 1$. Many gases represent substances of high transmissivity, for which $\tau \to 1$, and a blackbody approaches the ideal absorber, for which $\alpha \to 1$.

A good absorber is also a good radiator, and it may be concluded that the ideal radiator is one for which the value of α is equal to unity. When one refers to radiation as distinguished from absorption, the term emissivity ϵ is used rather than absorptivity α. The Stefan-Boltzmann law for the net rate of exchange of energy between two ideal radiators A and B is

$$q = \sigma(T_A^4 - T_B^4) \tag{4}$$

This may be modified for the nonideal case to read

$$q = \sigma \epsilon C_A (T_A^4 - T_B^4) \tag{4a}$$

where q = radiant-heat transfer, Btu/(hr)(sq ft)
C_A = configurational factor to allow for relative position and geometry of bodies (shape factor)
T_A and T_B = temperatures of bodies A and B, respectively, °R
σ = Stefan-Boltzmann constant = 0.173×10^{-8} Btu/(hr)(sq ft)(°R^4)

In application, recognition must be made of the fact that the radiators are nonideal. They are of nonoptimum geometry and position, absorption takes place in the intervening media, and the bodies themselves never possess emissivities equal to unity. Account of such things as these must be made through calibration.

If an ideal radiator is heated and the relative intensities at each wavelength are determined, an energy-distribution curve may be obtained. The rule governing this effect is the Wein displacement law, which may be expressed as follows:

$$E_\lambda = C_1 \lambda^{-5} e^{C_2/T} \tag{5}$$

where E_λ = energy emitted at wavelength λ
C_1 and C_2 = constants
e = base of napierian logarithms
T = absolute temperature of the body

Radiation Thermometer

A radiation thermometer consists of an optical system, used to intercept and concentrate a definite portion of the radiation emitted from the body whose temperature is being measured, a temperature-sensitive element, usually a thermocouple or thermopile, and an emf-measuring instrument. A balance is quickly established between the energy absorbed by the receiver and that dissipated by conduction through leads

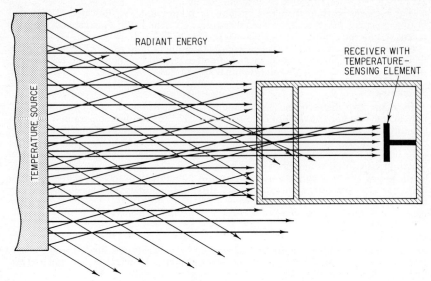

Fig. 10-8 A simplified form of total-radiation pyrometer.

and emission to surroundings. The receiver equilibrium temperature then becomes the measure of source temperature, with the scale established by calibration. Figure 10-8 shows, in simplified form, the method of operation of the total-radiation pyrometer.

Optical Pyrometer

Optical pyrometers use a method of matching as the basis for their operation. Generally, a reference temperature is provided in the form of an electrically heated lamp filament, and a measure of temperature is obtained by optically comparing the visual radiation from the filament with that from the unknown source. In principle, the radiation from one of the sources, as viewed by the observer, is adjusted to match that from the other source. Two methods are employed: (1) the current through the filament may be controlled electrically, through a resistance adjustment, or (2) the radiation accepted by the pyrometer from the unknown source may be adjusted optically by means of some absorbing device such as an optical wedge, polarizing filter, or iris diaphragm. The two methods are referred to, respectively, as the method using the variable-intensity comparison lamp and the method using the constant-intensity comparison lamp. In both cases the adjustment required is used as the means for temperature readout. Figure 10-9 illustrates schematically an arrangement of a variable-intensity pyrometer.

Special Problems

The number of special problems associated with temperature measurement is unlimited. Each instrument and application will have its own unique source of error; however, the most significant errors common to all will be discussed here.

The observed temperature readings should be corrected for instrumental errors using the calibration corrective values. Corrections at temperatures other than calibration temperatures should be determined by linear interpolation. Corrections for drift in calibration may be evaluated by periodic checking of the ice point or other convenient reference temperature and applying the observed change in correction at this temperature to all other correction values.

Basically, any temperature-measuring element senses temperature because heat is transferred between the surroundings and the element until some kind of equilibrium is reached. Error may be introduced by either of the three modes of heat transfer: convection, radiation, or conduction.

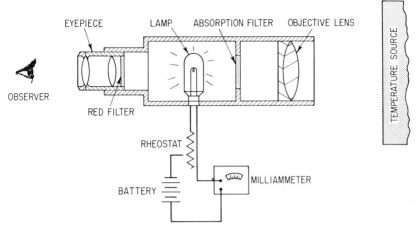

Fig. 10-9 Schematic diagram of an optical pyrometer.

The major heat flow, to and in some cases from the instrument probe, will be forced convection. This can be expressed by the following relation:

$$q = h_c A(t - t_p) \tag{6}$$

where q = heat transferred, Btu/hr
h_c = coefficient of heat transfer, Btu/(hr)(sq ft)(°F)
A = surface area of probe, sq ft
t = temperature of medium being measured, °F
t_p = temperature of probe, °F

Radiation between the probe and any source or sink of different temperature is a function of the difference in the fourth powers of the absolute temperatures. Therefore, it is generally true that radiation becomes an increasingly important source of temperature error as the temperatures and their differences increase. Increased temperature differences generally result from temperature extremes, either high or low, and in either of these cases, particular attention must be given to radiation effects.

Radiant-heat transfer is also a function of the emissivities of the members involved. For this reason, a bright, shiny probe is less affected by thermal radiation than is one tarnished or covered with soot.

Radiation error may be largely eliminated through proper use of thermal shielding. This consists in placing barriers to thermal radiation around the probe, which prevent the probe from "seeing" the radiant source or sink, as the case may be. For low-temperature work, such shields may simply be made of sheet metal appropriately formed to provide the necessary protection. At higher temperatures, metal or ceramic sleeves or tubes may be employed. In applications where gas temperatures are desired, care must be exercised so as not to cause stagnation of flow around the probe.

All temperature-measuring elements of the probe type must have mechanical support, and in general, some connection must be made to external indicating apparatus. Such connections provide conduction paths through which heat may be transferred to or away from the sensing element. Such transfer of heat will result in a discrepancy between the indicated temperature and that desired, namely, the temperature that would exist were the instrument not present. Factors influencing such error may be itemized as follows:

1. Conductivity of lead or support material
2. Lead and element sizes
3. Properties of surrounding media
4. Flow conditions over the probe

5. Presence of lead insulation or protective well
6. Configuration of the immersed leads
7. Temperature magnitudes and the form of temperature gradient along the leads or support
8. Depth of immersion of the probe

Measurement of Temperature in a Rapidly Moving Gas   When a probe is placed in a stream of gas, the flow will be partially stopped by the presence of the probe.   The lost kinetic energy will be converted to heat, which will have some bearing on the indicated temperature.   Two "ideal" states may be defined for such a condition.   A true state would be that observed by instruments moving with the stream, and a stagnation state would be that obtained if the gas were brought to rest and its kinetic energy completely converted to heat, resulting in a temperature rise.   A fixed probe inserted into the moving stream will indicate conditions lying between the two states.

An expression relating stagnation and true temperatures for a moving gas, assuming adiabatic conditions, may be written as follows:

$$t_t - t_s = \frac{V^2}{2g_cJc_p} \tag{7}$$

This relation may also be written as

$$\frac{t_s}{t_t} = 1 + \frac{(k-1)M^2}{2} \tag{8}$$

where t_s = stagnation or total temperature, °F
  t_t = true or static temperature, °F
  V = velocity of flow, fps
  g_c = gravitational constant, 32.2 ft/sec²
  J = mechanical equivalent of heat, ft-lb/Btu
  c_p = mean specific heat at constant pressure, Btu/(lb)(°F)
  k = ratio of specific heats
  M = Mach number

A measure of effectiveness of the probe in bringing about kinetic-energy conversion may be expressed by the relation

$$r = \frac{t_i - t_t}{t_s - t_t} \tag{9}$$

where t_i = temperature indicated by the probe, °F
  r = recovery factor

If $r = 1$, the probe would measure the stagnation temperature, and if $r = 0$, it would measure the true temperature.

Combining Eqs. (7) and (8), the following relationships are obtained:

$$t_t = t_i - \frac{rV^2}{2g_cJc_p} \tag{10}$$

or
$$t_s = t_i + \frac{(1-r)V^2}{2g_cJc_p} \tag{11}$$

The approximate range and accuracy of various temperature-measuring elements are given in Table 10-2.

TABLE 10-2 Approximate Range and Accuracy of Various Temperature-measuring Elements

Type	Range, °F	Accuracy, °F
Glass thermometers:		
Mercury-filled.	−38 to 760	0.5 to 2
Mercury- and nitrogen-filled . . .	−38 to 1000	0.5 to 10
Alcohol-filled	−95 to 150	1 to 2
Pressure-gage thermometers:		
Vapor-pressure type	20 to 400	2 to 10
Liquid- or gas-filled	−200 to 1000	2 to 10
Bimetallic thermometer	−100 to 1000	0.5 to 25
Thermocouples:		
Base metal.	−300 to 2000	0.5 to 20
Precious metal	−300 to 2800	0.5 to 20
Resistance thermometer	−400 to 1800	0.005 to 5
Thermistors	−150 to 500	°
Pyrometers:		
Optical	1400 up	20 for blackbody conditions
Radiation.	1000 up	20–30 for blackbody conditions

° Depends on aging.

PRESSURE MEASUREMENT

General Principles and Definitions

1. *Pressure* is defined as fluid force per unit area.

2. *Pressure relationships* (Fig. 10-10)

Differential pressure is the difference between any two pressures measured with respect to a common reference.

Absolute pressure is the differential pressure between any pressure and a perfect vacuum at a given point.

Gage pressure is the difference between absolute pressure and ambient atmospheric barometric pressure at a point.

Vacuum pressure is the difference between ambient atmospheric barometric pressure and a point below atmospheric pressure.

3. *Flow stream pressures*

Static pressure is pressure measured perpendicular to direction of flow.   This is the pressure you would sense if moving downstream with the fluid.

Total pressure is pressure in the direction of flow, where pressure as a function of direction is at a maximum.   Total pressure would be sensed if the stream were brought to rest isentropically.

Velocity pressure is the difference between static and total pressure measured at a specific region in the direction of flow.   It is called velocity head when measured in height of fluid.

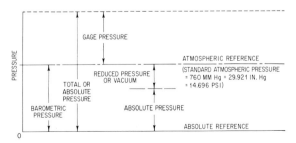

Fig. 10-10 Relations between absolute, gage, and barometric pressures.

Pressure Connections

1. *Sources of errors*

Flow errors—Leakage errors can be eliminated by proper sealing of connections. Errors due to friction, inertia, and lag errors in the gage piping, encountered in dynamic flow, can be minimized by using short, wide connecting tubes.

Turbulence errors—The static-pressure tap on the wall parallel to the flow should not be too large in order to prevent a disturbance in the flow, causing an inaccurate static reading; the tap, however, should be large enough to give a proper response. The area surrounding the pressure tap should be smooth to ensure that a burr or other obstruction will not affect the reading. The edge of the hole should be sharp and square. When the pressure is fluctuating, a damping device can be used to improve readability, although the accurate way would be to use a suitable recording instrument and determine the average pressure over a period of time.

2. *Static taps.* Static taps (Fig. 10-11a) should be at least 5 diameters downstream from symmetrical pipe fittings and 10 diameters downstream from unsymmetrical fittings, according to the ASME Power Test Code. Where possible, a weldolet or pipe coupling should be welded to the outside of the pipe and the hole then drilled through to the main pipe. Since the error increases with the velocity pressures, care must be taken in high-velocity areas to ensure sharp, square holes that are as small as possible (down to $1/16$ in.) to keep the disturbance and error to a minimum. In low-velocity areas, larger holes should be used to improve dynamic-pressure response and prevent clogging. When flow is nonuniform, several taps should be used along the periphery of the pipe.

3. *Static tubes.* Static tubes (Fig. 10-11b) are used for measurement of static pressure in a free stream such as on a moving plane. Static taps in the wall are preferable, since static tubes disturb the flow, making calibration necessary for accurate measurement. Unless one expects a static-pressure distribution, wall taps should be used.

4. *Impact tubes or pitot tubes.* An impact tube (Fig. 10-11c) faces directly into the flow, giving a total-pressure reading. Velocity pressure is determined by taking a static reading, preferably along a wall, and taking the difference; impact tubes can be used to get a velocity profile by traversing. Maximum velocity direction can be determined by rotating the tube.

5. *Piping arrangement.* Connecting piping (Fig. 10-11f) should be arranged to avoid liquid pockets in gas-filled lines and air pockets in liquid-filled lines. This is accomplished by having gas-filled lines sloping up to the measuring instrument and liquid-filled lines sloping downward to the instrument. Both types should have vents close to the instrument to bleed lines. More vents might be needed if lines must have dips or twists in them. For vacuum pressures an air bleed allowing very small flow should be provided near the instrument, to keep lines purged of condensate, etc., between readings. This can be accomplished by a valve, or a very small hole can be drilled near the top of the manometer, which would be closed or covered when taking a reading. In the case of mechanical or electrical transducers as measuring instruments, the same procedures hold true, but in hot-steam lines it might be necessary to loop the line and fill with water up close to the instrument to protect the instrument from the high temperature. For differential measurement the arrangement shown in Fig. 10-11e should be used to prevent and detect leakage.

Liquid-level Gage

1. A manometer measures pressure by balancing it against a column of liquid with a known density and height. Selection of the liquid is dependent on test conditions; however, it always must be more dense than the flowing fluid and immiscible with it. Other factors to consider are the specific gravity, the useful temperature range, the flash point, the viscosity, and the vapor pressure. The basic manometer liquids used are water (specific gravity 1), mercury (specific gravity 13.57), red oil (Meriam) (specific gravity 0.827), tetrabromo ethylene (specific gravity 2.95), and carbon tetrachloride (specific gravity 1.595). Special fluids are also available with specific gravities of 1.20

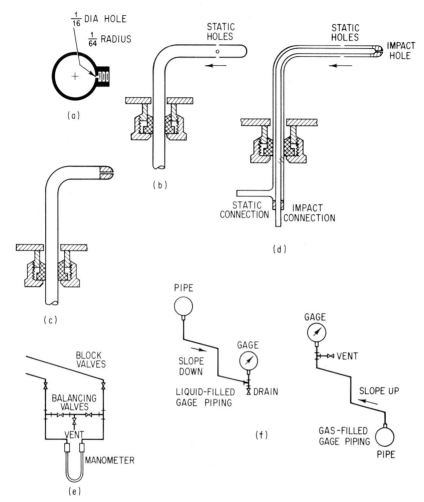

Fig. 10-11 (*a*) Static-pressure connection. (*b*) Static tube. (*c*) Impact tube. (*d*) Combination pitot–static tube. (*e*) Cross connection. (*f*) Typical pressure-gage piping arrangements.

and 1.75 (Ref. 4, page 10-21). The manometer fluid used must be kept pure to assure that the specific gravity remains constant.

2. The basic types of manometers are U-tube and cistern (Fig. 10-12).

In the U tube the pressure on one leg balances the pressure in the other leg. By performing a fluid balance and knowing the density of all fluids and their height, one can calculate the pounds per square inch difference between the two. Many times the second leg is open to atmospheric pressure so that the pressure difference represents gage pressure and must be added to barometric pressure to find the total pressure. When the second leg is connected to a pressure other than atmospheric, it is called a differential pressure and represents the direct difference between the two pressures.

In the well- or cistern-type manometer one leg has a cross section much larger than the other one. The zero adjustment in the cistern is usually made manually with an

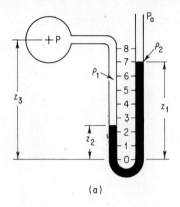

(a)

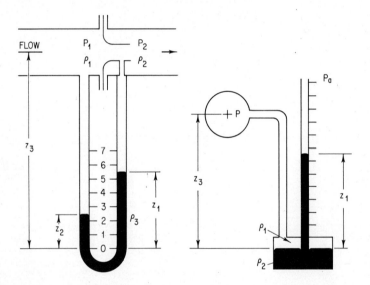

Fig. 10-12 Manometer types. (a) U-tube manometer, open to atmosphere. (b) Differential U-tube manometer. (c) Cistern manometer.

adjusting screw. Then the pressure is found by the following formula:

$$P = P_a + Z_1 \frac{g}{g_c} \rho_2 - Z_3 \frac{g}{g_c} \rho_1$$

where g = acceleration due to gravity
g_c = dimensional constant
ρ = density of liquid

Special types of manometers sometimes used for more accurate measurement include the inclined manometer, the micromanometer, and U tubes installed with hook gages, as well as many special types of manometers for vacuum measurement, which will be mentioned later.

3. Barometers are a special case of a manometer to measure atmospheric pressure.

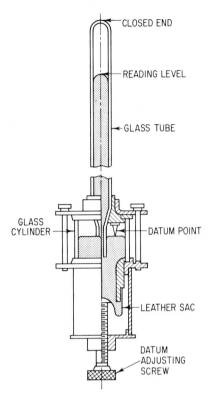

CLOSED END

READING LEVEL

GLASS TUBE

GLASS
CYLINDER

DATUM POINT

LEATHER SAC

DATUM
ADJUSTING
SCREW

Fig. 10-13 Fortin barometer.

A primary barometer would be a U tube with one end open to the atmosphere and the other end connected to a continuously operating vacuum pump.

In many cases a Fortin-type barometer (Fig. 10-13) is suitable.   In this case the mercury in the well is exposed to the atmosphere with the other end evacuated and sealed. All barometer readings should be corrected for temperature, local gravity, and capillary effect.   To give the correct atmospheric pressure, an aneroid barometer, which is a special type of elastic gage, is sometimes used in place of a manometer-type barometer because of the ease of transportation.

Dead-weight Tester and Gages

1. *Principle, design, and operation testers*

Dead-weight testers are the most common instrument for calibrating elastic gages with pressures in the ranges of 15 to about 10,000 psi or higher.

Dead-weight testers (Fig. 10-14) have a piston riding in a cylinder with a close clearance.   The total weight on the piston including that of the platform and the piston itself and any additional weights, divided by the cross-section area of the piston (which is usually an even fraction of inch such as $\frac{1}{8}$ sq in.), determine the pressure on the gage being tested.   It is necessary to have the piston in a vertical position and spinning freely when taking the measurement.   The inertia created by spinning minimizes the viscous drag on the piston by spreading oil around the diameter.   Maximum error is usually one-tenth of 1 percent of the pressure measured.

Operation.   To operate, put the desired weight on the piston, close the pressure-release valve, and pressurize the tester's fluid with the displacer pump or screw-type

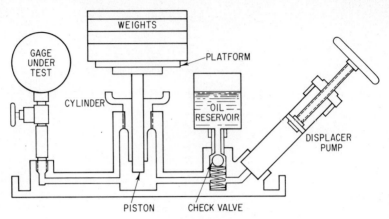

Fig. 10-14 Dead-weight tester.

ram until the weights are lifted and the piston is floating. Then slowly spin the piston and take your gage reading and compare it with the equivalent pressure created by the piston and weights. The gage reading must then be corrected accordingly.

Special testers include high-pressure, low-pressure, and the lever types. For very high pressure (above 10,000 psi) it is necessary to make use of a tester that makes adjustments to minimize the leakage and to correct for deformation of the piston and cylinder. Low-pressure testers (0.3 up to 50 psi are covered) use air as the working fluid for a more accurate measurement. Lever-type testers use a force-amplifying linkage to apply weight to the piston with an inertial wheel on a motor to keep the piston spinning freely.

2. *Dead-weight gages*

Dead-weight gages are mainly used to measure a relatively stable pressure so it can be maintained. These gages give very precise measurements but are not practical for a test with a wide range of pressures, since many weight changes would be necessary.

3. *Corrections*

Corrections include those necessary for local gravity, weight measurement, effective area, head, and buoyancy adjustments. The head correction is usually the only one necessary where accuracy of ¼ percent is satisfactory.

Elastic Gages

1. In elastic gages, an elastic member is caused to stretch or move by a given pressure. The movement is amplified through a linkage and usually is used to rotate a pointer indicating the pressure reading in relation to atmospheric pressure.

2. Bourdon gages (Fig. 10-15) contain a hollow tube curved in an arc that tends to straighten as internal pressure is applied, moving the linkage and pointer to indicate the pressure reading.

Differential as well as compound, vacuum, and straight-pressure bourdon gages are available. Differential-pressure gages have either the bourdon tube enclosed in a seal-pressurized case, or two bourdon gages—one subtracting from the other. Ranges go from 0 to 15 psig up to 0 to 100,000 psig as well as the vacuum range.

3. Bellows gages (Fig. 10-16) have a bellow or elastic chamber expanding to actuate the gage. They are usually used in low-pressure applications with maximum reading of about 50 psig.

4. Diaphragm gages (Fig. 10-17) use a flexible diaphragm as the inducer. This type is suitable for ranges from 0 to 1 in. Hg up to 200 psi. Variations of this gage are valuable in special cases where the process fluid must be kept separate from the gage as when the fluid is very hot (up to 1500°F with special modifications) or corrosive, or when the fluid would tend to clog other gages.

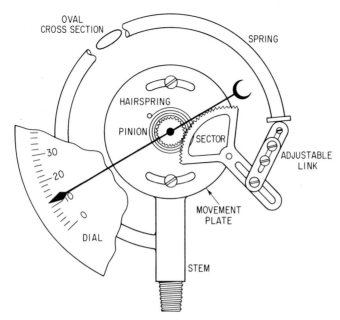

Fig. 10-15 Bourdon gage.

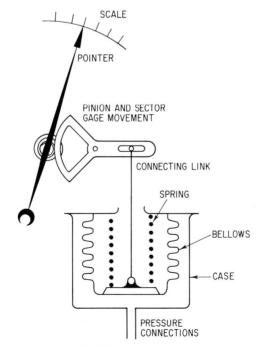

Fig. 10-16 Bellows gage.

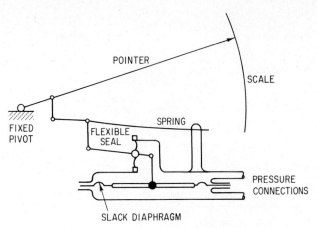

Fig. 10-17 Slack-diaphragm gage.

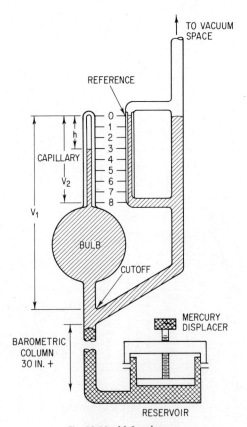

Fig. 10-18 McLeod gage.

5. All elastic gages must be calibrated continually to ensure accuracy. Accuracy to one-half of 1 percent or better of full scale can be obtained.

6. Gages must be bled for assurance that neither air nor water bubbles are present in the lines. To obtain a gage reading, first make sure the linkage is free. This is done with a light tap to the gage. When damping the gage needle by closing down on the inlet line, the needle is left fluctuating slightly to indicate the line is still open.

Special Measuring Devices

For low-pressure measurement the McLeod gage (Fig. 10-18) is a primary measuring device. The calibration is dependent only upon dimensional measurements. Other direct-reading pressure gages, for low pressure, are the mercury micromanometer, the Hickman butyl phthalate manometer, and the consolidated diaphragm comparator. Gages measuring properties directly convertible to pressure are the thermal-conductivity gages (thermocouple gage, Pirani gage), ionization gages (Phillips-Penning gage, Alphatron gage), and the molecular-vacuum gage.

Electrical transducers can be used on many pressure-measuring applications. Various types can be used with corrosive fluids and at high temperatures and pressures. The profession does not regard electrical transducers as the most accurate form of measurement. However, they do have advantages in some cases; for example, the readings they produce can be easily amplified and are suitable for input to continuous graphical plotting.

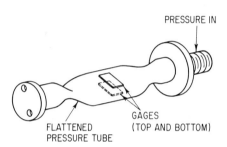

PRESSURE IN

FLATTENED PRESSURE TUBE

GAGES (TOP AND BOTTOM)

Fig. 10-19 Bonded strain gage.

Many of these gages measure resistance change of a wire or strain gage deformed by pressure. These instruments can be calibrated to measure pressure directly. There are two basic ways of mounting these gages. With bonded strain gages (Fig. 10-19) they are usually mounted on a diaphragm or tube that will deform as pressure is applied, changing the resistance of the gage. With unbonded strain gages (Fig. 10-20) a thin wire is usually wrapped around a sensing element that deforms and stretches the wire, changing its resistance, which can also be converted to pressure. Another special-type resistance gage for high-pressure reading is the bulk-modulus pressure gage (Fig. 10-21), which uses direct pressure on a loosely wound coil of fine wire to get a resistance change. The sensing mechanism is separated from the process fluid by a bellows. Other specialized types use differences in inductance or capacitance and correlate them to pressure.

References

1. T. G. Beckwith and N. Lewis Buck, "Mechanical Measurements," pp. 332–354, Addison-Wesley Publishing Company, Inc., Reading, Mass., 1961.
2. Consolidated Electrodynamics, Transducer, *General Catalog Bulletin* 1322, December, 1965.
3. ASME Power Test Code, Instruments and Apparatus, Part 2, Pressure Measurement, NSA, ASME, 1964.
4. *Meriam Standard Indicating Fluid Bulletin* IM-11.

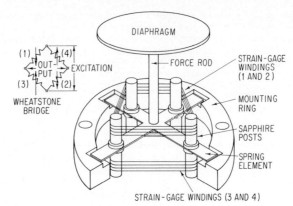

Fig. 10-20 Unbonded strain gage.

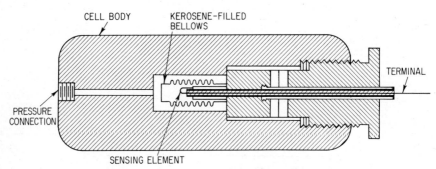

Fig. 10-21 Section through a bulk-modulus pressure gage.

FLOW MEASUREMENT

General

The three most extensively used types of flow-metering devices are the thin-plate square-edged orifice, the flow nozzle, and the venturi tube. They are differential-head instruments and require secondary elements for measurement of the differential pressure produced by the primary element. The Supplement to ASME Power Test Codes, Instruments and Apparatus (Ref. 1, page 10–27), describes construction of the above primary flow-measuring elements and their installation as well as installation of the secondary elements. The method of flow measurement, the equations for flow computation, and the limitations and accuracy of measurements are discussed. Charts and tables showing the necessary flow coefficients as a function of Reynolds number and diameter ratio β are included in the standards. Charts of the expansion factor for compressible fluids are given.

Some characteristic features of various types of primary elements are listed in the following:

Orifice. Simple, inexpensive, well-established coefficient of discharge, high head loss, low capacity for given pipe size, danger of suspended-matter accumulation, requires careful installation of pressure connections.

Flow nozzle. High capacity, more expensive, loss comparable with that of orifice, requires careful installation of pressure connections.

Venturi tube. High capacity, low head loss, has integral pressure connection, most expensive, greater weight and size.

Nomenclature

a = throat area of the primary element, sq in.
C = coefficient of discharge
d = throat diameter of the primary element, in.
D = pipe diameter, in.
$F = 1/\sqrt{1 - \beta^4}$, velocity-of-approach factor
F_a = thermal-expansion factor
h = manometer differential pressure, in.
h_w = manometer differential pressure, in. H_2O at 68°F
k = ratio of specific heats
$K = CF$ = combined-flow coefficient for orifices, velocity-of-approach factor included
n = numerical factor dependent upon units used
q = capacity of flow, gpm
Q_i = capacity of flow, cfm, at conditions i

$r = \dfrac{P_2}{P_1}$ = pressure ratio across flow nozzle, where P_1 and P_2 are absolute pressures

w = rate of flow, lb/sec
w_h = rate of flow, lb/hr
w_m = rate of flow, lb/min
Y = net-expansion factor for square-edged orifices
Y_a = adiabatic-expansion factor for flow nozzles and venturi tubes

$\beta = \dfrac{d}{D}$ = diameter ratio

γ = specific weight of flowing fluid at inlet side of primary element, lb/cu ft
γ_i = specific weight of flowing fluid at conditions i

Primary-element Construction and Installation

The primary element may be installed within a continuous section of pipe flowing full, or at the inlet or exit of a pipe or a plenum chamber. Orifice and venturi tube are usually installed within the pipe. The flow nozzle may be installed either way: within, at inlet, or at outlet of the pipe.

In De Laval's practice it is customary to use a venturi tube installed within a continuous section of pipe in pump-acceptance tests, and a flow nozzle at the exit of the discharge pipe in compressor-acceptance tests. However, other arrangements are also used. The construction of the primary elements and the example of their installation are given in the following paragraphs.

Orifice (Fig. 10-22) The recommended diameter ratio $\beta = d/D$ is from 0.25 to 0.75. The thickness of the orifice plate shall be not less than shown in the table below.

Pipe size, in.	Orifice thickness t, in.	
	Low temp, below 600°F	High temp, above 600°F
Up to 3	$3/32 \pm 1/32$	$1/4$
4–6	$5/32 \pm 1/32$	$3/8$
7–8	$1/4 \pm 1/16$	$1/2$
10 and over	$3/8 \pm 1/8$	$1/2$–$3/4$

Three types of pressure connections may be used: vena contracta taps, $1D$ and $\frac{1}{2}D$ taps, and flange taps. Appropriate discharge coefficients have to be used in each case.

Flow Nozzle The flow nozzle should be of either the low- or high-ratio, long-radius type as shown in Figs. 10-23 to 10-25. The diameter ratio β should be from 0.25 to 0.70, although ASME Power Test Codes (Ref. 2, page 10–27) recommend the β range between 0.40 and 0.60.

Venturi Tube The proportions of the standard-form (Herschel-type) venturi tube and its installation are shown in Fig. 10-25. Special forms (venturi-nozzle tube for high-

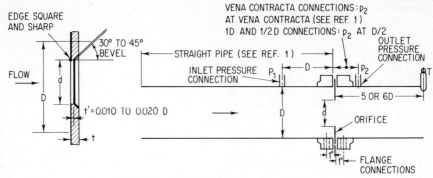

Fig. 10-22 Orific construction and installation.

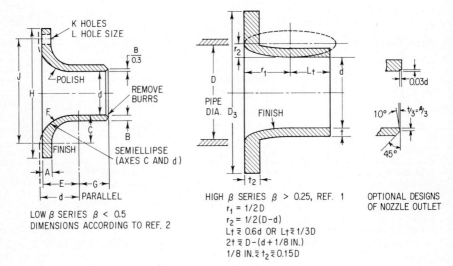

Fig. 10-23 Dimensional relations of ASME long-radius flow nozzles.

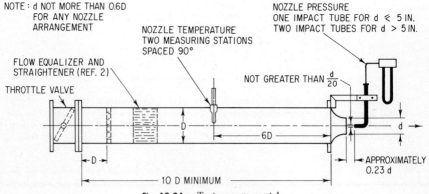

Fig. 10-24a Test arrangement A.

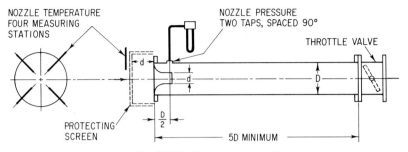

NOZZLE TEMPERATURE
FOUR MEASURING
STATIONS

NOZZLE PRESSURE
TWO TAPS, SPACED 90°

THROTTLE VALVE

d

d

D

PROTECTING
SCREEN

$\frac{D}{2}$

5D MINIMUM

Fig. 10-24b   Test arrangement *B*.

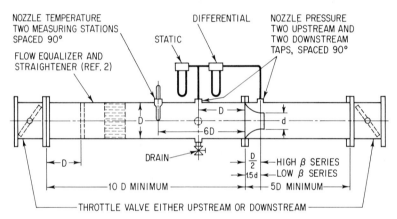

NOZZLE TEMPERATURE
TWO MEASURING STATIONS
SPACED 90°

FLOW EQUALIZER AND
STRAIGHTENER (REF. 2)

DIFFERENTIAL

STATIC

NOZZLE PRESSURE
TWO UPSTREAM AND
TWO DOWNSTREAM
TAPS, SPACED 90°

D

D

6D

d

D

DRAIN

$\frac{D}{2}$

15d

HIGH β SERIES

LOW β SERIES

D

10 D MINIMUM

5D MINIMUM

THROTTLE VALVE EITHER UPSTREAM OR DOWNSTREAM

Fig. 10-24c   Test arrangement *C*.

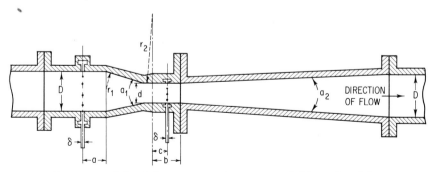

r_2

D

r_1 a_1 d

a_2

DIRECTION
OF FLOW

D

δ

δ

c

a

b

Fig. 10-25   Proportions of Herschel-type venturi tubes recommended by Technical Committee 30 on Measurement of Fluid Flow of the International Organization for Standardization. $a = 0.25D$ to $0.75D$ for 4 in. $\leqq D \leqq$ 6 in., $0.25D$ to $0.50D$ for 6 in. $< D \leqq$ 32 in., $b = d$, $c = d/2$, $\delta = ^3/_{16}$ to $^1/_2$ in. according to D, annular pressure chamber with at least four piezometer vents, $r_2 = 3.5d$ to $3.75d$, $r_1 = 0$ to $1.375D$, $a_1 = 21° \pm 2°$, $a_2 = 5°$ to $15°$.

pressure feedwater application, venturi-insert nozzle) may be used. They need individual calibration, however, while charts may be used for the standard form.

Calculation of Flow Rates

Incompressible Fluids The flow of any liquid through an orifice, flow nozzle, or venturi tube is determined by the following equation:

$$w = \frac{CaF_a n\gamma}{\sqrt{1-\beta^4}} \sqrt{2gh} \tag{1}$$

With the units in American practice, Eq. (1) is written

$$w_h = 359CFd^2F_a \sqrt{h_w\gamma} \tag{2}$$

Compressible Fluids To compensate for the change in specific weight as the fluid passes through the primary element, the equation must be modified by the expansion factor Y for orifices or Y_a for nozzles.

Orifices

$$w_h = 359CFd^2F_aY \sqrt{h_w\gamma} \tag{3}$$

Flow nozzles and venturi tubes

$$w_h = 359CFd^2F_aY_a \sqrt{h_w\gamma} \tag{4}$$

Quite often the flow coefficient $K = CF$ is specified for use in Eqs. (2) and (3) for orifices.

De Laval Applications With particular reference to the methods used at De Laval, the above equations assume the forms shown below.

Venturi tube. For measurement of the flow rate of water at 68°F with a *venturi tube* with mercury used as the manometer liquid, and if a value of 0.984 is used for the flow coefficient, Eq. (2) becomes

$$q = 19.79 \frac{d^2}{\sqrt{1-\beta^4}} \sqrt{h_0} \tag{5}$$

where h_0 = manometer differential pressure, in. Hg at 68°F

If water at a temperature other than 68°F is metered, a temperature correction should be made.

The coefficient of 0.984 is applicable for β values from 0.25 to 0.75 in pipes of 2 up to 32 in. provided the Reynolds number is greater than 200,000. The Hydraulic Institute Standards (Ref. 3, page 10-27) require a minimum velocity of 20 fps in the throat for the rated flow of the pump.

Flow nozzle. For measurement of airflow with *flow-nozzle* arrangement A (see Fig. 10-24a),

$$w_m = 5.983CFd^2Y_a \sqrt{h_w\gamma} \tag{6}$$

and

$$Q_i = \frac{w_m}{\gamma_i} \tag{7}$$

where

$$Y_a = r^{1/k} \left[\frac{k}{k-1} \frac{1-r^{(k-1)/k}}{1-r} \right]^{1/2} = \text{adiabatic-expansion factor} \tag{8}$$

The formula applies to subcritical flow with pressure ratio P_2/P_1 preferably greater than 0.7.

Unless the nozzle in this arrangement has been individually calibrated, the value of the flow coefficient should be taken as 0.99, provided that the throat Reynolds number exceeds 200,000. For nozzles within the pipe and using pipe taps, the coefficient of discharge for pipe Reynolds numbers above 100,000 varies from 0.980 to 0.993, depending on β.

Table 10-3 gives approximate flow rates for different nozzle sizes. It is useful for selecting a suitable nozzle for air tests with flow-nozzle arrangements A and B. It lists the basic design parameters of a long-radius low-β-series nozzle (see Fig. 10-23) for widely used flow rates.

TABLE 10-3 Long-radius Low-ratio Nozzle (Ref. 2)

d	A	B	C	E	F	G	H	J	K	L	Approx. flow rates, cfm	
											10 in. H$_2$O	40 in. H$_2$O
2.000	1.000	0.313	1.33	1.938	0.10	1.500	11.00	9.50	8	0.875	250	500
2.500	1.000	0.375	1.67	2.422	0.13	1.875	11.00	9.50	8	0.875	400	800
3.000	1.000	0.375	2.00	2.906	0.15	2.250	11.00	9.50	8	0.875	575	1,150
4.000	1.125	0.438	2.67	3.875	0.20	3.000	13.50	11.75	8	0.875	1,000	2,000
5.000	1.188	0.500	3.33	4.844	0.25	3.750	16.00	14.25	12	1.000	1,600	3,200
6.000	1.250	0.500	4.00	5.812	0.30	4.500	19.00	17.00	12	1.000	2,250	4,500
8.000	1.438	0.625	5.33	7.750	0.40	6.000	23.50	21.25	16	1.125	4,000	8,000
10.000	1.688	0.625	6.67	9.688	0.50	7.500	27.50	25.00	20	1.250	6,250	12,500
12.000	1.875	0.750	8.00	11.625	0.60	9.000	32.00	29.50	20	1.375	9,000	18,000
18.000	2.375	1.000	12.00	17.438	0.90	13.500	46.00	42.75	32	1.625	20,000	40,000
24.000	2.750	1.125	16.00	23.250	1.20	18.000	59.50	56.00	44	1.625	36,000	72,000

Orifice. Equation (2) is used for measuring the flow rate of water with *orifice* and Eq. (3) for measuring the rate of flow of air. Reference 1 gives the tables of the values of flow coefficient K for different pipe diameters as a function of diameter ratio β and pipe Reynolds number R_D. The excerpts from the tables in Ref. 1 are given in Table 10-4 for the three types of pressure-tap locations. The values below the stepped line are extrapolations and subject to twice the tolerance given in Table 10, Ref. 1.

TABLE 10-4 Values of Flow Coefficient K, Velocity-of-approach Factor Included, for 8-in. Pipe

β	Reynolds number R_D						
	10,000	50,000	100,000	200,000	500,000	10^6	10^7
	Flange taps						
0.250	0.6056	0.5992	0.5984	. . . . .	0.5978	0.5977	0.5976
0.500	0.6527	0.6284	0.6252	. . . . .	0.6229	0.6226	0.6223
0.750	0.9022	0.7565	0.7383	. . . . .	0.7272	0.7218	0.7202
	Taps at 1D and ½D						
0.250	0.6008	0.5976	0.5969	0.5963	0.5959	0.5956	0.5952
0.500	0.6326	0.6254	0.6237	0.6225	0.6214	0.6209	0.6200
0.750	0.7792	0.7533	0.7471	0.7428	0.7389	0.7370	0.7338
	Vena contracta taps						
0.250	0.6024	0.5977	0.5966	0.5958	0.5951	0.5948	0.5942
0.500	0.6355	0.6263	0.6241	0.6225	0.6212	0.6205	0.6193
0.750	0.7760	0.7517	0.7460	0.7419	0.7383	0.7365	0.7335

References

1. Supplement to ASME Power Test Codes, PTC 19.5; 4-1959, chap. 4, Flow Measurement, Part 5, Measurement of Quantity of Materials, Instruments, and Apparatus.
2. ASME Power Test Codes, PTC 10-1965, Compressors and Exhausters.
3. Hydraulic Institute Standards, 11th ed., 1965.

DATA PROCESSING ON ELECTRONIC COMPUTERS

The first and still alive computer is the Chinese abacus. In the mid-1600s, Pascal in France built the first machine designed to make addition. Charles Babbage, an Englishman, in 1822 built a difference engine, designed to compute the square of successive numbers. The engine's memory consisted of banks of wheels engraved with the 10 digits. He also had a vision of an analytical engine conceived to add, multiply, divide, and ask for more data. Babbage proposed to feed his engine with punched cards. This entirely mechanical machine was the forerunner of the modern computer.

In 1939, Aiken, with IBM support, conceived the digital computer, the Mark I, which was in operation at Harvard in 1943. The first electronic digital computer, named ENIAC, designed by Drs. J. P. Eckert and J. W. Mauchly, was put in operation in 1946 at the Moore School of Engineering, University of Pennsylvania. It required 19,000 vacuum tubes and hundreds of thousands of other electrical parts. Dr. John von Neumann developed the idea of the internally stored program where the directions for the computation, called instructions as distinct from data, are stored in the computer memory. The first computer, using internally stored instructions, was built at the Institute for Advanced Study at Princeton, N.J., in 1952.

The manufacture of electronic digital computers has grown into a multibillion-dollar business. The transistor has replaced the vacuum tube; the calculating speeds have greatly increased. The major companies engaged in manufacturing of electronic computers are International Business Machines Corp., Radio Corporation of America, General Electric, Burroughs, Control Data, Sperry Rand, Honeywell, Scientific Data Systems, and Electronic Associates.

There are two types of computers: the analog and the digital. Analog computers are basically machines which will duplicate physical phenomena. The word analog comes from analogy. An example is a wind tunnel. Such a computer is built to simulate electronically the conditions of a wind tunnel. Preliminary tests can be run in the analog computer.

Digital computers are basically high-speed calculating machines (Fig. 10-26). Digital by definition means "of numbers." The word "bit," the abbreviation for "binary digit," is being used in computer language. There are two binary digits, 0 and 1. Most digital computers operate on the binary system. A light switch is binary since it is either "on" or "off." The example which follows explains the system.

The number 2345 can be written as

$$2 \times 10^3 + 3 \times 10^2 + 4 \times 10^1 + 5 \times 10^0 = 2345$$

The number 10 is called the *radix* and is used in the decimal system.
The number 2345 written to the base 2 (binary) is

$$1 \times 2^{11} + 1 \times 2^8 + 1 \times 2^5 + 1 \times 2^3 + 1 \times 2^0 = 2345$$

Making a list of exponents in declining numerical order and of their respective coefficients from the above examples, it follows:

Decimal:	Exponent	3	2	1	0								
	Coefficient	2	3	4	5								
Binary:	Exponent	11	10	9	8	7	6	5	4	3	2	1	0
	Coefficient	1	0	0	1	0	0	1	0	1	0	0	1

As can be seen, for nonexisting exponents the coefficient of zero is inserted. Decimally, the coefficient 2345 remains the same, while in the binary system the number reads 100100101001. Since binary computers use "on" and "off" devices, the binary system becomes a necessity, as the number is defined by 1 and 0 or "off" and "on" written in numerical order.

Elements of digital computers are input, storage, control, arithmetic, and output (Fig. 10-27).

Input consists of two physical items: card, paper or magnetic tape, or a magnetic disk on which data are recorded, and a mechanical device to read and transmit data to computer storage.

The 80-column card makes it possible to record, in the form of punched holes, up to 80 characters. A digit requires a single punch in a column; the character two which

Fig. 10-26 IBM-1130 digital computer.

punches one of these is the zone punch (12, 11, or zero); the other is the numerical punch. The mathematical symbols need three punches in each column (Fig. 10-28). Punched cards were first used for large-scale data processing by Herman Hollerith in the census of 1890.

The eight-channel paper tape is the most widely used (Fig. 10-29).

The magnetic tape, also widely used, is shown in Fig. 10-30.

Storage, or memory, is the heart of the computer. Modern computer memories are made up of small ferromagnetic rings. All data and program instructions are stored in memory. The numbers are transmitted internally at time intervals as small as microseconds.

The control unit controls computer and input-output devices during the processing stage. It determines the sequence of operation and interprets and carries out the program instructions.

The arithmetic unit performs arithmetic and logical operations; it holds registers which temporarily store information to be used later.

Output, like input, involves two items: the medium on which the output is recorded, and a device required to accept the data from memory and create the output record. The types of output are punched cards, punched paper tape, magnetic tape and disk, high-speed printer up to 1,200 lines/min, and console typewriter.

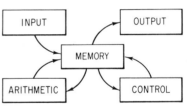

Fig. 10-27 Basic parts of the computer's operation. Arrows show flow of information. The memory has the key role in storing and releasing as necessary for computation.

The console typewriter is a tool for the operator or programmer during the computer operation and in debugging a new program. *Six channels (1,2,4,8,0,X) are used to record any number, letter, or special character.* The channel marked "Check" is intended to satisfy a validity check and will contain a punch whenever the basic code (1,2,4,8,0,X) consists *of an even number of holes.* The check hole is then added *to make an odd number of holes* so that every column can be checked when reading for the presence of an odd count. The "EL" channel is automatically punched to mark the end of a line or record on the tape. The lower four channels of the tape, excluding the sprocket or feed holes, are used to record numerical characters. For example, a hole in channel 2 represents a numerical "2." A combination of a "1" and a "2" punch represents a numerical "3." The X and 0 channels are used in combination with the numerical channels in recording alphabetic and special characters like the zone punches in the punched card previously discussed. Paper tape can be read directly into a *computer by a paper tape reader or* "converted" *to magnetic tape for introduction to the computer.*

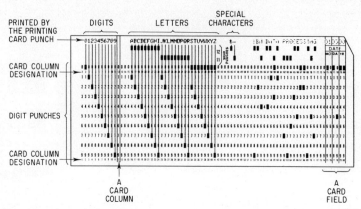

Fig. 10-28 A typical punched card. By using combinations of two holes, the decimal numbers, the alphabet, and several punctuation marks can be fed into computers and converted into electrical signals. By using combinations of three holes in each column, a great many mathematical symbols can be introduced.

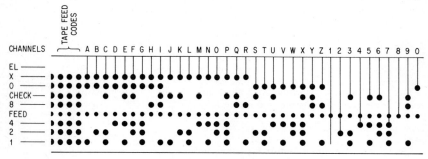

Fig. 10-29   Eight-channel paper tape.

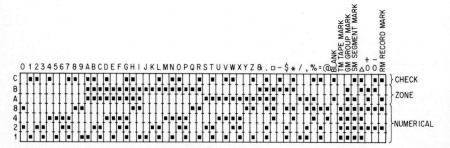

Fig. 10-30   Seven-channel magnetic tape.

Programming

Four basic steps are involved in the preparation of a computer program:

1. Problem definition
2. Preparation of a flow diagram of the logic to be followed by the computer
3. Writing the source program
4. Compiling the source program and checking out the object program on the computer

The problem to be processed on a computer must be well defined and elaborated in detail from the standpoint of mathematics and logic prior to a programming. A flow diagram is then prepared in accordance with the outline of the problem. The program consists of a series of instructions for the computer to perform the specified operations. These operations involve arithmetical operations, comparison, and iteration.

The program should be written in machine language which the computer understands. However, machine language is complex and involves many details. Because of this, special languages have been developed to simplify and speed up the programming.

Fortran (FORmula TRANslation) is the most widely used in engineering and scientific fields. Originally developed by IBM Corp., it is also being adapted by other computer manufacturers.

Unless otherwise specified, the computer processes the program instructions in sequence. A typical flow diagram for operations needed to calculate the area under a curve is shown in Fig. 10-31 and Fortran statements are listed in Fig. 10-32.

After the Source/Fortran/Program has been written, it must be compiled on the computer. The Fortran compiler (supplied by the computer manufacturer) translates the source program into the machine-language program, which is stored on cards, magnetic tapes, or disks. The compiler usually has built-in diagnostic tests to check for coding errors such as incorrect notation and punctuation. Following the compilation, the object program is read into the computer memory to execute the calculation, using any required data to produce the results, which are compared with manually computed data. When the program checking out is completed, the object program is released.

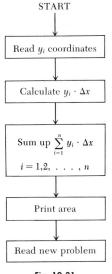

Fig. 10-31

```
   DIMENSION Y(20)
1  FORMAT(13)
2  FORMAT(8.3)
   DELX=0.5
3  SUM=0.0
   READ 1,N
   READ 2,(Y(I),I=1,N)
   DO 4 I=1,N
   SUM=SUM+Y(I)*DELX
4  CONTINUE
   PRINT 2, SUM
   GO TO 3
   END
```

Fig. 10-32

For more flexibility and programming-time saving, each Fortran program allows calling for subroutines. A subroutine is a computer program written to perform some frequently used operation. Subroutines for mathematical functions like square root, exponential, sine, cosine, arctangent, and natural logarithm are included in the Fortran compiler and are used by calling the subroutine by its name. Additionally, subroutines are also available for more complex operations like matrix inversion, solution of simultaneous linear equations, and statistical and Fourier analysis.

Index

Index

3